Managing Editor
Kirsteen McCue

Editor
Karen Marshalsay

Original Concept
Lynn Morrison

Researchers
Karen Abbott
Tommy Fowler
Elaine Hartley
Moira Mason
Sheila Osborne
Alasdair Pettinger
Sheila Tapp

Contributors
Ian Bone
Eilidh MacKenzie
Kenny Mathieson
Mary Miller
Matthew Rooke
Brigitte Strachan
Iain Sutherland
Rebecca Tavener
Sheila Wellington
John Williamson

SCOTTISH **MUSIC** HANDBOOK 1996

Scottish Music Information Centre Ltd
Glasgow

First published in 1995 by:
The Scottish Music Information Centre Ltd
1 Bowmont Gardens
Glasgow G12 9LR

THE SCOTTISH ARTS COUNCIL

Supported by Glasgow City Council

Foundation
for sport
and the arts

ISBN: 0-9525489-0-9

Typesetting: Rockmoor Ltd, Edinburgh

Design & layout: Fiona McIntyre & Allan J Hall

Cover design: Alastair Paul, Observatory Design

Printed & bound in the UK by:
The Cromwell Press

ACKNOWLEDGEMENTS

Scottish Arts Council
Foundation for Sport
    and the Arts
Glasgow City Council
Glasgow Trades House
    (Commonweal Fund)
Cunninghame District
    Council
Scottish Publishers
    Association

Ardival Harps
Balnain House
Peter Baxter
Alison Black
Adrian Clark
Arthur Cormack, Feisean
    nan Gaidheal
Dunkeld Records
Eclectic Records
Enterprise Music Scotland
Glasgow City Council
    Department of
    Performing Arts &
    Venues
Greentrax Records
Lesley Harrison
HI Arts
Tim Hobrough
Ken James
Klub Records

Danny Kyle
Barbara McDermitt
Eddie McGuire
Edmund May
Musicians' Union
Network Scotland
Isabel Paterson
Scottish Arts Council
    Helpdesk
Scottish Musicians
    Benevolent Fund
Springthyme Records
Temple Records
Training Access Point
Sheena Wellington
Graeme Wilson (Queen
    Anne High School)
Bobby Wishart
John Yule Harps

CONTENTS

CONTENTS

CONTENTS

The Scottish Arts Council welcomes the production of the *Scottish Music Handbook*. This *Handbook* is probably the most comprehensive single source of information on music in Scotland. Whilst there are a number of other publications which cover aspects of music in Scotland none of them contains the broad depth of information on offer - and if you can't find out what you want at first hand, the *Scottish Music Handbook* will guide you to someone else who can!

I think this book is valuable for the following reasons: firstly, it is the product of a database developed by the Scottish Music Information Centre to ensure that it has the best possible range of information at its fingertips for personal callers; secondly, whether you are a composer or performer, or involved in some other aspect of Scotland's music life, it will help to make sure that more people know about you and your work; and thirdly, not only will this *Handbook* help all of us involved in the business of music in Scotland make contacts with each other, it will also be a calling card working on Scotland's behalf abroad.

We are constantly being told information is power. Whilst ignorance may have been bliss a generation ago, in these fast moving times it is almost a sin. I hope that whether you are an entrant or a reader the *Handbook* will give you the power and support to make the most of the riches that music in Scotland has to offer.

Matthew Rooke
Music Director

Performing Arts
Department
Scottish Arts Council

SCOTTISH MUSIC HANDBOOK

T he *Scottish Music Handbook 1996* is the product of a database which has been developed at the Scottish Music Information Centre over the past year. At the Centre we felt the need to collate general contact details for musicians and musical organisations in Scotland in order to help in the answering of daily enquiries. We soon realised, however, that there was a need for this information to be made available to the general public in printed form.

The database has been built up from nothing, and even in this first year the number of entrants has far surpassed our estimation. What the *Handbook* shows most clearly is that music in Scotland is a thriving industry involving a large number of individuals and organisations. Moreover, it is illustrative of a new-found enthusiasm for collaboration that different musical forms are working more and more closely together - indeed, this is something of a recurring theme in the articles which introduce the different sections of the book.

This overlap of musical genres has made the task of classification a difficult one, but we believe that it was necessary to break down the listings into various categories in order to make the *Handbook* as useful to as many people as possible. While labels can never be completely satisfactory or precise for all eventualities they do make a large body of information much more accessible. The inclusion of a full index of both individuals and organisations lessens the chance of someone being 'missed' because of categorisation, and speeds up the location of particular entries if the name is already known.

To save any major duplication with other directories, particularly the *British Music Yearbook*, we decided that individuals and organisations would only be listed if they were based in Scotland or had a main contact address in Scotland. The only exceptions to this are the **Sources of Funding** and **Competitions** sections, as grants, funding bodies and competitions are often based outside Scotland but are still applicable to those living here.

Readers will also note that there are no listings of artists under **Light Music**, or **Rock and Pop**. There are listings in other sections of the *Handbook* which are applicable to these areas (e.g. **Festivals, Suppliers & Services** and **Venues** etc.), as well as informative articles and contact details for organisations which can supply further information. These are areas which we would like to be able to cover in more detail in future editions of the *Handbook* and in the on-going database at the Centre. The Music in Scotland Trust (MiST) produced *The Scottish Music Guide* for the first time in 1994. The *Guide* concentrates on the popular music industry in Scotland and gives listings and detailed profiles of individual artists and bands. The Trust works much more closely with this area of the music profession than the Scottish Music Information Centre and we therefore decided it would be an

unnecessary duplication to include such information in the *Handbook*. It is therefore timely that the Trust plans to produce a new edition of the *Guide* in 1996.

Each section of the *Handbook* is preceded by a brief article and a description of how to use the relevant listings, noting the different editorial decisions which apply. The *Handbook* is produced at a time of great change in Local Government in Scotland. Contact names and addresses of shadow officers were not available before clarifying information for print. The **Education** and **Venues** sections of the *Handbook* are the only sections affected and details are given where applicable.

While the *Handbook* is both categorised and indexed, readers who may wish to find specific combinations of information are welcome to contact the Centre where we can carry out searches on the database. In some instances people who are happy to be included on the database did not wish to have details printed in the *Handbook*. All the entries here have been checked by Centre staff during 1995 and the information is stored in accordance with the Data Protection Act.

We have created the database for use at the Centre and it is our intention to keep the information as up-to-date as possible and to continue to add to the sections presented here. This does, of course, rely to a certain extent on people involved in music in Scotland keeping the Centre informed of any changes and/or

developments. If you would like people to know about you or your group, venue, course etc. then please send details to the Centre and we will add them to the database.

The *Scottish Music Handbook 1996* is the first book of this kind that the Centre has produced. Its appearance is thanks primarily to support from the **Scottish Arts Council** and the **Foundation for Sport and the Arts**. The Centre would also like to thank **Glasgow City Council**, **Glasgow Trades House (Commonweal Fund)** and **Cunnighame District Council**. It has only been possible to produce the *Handbook* with a hard-working and dedicated team of collators, and with the help of many other **organisations** and individuals who are listed on its pages.

Kirsteen McCue &
Karen Marshalsay

Scottish Music Information Centre

October 1995

4

ORGANISATIONS

Scottish Music Information Centre

Reference Library and Sound Archive

with works by over 300 Scottish and Scotland-based composers, past and present. Catalogue extracts available free on request.

Information Database

with details of organisations, artists, promoters, venues, festivals, courses, and anything else relating to music-making in Scotland. Available as the *Scottish Music Handbook* from October 1995.

Music Current

a monthly guide to contemporary music events in Scotland.

Photocopying and Binding Service

catering for the specialist needs of the musician: producing high quality copies at competitive rates.

1 Bowmont Gardens   Glasgow G12 9LR

Tel: 0141-334 6393 (general enquiries)

0141-334 7730 (Handbook)

Fax: 0141-337 1161

Open: Mon-Fri (except Wed) 9.30am - 5.30pm

THE SCOTTISH **ARTS** COUNCIL

The **Scottish Music Information Centre (SMIC)** exists to document and to promote the works of Scottish and Scottish-based composers of all periods.

The Centre was founded in 1985 and grew from a collection - formerly the Scottish Music Archive - which was based at the University of Glasgow. The Centre now houses the largest single collection of music by Scottish and Scottish-based composers in the world, and its holdings include materials from the time of St Columba to the present day.

The library houses scores and parts (in printed and manuscript form), books and articles, microfilms, press-cuttings and recordings. We have biographical materials on over 200 composers and can provide detailed listings of the works they have written. Our visitors come to look at, read about and listen to Scottish music. The Centre also makes much of this music available to performers, by copying scores and parts and by hiring music. Lists of music for special occasions or for specific combinations of instruments can be produced from the Centre's catalogue. We work closely with professional and non-professional musicians, arts administrators and institutions, teachers, students and the general public.

The Centre circulates regular information about new Scottish music and composers. Our Information Officer, Librarian and Administrative Assistant can also provide answers to more general enquiries. The Centre produces a monthly newsletter, *Music Current*, which includes articles on new developments, opportunities and commissions, and lists performances of works by Scottish composers. This newsletter is distributed to individuals, venues and institutions at home and abroad.

Special projects are developed by the Centre to enhance interest and knowledge in the diversity of Scottish music and Scotland's musical heritage, and they are designed for national as well as international use. In 1992 the Centre developed the *Scotland's Music* Exhibition - telling the story of 3,000 years of Scottish music - which has toured Britain and abroad, and is still touring! During the same year the Centre worked with its Icelandic counterpart to organise a Festival of Icelandic and Scottish culture with a series of events in both countries. In the past two years the Centre has developed the *Scottish Music Handbook*, which, once more, illustrates how active music in Scotland is!

SCOTTISH MUSIC INFORMATION CENTRE

Under an enthusiastic Board of Directors, the Centre is subsidised by the **Scottish Arts Council** and is a member of the **International Association of Music Information Centres** and the **International Association of Music Libraries**.

For more information please contact: Kirsteen McCue (General Manager), Alasdair Pettinger (Information Officer), Deborah Harris (Administrative Assistant), or Catherine Owen (Librarian) at the **Scottish Music Information Centre**, 1 Bowmont Gardens, Glasgow G12 9LR.
Tel: 0141 334 6393
Fax: 0141 337 1161

7

INTERNATIONAL ASSOCIATION OF MUSIC INFORMATION CENTRES

The **International Association of Music Information Centres (IAMIC)** is a worldwide network of organisations promoting new music. Music information centres (or MICs as they call themselves) are multi-purpose resource centres: 'working collections' where related material such as scores, recordings, programme notes, biographical material, newspaper reviews, magazine articles, books, photos, and so on are collected together, generally on open access.

MICs are active in more than thirty countries internationally, documenting and promoting the music of that country or region, as well as co-operating internationally with the other centres on issues of common concern. Most MICs focus on contemporary art music, but this varies from country to country. Some, like **SMIC**, also have responsibility for folk music; some for everything from rock and pop through jazz to the so-called 'serious' end of things. In all countries, they serve as a focus of musical activity.

IAMIC was founded in 1958. The first meeting of 'National Music Centre Representatives' as they were then called, was organised by the International Music Council in co-operation with the Donemus Foundation, Amsterdam and the Dutch National Music Committee, with the aim of 'making available a wider knowledge of contemporary music'. Following the example shown by the work of Donemus, similar organisations were set up in other countries. In 1962, having decided that 'Music Information Centre' was a more apt description, it was decided to constitute the group formally as the **International Association of Music Information Centres**, affiliated to the **International Association of Music Libraries (IAML)**. This link continued until 1991, when IAMIC, by then with some forty member-organisations, voted to become a fully independent association under the aegis of the **International Music Council**. Close contact is still maintained with the International Association of Music Libraries, however, and the annual meetings of both organisations frequently run in parallel. In June 1995 for instance, **IAMIC** and **IAML** meet jointly, in Helsingor, Denmark.

Music information centres are open to the public and their extensive resources are at your service in person or by telephone, fax or mail. No matter what your query, the MIC of the country concerned will be able to assist you, or put you in touch with a more appropriate organisation. We look forward to hearing from you!

Eve O'Kelly, Secretary, **IAMIC Contemporary Music Centre**, 95 Lower Baggot Street, Dublin 2, Ireland.
Tel: 00 353 1-661 2105
Fax: 00 353 1-676 2639
E-mail: iamic@cmc.ie

THE SCOTTISH **ARTS** COUNCIL

The Scottish Arts Council welcomes applications for support from the following music funds:

Creative Artists' Bursaries
Bursaries to individual creative artists to devote time to new compositions.

Education and Outreach Projects
Grants to extend the range of participants in and audiences for music.

Performing Material Subsidy
Assistance to composers with the cost of preparing materials necessary for the performance of their work.

Performance Promotion
Assistance to selected promoters to enhance current spread of music provision throughout Scotland.

Music Commission Fee Subsidy
Assistance with the cost of commission fees for original compositions.

Traditional and Gaelic Music Development
Grants to activities aimed at passing on skills in traditional music.

Training and Travel Bursaries
Support towards travel and tuition costs incurred in the advancement of the professional musician's skill and expertise.

Recordings
Assistance to recording companies, music organisations and individuals towards the artistic costs incurred in making high quality recordings of music by Scottish composers.

Early Music Ensemble Development
Grants to assist the development of early music ensembles through coaching or training by leading musicians/directors.

Application forms and details of 1996/97 funds are available from The Music Office, Performing Arts Department, Scottish Arts Council, 12 Manor Place, Edinburgh EH3 7DD. Tel: 0131 226 6051 Fax: 0131 225 9833

THE SCOTTISH ARTS COUNCIL EXISTS TO CREATE A CLIMATE IN WHICH ARTS OF QUALITY FLOURISH AND ARE ENJOYED BY A WIDE RANGE OF PEOPLE THROUGHOUT SCOTLAND.

The **Scottish Arts Council (SAC) Help Desk** was founded in 1992. Since then it has gone from strength to strength, to become one of the foremost providers of information, primarily to the Scottish arts community, but also to individuals and organisations elsewhere who are interested in the arts in Scotland. It now helps around 4,000 people a year to find the information they need to operate effectively.

Essentially a direct line telephone enquiry service, providing a single point of access to the wealth of knowledge and resources available at **SAC**, it also responds to postal enquiries. It draws upon an extensive library, in-house databases, and the expertise of **SAC** art-form officers. Resources available include:

* A series of popular free factsheets, developed to answer the most common enquiries on funding, training, local government and the traditional arts

* Databases on Scottish Performing Arts Venues, Charitable Trusts and Foundations, Minority Ethnic Artists and Arts Organisations, and Consultants

* Contact lists for arts organisations, local authorities, partner agencies and a wide range of other bodies

* A comprehensive and easy to use "menu" of everything **SAC** has to offer designed to make obtaining information simple

* A free bi-monthly Information Bulletin which gives news from SAC and elsewhere, details of new policy and research initiatives, awards and funding, training and conferences, new contacts for people and organisations, and publications

A wide range of the services available will be of interest to those working in the music industry, whether as individuals or as part of an organisation, and the **Help Desk** already regularly assists individual musicians, orchestras, ensembles, festivals and others.

The **Help Desk** should be the first port of call for anyone seeking to know about funds available for the support of musical projects. In addition to supplying guidelines and application forms for all of **SAC**'s own schemes, Help Desk staff will be able to suggest alternative sources of funding, and provide the relevant contacts. For people looking to further develop their careers through training, the **Help Desk** has full information on a wide range of available courses. For those wishing to organise a tour or set up a

SCOTTISH ARTS COUNCIL HELP DESK

performance, Datavenue, one of the **Help Desk**'s largest databases, may be able to help with lists of suitable venues and promoters.

Whatever the query, the **Help Desk** will endeavour to deal with it courteously and as soon as possible. In cases where **Help Desk** staff do not have the answer, they are almost always able to use their extensive range of contacts to suggest a more appropriate source for the caller to try.

In summary, the **Help Desk** helps to ensure that Scotland's arts sector is both efficient and effective, by providing timely, accurate and essential information to those who work in it. The **Help Desk** is open Monday to Friday from 10am to 12pm, and 2pm-4pm, and can be reached on direct line (Tel: 0131 243 2444), or by writing to the **Help Desk** Administrators - Virginie Renard and Anne Marie Allan (job share) - **Scottish Arts Council**, 12 Manor Place, Edinburgh, EH3 7DD. An answering machine operates outside of normal working hours. Christine Galey is the Information Officer.

11

INTERNATIONAL CULTURAL DESK

Launched in June 1994, the **International Cultural Desk** is the first central clearing house in Scotland for information about international opportunities for the arts and cultural services sector. *The Charter for the Arts in Scotland* recognised the importance of the international perspective to Scottish arts and artists and identified a very strong interest among Scottish arts and cultural organisations, in developing a mechanism to promote more international collaboration. In response to this need the **International Cultural Desk** was established as a three year pilot project jointly funded by the **British Council**, the **Scottish Arts Council** and the **Scottish Museums Council** with additional funding from **Scottish Enterprise National** and **Highlands and Islands Enterprise**. Its aim is to assist the Scottish arts and cultural community to operate more effectively in an international context by providing timely and targeted information and advice. The Desk deals with all art forms and arts practices including museums and galleries but excluding film where the **Scottish Film Council** provides its own information service.

If you are planning an international project and would like to know more about international festivals, venues, sources of funding and other international opportunities contact the **International Cultural Desk** for information and advice. The Desk publishes a bimonthly information update - *Communication* - which brings together for the first time details about forthcoming international opportunities across the whole range of cultural and artistic activity. It includes the latest news on European Union Funding and Cultural Policy, and details international opportunities under the following headings: Awards; Exchanges; Commissions; Residencies; Competitions; Conferences; Courses/ Workshops; Exhibitions; Festivals; Internships; Networks; Partners for Collaborations; Publications; Special Events. An annual subscription to *Communication* provides you with 6 issues at an annual rate of £8.00 (individuals); £20 (non-profit organisations); £40 (others). For the blind and partially sighted an audio cassette or large print copy will be available on request. The bulletin includes a section which is reserved for Scottish artists, arts and cultural organisations who are currently developing international projects and would like to share their experience, exchange information or inform colleagues about their international activities. If you would like to be listed, contact the Desk for a Scotland International registration form.

The **International Cultural Desk** is accessible by telephone, letter or by appointment. For further details contact Hilde Bollen, Development Manager, or Anne Robb, Information Assistant at the **International Cultural Desk**, 6 Belmont Crescent, Glasgow G12 8ES.
Tel: 0141 339 0090
Fax: 0141 337 2271

What has music to do with **Disability Scotland**? The link is provided by the disabled 10 per cent of our population.

Many arts providers have accepted that because they are in receipt of public funding they have a responsibility to provide access to their work to all members of the community. Recognising the difficulties of the buildings they have inherited, arts managers have taken steps to make them accessible to the disabled.

But what is disability? You might not consider that an elderly relative, whom you have known all your life, to whom you now have to speak very clearly and distinctly, and who has a bit of trouble getting about, is disabled, but the Social Work Department and many other agencies almost certainly will.

Contrary to the stereotype 'Disabled = wheelchair user,' there are many disabilities which do not involve using a wheelchair. Some think that being blind is being marooned in a totally dark void, when in fact the term 'blindness' covers such visual impairments as tunnel vision.

Stereotypes are very handy. But they prevent clear thinking. And they influence the way decision makers make their decisions. To explode the stereotypes it can be helpful to think of disability as a continuum ranging from slight to severe, rather than to divide the world into two groups of disabled and non-disabled people. No one is perfect, after all. Equipment, the environment and other people can all play an important role in enabling the person with a disability to lead an independent life.

A large proportion of the population has a hearing impairment, though only a small number can be described as having a listening disability. There is widely available technology to enhance available hearing in the form of induction loops and infra-red systems.

Again, despite the common expression 'confined to a wheelchair', far from being a prison, the wheelchair is a liberating mechanism, taking its user beyond home and hospital. What does confine a wheelchair user is a flight of steps on the front of a concert hall rather than level access. And life can be made much more straightforward with the assistance of other people, such as audio describers for the visually impaired and sign language interpreters for the profoundly deaf.

There is an important distinction to be made between the cause and effect of disability. In most cases the reason why the person uses the wheelchair is not particularly relevant. The traditional medical

DISABILITY SCOTLAND

model of disability is that the individual has to change, or be changed by professionals through rehabilitation or cure. In other words, disability has been seen as the problem of the individual. The social model of disability suggests that it is economic and social barriers which stop people with disabilities from participating fully in society. It is not the medical condition which prevents participation, but environments and attitudes.

To encourage society to accept responsibility for disability, **Disability Scotland** will continue to support the efforts made by the music business to enable disabled people to participate as performers and audiences, and will continue to campaign for greater efforts.

For further information on the activities of **Disability Scotland** contact Robert Pickles at the organisation's main office in Princes House, 5 Shandwick Place, Edinburgh EH2 4RG. Tel/ Minicom: 0131 229 8632 Fax: 0131 229 5168

MUSICIANS' UNION

The **Musicians' Union** (**MU**) has been in existence now for over 100 years. From its humble origins in a pit orchestra in Manchester it has grown into the largest and most representative professional organisation for musicians in Europe.

It has branch offices throughout the UK and in Scotland is based at the Glasgow Office.

Scotland was one of the first areas to become involved in the new Amalgamated **Musicians' Union** and there has been an office in Glasgow since 1893. We now have branches in Inverness, Aberdeen, Dundee, Perth, Stirling, Motherwell, Edinburgh, Falkirk, Cumnock and North Ayrshire. The full-time official and Scottish Organiser is currently Ian Smith.

The Union began life trying to secure a reasonable living wage for working musicians, and times haven't changed! The Union's role in promulgating rates of pay for engagements and negotiating contracts of employment with industry managements - orchestras, opera companies, ballet companies etc - has never been more valued.

Every payment that a musician and in many instances a teacher, or composer, or copyist, or arranger receives has been negotiated by the Union on their behalf. We deal on a day to day basis with employers, the media; BPI, BBC, ITV, both radio and television, the rights collection agencies **MCPS** and **PRS**, and any organisation that employs musicians directly or indirectly. We also police venues, from concert halls to small clubs, to ensure that proper conditions and rates of pay apply to the employment of musicians whether it be the Royal Scottish National Orchestra, Scottish Opera, Carol Kidd's Trio, Bobby Harvey's Ceilidh Band or Wet Wet Wet.

The Union now has a wide range of services to offer to our members; the most used being our legal services. We handle hundreds of claims throughout the UK annually, ranging from simple non-payment and the vetting of contracts to major contractual disputes which can only be settled in court. The legal service is available to all members as is free accountancy and tax advice.

We now have a major insurance agency working exclusively for the Union providing free cover for up to £500 worth of instruments or equipment. Public liability insurance up to £1 million is available to all members as part of their membership. We can also offer all types of insurance from car to private health schemes at specially negotiated rates.

We offer further health advice through the British Performing Arts Medicine Trust and a Union brokered scheme provides volunteer GPs throughout the country to deal with the particular needs of today's musician.

In the field of education we deal with directors of education in ensuring that our members who are instrumental teachers have proper contracts of employment and are properly recognised as full time teaching staff.

The Union has within its organisation specialist sections which cover Education, Jazz, Writing, Session Musicians, Theatre, Opera and Ballet, Orchestras and Media. Each section is served by representative committees made up of the members and specialists in those fields to properly serve those areas and keep up to date with any changes to the work pattern which may occur.

The **MU** provides directories free of charge and issues a quarterly magazine in addition to the branch newsletters which each individual branch circulates to its members.

We also provide career advice and hold workshops and seminars on a regular basis to help youngsters know more about all aspects of the music business - not just performance. We are represented on many committees to ensure that the views of musicians are well represented, e.g. SCOTVEC which provides modules for HNC and HND qualifications.

The Union therefore is an essential organisation to anyone considering a career which has anything to do with music - performing, writing, teaching, arranging - even DJ rapping! We can provide all the services and advice that the professional will need, whatever rung of the ladder he or she happens to be on. Many of our members enjoy the full range of services the Union offers.

If you are contemplating a career in music, then there are many people and organisations that you should speak to, but high on the list - perhaps No. 1 - should be the **Musicians' Union**.

Contact our full-time official at the Glasgow Office and he will be happy to advise you and, if appropriate, put you in touch with the Branch Secretary in the area most convenient to you and your needs. The **Musicians' Union** is the only organisation that can

MUSICIANS' UNION (CONTD)

ensure that the provision of the enjoyment of Live Music in all its forms continues to flourish throughout Scotland. The Scottish Organiser is Ian Smith at the **Musicians' Union**, 11 Sandyford Place, Glasgow G3 7NB. Tel: 0141 248 3723. Fax: 0141 204 3510.

THE MUSICIANS' UNION EUROPE'S LARGEST REPRESENTATIVE ORGANISATION FOR MUSICIANS KEEPING MUSIC LIVE!

MUSICIANS' UNION

FREE LEGAL ADVICE : CONTRACT VETTING etc.
FREE ACCOUNTANCY AND TAX ADVICE
FREE PUBLIC LIABILITY INSURANCE : £1M BENEFIT
1st £500 OF INSURANCE COVER : FREE BENEFIT,
CAREER ADVICE AND MUCH MUCH MORE

**FOR ALL DETAILS OF MEMBERSHIP etc
CONTACT IAN SMITH or FRANCESCA HOWELL
On 0141-248 3723   Fax: 0141-204 3510
11 SANDYFORD PLACE, GLASGOW G3 7NB**

*IF YOU ARE A PERFORMER, WRITER, TEACHER - EVEN A RAPPER!
WE CAN MEET YOUR NEEDS*

15

The **Scottish Musicians' Benevolent Fund** (SMBF) exists to alleviate hardship and to provide help for Scottish professional musicians, and their dependants, in need.

In 1994 the Fund gave £20,000 in grants to the ill, elderly or needy, and to some who were still active but in temporary difficulties. With the caring support of the Fund's Visitor, 65 musicians or their dependants were helped by the **Scottish Musicians' Benevolent Fund** in that year. Beneficiaries included classical, jazz and folk musicians, composers and dependants of musicians.

The Fund is independent of, but works in close co-operation with, the much larger **Musicians' Benevolent Fund** based in London. The Scottish Fund deals with all the London Fund's beneficiaries living in Scotland. An important development in 1991 was the employment of a trained visitor, serving both Funds.

The origins of the **Scottish Musicians' Benevolent Fund** are traced to 1918 and Dr Henry G Farmer, who was then the President of the Glasgow branch of the **Musicians' Union**. It was not until 1953 that the Fund became known as the **Scottish Musicians' Benevolent Fund**. Dr Farmer was the Honorary President until his death in 1965.

Sir Alexander Gibson, who loyally supported and worked to promote the Fund, succeeded Dr Farmer as Honorary President and a Trustee until his untimely death in January 1995. It was Sir Alex's wish and that of his family that the **SMBF** particularly be remembered at that time. On St Cecilia's Day in 1993 he conducted the four premier orchestras of Scotland in a memorable Gala Concert in Glasgow Royal Concert Hall to celebrate the 75th Anniversary of the Fund.

Neill Aitken, who was appointed as Honorary Secretary and Treasurer in 1950 and latterly as a Trustee until his death in 1984, saw the fund develop over the 34 years he was involved. Under the current chairmanship of Malcolm McIver and six other dedicated Trustees progress continues. In addition to the basic grant-making policies, the Fund seeks ways in which to help beneficiaries and is, for instance, able to organise holidays for some who would not otherwise have the opportunity for a break or to meet with fellow musicians or their dependants.

The **Scottish Musicians' Benevolent Fund** invites applications from, or on behalf of, necessitous Scottish professional musicians and their

SCOTTISH MUSICIANS' BENEVOLENT FUND

dependants, and the Fund seeks continued financial support in order that help can be given to those in need and whose music we have enjoyed.

Can we help you? - or - Can you help us to help?

All enquiries to Allan M Barns-Graham, Honorary Secretary & Treasurer, Scottish Musicians' Benevolent Fund, c/o Carbeth Guthrie, Blanefield, Nr Glasgow G63 9AT.
Tel: 01360 771168
Fax: 01360 770671

17

The **Incorporated Society of Musicians (ISM)** is the UK's professional association for all musicians.

It exists to promote the art of music and maintain the honour and interests of the music profession. It has three main objectives: to represent and protect all those who work with music; to improve and enhance standards within the profession; and to offer its members the best possible range and quality of benefits. It aims to maintain the highest levels of professionalism, both in the services it provides for its subscribers, and in its members' own dealings with their clients.

The **ISM** is a genuinely independent musical association, with no political or other ties. It is run by a Council of elected members, every one of whom is an active professional musician, from all over the country (the two current Scottish representatives, James Boyd and John Hearne, cover West and East Scotland respectively). To maintain the Society's long tradition of excellence, it gives particular attention to ways of improving members' experiences, achievements and qualifications. This enhances the reputation of the Society as a whole, and of its members as individuals, in the world of professional music.

Musicians who are **ISM** members, whether performers, composers, teachers or lecturers, receive complete professional support throughout their careers. The **ISM**'s extensive membership benefits include a free 24-hour legal helpline, free public liability cover, and other exclusive insurance schemes, tax advice, standard contracts, help with career development and a range of valuable discounts. Unpaid fees are recovered, contractual disputes resolved and unfair dismissals challenged. Three specialists sections - for performers and composers, private teachers and musicians in education - coordinate policy, and organise conferences and seminars, on topical issues. Publications include promotional registers, advisory pamphlets on professional issues such as copyright and noise nuisance, the monthly *Music Journal*, and *Careers with Music*. The **ISM**'s recommendations on minimum fees are recognised nationally; its working agreements with major employers set out a clear framework for individual negotiations.

In addition to providing comprehensive legal and technical services to more than 4,000 full members, the **ISM** speaks on behalf of the music profession as a whole when dealing with central and local government, the media and the public.

INCORPORATED SOCIETY OF MUSICIANS

The **ISM**'s work is helped by special membership groupings for students and non-professionals. There is also a unique corporate members' section, which embraces some 150 bodies such as manufacturers, businesses, colleges, musical organisations and conservatoires (including the **RSAMD**, whose Principal, Dr Philip Ledger CBE, was President of the **ISM** in 1994-95).

A network of 47 local Centres across the UK keeps members in touch with each other, and averts the danger of loneliness and isolation by organising professional and social events. The **ISM**'s five Centres in Scotland are based in Aberdeen, Edinburgh, Glasgow, Inverness and Tayside.

If **ISM** members and their dependants encounter hardship or misfortune, the **ISM**'s Benevolent Fund can provide financial assistance.

The subscription for full membership of the **ISM** costs around £6 a month, and can be paid in monthly instalments. Even as simply an insurance scheme - and it is much more than that -

19

INCORPORATED SOCIETY OF MUSICIANS (CONTD)

membership offers excellent value to professional musicians. If members ever meet with problems in their careers, or need expert advice, they can be sure that the Society will be there to help.

To inquire about the **ISM** and its services, and to find out how to join, write to Neil Hoyle, Chief Executive, **ISM**, 10 Stratford Place, London, W1N 9AE.
Tel: 0171 629 4413
Fax: 0171 408 1538

What is the role of **Performing Right Society** and how can it be of use to you?

If music be the food of love . . . One evening in the early 19th Century a young French composer was dining out with a young lady in an atmospheric Parisian restaurant where the good food and wine were augmented by the music being played by the resident orchestra. On this particular night the music that was entertaining the diners was written by the composer in question. When presented with the bill for his meal, the composer declined to pay until he had been paid for the use of his music.

From the ensuing uproar the concept of a 'performing right' was established in France. The right of composers (and their publishers) to control and be rewarded for public performance in the UK was protected by the 1911 Copyright Art, and has continued to be protected in the 1956 and the 1988 Acts.

What is *PRS*?

PRS is the UK association of composers, songwriters and music publishers. It administers the 'performing right' in their music. There are similar performing right societies throughout the world. By agreement with them, **PRS** represents their members in its territory and is

represented by them in theirs. At any one time **PRS** licenses millions of compositions - everything from an advertising jingle to entire symphonies, with every kind of pop/rock/jazz and folk music in between.

Why does PRS exist?

Whenever copyright music is heard in public the people who own the copyright in the work are entitled by law to give permission and should get paid by the music user. However, the people who create and publish the music need help to give that permission (that is to license their music) and to collect the fees due. So they give **PRS** the right to do both on their behalf. The common misconception is that music is public property and **PRS** exists to remind people that music doesn't just appear out of thin air. Until composers, authors and music publishers came together to exercise their rights, through societies such as **PRS,** there was very little the individual creator could do to collect what was rightfully due from performances of copyright music. The words 'rightfully due' are important, particularly today - in a world where increasingly easy access to music in a wide variety of forms just reinforces the public's long preferred misconception that musical performance belongs to everyone and no one and should therefore somehow

PERFORMING RIGHT SOCIETY

be 'free'. A composer or songwriter works to write music, and time and money are invested in it by the creators and the publishers. These people, just like any other producers of goods and services, are entitled to payment for the use of the product of their labours.

How are the royalties collected?

PRS issues licences to those who wish to use copyright music. All premises that use music in public (which has been defined through the courts as anywhere outside the domestic circle) require a **PRS** licence. The same is true of broadcasters including those providing a cable service.

How are the royalties distributed?

As **PRS** makes no profits for itself, all money collected is paid out as royalties after deduction only of its operating costs. At the **PRS** head office in London, an advanced computer system keeps records of all musical works composed by **PRS** members plus information on licences and broadcasts.

As far as possible, the net royalties are distributed to **PRS** members in accordance with the extent to which their works have

PERFORMING RIGHT SOCIETY (CONTD)

been broadcast or publicly performed. In some cases, it is not possible to find out every detail of performances. **PRS** then uses 'samples' to allocate royalties, and also draws on record sales charts and other relevant information.

When should you become a ***PRS*** *member?*

Once a songwriter is gaining some success and has at least three works that are performed in public or broadcast, he/she should contact **PRS** for details of how to become a member. The current admission fee is £50 for a writer and £250 for a publisher.

How can I obtain further information about ***PRS****?*

Contact the **PRS** office in Scotland - **PRS**, 3 Rothesay Place, Edinburgh, EH3 7SL (Tel: 0131 226 5320, Fax: 0131 220 4521). **PRS** has a range of literature which is available free of charge including: ***PRS*** *Yearbook,* ***PRS*** *Members' Handbook,* ***PRS****: The Movie* (film available on video formats on free loan), and leaflets including *What is* ***PRS****?, Music, the Law and You!, Music in Theatres,* and ***PRS*** *Live Music Distribution Policy.*

MECHANICAL COPYRIGHT PROTECTION SOCIETY

The Mechanical Right directly or indirectly affects almost everyone involved in the business of creating, publishing, dubbing or recording music.

However, many still regard the whole issue as a confusing minefield. It's actually simpler than most people think.

The legal situation is quite clear. The owner of the copyright in a musical work, whether he or she is the creator or a publisher to whom the rights have been assigned, must be approached for permission prior to any recording or copying of that work, and a fee, or *royalty*, negotiated for its use. This holds true as much for film, television and video producers, advertising agencies, background music suppliers, broadcasters, karaoke recording companies and computer software manufacturers as it does for the record industry, which is understandably the largest user of music.

What then, if you have written a song and someone wants to record and release it? How will they know where to reach you, and how much should you ask for in the way of royalties? Or, for that matter, if you want to release your own record, and one of the tracks is an Elton John cover - will you be able to find out who the publisher is, will you be allowed to use it and will it cost the earth? Maybe you want to use a piece of music on a television production, or an advert or corporate video. Infringing copyright is a serious matter - how can you use the music you want legally, without a lot of hassle?

This is where the **Mechanical Copyright Protection Society**, or **MCPS**, as it's better known, comes in. Music copyright owners, whether they be songwriters, composers, lyricists or the music publishers to which they have assigned their works, join **MCPS** and give the Society a mandate to issue licences and collect royalties for the use of their works wherever they are recorded or copied. Thus, the record and video companies, broadcasters, multimedia producers and other commercial users of music can, in most cases, have access to whatever music they need by completing a very straightforward licence application and paying a fair and reasonable royalty. The copyright owners are thus able to get on with their day-to-day business in the knowledge that **MCPS** is continually monitoring the use of their works both in the UK and, by way of reciprocal agreements with overseas societies, all around the world.

MCPS membership, which is free, is advisable for any music copyright owner whose works are being commercially recorded, dubbed or copied by anyone other than themselves. It makes little sense, for example, for a band releasing their own album to ask **MCPS** to collect royalties from their own label to pay themselves. However, the band may be making other recordings of the songs for radio, television or video which would attract mechanical royalties, or another artist might cover one of the songs. In these cases, the writer-members of the band should join and exclude their own label from collection. Remember also that where writers and composers have assigned their works to publishers, **MCPS** membership is only relevant to the publishers, as they will have become the copyright owners of these works.

The **MCPS** licensing schemes vary, depending on what the music usage is for, but none are particularly complicated. Duncan McCrone is **MCPS**'s Manager in Scotland, and is always available to give free advice on all matters relating to mechanical rights. He is based in Central Scotland, and can be contacted via **MCPS** Headquarters at Elgar House, 41 Streatham High Road, London SW16 1ER.
Tel: 0181 769 4400
Fax: 0181 769 8792

23

ENTERPRISE MUSIC SCOTLAND

Enterprise Music Scotland (**EMS**) was set up in 1992 to support, co-ordinate, and develop a large network of promoting organisations in Scotland.

These music clubs, music societies and arts guilds form an integral part of local music promotion in Scotland.

A principal objective of **EMS** is to support and to build on the work of voluntary music promoters. Each year it supports around 400 classical music concerts in a variety of locations throughout Scotland. **EMS** seeks to assist these voluntary promoters in the work they do in bringing live music performances to local audiences and in their efforts to encourage as many people as possible to enjoy live music performances of the highest quality.

EMS provides financial support, from funds provided by the **Scottish Arts Council**, for voluntary promoters in the form of grants towards costs of promoting professional performances. Generally, grants are available for a season of concerts and one-off concerts can be considered. Application forms and a set of **EMS** guidelines concerning funding, are available from our office.

EMS provides information support and encourages information sharing between promoters. Each year **EMS** undertakes a tours co-ordination process, designed to pool resources of promoters and assist in their touring arrangements. Part of this process involves the production of the *Scottish Tours Book* (published in September each year), which is designed to provide promoters with the information they require about performers who wish to tour in Scotland. It is also an opportunity for performers to introduce themselves to music clubs. Allied to this is the national Tours Planning Conference in November each year where plans and arrangements for tours in the following season are laid.

EMS has strong commitments to developing live music performances in Scotland through the extension in the number of voluntary promoters. The maintenance of existing audiences and encouragement for new audiences for performances is a high priority. Funds and support are available to help with the establishment of new promoting organisations and **EMS** would like to hear from individuals and organisations who may be interested in bringing live music performances to their own community.

This large network of promoting organisations and the associated concerts provides a unique opportunity for audiences in Scotland to hear high quality performances locally. **EMS** especially encourages performances by Scottish-based performers and of contemporary and lesser-known works.

If you would like to know more about **EMS** and our activities please contact: Ronnie Rae, **Enterprise Music Scotland**, Westburn House, Westburn Park, Aberdeen AB2 5DE. Tel: 01224 620025 Fax: 01224 620027

24

NFMS Scotland is the Scottish arm of the **National Federation of Music Societies** which represents some 1,500 voluntary music organisations throughout the UK and can justly claim to be 'the National Voice of Music Making'.

The membership now includes not only choral, orchestral and music societies, but also steel bands, gospel choirs, wind bands - a whole range of different genres of performance.

The **NFMS** has three main functions. Firstly to ensure that the voice of the amateur musician is heard at all levels from government downwards through advocacy, representation and lobbying. No less important is the provision for **NFMS** members: a comprehensive package of artistic, legal, financial and information services. Last, but by no means least, the **NFMS** is committed to ensure that music societies not only survive but also thrive. To that end, an ongoing Training and Development programme means that members are equipped with the necessary skills to attract audiences, members and funding, in addition to practical training aimed at improving performance. This particular aspect of the Federation's work has been supported over the past three years by substantial sponsorship from British Telecom under the banner 'Making More of Music'.

NFMS Scotland currently has 106 affiliated societies from Shetland to Dunbar, whose interests are served by an enthusiastic 24-strong committee. Every member society in Scotland is allocated a Visitor, a member of the Scottish Committee who is available to offer help and advice, to ensure that each society is reaping maximum benefit from **NFMS** membership and to encourage every group to achieve its full potential in all aspects of its work. Visitors are only a telephone call away should a query or a problem arise and if they do not have the answer they will discover who can provide the relevant information.

To keep members in touch with the activities of fellow-performers and promoters the Scottish Newsletter comes free to every Scottish member society three times a year. It incorporates a concert diary for the relevant period and provides a means of communicating information on the work of the Scottish Committee. Members also receive the *NFMS News* from Francis House, the Federation's Head Office in London, and this highlights the issues which are pertinent to all members of the **NFMS** throughout the UK.

Each spring there is the opportunity for delegates from all societies to meet each other at the annual

NATIONAL FEDERATION of MUSIC SOCIETIES

Scottish Conference which visits a different part of the country each year. After a brief Annual Business Meeting, the remainder of the day is spent in a discussion of issues of significance to member societies and occasionally the entire day is devoted to a participatory activity such as a Choral Workshop. However, useful as the discussions and workshops are, the principal benefit to be gained from such a conference is the opportunity to meet people with similar interests and enthusiasms, to hear about successes, to share problems, air grievances and, hopefully, leave with some fresh ideas. The same is true of the National Conference, normally held at the end of September, when delegates from the length and breadth of the UK converge for a weekend of discussion sessions, seminars and workshops. In 1994 this Conference was held in Edinburgh.

Performing societies in Scotland can apply for financial assistance towards concert expenses including professional concert, rehearsal and tuition fees, hire of venues and the costs of music and publicity. The funding for this comes from

NATIONAL FEDERATION of MUSIC SOCIETIES (CONTD)

the **Scottish Arts Council** on whose behalf **NFMS Scotland** administers the Financial Aid Scheme for choral and orchestral societies and also funding for amateur opera.

Whether in a remote location or in a city centre, all societies can benefit equally from the advice and expertise available from the Federation. Performing societies can save substantial sums by taking advantage of concessionary rates negotiated for the engagement of **Musicans' Union** members, and all societies can benefit from the highly competitive Block Insurance Scheme, the Performing Rights Scheme and the Programme Note Bank. Membership subscriptions are banded, so that even the smallest organisation can afford to join and take advantage of these money-saving opportunities. **NFMS Scotland** has a Recruitment and Liaison Officer who will be happy to deal with enquiries and can arrange for a visit from a member of the Scottish Committee.

The **NFMS** is proud of the fact that in many communities the only live music is provided by an **NFMS** member society. To quote the President of **NFMS**, Sir Peter Maxwell Davies, 'Where **NFMS** is active music becomes alive!'

For further information contact: The **National Federation of Music Societies**, Francis House, Francis Street, London SW1P 1DE (Tel: 0171 828 7320, Fax: 0171 828 5504), or **NFMS Scotland** Recruitment and Liaison Officer, Miss Isobel Crawford, 9 Beansburn, Kilmarnock KA3 1RN, Ayrshire (Tel: 01563 520538).

ARTISTS

Editorial Notes

The chapter is divided into various categories depending on the type of music involved, e.g. classical, jazz etc. Each category is further subdivided as necessary so that similar types of groups, orchestras, or players of the same instrument are grouped together and listed by alphabetical order. If you wish to find a classical violinist for example, then you should look at the 'Violin' section of the Classical category. If you wish to find a particular artist but are unsure where exactly they would be placed then check the index for the page reference number.

In some sections, mainly Classical and Folk and Traditional, the listings also include useful contacts. These are organisations which work in that particular field of music and may be able to answer queries not covered in the *Handbook*.

Some sections are less well represented than others and it is our hope to expand and develop these areas in future editions.
The category divisions are as follows:

CLASSICAL
COUNTRY MUSIC
EARLY MUSIC
FOLK AND TRADITIONAL
JAZZ
LIGHT MUSIC (article only, no listings)
MUSIC FROM OTHER CULTURES
ROCK/POP (article only, no listings)
COMMUNITY.

Classical Music in Scotland

by Mary Miller

Bernard Levin announced recently, in his newspaper column, that music had stopped. Recent English composition, he pronounced, was negligible; nothing half decent had been written since Benjamin Britten's death.

Mr Levin, step North. In Scotland, we bask in a honeypot of creativity, both in terms of composition and its performance. We have composers of both intellect and glamour, powerfully individual voices who produce music which communicates in a language which everyone - from telecentric child to reactionary grandmother - can appreciate. This is neither contrived, nor a compromise in each composer's truth - simply that in Scotland we have, perhaps, a more defined, more proudly held sense of culture, and a landscape which, both politically and physically, seems to provoke a particularly open and glowing creativity.

So, we have innumerable talented young composers who have become leaders, inspirers, even entrepreneurs. We have composer-led ensembles, like the **Chamber Group of Scotland**, and orchestras like the **Scottish Chamber Orchestra** which is encouraging a new breed of musician who performs, composes and works in the wider community. We have a **BBC Scottish Symphony Orchestra** which, by its own vivacious playing standard and unswerving commitment to new Scottish work, has pulled away from the threat of extinction, and a **Royal Scottish National Orchestra** recently re-vitalised. And we have a **Scottish Opera**, which, if like its colleagues nationwide it struggles financially, is bold in its style and outlook.

It does perhaps take a major festival such as Edinburgh's for us to realise that what treasure we have, in terms of performance, is not an admirable 'regional' achievement, but an international resource. For the triumphs of Scottish composition, this year's BBC *Fairest Isle* celebrations tell their own story - our composers, both in Scotland, or those who have chosen to make their homes here, are represented in force on Radio 3's airwaves, and at the Proms. Yet still they depend on London publishers for recognition: a Scottish based, respected and effective publishing facility must surely come soon.

Our music education system may quiver as it anticipates the full thrust of regional change, but what we have we must appreciate and cherish: a network of dedicated teachers, a catalogue of fine ensembles in jazz, classical, traditional music and brilliant brass band. There is a rising standard of entrant to the **Royal Scottish Academy of Music and Drama**, where the new Sir Alexander Gibon opera school will pay tribute to the ability of young Scottish singers, and where our established composers teach their aspirators. So the wheel of creativity turns.

Our contemporary music is fit and well muscled with a number of fine ensembles working in its support: The **Chamber Group of Scotland**, directed by two of Scotland's foremost composers, James MacMillan and Sally Beamish, plus cellist Robert Irvine, is evangelical in the performance of Scottish contemporary work, and enterprising in the pursuit of performing formulae, experimenting both with venues and visual effects. The **Hebrides Ensemble** also dedicates time to Scottish work, planning programmes which juxtapose with care such work with like-minded works elsewhere.

ARTISTS

Both ensembles refuse to ghetto-ise the new, blending it with masterpieces and rarities from the past. The **Paragon Ensemble** is even broader in the scope of work which it embraces - tackling opera and music theatre, and undertaking brilliant work in the community. It is also a brave commissioner of new native work, and champions the younger generation of Scottish composers, whom it incorporates into its community programme.

The **Yggdrasil Quartet of Aberdeen**, recently appointed to the city as the result of an innovative three-way partnership between the city, the University of Aberdeen and the Scottish Arts Council, may set a benchmark for string playing throughout the land, and the **Edinburgh Quartet** continues to play to a dedicated audience.

The choral tradition continues, though not, as John Purser's *Scotland's Music* reminds us, with the fervour of pre-war times. The **Edinburgh Festival Chorus**, with sections combining from Glasgow, Edinburgh and Aberdeen, produces both might and sophistication and is in superb form with David Jones as its new director. Edinburgh, Glasgow and Dundee have vibrant choral unions, and Glasgow has the all-male, rich voiced **Glasgow Philharmonic Choir**. The main cities all foster smaller ensembles too.

The **Royal Scottish National Orchestra Chorus**, directed by Christopher Bell, is magnificent, and has worked indefatigably to overcome the vicissitudes of Glasgow Royal Concert Hall's unwelcoming acoustic for voices. The **Scottish Chamber Orchestra Chorus**, formed from the somewhat smouldering ashes of the Scottish Philharmonic Singers, has not yet entirely found form after the changes of musical direction, but is working hard with new director Tim Byram-Wigfield. And **Cappella Nova**, with Alan Tavener's fastidious direction, continues to explore repertoire from Carver to Cage. The standard varies depending on the voices available, but at best this ensemble is elegant and inventive.

It is customary, in such perorations, to settle for a key word. In 1995, it is no struggle: in Scotland we have, now, collaboration - orchestras combining in well planned series, medias mixing, folk bands working with their fellows from the symphony platform, jazz artists writing for classical violinists, and players crossing other boundaries, thinking about presentation, considering dress, lighting and choice of venue.

What we need is confidence not self-congratulation, focus not fashion, and a national commitment to art, as opposed to entertainment.

For if entertainment is fun for the moment, art is what changes lives and sustains a great country's culture. Let's hear it.

AGENTS

Louise Naftalin Arts Consultancy and Management
Agent for classical artists and ensembles. All aspects of marketing, publicity and promotion undertaken.
537 Sauchiehall Street, Glasgow G3 7PQ
Tel: 0141 248 1611 Fax: 0141 248 1989

Pitch Perfect
Providers of sopranos, string quartets, tenors or trios for corporate entertainment and weddings; promoters of full-scale choral and symphonic concerts.
5 Aytoun Road, Glasgow G41 5RL
Tel: 0141 423 5577 Fax: 0141 423 5544
Contact: Lesley Boyd (Director) or Scott Cooper (Director)

Sonata Ltd
Arranges tours by musicians and ensembles from mostly Eastern Europe, including St Petersburg Glinka State Choir and Shostakovitch Quartet with promoters and festivals such as Mayfest, South Bank, Bath Festival etc. Particularly help young musicians' careers, representing Victoria Imadko (conductor), Graf Mourja (violin). Assists in touring the CIS.
11 North Park Street, Glasgow G20 7AA
Tel: 0141 946 7034

BRASS/ SILVER BANDS

Annan Town Brass Band
A long-serving brass band with wide repertoire. Annual concert in April, many other concerts, gala days, contests, church services etc. throughout the year. Contact for further details or invitations!
4 Newington Avenue, Annan, Dumfriesshire DG12 5AX
Tel: 01461 203190
Contact: Samantha Denner

Barrhead and District Brass Band
71 Tantallon Drive, Paisley, Renfrewshire PA2 9HS
Tel: 0150 581 4502
Contact: Thomas Allan (Secretary)
Tel: 0141 308 2433 (W)

Bo'ness and Carriden Brass Band
Winner of the Scottish Brass Band Championship 1995.
29 Elizabeth Avenue, Grangemouth, Stirlingshire FK3 9DD
Tel: 01324 472512
Contact: James Allan (Secretary)

Campbeltown Brass
Members of the Scottish Amateur Brass Band Association. Rehearsals: Thursday evenings. For details of activities/concerts etc. contact Band Manager.
17 Crosshill Avenue, Campbeltown, Argyll PA28 6LH
Tel: 01586 554356
Contact: Gordon Evans (Band Manager)

City of Edinburgh Brass Band
Offers opportunity to explore the brass band repertoire. Rehearsals: 8.00 - 9.30pm, Community Centre, Albion Place, Calton, Edinburgh. Some ability to play a brass instrument required.
30 Morningside Park, Edinburgh EH10 5HB
Tel: 0131 447 4791
Contact: Arnold Myers or Charles Easton (Secretary)

Clydebank District Band
Founded 1891. 25-strong. Meets: Wednesday and Sunday evenings in own hall, Second Avenue, Clydebank. Conductor:Eric Dunlea. Regular competitors in Scottish championships (winners 17 times). Beginners' band meets Thursdays under David Neil.
111a Kirkwood Avenue, Clydebank, Dunbartonshire G81 2LL
Tel: 0141 952 6839
Contact: George Fleming (Treasurer)

Cowdenbeath Brass Band
Band meets twice weekly: Thursday 7 - 9 and Sunday 5 - 7.
3 Husband Place, Dunfermline, Fife KY11 4XN
Tel: 01383 728760 / 515818
Contact: John Todd (Secretary)

Creetown Silver Band
Cairnlea, Machermore, Newton Stewart, Wigtownshire DG8 7AR
Tel: 01671 403306
Contact: Gillian McKnight (Secretary)

Croy Parish Silver Band
Traditional brass band formed in 1875.
12 Craiglinn, Condorrat, Cumbernauld, Glasgow G68 9AD
Tel: 01236 728951
Contact: James O'Donnell (Secretary)

Dalkeith and Monktonhall Colliery Brass Band
57 Gardiner Road, Prestonpans, East Lothian EH32 9HG
Tel: 01875 812705
Contact: Lawrence Blair (Secretary)

Dalmellington Brass Band
24a Eglinton Terrace, Ayr KA7 1JJ
Tel: 01292 265188
Contact: Jan Murray (Secretary)

Dumfries Town Band
Willing to take on all types of engagements (parades, concerts, songs of praise, gala days etc). Around half the present membership is of school age. Experienced players welcome. Training given to beginners.
42 Hardthorn Crescent, Dumfries DG2 9JD
Tel: 01387 253817
Contact: William Little (Secretary) or Margaret Williamson Tel: 01387 261257

Dunaskin Doon Brass Band
17 Cargill Road, Maybole, Ayrshire KA19 8AF
Tel: 01655 882188 Fax: 01655 882188
Contact: Hugh White (Secretary)

Dundee Instrumental (St. Margaret's) Brass Band
Meets: Thursdays 7.30pm, Band Room, Lochee Park Pavilion.
74 Harrison Avenue, Dundee DD2 3SU
Tel: 01382 828081
Contact: Angus McKay (Secretary)

Dunfermline Town Brass Band
All types of engagements carried out eg. galas, concerts, hospitals and old folks homes, and all events considered individually. Learners' class for all ages: Tuesdays 5.30 - 7pm at the band hall.
29 Standing Stone Walk, Dunfermline, Fife KY11 4RG
Tel: 01383 727626
Contact: Dorothy Hall (Secretary)

ARTISTS CLASSICAL

33

Elgin City Brass Band

Small brass band which has been in existence since before the turn of the century. Performs wherever appropriate, mostly at church services and fêtes, hospitals, concerts and in parks in the summer, with or without a fee depending on circumstances.

17 Perimeter Road, Pinefield, Elgin, Moray IV30 3AF
Contact: Heather Park Tel: 01343 549251

Fauldhouse Miners' Brass Band

4 Moorelands, Addiewell, West Calder, West Lothian EH55 8HU
Tel: 01501 762516
Contact: John Kelly (Secretary)

Greenhall Youth Brass Band

2 Mortonhall Park Gardens, Edinburgh EH17 8SL
Tel: 0131 664 5125
Contact: John Robertson (Secretary)

Hawick Saxhorn Band

Young band - old history, established 1855. A marching band. A concert band. A competitive band. Available for engagments. Bandmaster Robert J Hume.
24 Chay Blyth Place, Hawick, Roxburghshire TD9 8HX
Tel: 01450 374711
Contact: Margaret Potts or Mrs G C Tait Tel: 01450 376196

Jedforest Instrumental Band

28 Howden Crescent, Jedburgh, Roxburghshire TD8 6JY
Tel: 01835 862565
Contact: William Renilson (Secretary)

Johnstone Silver Band

8 Milliken Place, Kilbarchan, Johnstone, Renfrewshire PA10 2AN
Tel: 01505 734422
Contact: Mrs C Maxwell (Secretary)

Kilmarnock Concert Brass

53 Harperland Drive, Kilmarnock, Ayrshire KA1 1UH
Tel: 01563 534225
Contact: Andrew Keachie (Musical Director) or Jamie Quin (Band Secretary) Tel: 01563 534854

Kirkintilloch Brass Band

Formed 1890. Scottish National Champions (1984, 1985, 1990). Represented Scotland at the National Championships in Denmark, Wales, Holland and Luxembourg. Also made TV appearances, radio broadcasts and recordings. Kirkintilloch Kelvin Brass is the junior section.
62 Fellsview Avenue, Kirkintilloch, Glasgow G66 2LX
Tel: 0141 776 3395 (H) / 248 5811(W)
Contact: Peter Fraser MBE (Secretary)

Langholm Town Brass Band

12 Charlotte Street, Langholm, Dumfriesshire DG13 0DZ
Tel: 013873 80425
Contact: Christine Calvert (Secretary)

Lochgelly Brass Band

3 Hailes Place, Dunfermline, Fife KY12 7XS
Tel: 01383 737293 Fax: 01383 737293
Contact: Susan Shepherd

MacTaggart Scott Loanhead Silver Band

Founded 1943. Activities include competing (4th section Scottish Champions 1992) and concerts. Available for concert and marching engagements. One recording *Impressions in Brass* (1994). Also junior training band with tuition for beginners. New members always welcome.
Mansfield Villa, 23 Polton Road, Loanhead, Midlothian EH20 9BU
Tel: 0131 440 3830 Fax: 0131 452 8272
Contact: Alan MacLaren (Secretary)

Murray International Whitburn Band

1995 was the band's 125th year. 1954 first Scottish band to win a national title. Won national and European awards. Draws members from all over Scotland. Performs in many concert venues. Involved in the annual Malcolm Sargent Cancer Fund concert in the Glasgow Royal Concert Hall, 1995.
Cumloden, 106 Sheephousehill, Fauldhouse, Bathgate EH47 9EL
Tel: 01501 771616
Contact: Archibald Simpson (Secretary)

Musselburgh and Fisherrow Trades Brass Band

35 Fowler Street, Tranent, East Lothian EH33 1BT
Tel: 01875 613565
Contact: James Stewart (Secretary)

Newland Concert Brass (Bathgate)

40 Edinburgh Road, Bathgate, West Lothian EH48 1BA
Tel: 01506 633025
Contact: Jim Gill (Secretary)

Newtongrange (B and C Decorators) Silver Band

Available for all types of engagements and church wedding services etc.
21 Galadale Crescent, Newtongrange, Dalkeith, Midlothian EH22 4RR
Tel: 0131 663 6763
Contact: Terry Smith (Secretary) or David O'Connell Tel: 0131 663 1430

Penicuik Silver Brass Band

16 Greenhillk Park, Penicuik, Midlothian EH26 9EX
Tel: 01968 673976
Contact: Janice Fleming

Perth Silver Brass Band

Experienced players and beginners required for fourth section band with busy competition and engagement calendar. Practice nights: Wednesday 7.30pm, Friday 7pm at the RASC Memorial Club, 10 St Leonards Bank, Perth. Available for all types of engagement.
7 Tummel Road, Letham, Perth PH1 2HQ
Tel: 01738 33026
Contact: Jane Dewar (Secretary) or Mr A Kelly Tel: 01738 583122

Perthshire Brass

Lauderdale, 24 Tibbermore Gardens, Perth PH1 2BX
Tel: 01738 622596
Contact: James Harker (Chairman)

Renfrew Burgh Band

43 Cockles Loan, Renfrew PA4 0PA
Tel: 0141 886 3148
Contact: Harry Peckham (Secretary)

Sanquhar and District Silver Band

39 Waugh Drive, Sanquhar, Dumfriesshire DG4 6AQ
Tel: 01659 50660
Contact: Margaret MacCormick (Secretary)

ARTISTS

CLASSICAL

St. Ronan's Silver Band
Available for festivals, gala days etc. One of the oldest established bands in Scotland, its members meet every Friday 7 - 9 pm in the Band Hall, Hall Street, Innerleithen. New members always welcome. Beginners meet Tuesdays. Regular concerts and public appearances.
1 Horsbrugh Street, Innerleithen, Peeblesshire EH44 6LF
Tel: 01896 830577
Contact: Keith Belleville (Secretary)

Tayport Instrumental Brass Band
Rehearsals 7.30 - 9.30 pm Monday and Thursday, Band Hall, Maitland Street, Tayport.
7 Woodhaven Terrace, Wormit, Fife DD6 8LD
Tel: 01382 541416
Contact: Mr A Smart (Secretary)

UDI Brass (Aberdeen) Brass Band
Aims to encourage and foster interest in brass band music and to provide special instruction in the playing of brass band instruments. The band, or a smaller group, can cover a wide range of musical styles and can entertain at a variety of functions.
50 Claremont Street (GF/R), Aberdeen AB1 6RA
Tel: 01224 587896
Contact: Pauline Ann Craib (Secretary)

MILITARY BANDS

The Band of HM Royal Marines Scotland
Can provide an ensemble to suit many occasions from a jazz trio to a full symphonic band and including fanfare teams, dance/big bands, chamber groups and marching bands.
HMS Cochrane, Rosyth, Fife FY11 2XT
Tel: 01383 412121 x62052
Contact: Lt Christopher Davis
Tel: 01383 424394 or Band Colour Sergeant John Bushell
Tel: 01383 412121 x62052

WIND BANDS

Dunbartonshire Concert Band
Community band which offers the opportunity to players of a wide range of ages and musical ability to play in a wind band. Has a varied programme of performances given in concert, at festivals and at clubs, and for charities. Rehearsals on Saturdays, 10am - 12.30pm, Cairns Church, Milngavie.
10 Kelvin Drive, Glasgow G20 8QG
Tel: 0141 946 2762
Contact: Richard Phelps (Secretary)

Glasgow University Wind Band
Under the auspices of the University Music Club. Repertoire covers standard and new works. No auditions. Membership open to all students, staff, graduates, and employees of the university. Rehearsals: Mondays, 5 - 7pm, Concert Hall, for first two terms. One concert around March.
Music Department, 14 University Gardens, Glasgow G12 8QE
Tel: 0141 330 4093 Fax: 0141 307 8018
Contact: Stephen Broad (Conductor) or Andrea Possée (Music Club Secretary)

Glasgow Wind Band
Formed 1972. Provides an opportunity for senior school pupils, students and adult members of the public to play in a symphonic band. Termly concerts, national competition, annual major concert, new commissions and residential weekends. Meetings: Mondays, 7 - 9.30pm, Hillhead High School. Subscription fee.
c/o Paul Stonelake, 40 Lansdowne Crescent, Kelvinbridge, Glasgow G20 6NH
Tel: 0141 337 3673
Contact: Kevin Price (Musical Director)
Tel: 01360 311215

Leith Community Concert Band
Rehearsals: 7.45 - 9.45pm St Margaret's Episcopal Church Hall, Easter Road. Grade 8 diploma preferred, Grade 6 minimum. Small membership fee, paid weekly. Auditions by arrangement with the Director of Music.
2 Wellington Place, Leith, Edinburgh EH6 7EQ
Tel: 0131 554 0568 / 455 3322(day)
Contact: F W Frayling-Kelly (Director of Music/Chairman)

Strathclyde University Wind Band
Repertoire firmly in the symphonic wind band tradition, together with opportunities for smaller ensemble work such as brass ensembles and wind ensemble. Rehearsals: Tuesdays, 5 - 7pm. Annual membership fee, concession for students.
Director of Music , University of Strathclyde, Livingstone Tower, Richmond Street, Glasgow G1 1XH
Tel: 0141 552 4400 x3444
Fax: 0141 552 4053
Contact: Alan Tavener (Director of Music)

Trinity Concert Band
Formed by FPs of Trinity Academy but all welcome. Interested in those who learned to play as adults. No auditions. Rehearsals: 7.30pm, Mondays, Trinity Academy, Craighall Ave. Small membership fee payable weekly.
4 Broomyknowe, Colinton EH14 1J2
Tel: 0131 441 7509 / 0131 552 8101(day)
Contact: Ian Cameron (Chairman)

BARBERSHOP CHOIRS

Forth Valley Chorus
Ladies barbershop chorus. 44 voices. 1993 Gold Medal UK Champions. Went to Reno, Nevada, November 1994 to compete in the International Championship. Available to perform. Fees from £50. Rehearsals: 7.15pm, Thursdays, Broughton High School, Carrington Road, Edinburgh. Standards: must have a good ear. Sponsors: Foundation for Sport and the Arts.
43/2 South Gyle Park, Edinburgh EH12 9EW
Tel: 0131 334 4723 / 0131 229 8711(day)
Contact: Margaret Dickson (Secretary)

ARTISTS

CLASSICAL

35

Rolling Hills Barbershop Chorus

Male voice choir singing in barbershop style at charity events, clubs, concerts etc. Song parts recorded on tape for members to learn. Rehearsals: Friday 7-9pm, the King's Building, West Mains Road, Edinburgh. Requirements: sing a note on pitch. Small membership fee, new members welcome - come and have fun!

5 Grigor Gardens, Edinburgh EH4 2PA
Tel: 0131 539 2848
Contact: Joe Nelson or Bill Harvey
Tel: 01896 831112

ARTISTS

CLASSICAL

CHAMBER CHOIRS

Glasgow Chamber Choir

30-strong chamber choir. Meets Thursdays St Aloysius, Garnethill. At least three annual concerts. Repertoire from early music through Bach and the classics to contemporary. Performed Edinburgh Festival Fringe. 1995 new Maunder edition of Mozart's *Requiem*. April 1996, *St John Passion*.
47 Deanston Drive, Shawlands G41 3AG
Tel: 0141 649 0507
Contact: Robert Marshall (Director)

Glasgow University Chamber Singers

Formed in 1992. A membership of 16 voices. Broad range of music covered outwith regular choral society repertoire. Auditions in early October at the Music Department. Termly subscription.
c/o The Concerts Organiser, University Concerts Office, 14 University Gardens, Glasgow G12 8QE
Tel: 0141 330 4092 Fax: 0141 307 8018
Contact: Judy Kilpatrick (Concerts Organiser) or Graham Hair (Director)

Glasgow University Chapel Choir

Membership open to all people associated with the University. No auditions, though some choral experience desirable. Rehearsals: Thursdays, 5.15 - 7pm, the Concert Hall. Concerts usually December and March.
c/o The Concerts Organiser, University Concerts Office, 14 University Gardens, Glasgow G12 8QE
Tel: 0141 330 4092 Fax: 0141 307 8018
Contact: Judy Kilpatrick (Concerts Organiser) or Stuart Campbell (Director)

Rudsambee

12-voice *a cappella* choir with wide-ranging repertoire, including Gaelic *puirt-a-beul* (mouth music), Southern African anthems, medieval secular and religious music, original settings of poems - whatever works for them! Perform in pubs, clubs, festivals etc. New members welcome - some experience of sight-reading preferred. Rehearsals: 8.30 - 10.15pm, Mondays.
13 Kilmaurs Road, Edinburgh EH16 5DA
Tel: 0131 662 0574
Contact: Sheena Phillips (Conductor/ Arranger)

Scottish Chamber Choir

25 voice choir. Performs mainly in and around Edinburgh, including Festival Fringe. Varied repertoire from contemporary to 16th c. Conductor for 1994-5 is Philip Sawyer; accompanist, Iain Ogg. Rehearsals: Mondays 7.30 - 9.30pm, Fettes College, Carrington Road, Edinburgh. Auditions usually in September. Audition of prepared piece plus sight reading required. Membership fee.
5 Hunt Place, Crossford, Fife KY12 8QG
Tel: 01383 729777 / 821921 (day)
Contact: Frank Lucas (President) or Bill Wood (Secretary) Tel: 0131 339 7663

Stonehaven and District Choral Society

531 Holburn Street, Aberdeen AB1 7LH
Tel: 01224 574979 (H)
Contact: Patricia Reed

GENERAL CHOIRS

Aberdeen Bach Choir

Two recitals a year. Choir re-formed in 1956 so 1996 is 40th anniversary year. Repertoire covers Renaissance to 20th c. This session Purcell, Monteverdi, Bach and the first Scottish performance of the recently edited Michael Haydn *St Teresa Mass*. Conductor James Lobban.
Linshart, 113 Station Road, Ellon AB41 9AZ
Tel: 01358 721568
Contact: Lesley Robertson (Secretary) or James Lobban (Conductor) Tel: 01224 638898

Aberdeen Choral Society

110 strong, meets on Mondays in Langstane Kirk Hall. Two annual concerts at Christmas and Spring. Conductor Alastair McDonald. Repertoire covers major choral works. *Messiah* performed every Christmas. 1996, 50th anniversary season, Vaughan Williams' *Serenade to Music*, Parry's *Blest Pair of Sirens*, Elgar's *The Music Makers* and first performance of commission from Lyell Cresswell.
17-18 Golden Square, Aberdeen AB9 8NY
Tel: 01224 632032 (day) / 713732 (eve)
Contact: Graham Mountford (Secretary)

Angus Choral Society

A 60-strong group of enthusiastic singers of wide age range who enjoy and appreciate choral music, and like to share their joy and pleasure with others throughout the community.
8 East Hillbank, Kirriemuir, Angus DD8 4HQ
Tel: 01575 572324 Fax: 01575 575158
Contact: Anne Smith (Secretary)

Anstruther Philharmonic Society

Formed in 1892. One major concert in March, as well as a less formal pre-Christmas performance. Membership extends from St Andrews to Leven.
Murrayfield, 34 James Street, Pittenweem, Fife KY10 2QW
Tel: 01333 310194
Contact: Dr A S L Kennedy (President) or Mrs A Robertson Tel: 01333 311821

Ayr Choral Union

21 Hillhouse Gardens, Barassie, Troon, Ayrshire KA10 6SZ
Tel: 01292 311351
Contact: V B M McLeonard (Secretary)

Bearsden Burgh Choir

Formed 1968. Weekly rehearsals, Wednesday evenings in Milngavie Town Hall, September - May. Two oratorio concerts each year (Christmas and Easter) as well as numerous charity/fun concerts. Musical Director: James Hunter. Honorary President: Agnes Duncan, MBE. Accompanist: Anne Crawford.
5 Daleview Avenue, Glasgow G12 0HE
Tel: 0141 226 5511(day) / 339 4567(eve)
Contact: Miss V A Klimowicz (Hon Secretary) or Anne or Alan Foulis
Tel: 0141 956 3092

Buckie Choral Union

13 Sterlochy Street, Findochty, Buckie, Banffshire AB5 2PQ
Tel: 01542 832930
Contact: Mrs E M Davidson (Secretary) or Dr A Silbergh Tel: 01542 831030

Cadenza Choir

Formed 1993 by singers who wished to sing to a high standard. Mixed repertoire from Renaissance to popular, including choral classics like Fauré's *Requiem*. Three main concerts a year, plus several for charity. Rehearsals on Wednesday evenings in central Edinburgh. Small membership fee. Short entrance audition.
3 Mavisbank Place, Edinburgh EH18 1DQ
Tel: 0131 663 1278
Contact: Graham Lovett

Call that Singing!

Rehearsals: most Mondays at 7.15 pm, John Anderson Building, Strathclyde University, Taylor Street (off Cathedral Street). Always looking for more people to join. Everyone, regardless of age and singing experience, is welcome. No auditions, no sight reading. Lots of fun.
c/o SCET, 74 Victoria Crescent Road, Glasgow G12 9JN
Tel: 0141 337 3336 Fax: 0141 334 6519
Contact: Sue Hillman (Project Director) or Joe McGinley (Musical Director)

Cappella Nova

An *a cappella* specialist ensemble of 3 to 18+. Repertoire prinicpally of early and contemporary music. Winners of PRS Enterprise Awards for commitment to contemporary music and a Glenfiddich Living Scotland award for recording Scottish early music. CDs on the ASV Gaudeamus and Linn Record labels.
172 Hyndland Road, Glasgow G12 9HZ
Tel: 0141 552 0634 / 357 0052
Fax: 0141 552 4053
Contact: Alan Tavener (Director) or Rebecca Tavener (Manager)

Choir of St Paul's Episcopal Cathedral (Dundee)

The choir, consisting of boys and men, primarily performs music to a professional standard for the cathedral services in the Anglican Choral Tradition. It also performs widely all over Scotland both in sacred and secular settings. Two recent recordings and tour of USA.
Binrock Lodge, 454A Perth Road, Dundee DD2 1NG
Tel: 01382 669331
Contact: Mark Hindley (Organist and Master of Choristers) or Cathedral Office Tel: 01382 224486

The City of Glasgow Chorus

Independent chorus - gives around 12 concerts each season. 150 members. In addition to its own promotions, sings regularly with The City of Glasgow Philharmonic Orchestra and Opera-in-Concert. Has appeared with the RSNO and Scottish Opera Orchestra. Rehearsals: Tuesdays, city centre.
14 Hyndland Road, Glasgow G12 9UP
Tel: 0141 339 6153 / 334 9588
Contact: Graham Taylor (Musical Director)

Clydebank District Choir

50-strong mixed choir. Meets: Tuesdays, Clydebank Town Hall. Repertoire: part songs, covering a wide range of styles including songs from the shows, Scots songs, sacred, and folk songs. Two per year concerts at Christmas and spring as well as other smaller concerts throughout the year.
Flat 1, 10 Dorset Square, Glasgow G3 7LL
Tel: 0141 221 8837
Contact: Cameron Murdoch (Conductor)

Clydebank Male Voice Choir

Formed in January 1900, the first in Scotland, and has given many concerts, radio and television broadcasts.
29 Hawick Street, Yoker, Glasgow G13 4EL
Tel: 0141 952 5849
Contact: John Billings (Secretary)

The Crescent Singers

Perform three times per season: Festival of Carols (Christmas), choral concert with orchestra (Easter), and a concert of part-songs, folk-song arrangements and songs from shows (mid-June). Rehearsals: Wednesdays, 7.30 - 9.30pm in St James Church Hall, Portobello September-June. No auditions. Small membership fee.
52 Haymarket Terrace (T/L), Edinburgh EH12 5LA
Tel: 0131 337 4750 / 337 4750
Contact: Brian Hamilton (Musical Director)

Cumbernauld Choir

50-60 members rehearse Tuesdays St Mungo's Church, Cumbernauld. Conductor James Whyte. Major works *The Creation*, *Messiah*, and the requiems of Mozart, Verdi and Fauré. Considering a lighter programme to encourage new members. Always accompanied by Edinburgh University Orchestra.
29c Braeface Road, Seafar, Cumbernauld G67 1HJ
Tel: 01236 727706 (day) / 720905 (eve)
Contact: Margot Pinkerton (Secretary)

Cunninghame Choir

Meets in Beith Community Centre, Wednesday evenings, September - May. Gives two concerts (with orchestral accompaniment) each year in various locations in North Ayrshire. Mainly classical music, from Monteverdi to MacMillan. New members (SATB) always welcome.
40 Morven Avenue, Paisley PA2 8DR
Tel: 0141 884 5008
Contact: John Turner (Secretary)

ARTISTS
CLASSICAL

37

ARTISTS

CLASSICAL

Cupar Choral Society

70-strong oratorio choir. Meets: Monday evenings St John's Church Hall. Performances usually December and March. Conductor: Richard Galloway.
63 St Michaels Drive, Cupar, Fife
Tel: 01334 653667
Contact: Pat Ritchie (Hon Secretary)

Dalry Singers

A small choir for people over 50 years old. Frequently performs concerts for old peoples' clubs, homes etc. Rehearsals: 10am - 12 noon at Dalry House, Orwell Place, Edinburgh. Any standard welcome.
Speedyburn House, Gifford, East Lothian EH41 4QL
Tel: 0162 081363
Contact: Mrs McIndoe (Conductor) or Dalry House Tel: 0131 337 5252

Dingwall and District Choral Society

Pear Cottage, 62 Saltburn, Invergordon, Ross-shire IV18 0JY
Tel: 01463 81317 (day) / 01349 61673 (eve)
Contact: Mr N Bolton

Dumfries Choral Society

90-strong mixed voice choir performing regularly with professional artists in Dumfries and the surrounding area. 1995/6 proramme includes Rutter's *Requiem*, Fauré's *Requiem*, Bizet's *Te Deum*, Verdi's *Te Deum*, and Puccini's *Messa di Gloria* and two carol concerts. Conductor: Jean Mason. Assistant Conductor: Nick Riley. Rehearsal Accompanist: Margaret Tarbitt.
Braeside, Virginhall, Thornhill, Dumfriesshire DG3 4AD
Tel: 01387 253820 (day) / 01848 6330821(eve)
Contact: Mr G A Creamer (Secretary)

Dundee Choral Union

Around 140-strong meets Mondays 7.30pm in Music Centre, Bell Street. Musical director: Neil Mantle. Christmas 1995, *Messiah*. Spring 1996, Vaughan Williams' *Sea Symphony* and Elgar's *The Music Makers*. Performances in the Caird Hall.
Greywood, 31 Flass Road, Wormit, Fife DD6 8NL
Tel: 01382 541293
Contact: Kay Simpson (Secretary)

Dunfermline Choral Union

100-strong meets Mondays in the Music Institute, Dunfermline, 7.15pm. Conductor: Mandy Miller. Two annual concerts: Christmas, carols at Dunfermline Abbey and spring, Carnegie Hall. Spring 1996 features Poulenc *Gloria* and first performance of Bruce Fraser's *Magnificat*.
3 Sycamore Grove, Dunfermline KY11 5AD
Tel: 01383 725409
Contact: Margaret Murray (Secretary)

Edinburgh Festival Chorus

Concerts at Usher Hall, Edinburgh, during festival with major international orchestras and conductors. Also touring. Chorus Master: David Jones. Rehearsals: Tuesday 7.00 - 9.30pm, Stockbridge Parish Church, Edinburgh; Monday 6.30 - 9pm, Scottish Opera Centre, Elmbank Crescent, Glasgow. Good voice and competent sight reading required. No membership fee. Audition dates flexible.
Edinburgh Festival Society, 21 Market Street, Edinburgh EH1 1BW
Tel: 0131 226 4001 Fax: 0131 225 1173
Contact: James Waters (Associate Director) or Margery Ramsay (Chorus Secretary)

Edinburgh Royal Choral Union

An auditioned choir of 140, established in 1840 and continuing to aim for a high standard of performance. Promotes own concerts and engages professional conductors, orchestras and soloists. Varied repertoire which includes the large classical choral works and works commissioned by the choir.
43 Inverleith Gardens, Edinburgh EH3 5PR
Tel: 0131 552 3874 Fax: 0131 332 3940
Contact: Lilian Davidson (Admin Secretary)

Edinburgh Singers

Conductor: Mary Carmichael. Varied repertoire including classical works, Scottish songs, songs from musicals, folk songs. Concerts on request. Performed major works in Queens Hall, Usher Hall, Greyfriars Kirk. Aim: the enjoyment of singing. Rehearsals: Thursday 7.30 - 9.30pm, Bruntsfield Hall, Barclay Church, Edinburgh. Applicants must be able to sing in tune (auditions). Small membership fee.
4 Boroughloch Square, Edinburgh EH8 9NJ
Tel: 0131 667 9124 / 650 3536 (day)
Fax: 0131 662 0240
Contact: Ronnie Dow (Chairman) or Aileen Chree

Edinburgh Telephone Choir

Mixed choir (SATB). Free concerts throughout the season (October to March) on request. Performance held in the Churchhill Theatre each April. Rehearsals: Monday evenings, 7.30pm, GPO Dining Annexe, North Bridge Entrance, Edinburgh. Ability to read music not essential, mainly enthusiasm required. Small membership fee. No auditions.
10 Duddingston Square West, Edinburgh EH15 1RS
Tel: 0131 669 2948
Contact: T J Muirhead (Secretary) or T J M Moar Tel: 0131 669 6689

Edinburgh University Musical Society Chorus

Rehearsals: 5.15 - 6.45pm, Thursdays, Chaplaincy Centre, Potterrow Union, Bristo Square, Edinburgh. Membership open to anyone. Emphasis on enjoyment, but weekly commitment is important. Membership of EUMS entitles person to cheap tickets at other EUMS events.
c/o Faculty of Music, Alison House, 12 Nicolson Square, Edinburgh EH8 9DF

Edinburgh University Renaissance Singers

Choir made up of approximately 30 members - students and others. Concentrates on renaissance and early baroque music. Two concerts or so per term. Rehearsals: 6 - 8pm, Wednesdays, Music Faculty, Alison House, 12 Nicolson Square, Edinburgh. Reasonable sight reading required. Small membership fee. Auditions: contact conductor.
41 Montague Street, Edinburgh EH8 9QS
Tel: 0131 667 7853 / 650 2429 (day)
Contact: Noel O'Regan (Conductor)

Falkirk Caledonia Choir

60-strong meets on Mondays, 7.30 in Comely Park School, Falkirk. Conductor: David Malloch. Two main concerts, Christmas and spring. Repertoire mainly shorter pieces such as folk songs, part songs, religious music, motets and Scots song.

6 Gartcows Drive, Falkirk FK1 5QQ
Tel: 01324 623006
Contact: Alex Logie

Falkirk Festival Chorus

60-strong oratorio choir. Meets Sundays 3 pm in Falkirk Old and St Modan's Parish Church hall. Annual concerts in May at Falkirk Festival and Christmas. Other concerts arranged. Most recent performance, Dvorak's *Stabat Mater*, next Brahms' *Requiem*. Conductor: Robert Tait.

1 Westerglen Road, Falkirk FK1 5ND
Tel: 01324 625284
Contact: Norah Summers (Hon Secretary)

Garnock Choral Society

Choral singing. Annual concert in April, smaller concerts when required.

Ellenlea, 6 John Gregor Place, Lochwinnoch, Renfrewshire PA12 4HO
Tel: 01505 843252 (ans mac)
Contact: Helen Scott

Glasgow Cathedral Choral Society

Formed 1938 to perform large-scale sacred music. Working with the Virtuosi of Scotland, pioneered the performance of baroque works with an authentic orchestra. The choir's conductor John Turner is organist of the cathedral and a lecturer at the RSAMD.

80 Lawers Road, Bearsden, Glasgow G61 4LG
Tel: 0141 946 6389
Contact: Carol Nuttall

Glasgow Jewish Choral Society

Around 60 members. Rehearse Wednesdays, Newton Mearns Synagogue. Annual charity concert, City Hall, March. Other concerts throughout the year as required. Conductor: Edward Binnie. Repertoire covers wide range of Jewish and Israeli music, folk songs, and operatic pieces. Sing in many languages. Winners of Orpheus Trophy Glasgow Music Festival 1994.

26 Dalziel Drive, Glasgow G41 4PU
Tel: 0141 423 5830
Contact: Judith Tankel

Glasgow Philharmonic Choir

65-strong male voice choir. Meets Tuesdays, 7.30, Dalintober Hall, CWS Building, Morrison Street. One spring and two Christmas annual concerts plus three or four throughout the year for good causes. Repertoire covers the male voice spectrum including ballads, Scots song, light classics and items from the Welsh male voice collection. Conductor: David Hamilton.

5 Ormonde Avenue, Netherlee, Glasgow G44 3QU
Tel: 0141 633 0098
Contact: Norman MacGilp (Secretary)

Glasgow Phoenix Choir

Founded 1951. Repertoire includes Scottish folk songs, sacred and secular music spanning five centuries, and popular contemporary music. Spring and Christmas concerts are held in the Glasgow Royal Concert Hall. Other performances and tours are undertaken. Recording *Feel Good* on Lochshore label. Conductor: Marilyn Smith. Accompanist: Cameron Murdoch.

Flat 14, Cardell, Wemyss Bay Road, Wemyss Bay PA18 6AD
Tel: 01475 520876
Contact: Flora Harrison (General Secretary)

Glasgow University Choral Society

Membership open to all people associated with the University. No auditions, though some choral experience desirable. Rehearsals: Thursdays, 5.15 - 7pm, the Concert Hall. Concerts usually December and March.

c/o The Concerts Organiser, University Concerts Office, 14 University Gardens, Glasgow G12 8QE
Tel: 0141 330 4092 Fax: 0141 307 8018
Contact: Judy Kilpatrick (Concerts Organiser) or Myra Soutar (Conductor)

Haddo House Choral and Operatic Society

Haddo House, Aberdeen AB41 0ER
Tel: 016515 851 666
Contact: Mrs M B Longley (Secretary)

Hadley Court Singers

36-40 members. Two main concerts, Christmas and spring. Toured France and Germany. Reached the televised stage of Sainsbury Choir of the Year in 1990. Rehearsals: 7.30 - 9.30pm, Wednesdays, Holy Trinity Church, Church Street, Haddington, East Lothian. New members welcome, especially young people. Auditions as required. Membership fee.

21 Clifford Road, North Berwick, East Lothian EH39 4PW
Tel: 01620 892047
Contact: Alistair Munro (Secretary)

Helensburgh Dorian Choir

Long established amateur choir of about 60 singers. Wide repertoire from Bach to the Beatles. Aim is to enjoy singing with others and to entertain as wide an audience as possible.

Tigh na Mara, Rosneath, Helensburgh, Dumbartonshire G84 0PX
Tel: 0143684 831889
Contact: Anne Hollingsworth (Secretary)

Helensburgh Oratario Choir

Since 1973 the Choir has presented over 70 major choral works spanning four centuries with support from professional soloists and instrumentalists. Three recordings, broadcasts on radio and television. Also performs outwith Helensburgh and gives charity concerts.

13 Cumberland Avenue, Helensburgh G84 8QS
Tel: 01436 678248 (eve)
Contact: Richard Hassall or Martin Speller (Musical Director)
Tel: 01436 676279 (eve)

Hutchesons' Choral Society

An independent society meeting on Monday evenings during term time. Wide repertoire including Scottish premieres in major venues. No auditions. New members always welcome. Modest annual subscription, free to under 18s and those in full time education. 1995-96 season includes *Carmina Burana* and Vaughan Williams' *Mass in G Minor*.

Hutchesons' Grammar School, 21 Beaton Road, Glasgow G41 4NW
Tel: 0141 423 2933 Fax: 0141 424 0251
Contact: The Director of Music or The Administrator

ARTISTS

CLASSICAL

39

ARTISTS

CLASSICAL

Ingle Neuk Singers
Give 8-11 concerts each year, mainly to senior citizen meetings, consisting of light classical short songs. Rehearsals: 2.00 - 3.00pm, Tuesdays, Davidsons Mains Parish Church Hall. Some ability to read music required. Small membership fee. No auditions. Roughly 24 members.
20 Barnton Court, Edinburgh EH4 6EH
Tel: 0131 339 7188
Contact: Ruth Goudie (Conductor)

Inverness Choral Society
1995 marks the 75th anniversary of the society, which has a current membership of 140.
2 Woodside Crescent, Scorguie, Inverness IV3 6NR
Tel: 01463 224583
Contact: Margaret Harding

Inverness Singers
Founded 1972 with the object of singing together for enjoyment. Two concerts each year - a Christmas carol concert in St Andrew's Cathedral, Inverness and a spring concert in March.
c/o Holmknowe, 78 Culloden Road, Balloch, Inverness IV1 2HH
Tel: 01463 791102
Contact: Anne Lee (Secretary)
Tel: 01463 791102 or Margaret Young (Librarian/Dep Secretary) Tel: 01463 232835

John Currie Singers
Founded 1968. Professional ensemble, 16 singers and chamber orchestra. Commissioned many new works from composers including Wilson, Cresswell, McMillan and McLeod. Repertoire: baroque and classical works including: *Messiah*, the Haydn masses, Monteverdi *Vespers*, and the major works of Bach.
The Old Schoolhouse, Ballintuim, Blairgowrie PH10 7NJ
Tel: 01250 886234 Fax: 01250 886327
Contact: John Currie (Artistic Director / Administrator)

Jubilo
Mixed voice choir of about 80 members. Conductor: Walter Thomson. Annual family Christmas Carol Concert plus a spring concert, as well as fundraising concerts and others. Rehearsals: 7.30 - 10pm, Sundays, Blackhall St Columba's Church, Edinburgh. Ability to read music and to sing in tune required. Auditions by arrangement. Wide repertoire.
5 Ravelston House Drive, Edinburgh EH4 3LT
Tel: 0131 332 4477 / 555 0616 (am only)
Contact: Elspeth Williamson (Chairman)

The Kilbarchan Singers
Founded by Ian McCallum (1982) to satisfy the needs of singers who wished to sing *a capella* (mostly) and raise money for charities. Repertoire extends from Monteverdi via Bach to Messiaen including early and recent Scottish music. Venues include Glasgow and St Giles Cathedrals, the Burrell, Kelvingrove and Pollock House.
1 Langside Park, Kilbarchan, Renfrewshire PA10 2EP
Tel: 01505 704688
Contact: Ian McCallum (Musical Director)

The Kilmallie Singers
Choral Society of approximately 50 members meeting in Caol Church Hall, Fort William, Thursdays 7.30pm. Perform major choral works (spring) and Christmas carol concert. Occasional lighter concerts in outlying areas of Lochaber.
Abrach House, 4 Caithness Place, Fort William PH33 6JP
Contact: Heather Moore Tel: 01397 702535 or Judith Pashley Tel: 01397 705499

Kirkcaldy Choral Union
26 Ramsay Road, Kirkcaldy KY1 1TZ
Contact: Mr T Drummond (Secretary)

Leith Senior Citizens Choir
Entertains one afternoon weekly September - April in hospitals, community centres, church meetings etc. Rehearsals: 1.30 - 3.00pm, Tuesdays at South Leith Parish Church Hall. People interested in joining a happy choir and especially if you sing alto, tenor or bass are welcome. Ability to read music not necessary.
South Leith Parish Church Hall, Henderson Street, Leith
Tel: 0131 661 5313

Lerwick Choral Society
50-strong choir. Meets Islesburgh Community Centre, Lerwick on Mondays at 7.30pm. Two annual concerts in May and December. Conductors Gordon Yeaman and Bob Heaton. Repertoire is a mixture of light and classical music.
Wick, Gulberwick, Shetland ZE2 9JX
Tel: 01595 694387
Contact: Marion Ockendon (President)

Linn Choir
Founded 1948. Mixed voice choir of around 65 voices. Rehearsals on Wednesdays in Pollokshaws Methodist Church Hall at 7.15pm. New voices welcome. Around 7-8 concerts a year, many for charity, at various venues in and out of Glasgow. Regular conductor: Dr Harry Gardner.
39 Cloan Crescent, Bishopbriggs, Glasgow G64 2HN
Tel: 0141 772 3922
Contact: Flo Allan (Secretary)

Milngavie Choir
10 McGrigor Road, Milngavie, Glasgow G62 7LD
Contact: John Townson Tel: 0141 956 3440

Montrose and District Choral Society
28 Tailyour Crescent, Montrose DD10 9BL
Contact: J Stewart (Secretary)

Moravian Singers
All-female choir of forty rehearses September to April on Mondays in the Town Hall Elgin. Repertoire covers Renaissance to contemporary. Three concerts per year at autumn, Christmas and Easter.
34 McIntosh Drive, Elgin IV30 3AW
Tel: 01343 545637
Contact: Gavin Currie

New Kilpatrick Singers
Small group of mixed voices performing a very varied programme from classical to pop, performing regularly throughout Scotland.
13 West Chapelton Ave, Bearsden, Glasgow G61 2DJ
Tel: 0141 942 6963
Contact: Mrs M I White (Secretary) or Mrs T Nixon (Leader) Tel: 0141 942 5607

Northern College Choir Aberdeen Campus
Regular performer in the NE of Scotland, comprising students and staff of the college. Recent performances include Bach's *Magnificat* and music by Ronald Stevenson.
Northern College, Hilton Place, Aberdeen AB9 1FA
Tel: 01224 283601 Fax: 01224 283576
Contact: Pete Stollery (Performance Co-ordinator) or Dundee Campus Tel: 01382 464000

Paisley Abbey Choir

The choir can be traced back to the 14th c. and still provided choral services after the Reformation. Now the choir has broadcast on radio and television and made several recordings. Wide repertoire, often encompasses larger works with orchestra both in a liturgical and concert concept.
The Abbey, Paisley PA1 1JG
Tel: 0141 889 3528 Fax: 0141 887 3929
Contact: George McPhee MBE

Perth Choral Society

Performs three concerts per year: two of mainly sacred or oratorio works and one family carol concert at Christmas. Works performed in 1994/5 were: *Christmas Oratorio* (Bach) and *Elijah* (Mendelssohn). Plan to perform *Requiem* (Fauré) 1995/6.
Carngeal, Almondbank, Perthshire PH1 3NP
Tel: 01738 22807 (eve)
Contact: Mrs N Collins (Hon Secretary)

The Practice Choir

Director: Nicholas Jones. Aims to develop in people with an interest in singing but with little or no previous training, the skills and confidence to be successful in auditioning for major Scottish Choirs. The choir presents at least one major public performance each year in Edinburgh.
9 Craigleith Crescent, Edinburgh EH7 3JJ
Tel: 0131 539 2718
Contact: Brian Thornton (Chairman)

Queens Cross Chorus

Founded with orchestra in 1981 to perform an annual concert for charity in Queens Cross Church, Aberdeen. Around 70 strong. Rehearse in the church for six weeks before the February concert. Conductor Geoffrey Atkinson.
Queens Cross Church, Albyn Place, Aberdeen AB1 1UN
Tel: 01224 644742
Contact: Elspeth Mogendorff (Secretary)

Roxburgh Singers

Formed in 1962 to sing at the Hawick Music Club. Current Musical Director: Dr Garrett O'Brien (since 1983). Repertoire ranges from *Messiah* to madrigals to modern, with research into Scottish music, and arrangements by the conductor.
5 Riverside Drive, Denholm, Hawick TD9 8NE
Tel: 01450 870313
Contact: Ralph Kyte (Publicity Secretary)

Royal Scottish National Orchestra Chorus

73 Claremont Street, Glasgow G3 7HA
Tel: 0141 226 3868 Fax: 0141 221 4317

Schola Cantorum of Edinburgh

Perform works from early *a cappella* polyphony and orchestrally accompanied baroque cantatas to newly commissioned works by both young and established composers. Have performed annually (since 1992) at the Edinburgh International Festival. In 1995 became the Edinburgh Festival Theatre's Singers in Residence.
10 Hermand Terrace, Edinburgh EH11 1QZ
Tel: 0131 346 2476 Fax: 0131 539 9134
Contact: Eric Ibler (Artistic Director)

Scottish Chamber Orchestra Chorus

Gives regular concerts throughout Scotland with the SCO and world-class conductors and soloists. Occasionally tours abroad with the SCO. Rehearsals: 7.15pm, Mondays, Methodist Church, Nicolson Square, Edinburgh. Standards: good choral singers required. Auditions by appointment with the Secretary. No membership fee.
4 Royal Terrace, Edinburgh EH7 5AB
Tel: 0131 557 6800 Fax: 0131 557 6933
Contact: Timothy Byram-Wigfield (Chorus Master) or Sheila Young (Chorus Secretary)

The Scottish Concert Choir

An occasional large scale choir, specialising in unusual but major performances (*African Sanctus*, Lloyd Webber *Requiem* etc).
c/o 134 Marchmont Road, Edinburgh EH9 1AQ
Tel: 0131 447 9341 Fax: 0131 452 9383
Contact: Brian Allingham (Secretary) or M Allingham Tel: 0131 225 8147

St Giles' Cathedral Choir (Edinburgh)

St Giles' Cathedral, High Street, Edinburgh EH1 1RE
Tel: 0131 225 4363
Contact: Herrick Bunney Tel: 0131 337 6494

Strathaven Choral Society

Established 1972. Now the largest choir of its type in Lanarkshire with a membership of 80-90. Mounts two professional concerts each season performing a wide range of works from baroque to contemporary. Membership enquiries welcome from age 17 upwards. Rehearsals: Monday (August - May). Conductor: David Hamilton.
24 Crofthead Street, Strathaven, Lanarkshire ML10 6BB
Tel: 01357 22118
Contact: Mrs C Gow (Secretary) or Mrs L Young Tel: 01357 22138

Strathclyde University Chamber Choir

Repertoire from Renaissance to 20th c. Regular tours in the UK and abroad, notably to sing the services in English cathedrals. Rehearsals: Tuesdays, 7.30-10 pm. Annual membership fee, concessions for students.
Director of Music , University of Strathclyde, Livingstone Tower, Richmond Street, Glasgow G1 1XH
Tel: 0141 552 4400 x3444
Fax: 0141 552 4053
Contact: Alan Tavener (Director of Music)

Strathclyde University Chorus

Light and popular music rehearsed and performed in unpressured conditions. No entrance requirements. Vocal and music reading coaching provided. Annual membership fee, concession for students. Rehearsals: Mondays, 5 - 7pm.
Director of Music, University of Strathclyde, Livingstone Tower, Richmond Street, Glasgow G1 1XH
Tel: 0141 552 4400 x3444
Fax: 0141 552 4053
Contact: Alan Tavener (Director of Music)

Thomas Coats Memorial Choral Society

Mixed chorus, non-denominational. Meets January to March in Thomas Coats Memorial Church on Tuesday evenings. Concert at end of March with professional orchestra, classical repertoire (Palestrina to Rutter).
40 Morven Avenue, Paisley PA2 8DR
Contact: Karen Turner

ARTISTS
CLASSICAL

41

Westerton Male Voice Choir

Around 40 members. Meets on Tuesdays at 7.30 in St Andrew's College. Around ten concerts a year for music clubs, women's guilds and other places to which the choir is invited. Repertoire covers the light classics and modern song settings. Conductor: Gavin Settle.
31 Rubislaw Drive, Bearsden, Glasgow G61 1PS
Tel: 0141 942 3802
Contact: D MacFarlane

ARTISTS

CLASSICAL

OPERA

Caledonian Opera

Gives a short season of fully staged performances each year for private or corporate entertainment, featuring British singers and small chorus with piano accompaniment from MD Gerald Martin Moore. Repertoire includes works by Mozart, Donizetti and Puccini. Opera gala concerts also a speciality.
House of Schivas, Ythanbank, Ellon, Aberdeenshire AB41 0TN
Tel: 01358 761224 Fax: 01358 761488
Contact: Scott Cooper (Company Manager) or Innes Catto

Edinburgh Grand Opera

A chorus based company producing major repertoire operas with the help of professional music directors, directors and singers and a full size orchestra. Annual performances in the King's Theatre, Edinburgh.
c/o Allingham, 20 Manor Place, Edinburgh EH3 7DS
Tel: 0131 225 8147 Fax: 0131 452 9383
Contact: Mrs M Allingham (Secretary)

Edinburgh University Opera

A student opera group producing non-standard operas. Productions include Handel's *Athalia*, Purcell's *King Arthur* and *The Beggar's Opera*. Stage one large scale show per year in mid-February with possibly one other smaller scale production in the summer.
c/o Allingham, 20 Manor Place EH3 7DS
Tel: 0131 225 8147 Fax: 0131 452 9383
Contact: Mr B Allingham Tel: 0131 447 9341

Fife Opera

Musical Director, Graeme Wilson. Promotion and performance of opera in Fife. Recent productions include *The Bartered Bride*, *La Traviata*, *Cavelleria Rusticana*. Additional performances include an annual Christmas concert and other occasional concert performances. Performance of *The Merry Widow* in the Adam Smith Theatre, Kirkcaldy 8-11 November 1995.
36 Bourtree Brae, Lower Largo, Fife KY8 6HX
Tel: 01333 320282
Contact: Mrs E M Taylor

Opera West

Founded 1986, now established as a major company in south west Scotland. Mixture of local, national and international performers.
14 Ashgrove Street, Ayr KA7 3AQ
Tel: 01292 264489 Fax: 01292 282424
Contact: Raymond Bramwell (Artistic Director) or Marilyn de Blieck (Director of Productions)

Paragon Ensemble Scotland

Regularly performs new work in concerts, music theatre, opera, education and the community. With a flexible repertoire ranging from small chamber ensembles to music theatre productions, the company tours nationally and internationally, as well as promoting its own subscription series.
2 Port Dundas Place, Glasgow G2 3LB
Tel: 0141 332 9903 Fax: 0141 332 9904
Contact: Margaret Paterson (General Manager) or David Davies (Artistic Director)

Pocket Opera

A small scale opera company devoted to producing rarely performed operas.
20 Manor Place, Edinburgh EH3 7DS
Tel: 0131 447 9341 Fax: 0131 452 9383
Contact: Mr B Allingham Tel: 0131 225 8147

Scottish Opera

Scotland's national opera company. Over 70 major performances each season in Glasgow, Edinburgh, Aberdeen, Inverness and Newcastle. Employs over 200. Scottish Opera-Go-Round performs at smaller venues. Scottish Opera For All works extensively in the community. Owners of Theatre Royal, Glasgow. Annual income £8 million.
39 Elmbank Crescent, Glasgow G2 4PT
Tel: 0141 248 4567 Fax: 0141 221 8812
Contact: Richard Jarman (General Director) or Roberta Doyle (Head of Marketing and Press)

The Southern Light Opera Company

Rehearsals: 7.30pm at Firrhill Day Centre, 257 Colinton Road, Edinburgh.
7 Caledonian Crescent, Edinburgh EH11 2DD
Tel: 0131 337 1489
Contact: C W Melville (Secretary)

CHAMBER ORCHESTRAS

The Edinburgh Chamber Orchestra

Four annual performances (October-June) of predominantly 18th c. music. Permanent string section (6.6.4.5.2), wind added as required. Will accept engagements in Scotland. Rehearsals: Wednesdays, 7.30 - 10.00pm, Chapter House, St Mary's Cathedral, Palmerston Place, Edinburgh.
c/o St Mary's Cathedral, Palmerston Place, Edinburgh EH12 5AW
Contact: Dr Alberto Massimo (Musical Director) Tel: 0131 668 3390

Edinburgh University Chamber Orchestra

Rehearsals: 6.30 - 9.30pm, Tuesdays, Reid Concert Hall, 14 Bristo Square, Edinburgh. Standard: Grade 8 upwards. Membership fee. Audition dates during October, sign up at Freshers Fair. Several concerts per year with guest conductors. Available for hire all areas of Scotland.
c/o Faculty of Music, Nicolson Square, Edinburgh EH8 9DF
Contact: Ben Larpent

Edinburgh University String Orchestra

Rehearsals: 2 - 5pm Wednesdays, Reid Concert Hall. Founded 1991 by Emre Araci. Grade 8 preferable, all players audition each year. Regular concerts given each term, plus annual Scottish tour. Wide repertoire, ranging from Bach to Finzi, Vivaldi to Leighton.
c/o Faculty of Music, Alison House, 12 Nicolson Square, Edinburgh EH8 9DF
Contact: Emre Araci

Fife Sinfonia

A mid-sized semi-professional orchestra performing mainly in Fife. Two concerts annually, plus accompanying Fife Opera. Regular conductor: John Steer. Educational involvement with Arts in Fife, including *Tam* with primary school children and commission from Alasdair Nicolson. Often gives young local soloists opportunity to perform.
17 Main Street, Dunshelt, Fife
Tel: 01337 828005
Contact: Helen McGregor (Secretary)

Glasgow Chamber Orchestra

Established for c.30 years. In 3 concerts per annum, usually in the Stevenson Hall of the RSAMD, presenting programmes of popular classical music, often with soloists, and less familiar pieces, some by contemporary Scottish composers.
11 Deanwood Avenue, Netherlee, Glasgow G44 3RL
Tel: 0141 637 4158
Contact: Hugh Levey (Chairman)

Glasgow Sinfonia

Amateur chamber orchestra. Founded in 1986. Performs all types of music from Bach to Bartók. Rehearsals in Maryhill Community Central Hall on alternate Sunday afternoons.
21 Barnton Grove, Edinburgh EH4 6EQ
Tel: 0131 339 2065
Contact: Lesley Roe

Lochaber Community Orchestra

1995/6 sees their fifth season. Rehearsals: Mondays 7.15pm, Lochaber High School. Varied repertoire from baroque to musicals.
Newhouse, Ballachulish, Argyll PA39 4JR
Tel: 01855 811507 Fax: 01855 811507
Contact: Mary Anne Alberger (Conductor)

ARTISTS

CLASSICAL

Moray Chamber Orchestra

*Kildonan, Young Street, Elgin, Moray
IV30 1TH*
Tel: 01343 543531
Contact: Peter Zanrè (Director)

New Edinburgh Orchestra

A new chamber orchestra of 40 players in its first season. Audition necessary. Repertoire contains works by Mozart, J C Bach, K F Abel and C P E Bach. Aims to have a varied concert season, promoting new and contemporary works as well as performing the old timeless classics.
22a Fettes Row, Edinburgh EH3 6RH
Tel: 0131 558 3932
Contact: Alexander Ackland (Orchestral Manager)

Peebles Orchestra

Repertoire mainly 18th c. Rehearsals: Wednesdays, 6.00 - 6.30pm (Beginners Group), 6.30 - 7.30pm (Youth Orchestra), 7.30 - 9.30pm (Peebles Orchestra) at Priorsford School, Peebles. Players of any standard welcome. Membership fee.
*c/o Claire Garnett, Glenternie Lodge,
Manor Valley, Peebles EH45 9JN*
Tel: 01721 740256
Contact: Claire Garnett or Malcolm Porteous Tel: 0131 447 0539

Scottish Chamber Orchestra

Principal Conductor (from 1996): Joseph Swenson. Conductor Laureate: Sir Charles Mackerras. Composer Laureate: Sir Peter Maxwell Davies. Affiliate Composer: James McMillan. Chair: Donald Macdonald. Regular seasons of concerts in major towns and a tour of the north of Scotland as well as numerous educational workshops are given annually.
4 Royal Terrace, Edinburgh EH7 5AB
Tel: 0131 557 6800 Fax: 0131 557 6933
Contact: Roy McEwan (Managing Director) or Barry Kempton (Concerts Director)

SYMPHONY ORCHESTRAS

BBC Scottish Symphony Orchestra

Conductor Laureate: Jerzy Maksymiuk. Associate Conductor: Martyn Brabbins. Associate Composer/Conductor: Tan Dun. Founded in 1935 as Scotland's first full-time professional orchestra. It was originally studio-based but now has an ever-increasing public concert schedule throughout the UK. Most performances are broadcast on radio or television, usually Radio 3.
*BBC Scotland, Queen Margaret Drive,
Glasgow G12 8DG*
Tel: 0141 338 2606 Fax: 0141 307 4312
Contact: Hugh Macdonald (Head of Music) Tel: 0141 338 2489 or Alan Davis (Manager) Tel: 0141 338 2606

City of Glasgow Philharmonic Orchestra

Established in 1988 under the artistic direction of founder-conductor Iain Sutherland. Since 1992 managed by the City of Glasgow Philharmonic Foundation with funds from Glasgow City Council and private sector sponsorship. Concerts regularly broadcast. Video, CDs include *Flower of Scotland, The Pilgrim.*
Principal Conductor and Artistic Director Iain Sutherland, c/o City of Glasgow Philharmonic Foundation, 2 Port Dundas Place, Glasgow G2 3LB
Tel: 0141 353 1475 Fax: 0141 353 3705
Contact: Duncan McCallum (General Manager) or Gordon Jack (Orchestral Manager)

Claremont Amateur Light Orchestra

Rehearsals: Thursdays, 7.30 - 9.30pm at Leith St Andrew's Church Hall. Small membership fee, and open to musicians of any standard. No auditions.
*40 Longformacus Road, Edinburgh
EH16 6SE*
Tel: 0131 664 2996 (eve) / 557 1100 (day)
Contact: Jim Glancy (Band Member)

Colinton Amateur Orchestral Society

Rehearsals: 7.30pm, Tuesdays at St. Cuthbert's Episcopal Church Hall, Colinton, Edinburgh. Players of all standards welcome, no auditions. Vacancies for horn, bassoon, violins, violas and cellos. Small membership fee.
*9 Greenhill Terrace, Edinburgh
EH10 4BS*
Tel: 0131 447 1135
Contact: Monica Miller (Secretary)

Dalkeith Symphony Orchestra

Founded in 1975 by Malcolm Porteous. General 19th c. repertoire. 80/90 players of all ages brought together from a wide area for a few rehearsals and two performances (late May/June). Membership usually by invitation, but keen players can make known their interest in being invited.
*3 Hermitage Gardens, Edinburgh
EH10 6DL*
Tel: 0131 663 7784 / 447 0539 (eve)
Contact: Malcolm Porteous (Musical Director)

Edinburgh Symphony Orchestra

Rehearsals: 7.30 - 10.00pm, St Peter's Church Hall, Lutton Place, Edinburgh. Standards required: Grade 7 upwards. Auditions held October to May. String players always needed, percussionists often needed, and sometimes vacancies for trumpet players. Waiting list for other woodwind and brass. Membership fee.
11 Inverleith Row, Edinburgh EH3 5LS
Tel: 0131 556 1508
Contact: Dr Carolyn Dyson

Glasgow Orchestral Society

Glasgow's oldest amateur orchestra, founded 1870. Rehearsal and performance of classical music, both of standard and contemporary repertoires. Three concerts per year usually in December, February and May. Rehearsals: Mondays, 7.30 - 9.30pm at Community Central Hall, 304 Maryhill Road, Glasgow. Subscription: waged £50, unwaged £15.
*47 Durness Avenue, Bearsden, Glasgow
G61 2AL*
Tel: 0141 942 7754
Contact: Donald Gibson (Secretary)

ARTISTS

CLASSICAL

Glasgow Senior Citizens' Orchestra

Formed 28 years ago. Performs a wide range of music at old people's clubs and special events. Rehearsals: September - May, Tuesdays and one other afternoon at Strathclyde Arts Centre, Washington Street. Membership free.

67 Larchfield Avenue, Glasgow
G77 5QN
Tel: 0141 639 6333
Contact: Mrs J M Dee (Secretary)

Glasgow Symphony Orchestra

Founded 1975. Repertoire includes many major works (Beethoven, Tchaikovsky, Dvorák, Vaughan Williams, Rachmaninov). Three concerts a year in March, June and December. Open to all. Rehearsals: Tuesdays, 7.30 - 9.30pm, Notre Dame High School, Hillhead. All welcome, especially strings. Annual subscription.

104 Weymouth Drive, Glasgow G12 0EN
Tel: 0141 339 1297
Contact: Tom Kent (Conductor) or Dorothy Gunnee Tel: 0141 778 4458

Glasgow University Orchestra

Conductors: Marjorie Rycroft, Myra Soutar. Auditions usually held first week of October. Rehearsals: Tuesdays, 6 - 8.30pm, Concert Hall. Concert dates usually in November and February. Termly subscription.

c/o The Concerts Organiser, University Concerts Office, 14 University Gardens, Glasgow G12 8QE
Tel: 0141 330 4092 Fax: 0141 307 8018
Contact: Judy Kilpatrick (Concerts Organiser)

The Kelvin Ensemble

The student chamber orchestra of Glasgow University. Established 1991 to bring classical music on campus. Programmes have included music by McGuire, Hummell, Mendelssohn and Prokofiev.

35 Thorn Road, Bearsden, Glasgow G61 4BS
Tel: 0141 942 7438
Contact: Arthur Doyle (Orchestra Manager) or Suzanne Moir (Tickets and Sponsorship) Tel: 0141 946 7640

Kirkcaldy Orchestral Society

Rehearsal and performance opportunities for an average 70 players a week. Five performances a year including an open night/repertoire rehearsal. Commissions in recent years from Bruce Fraser, William Sweeney and Eoin Hamilton (1994 - *Episodes* for percussion ensemble and orchestra).

20 Balwearie Gardens, Kirkcaldy KY2 5LU
Tel: 01592 264841
Contact: William Ritchie CBE (Chairman) or Graeme Wilson (Musical Director) Tel: 0592 265714

Northern College Chamber Orchestra Aberdeen Campus

Made up from students at the college, regularly accompanies the Northern College Choir. Recent performances include music by Mozart and Dvorak as well as compositions by students.

Northern College, Hilton Place, Aberdeen AB9 1FA
Tel: 01224 283601 Fax: 01224 283576
Contact: Pete Stollery (Performance Co-ordinator) or Dundee Campus Tel: 01382 464000

Perth Symphony Orchestra

Formed 1951, first concert in February 1953. The orchestra has amateur status with a regular membership of over 50 players, rehearses on Wednesday evenings and gives 2 concerts a year in November and February.

Whitelaw House, Orchil Road, Auchterarder PH3 1LS
Tel: 01738 639436 / 01764 662243
Contact: H Johnson (Secretary)

Queens Cross Orchestra

Founded with chorus in 1981 to perform an annual concert for charity in Queens Cross Church, Aberdeen. Around 60 strong. Rehearse in the church for six weeks before the February concert. Conductor: Geoffrey Atkinson.

Queens Cross Church, Albyn Place, Aberdeen AB1 1UN
Tel: 01224 644742
Contact: Elspeth Mogendorff (Secretary)

Riddle's Court Community Orchestra

Rehearsals: 2.00 - 4.00pm, Mondays at Riddle's Court. Adequate standards expected. Small membership fee. No auditions.

322 Lawnmarket, Edinburgh EH1 2PQ
Tel: 0131 225 4411
Contact: E Bennet (Secretary) Tel: 0131 661 9038

Royal Scottish National Orchestra

Principal Conductor/Music Director: Walter Weller. Principal Guest Conductor: Alexander Lazarev. Conductor Laureate: Neeme Jarvi. Concert Manager: Patricia Gillies. Orchestra Manager: Elaine Thomson. Marketing Officer: Fiona Ferguson. Chair: Morrison Dunbar. Chief Executive: Paul Hughes.

73 Claremont Street, Glasgow G3 7HA
Tel: 0141 226 3868 Fax: 0141 221 4317
Contact: Jacqueline Noltingk (Head of Planning) or Valerie Carlaw (Head of Marketing)

Scottish Sinfonia

Gives 5 concerts a year with a professional conductor and leader. Previous programmes have included 8 Mahler symphonies. Rehearsals: Sunday afternoons for 3 weeks before concerts. Applications for audition from experienced players welcome.

220 Bruntsfield Place, Edinburgh EH10 4DE
Tel: 0131 229 9832
Contact: Margot Cruft (Secretary)

St Andrew Amateur Orchestral Society

Rehearsals: 7.30 - 9.30pm, Tuesdays at St James Gillespie's High School, Lauderdale Street, Edinburgh. String players particularly needed - especially violins. Small membership fee. No formal standard required. 2 concerts a year.

22 Gillespie Crescent, Edinburgh EH10 4HU
Tel: 0131 229 9593
Contact: Brenda Rowan (Secretary) or John Bedford Tel: 01875 830292

St James Orchestra

Have given concerts in Paisley for over 25 years. Rehearsals: Sundays, 2.30 - 5pm, St James Church, Paisley. Membership subscription.

3 Castleview, Stanely Green, Paisley PA2 8ED

Contact: Tom Ferguson Tel: 01505 816132

Stockbridge and Newtown Community Orchestra

Rehearsals: 7.30 - 9.00pm, Thursdays, at St Stephen's Church, St Stephen's Street, Stockbridge. No auditions. Formed in January 1995 to integrate people of all ages and of all standards in musical activity. Work closely with local composers.

8c Abercromby Place (basement), Edinburgh EH3 6LB

Tel: 0131 556 5794

Contact: Grace Conway (Co-ordinator)

Strathclyde University Orchestra

Programmes drawn from the standard symphonic repertoire, as well as baroque and contemporary works. Annual membership fee, concessions for students. Rehearsals: 5 - 7pm Tuesdays.

Director of Music, University of Strathclyde, Livingstone Tower, Richmond Street, Glasgow G1 1XH

Tel: 0141 552 4400 x3444 Fax: 0141 552 4053

Contact: Alan Tavener (Director of Music)

INSTRUMENTAL DUOS

Andrew Hardy and Murray McLachlan

Andrew Hardy (violin) is an American based in Europe pursuing a solo career after holding many concert-master posts with American and German orchestras. Murray McLachlan (piano) has been concert soloist with the RPO, SCO, BBC SSO and the Manchester Camerata. Both have wide reputations as performing and recording artists.

Banrye Cottage, 5 Holburn Place, Aberdeen AB1 6HG

Tel: 01224 587610 Fax: 01224 587610

Contact: Murray McLachlan

Anne Evans and Dick Lee

Anne Evans (flute, piano); Dick Lee (clarinet, bass clarinet, recorder, saxophone). Repertoire ranges from Handel and Telemann to such diverse 20th c. masters as Eric Satie and Benny Goodman. Dick Lee's compositions and arrangements of jazz classics are also included.

1 Cheyne Street, Edinburgh EH4 1JA

Tel: 0131 332 8083

Contact: Anne Evans

Argondizza Duo

Peter Argondizza (guitar) and Pauline Dowse (cello). Argondizza is currently a lecturer in music at Strathclyde University and Dowse is principal cello with the Royal Scottish National Orchestra. They are available as a duo or augmented with other players for trios, quartets and quintets.

26 Woodcroft Avenue (3/2), Broomhill, Glasgow G11 7HY

Tel: 0141 357 1428

Contact: Peter Argondizza

Chord 'n' Blew

Rosemary Lock (flute), Anne Chaurand (guitar). Formed 1993, combining the contrasted experiences of an orchestral flautist and guitar soloist and chamber musician. Given numerous recitals and featured on BBC radio. Aim to create and informed and informal atmosphere, and offer recitals with educational workshops.

46 Glasgow Road, Blanefield, Stirlingshire G63 9BP

Tel: 01360 770241

Contact: Rosemary Lock

David Nicolson and Eluned Pierce

Flute and harp duo. Experienced soloists in their own right who have combined to give recitals both in the UK and abroad. Play all the standard repertoire and have commissioned new works. Work to date includes recitals, lunch-time concerts, lecture recitals and coaching.

14 Nile Grove, Edinburgh EH10 4RF

Tel: 0131 447 3398 Fax: 0131 447 3398

Contact: David Nicholson

Duo Paganini

Angus Ramsay (violin) and Phillip Thorne (guitar) are both on the staff at the RSAMD and are well-known soloists. Formed in 1994, the duo is dedicated to performing the wealth of relatively unknown music for violin and guitar by Paganini and his contemporaries.

2 Staik Hill, Lanark ML11 7PW

Tel: 01555 662645

Contact: Angus Ramsay

Eira Lynn Jones and Mary Ann Kennedy

The duo first collaborated on the première of a work for two harps by Edward McGuire commissioned with SAC funding for the RNCM's international harp week 1994. Drawing on a Celtic and classical background they aim to explode the myth of the angelic harpist!

c/o 18 Glencairn Drive, Pollokshields, Glasgow G41 4QN

Tel: 0141 423 6585

Contact: Eira Lynn Jones Tel: 0161 471 1148 or Mary Ann Kennedy Tel: 01808 521424

Geoffrey Haydock and Penelope Smith

Geoffrey Haydock is principal clarinet with the BBC SSO which he joined in 1969. He is also known for involvement in chamber ensembles and solo concerto broadcasts. Penelope Smith has appeared on television accompanying Jack Brymer, Moira Anderson, Douglas Boyd and Marisa Robles.

17 Douglas Muir Drive, Milngavie, Glasgow G62 7RJ

Tel: 0141 956 4685

Contact: Geoffrey Haydock

Gillian Leonard and Bob Howie/Barbara Payne

Gillian Leonard: two degrees in flute performance from Northern Illinois University; taught at Northern College for 7 years; founder member of Sequoia, a chamber music ensemble. Bob Howie: recently retired from Northern College. Barbara Payne: Polish pianist with an international career, currently teaching at Northern College.

Resthivet Cottage, Pitcaple, Inverurie AB51 5DT

Tel: 01467 681298 Fax: 01467 681298

Contact: Gillian Leonard

ARTISTS
CLASSICAL

47

INSTRUMENTAL DUOS (CONTD)

ARTISTS

CLASSICAL

Helen Hossack and Charlotte Brennand

Violin and piano. Studied at the RSAMD and were awarded scholarships for advanced studies at the Royal Academy of Music, London, where they formed a duo in 1994. Helen performed regularly as leader of the Mansbridge Quartet and freelances with the Scottish orchestras. As a member of Intermezzo, Charlotte performs regularly throughout Britain.
9 Victoria Terrace, Menstrie, Clackmannanshire FK11 7EE
Tel: 01259 762333 / 0973 337267 (mobile)
Contact: Helen Hossack or Charlotte Brennand Tel: 0171 359 3167

Jack Keaney and Jean Hutchison

Piano duo.
17 Kensington Gate, Glasgow
Tel: 0141 334 3763
Contact: Jack Keaney

Joy Watson and Neil McFarlane

After winning a prize at the Lionel Tertis viola competition in 1984, Watson left her position as assistant principal viola (BBC SSO) to pursue more recital and freelance engagements. McFarlane is an experienced accompanist, having won prizes at the RSAMD. First BBC recital 1987.
38 Thornwood Drive, Thornwood, Glasgow G11 7UE
Tel: 0141 339 2168
Contact: Joy Watson

Lucy Russell and David McGuinness

19 Havelock Street, Glasgow G11 5JF
Tel: 0141 339 0605
Contact: David McGuinness

Mitchell Neave Duo

Flute and guitar duo. Performs widely, giving recitals for international festivals, music societies, the National Trust and local authorities. Also present educational workshops and regularly broadcast on the BBC and independent radio. Diverse repertoire from Bach, Paganini and Piazolla to McGuire and Takemitsu.
28 Bellwood Street, Shawlands, Glasgow G41 3ES
Tel: 0141 649 9236
Contact: Alison J. Mitchell or Allan Neave Tel: 01382 453353

Morley Duo

Michael Kellett (violin), Stephen Adam (piano). Whilst the Classical and Romantic repertoire forms the basis of their programmes, they particularly enjoy introducing audiences to the more attractive works of the 20th c. Kellett and Adam are principal players with Scottish Opera Orchestra and a programme of music by operatic composers is available.
35 Camphill Avenue, Langside, Glasgow G41 3AX
Tel: 0141 632 9115 Fax: 0141 632 9115
Contact: Stephen Adam (Pianist) or May Biggam (Manager) Tel: 0141 427 4836

Murray McLachlan and George Donald

Four hands at one piano. Murray McLachlan is a well known performing and recording artist and George Donald is a member of Scotland The What. Programmes include music from France as well as Mozart, Schubert, Rachmaninov and Grainger.
Banrye Cottage, 5 Holburn Place, Aberdeen AB1 6HG
Tel: 01224 587610 Fax: 01224 213241
Contact: Murray McLachlan

Robert and Mary Fleming

A varied programme with violin, clarsach, piano and song. Repertoire covers light and Scottish classical music. Performances usually in music clubs and arts guilds throughout Scotland.
80 High Street, Montrose, Angus DD10 8JF
Tel: 01674 674719
Contact: Robert Fleming

Saxophone Classique

Philip Greene (saxophone) and Audrey Innes (piano) present a varied programme of arrangements and original works for classical saxophone. Extensive repertoire with major works from France, America, Canada and Britain. Concert programmes can include pieces for soprano, alto or tenor saxophones and solos for piano.
16 Learmonth Terrace, Edinburgh EH4 1PG
Tel: 0131 332 0481
Contact: Philip Greene

Scott/McFarlane Duo

Hector Scott and Neil McFarlane are experienced in Scottish music and arts clubs and have recently issued a CD *300 Years of Music from Scotland*, commissioned by the Bank of Scotland to commemorate its Tercentenary. Flexible programming, ranging from traditional to contemporary.
38 Queen's Crescent, Edinburgh EH9 2BA
Tel: 0131 667 8417 Fax: 0131 667 8417
Contact: Dr E A J Scott

Scottish Guitar Duo

Phillip Thorne and Selina Madeley are both on the staff at the RSAMD. Specialise in the music of contemporary Scottish composers and the 19th c. repertoire. Recorded the music of Edward McGuire and John Maxwell Geddes.
25 Brockwood Avenue, Penicuik, Midlothian EH26 9AL
Tel: 01968 673470
Contact: Phillip Thorne

The Silver Duo

Noreen Silver (cello) and Phillip Silver (piano) perform programmes emphasising both familiar and lesser known works from the classic, romantic and contemporary periods. They have performed in Glasgow, London, Frankfurt, Jerusalem and Boston. Broadcasts on BBC Radio 3 and in America, Israel, Sweden and Belgium. CDs available.
4 May Terrace, Glasgow G42 9XF
Tel: 0141 632 0517 Fax: 0141 632 0517
Contact: Phillip Silver

Stanzeleit-Fenyó Duo

Formed 1989 at the Bartók Seminar in Hungary and have since performed in Germany, Austria, Spain, USA and the UK, broadcasting for the BBC and Hungarian Radio. Have recorded all works for violin and piano by Bela Bartók (ASV). Currently recording an anthology of works by British composers (United).
17 North Gardner Street, Hyndland, Glasgow G11 5BU
Tel: 0141 339 2708 Fax: 0141 339 2708
Contact: Gusztáv Fenyó

48

Timothy Gill and Murray McLachlan

Timothy Gill (cello) studied at Cambridge University and the RAM. He has won a number of prizes and scholarships. Murray McLachlan (piano) is well known as a performing and recording artist. The duo made a successful début on London's South Bank.

Banrye Cottage, 5 Holburn Place, Aberdeen AB1 6HG
Tel: 01224 587610 Fax: 01224 587610
Contact: Murray McLachlan

The Trabichoff Duo

Geoffrey Trabichoff and his daughter Nina established the violin/viola duo following the success of their joint performance of Mozart's *Sinfonia Concertante*. Repertoire ranges from Baroque to the present day. Inaugural concert March 1995 in Troon with pianist Julia Lynch.
40 Woodend Drive, Glasgow G13 1TQ
Tel: 0141 959 3496
Contact: Judy Trabichoff

Trabichoff/Stafford Duo

Violin and piano duo of many years', experience performing throughout Scotland. Wide-ranging repertoire, which includes theme concerts, and have recorded for BBC Radio 3.
40 Woodend Drive, Glasgow G13 1TQ
Tel: 0141 959 3496
Contact: Judy Trabichoff

Veronica Henderson and Murray McLachlan

Veronica Henderson (cello) and Murray McLachlan (piano) met as students at Cambridge University. Both have solo careers and as a duo have had successful recital tours of Scotland as well as a performance at the Edinburgh Festival Fringe.
Banrye Cottage, 5 Holburn Place, Aberdeen AB1 6HG
Tel: 01224 587610 Fax: 01224 587610
Contact: Murray McLachlan

William Conway and Peter Evans

Cello and piano. Conway has appeared at festivals and concert halls in Scotland and London and recorded Peter Maxwell Davies' cello concerto which was specially written for him. Evans has given concerts throughout UK, Europe, USA, CIS, Japan and has many recordings and broadcasts. Artistic co-directors of the Hebrides Ensemble.
9 Sciennes Gardens, Edinburgh EH9 1NR
Tel: 0131 667 4630 Fax: 0131 667 4630
Contact: William Conway

VOCAL DUOS

The Coates Duo

Husband and wife Leon and Heather perform in music clubs sometimes with an added solo instrument. Heather Coates has performed with choral societies throughout Scotland and Leon Coates lectures in music at Edinburgh University as well as being organist and choirmaster of St Andrew's and St George's Church.
35 Comely Bank Place, Edinburgh EH4 1ER
Tel: 0131 332 4553
Contact: Leon Coates

Viva Voce

Perform a selection of songs and duets to suit a wide range of tastes. Fiona Lindsay and Mhairi Lafferty perform regularly throughout Scotland and Isobel Anderson teaches piano at RSAMD. Together they perform songs and duets to suit a wide range of tastes.
103 Larkfield Road, Lenzie, Glasgow G66 3AS
Tel: 0141 776 6635
Contact: Fiona Lindsay

MIXED DUOS

Alison Donaldson with accompanist

Appeared in concert, recital, oratorio, opera and musical revue throughout the country. Programmes include: *A Tribute to Jenny Lind, The Victorian Soirée, Viennese Nights,* and *A Scottish Celebration.* CD/cassette: *Mid Pleasures and Pains.*
21 Lynn Drive, Eaglesham, Glasgow G76 0JJ
Tel: 013553 02869
Contact: Alison Donaldson

Company Two

Fiona Mitchell (soprano) and Andrew Nicol (piano). Evenings of Scottish music or Cole Porter and Jerome Kern. Fiona Mitchell studied RSAMD. Performs throughout Scotland, oratorio, concert opera, leider and cabaret. Accompanist Andrew Nicol has appeared with Linda Ormiston, Donald Maxwell, Mary Sandeman and with his father, tenor James Nicol.
5 Little Road, Edinburgh EH16 6SH
Tel: 0131 467 3616
Contact: Fiona Mitchell

Duo Amati

Elizabeth Ann Binks, member of Scottish Opera, and Christine Greig have a wide repertoire and perform on both sides of the border.
37 Dudley Drive (0/2), Hyndland, Glasgow G12 9RP
Tel: 0141 334 7645
Contact: Elizabeth Ann Binks

Kelda Ruth Miller and Catherine Muir

Miller (lyrical mezzo-soprano) and Muir (piano) formed a year ago. Recitals include parlour and salon pieces; repertoire from early Bel Canto arias through to German lieder, French chansons, British songs, romantic musical numbers and traditional folk song arrangements (mainly Scots). No calls on Sunday please.
35 Lansdowne Crescent, Glasgow G20 6NH
Tel: 0141 339 8499
Contact: Kelda Ruth Miller or Catherine Muir Tel: 0141 647 8973

ARTISTS

CLASSICAL

ARTISTS

CLASSICAL

Lewis Allan and David Murray

Recitals usually contain a delightful blend of classical (Handel, Mozart, Schumann, Fauré, Wolf, R Strauss, Quilter, Britten and others) and music theatre as well as Burns' songs and operetta. The repertoire is extensive and can usually accommodate special wishes.

88 Shawwood Crescent, Newton Mearns, Glasgow G77 5NB
Tel: 0141 639 5433
Contact: Lewis Allan Tel: 0585 423 214 (mobile)

Lydia Flett and Penelope Smith

Lydia Flett has given concerts for the National Trust and Arts Guilds throughout Scotland and performs as soloist for choral societies and the Salon Orchestra. The accompanist Penelope Smith works with several Scottish orchestras, appears on television and has taken part in almost 2,000 radio broadcasts.

2 Lindsay Drive, Kelvindale, Glasgow G12 0HB
Tel: 0141 357 1423
Contact: Lydia Flett

Nigel Boddice, John Langdon and Friends

Nigel Boddice (trumpet) and John Langdon (organ) both play regularly throughout Scotland individually and as a duo. In particular, their programme *The Golden Age of Trumpet* includes works by Bach, Handel and Vivaldi, with additional friends popping in to sing!

c/o 16 Lindsay Place, Kelvindale, Glasgow G12 0HX
Tel: 0141 357 1826 Fax: 0141 357 1826
Contact: Anne Cumberland

Patricia MacMahon and Walter Blair

Patricia MacMahon (soprano), Walter Blair (piano) are well-known artists who have established a high reputation for versatile and popular performances. Programmes can include combinations of Lieder, Italian arias, English, French, Italian and Spanish music as well as folk music and a special children's programme.

Banavie, Broomknowe Road, Kilmacolm PA13 4HX
Tel: 01505 872391
Contact: Patricia MacMahon

Sandra Porter and Graeme McNaught

As soloists the artists work with major orchestras and ensembles and have performed in Europe, the Middle East and Japan. Together they perform a wide repertoire emphasizing 19th and 20th c. voice and piano pieces from Scottish composers.

27 Victoria Road, Burnside, Glasgow G73 3QF
Tel: 0141 647 3464
Contact: Sandra Porter

Tour de Four

A musical celebration of the lives and songs of four great entertainers: Joyce Grenfell, Gracie Fields, Gertrude Lawrence and Beatrice Lillie; given by Linda Ormiston and accompanied by John Scrimger.

39 Colinhill Road, Strathaven ML10 6HF
Tel: 01357 21401 Fax: 01357 29719
Contact: Linda Ormiston or John Scrimger Tel: 01738 631367

Zarabanda

Roger Quin (guitar) and Fiona Mitchell (soprano). Repertoire covers Rennaisance to the present day. Performs in music clubs and tours throughout Scotland. Fiona Mitchell is a soloist in oratorio, concert opera, lieder and cabaret. Roger Quin teaches guitar at Napier University and the duo performs some of his compositions.

89c Grange Loan, Edinburgh EH9 2ED
Tel: 0131 667 7017
Contact: Roger Quin

INSTRUMENTAL TRIOS

Aberdeen Trio

Violin/Cello/Piano
14 Giffordgate, Haddington, East Lothian EH41 4AS
Tel: 01620 824618
Contact: Raymond Dodd or Bryan Dargie Tel: 01224 635792

The Ailsa Ensemble

Lawrence Gill (clarinet), Michael Beeston (viola), Isobel Anderson (piano). Formed to play at the Westbourne Music Series in Glasgow. Many former collaborations between the players in different combinations. All three teach at the RSAMD. Also available with Irene Drummond, soprano.

119 Craigleith Road, Edinburgh EH4 2EH
Tel: 0131 332 8691 Fax: 0131 332 8691
Contact: Michael Beeston

Classic Trio

Geoffrey Haydock (clarinet) principal BBC SSO. Alexander Volpov (cello) from the former USSR now lives in Scotland. Penelope Smith (piano).

17 Douglas Muir Drive, Milngavie, Glasgow G62 7RJ
Tel: 0141 956 4685
Contact: Geoffrey Haydock

The Kegelstatt Trio

James Durrant (viola) was head of strings at the RSAMD. Geoffrey Haydock is principal clarinet with the BBC SSO. Penelope Smith has a UK-wide reputation as an accompanist. Formed in 1978, the trio have established a reputation performing and broadcasting.

17 Douglas Muir Drive, Milngavie, Glasgow G62 7RJ
Tel: 0141 956 4685
Contact: Geoffrey Haydock

The Leda Piano Trio

London South Bank début led to engagements throughout the UK and tours abroad for British Council, BBC broadcasts, many commissions (eg. Sally Beamish, Edward Harper) and CD of 18th c. Scottish works. Programming explores neglected works. String players principals from the Scottish Chamber Orchestra.

107 Woodhall Road, Colinton, Edinburgh EH13 0HP
Tel: 0131 441 4247
Contact: Peter Campbell Kelly (Administrator) or Kate Thompson

Merlyn Trio

Formed in 1992. Consists of Daphne Godson (violin), a former Gertler pupil, Patricia Hair (cello) former Navarra pupil and member of various Scottish chamber ensembles and Leon Coates (piano), an Edinburgh University lecturer in music.

35 Comely Bank Place, Edinburgh EH4 1ER
Tel: 0131 332 4553
Contact: Leon Coates

50

The Rachmaninov Trio

Lev Atlas (violin/viola), Alexander Volpov (cello), Phillip Silver (piano). Repertoire ranging from works of Rachmaninov, Tchaikovsky, Mozart and Brahms to composers such as Sviridov, Moscheles, Gershwin and Bernstein. Future engagements include tour of Germany and Switzerland to promote new CD. Recently appointed Trio in Residence at University of Strathclyde.
537 Sauchiehall Street, Glasgow G3 7PQ
Tel: 0141 248 1611 Fax: 0141 248 1989
Contact: Louise Naftalin

The Scottish Flute Trio

The Scottish Flute Trio has broadcast on BBC Radio and performed throughout Scotland to great acclaim. Programmes with guitar, piano or harp can be offered over a wide range of music, from Russian classics to traditional Celtic music and baroque to the avant-garde, using concert flutes, piccolos and alto flute.
213 Wilton Street, Glasgow G20 6DE
Tel: 0141 946 9070
Contact: Jacqueline Inglis

Trio Ecosse

Richard Chester (flute), James Durrant (viola), Phillip Thorne (guitar). Repertoire concentrates on the work of contemporary Scottish composers, much of which is written for the trio. Other repertoire includes the wealth of 19th c. works written for this very popular combination.
25 Brockwood Avenue, Penicuik, Midlothian EH26 9AL
Tel: 01968 673470
Contact: Phillip Thorne

Trio Papageno

Jean Murrray (flute), Mark Bailey (cello) and Audrey Innes (piano) are available for performances at music clubs, festivals etc, offering varied priogrammes mixing trios with duos for flute and piano, and duos for cello and piano.
11 Melville Place, Edinburgh EH3 7PR
Tel: 0131 226 3392
Contact: Jean Murray

Trio Raro

Name and inspiration from Robert Schumann. Comprises Peter Markham (2nd violinist Edinburgh Quartet); Gillian Thomson (former principal cellist with Scottish Baroque Ensemble) and Sheena Nicoll (piano). Varied programmes from rarely performed and mainstream repertoire, eg. *Trios by Women Composers, Scandinavian Composers, Gems from Romantic and Classical Literature.*
19 Rothesay Terrace, Edinburgh EH3 7RY
Tel: 0131 225 3393 / 01576 300357
Fax: 01576 300357

MIXED TRIOS

The Caledonian Trio

Fiona Mitchell and Margaret Aronson (sopranos), Stuart Montgomery (piano). Friends and colleagues since 1985. Although classically trained, the repertoire ranges from the classics to show music. Classical programme of Mozart, Puccini, Strauss, Britten, Chopin, Liszt, Brahms. *Down Memory Lane*, Gershwin, Porter, Kern, Mayerl, Novello, Lehar etc.
5 Little Road, Edinburgh EH16 6SH
Tel: 0131 467 3616
Contact: Fiona Mitchell

Csardas

Sheila Osborne (mezzo-soprano), Bernard Docherty (violin) and Stephen Adam (piano) have made several broadcasts on radio and performed at music clubs, festivals, concert halls and theatres throughout the UK. The emphasis is on well-known pieces programmed into themes, e.g. Gypsy, Viennese, Russian. School programme (Gypsy) also available.
2 Falkland Avenue, Newton Mearns, Glasgow G77 5DR
Tel: 0141639 3176
Contact: Sheila Osborne

Lallan' Voices

Sarah-Jane Dale (soprano), Dirk Paterson (tenor) and Neil McFarlane (piano). 4 programmes: A *Soirée of Scottish Song*, and its influences on mainstream European composers; *Mendelssohn Maximus*, tales and songs of their epic journey through Scotland; *A Rantin' Rovin'*, Burns; *Technicolour Trews!* the renaissance of Scottish culture in the 20th c.
South Rowantree, Gatelawbridge, Thornhill, Dumfriesshire DG3 SEA
Tel: 01848 330396 Fax: 0171 873 7374
Contact: Dirk Paterson Tel: 0181 907 9182 or Sarah-Jane Dale Tel: 01737 249 839

The Music Box

Formed in 1977 by Linda Ormiston, Donald Maxwell and John Scrimger. Since then they have performed from Penzance to Thurso and from Swansea to Schweinfurt with frequent appearances at Prom concerts and at the Edinburgh Festival, 1992-95.
39 Colinhill Road, Strathaven ML10 6HF
Tel: 01357 21401 Fax: 01357 29719
Contact: Linda Ormiston

Trio Drummond Cairns McNaught

Irene Drummond (soprano), Christine Cairns (mezzo soprano) and Graeme McNaught (piano) are 3 experienced concert and recital artists who have combined to present programmes of songs, duets and piano solos, ranging from Schubert, Schumann and Brahms to Kern, Bernstein and Gershwin. Appearing in Europe, North America and Asia.
Carroll Artist Management, 25 Coates Gardens, Edinburgh EH12 5 LG
Tel: 0131 337 4705 Fax: 0131 337 4740
Contact: Frank Carroll (Management)

Trio Serenata

Integrate the familiar with the unfamiliar. Performed from village halls to Glasgow Royal Concert Hall. Repertoire ranges from Victorian, Scottish and Robert Burns to French and Viennese music. CD/ cassette: *Mid Pleasures and Pains.*
Alison Donaldson (Soprano), George MacIlwham (flute), David Murray (piano).
21 Lynn Drive, Eaglesham, Glasgow G76 0JJ
Tel: 013553 02869
Contact: Alison Donaldson

ARTISTS
CLASSICAL

51

Vocalise

Patricia MacMahon (soprano), John Cushing (clarinet), Walter Blair (Piano). Gaining a reputation for versatile and varied concerts. Programmes include Schubert, McCabe, Cooke, Spohr, Tate, Jacobs, Kern.
Banavie, Broomknowe Road, Kilmalcolm, Renfrewshire PA13 4HX
Tel: 01505 872391
Contact: Patricia H MacMahon

ARTISTS
CLASSICAL

INSTRUMENTAL QUARTET

Alison Jane Mitchell with members of the Edinburgh Quartet or Morley String Quartet

The chamber ensemble of flute and string trio with members of the Edinburgh Quartet or the Morley String Quartet, depending on their availability, perform flute quartet masterpieces from amongst others Haydn and Mozart and include newly commissioned Scottish works. Available for recitals, masterclasses and educational workshops.
28 Bellwood Street, Shawlands, Glasgow G41 3ES
Tel: 0141 649 9236

Allegro

String quartet of 2 years' standing offering classical recitals and a mixture of light and classical music for weddings, corporate functions etc. Requests gladly accommodated. Quartet made up of RSAMD graduates.
6/2 Buccleuch Street, Cowcaddens, Glasgow G3 6NR
Tel: 0141 332 0688 / 0374 607304 (mobile)
Contact: Ellen Rothwell

The Edinburgh Quartet

35th birthday in 1995. Travels widely throughout the UK and abroad. Broadcast frequently for British and foreign radio stations. Miles Baster (first violin), Peter Markham (second violin), Michael Beeston (viola) and Mark Bailey (cello).
119 Craigleith Road, Edinburgh EH4 2EH
Tel: 0131 332 8691 Fax: 0131 332 8691
Contact: Kenneth Main (Administrator)

Figaro Flute Quartet

Jean Murray (flute), Ian Laing (violin), Julian Marshall (viola) and Pat Hair (cello) are available for performances at music clubs and festivals, also weddings, dinners etc. within a 50 mile radius of Edinburgh. Their programmes, based around the flute quartets of Mozart, also include duos and trios.
11 Melville Place, Edinburgh EH3 7PR
Tel: 0131 226 3392
Contact: Jean Murray

Inchcolm

Anne Evans (flute); Dick Lee (clarinets); Nigel Richard (cittern, bagpipes); Wendy Weatherby (cello). Explores the area of music where classical/contemporary meets traditional/folk. Repertoire ranges from Corelli to Bartók, O'Carolan to Davy Graham, and includes original compositions by the group.
1 Cheyne Street, Edinburgh EH4 1JA
Tel: 0131 332 8083 Fax: 0131 332 8083
Contact: Dick Lee or Nigel Richard
Tel: 0131 551 1726

Just Flutes

New flute quartet with a wide and varied repertoire, easily adapted to suit any occasion. Performed throughout Scotland. Won a scholarship in July 1994 to travel to the Banff Centre for the Arts in Canada.
2 Napiershall Street (T/L), Kelvinbridge, Glasgow G20 6HQ
Tel: 0141 332 6467
Contact: Michelle McCabe

The Kilarney Quartet

Neil McFarlane (piano), Ruth Morley (flute), Karen Murdoch (clarinet) and Mary James (oboe). Tunnell and Hattori award winners. Broadcast for BBC and given concerts for many music societies and the Edinburgh Fringe, as well as educational tours for primary children.
G/R 8 Garrioch Crescent, North Kelvinside, Glasgow G20 8RR
Tel: 0141 946 1848
Contact: Neil McFarlane

Kist of Musick

Active for 12 years. Specialises in Scottish baroque chamber music. Two violins, cello and harpsichord. SAC tours, Reid Memorial Concerts, British Council trip to Czechoslovakia. Broadcast BBC Radio Scotland especially *Scotland's Music* series. Repertoire covers McGibbon, Oswald, Earl of Kelly, Sir John Clerk; also Corelli, Vivaldi, Handel, Purcell.
35 Mountcastle Terrace, Edinburgh EH8 7SF
Tel: 0131 657 2097 Fax: 0131 313 1388
Contact: Alastair Hardie

The Morley String Quartet

Prizewinning quartet which has performed in Russia and regularly at music clubs throughout the UK, broadcast on BBC Radio Scotland, and recorded a CD/cassette of popular encores. Music ranges from Mozart to Shostakovitch. New works occasionally premièred. Michael Kellett (violin 1), Frances Pryce (violin 2), Pat Field (viola), Stephen Adam (cello).
35 Camphill Avenue, Langside, Glasgow G41 3AX
Tel: 0141 632 9115 Fax: 0141 632 9115
Contact: Michael Kellett (Leader) or May Biggam (Manager) Tel: 0141 427 4836

Quartz String Quartet

String quartet of SCO players very much involved in education. Concerts and workshops, many of which are given in schools, are presented with a relaxed approach and an emphasis on making more accessible the variety of music presented.
89 Main Street, Aberdour, Fife KY3 0VQ
Tel: 01383 860 226
Contact: Steve King

Saltire String Quartet

Currently Quartet in Residence at the Queen's Hall, Edinburgh, this group of young players drawn from the BT Scottish Ensemble covers both traditional and contemporary music, in engagements throughout Scotland and broadcasts on BBC Radio 2 and Radio Scotland.
38 Queen's Crescent, Edinburgh EH9 2BA
Tel: 0131 667 8417 Fax: 0131 667 8417
Contact: Dr E A J Scott

The Scottish Saxophone Quartet

Founded 1976. Programmes are wide ranging and include arrangements from the 17th c. through the standard classical repertoire to popular style. Concerts include demonstrations and introductions. The group specialises in lecture recitals for schools.
Younger Hall Music Centre, University of St Andrews, Fife KY16 9AJ
Tel: 01334 462226 Fax: 01334 462570
Contact: Gillian Craig

Yggdrasil Quartet of Aberdeen

Swedish quartet from 1995 in three-year residency at Aberdeen to stimulate university music, workshops, masterclasses and projects both in the city and around Scotland.
Marischal College, Broad Street, Aberdeen AB9 1AS
Tel: 01224 273098 Fax: 01224 273098

MIXED QUARTETS

Ballads, Songs and Snatches

Kirsteen Grant (soprano), Anne Crawford (piano), Christine Forshaw (flute) and Gordon McCorkindale (reader) provide entertainment in music and word on a variety of topics, either as an hour's programme or as a complement to a first half recital.
25 Gartconnell Road, Bearsden, Glasgow G61 3BZ
Tel: 0141 942 7603
Contact: Kirsteen Grant

The Blind Date

Comedy show, devised and directed by tenor Stuart Patterson who joins forces with Eleanor Bennett (soprano), John Kitchen (harpsichord) and Robert Phillips (lute). Purcell, Handel and Monteverdi as you've never heard them before. As seen at the Glasgow International Early Music Festival and Covent Garden Festival.
c/o Pitch Perfect, 5 Aytoun Road, Glasgow G41 5RL
Tel: 0141 423 5577 Fax: 0141 423 5544
Contact: Lesley Boyd (Director) or Scott Cooper (Director)

The Lydian Ensemble

The combination of flute, clarinet and piano with a soprano makes possible a wide and varied repertoire with special arrangements and compositions. Performances are given as a duo, trio and quartet.
2 Lindsay Drive, Kelvindale, Glasgow G12 0HB
Tel: 0141 357 1423
Contact: Lydia Flett or George McIlwham
Tel: 0141 942 6779

Sincerely, Edvard Grieg

A complete evening programme lasting 90 minutes (plus interval). Readings from the composer's letters and articles linked by a selection of his songs and piano music. Fiona Lindsay (soprano), Robert Howie (piano), Margaret Hearne (reader) and John Hearne (reader).
Longship Music, Smidskot, Fawells, Keith hall, Inverurie AB51 0LN
Tel: 01651 882274 Fax: 01651 882274
Contact: John Hearne

Stanza

Peter Alexander Wilson (tenor), Peter Thomson (baritone), Crawford Logan (speaker) and Richard Honner (piano). All experienced performers in their own right who have worked with many leading opera companies. Offer programmes such as *Wine, Women ...but mostly Song*, *The Victorian Experience*, *A Celebration of Christmas*, and *The Joy of Springtime*.
Flat 6, 15 Forbes Place, Paisley PA1 1UT
Tel: 0141 887 5460 / 889 2536
Contact: Peter Alexander Wilson

INSTRUMENTAL ENSEMBLES

Allander Ensemble

Formed in 1984 and takes its membership from principal players of the Royal Scottish National Orchestra. Directed by the orchestra's leader Edwin Paling. The versatility of the ensemble enables it to cover a wide and varied repertoire ranging from trios to octets.
Edwin Paling, Royal Scottish National Orchestra, 73 Claremont Street, Glasgow G3 7HA
Tel: 0141 632 0567
Contact: Edwin Paling

Arcadian Ensemble

Brian Hale (violin), Philip Burrin (violin), Hilary Thornton (viola), Angela Turner (cello), augmented by others as required. Recent concerts have included works by Brahms, Elgar and Mozart.
Keeper's Cottage, Blackcraig, Ballintuim, Perthshire PH10 7PX
Tel: 01250 886 225
Contact: Hilary Thornton or Brian Hale
Tel: 0131 447 5307

Athenaeum Brass

Formed in 1985 at the RSAMD. The members of the quintet are now professional musicians and give regular music club recitals and community concerts all over Scotland. Their varied repertoire spans 400 years and ranges from Renaissance and classical to jazz and contemporary music.
21 Cartha Street, Shawlands, Glasgow G41 3HH
Tel: 0141 649 0754
Contact: Francis Magee

Avison String Ensemble

An eleven-player string ensemble, formed in 1982, performing in Fife and in other parts of Scotland. Repertoire extends over four centuries and includes music by Ian Whyte and, in particular, by Eoin Hamilton.
18 Balwearie Gardens, Kirkcaldy, Fife KY2 5LU
Tel: 01592 265714
Contact: Graeme Wilson (Director)

Baroque and Blue

Westlands, 14 Victoria Road, Dumfries DG2 7NU
Tel: 01387 54991
Contact: Mrs J Riley

BT Scottish Ensemble

Repertoire from baroque to contemporary, directed by violinist Clio Gould. Composer in Residence: Dave Heath. Records with Virgin Classics. Broadcasts on BBC television and radio and promotes series in all major Scottish cities.
2 Anchor Lane, Glasgow G1 2HW
Tel: 0141 221 2222 Fax: 0141 221 4444
Contact: Roger Pollen (Managing Director) or Jane Greig

Caledonia Brass

Formed in 1979 by members of the NYOS. Repertoire of over 200 pieces. Recitals given throughout the UK at several major festivals, clubs and societies, as well as numerous radio and television broadcasts.
680 Anniesland Road, Glasgow G14 0XR
Tel: 0141 954 8757
Contact: Joan Morrison or Alan Fernie
Tel: 0131 551 3887

Cello Spice

Established professional group performing and promoting the large repertory of original compositions for cello ensemble from the 18th c. to contemporary, plus arrangements of salon and popular music for three, four and up to twelve or more cellists. Programmes flexible in content, length and numbers of performers. First commercial CD, 1995.
The Corner House, Murthly, Perthshire PH1 4EL
Tel: 01738 710378
Contact: Avril Lloyd (Administrator)

ARTISTS
CLASSICAL

53

Celtic Clarinets

Recently formed clarinet quartet whose members have been brought together after completing their studies. Can create a backdrop for a host of occasions such as recitals, dinners and exhibitions.
26 North Dumgoyne Avenue, Milngavie, Glasgow G62 7JT
Contact: Eleni Panaretou

Chamber Group of Scotland

Founded 1991. Patron: Sir Peter Maxwell Davies. Artistic directors: Sally Beamish, Robert Irvine, James MacMillan. Promotes chamber music, particularly contemporary Scottish. Heard regularly on Radio Scotland and Radio 3. Appeared at major Scottish festivals including Edinburgh Festival. Winners of Mayfest Paper Boat award.
40 Braeside Place, Milngavie G62 6LJ
Tel: 0141 956 2618 Fax: 0141 956 2618
Contact: Carole Allen (Administrator) or Robert Irvine Tel: 0360 440165

Concerto Caledonia

Début at the Edinburgh International Festival in 1992. Focus for many of the most experienced of Scotland's baroque music specialists, through broadcasts, recordings and occasional concerts.
36 Station Road, Bearsden, Glasgow G61 4AL
Tel: 0141 942 0239
Contact: Carolyn Sparey-Gillies or David McGuinness Tel: 0141 339 0605

Flaxton Ensemble

Formed 1983. Fiona Chisholm (flute); Sheila Laing (oboe); Tom Hay (clarinet); Lesley Wilson (bassoon); John Wilson (french horn). Performed at music clubs and arts guilds throughout Scotland, and also under the auspices of the National Trust for Scotland. Premièred *Untold* by James MacMillan (1988), commissioned by Ayr Arts Trust and SAC.
1a St Leonard's Road, Ayr KA7 2PR
Tel: 01292 265298
Contact: Tom Hay

Glasgow Viennese Strings

Performs all over Scotland the easily accessible yet seldom heard literature of the Viennese school (Mozart, Lanner, Schubert, Strauss) using a varied and informal style.
2 Staikhill, Lanark ML11 7PW
Tel: 01555 662645
Contact: Angus Ramsay

Hebrides Ensemble

Founded 1991 by William Conway and Peter Evans. Programme emphasis on Scottish-based composers and covering a wide range of periods and styles. Promotes a concert series. Appeared at Edinburgh Festival, Glasgow Mayfest and music clubs throughout the country. BBC Radio 3 broadcasts and appearances on BBC TV.
25 Coates Gardens, Edinburgh EH12 5LG
Tel: 0131 337 4740 Fax: 0131 337 4740
Contact: Frank Carroll (Manager)

The McGibbon Ensemble

Recitals of Scottish music, mainly 18th c. Performances include: BBC in 1992, as part of John Purser's *Scotland's Music* series; Reid Memorial Concert at Edinburgh University in 1995; two commercially available cassettes.
2/3 Craufurdland, Braepark Road, Edinburgh EH4 6DL
Tel: 0131 317 9191
Contact: Bryce Gould or Dr David Johnson (Director) Tel: 0131 667 7054

New Torphin Music Group

A string, wind and piano band of eight to ten players. Music is varied, but mostly 18th c. Meetings on alternate Thursday evenings throughout the year.
58 Greenbank Crescent, Edinburgh EH10 5SW
Tel: 0131 447 3752
Contact: G. Sclare (Convener)

The Nielsen Wind Consort

Wind quintet, formed whilst studying at the RSAMD. Repertoire suited to a variety of occasions such as recitals and galas. Past performances have included recitals for Margaret Thatcher and the Queen.
119 Novar Drive, Hyndland, Glasgow G12 9SZ
Tel: 0131 339 1408
Contact: Rachel Forbes

Northern College 20th Century Ensemble Aberdeen Campus

A group of staff and students from Northern College dedicated to bringing contemporary music to a wider audience by means of exciting and innovative performances. Recent repertoire includes music by Steve Reich, Graham Fitkin, Arvo Part, Rebecca Rowe and music by members of the ensemble.

Northern College, Hilton Place, Aberdeen AB9 1FA
Tel: 01224 283601 Fax: 01224 283576
Contact: Pete Stollery (Performance Co-ordinator) or Dundee Campus Tel: 01382 464000

The North Winds

Wind quintet. Programmes contain a variety of wind music, trios, quartets and quintets, from the 18th c. to the present day. The group aims to transmit its tremendous sense of enjoyment in the music to the audience. Spoken introductions by Bruce Gordon.

1 Cheyne Street, Edinburgh EH4 1JA
Tel: 0131 332 8083
Contact: Anne Evans

One Voice

Contemporary Scottish music ensemble, with a large part of their repertoire by composers working in Scotland. A cross-over ensemble aiming to break down barriers between music genres and catalysing cooperation between community groups through music. Recording: *One Voice* available from the ensemble.

99 Lothian Road, Edinburgh EH3 9AN
Tel: 0131 228 3706 Fax: 0131 650 6516
Contact: Jeremy Cull Tel: 0131 661 5377 or Geraint Wiggins Tel: 0131 650 2722

Out to Play!

Wind ensemble of 2-5 players, with or without piano. Light and classical repertoire.

Ennets Farm, Tornaveen, Torphins, Kincardineshire AB31 4PE
Contact: Margaret Preston
Tel: 013398 83401

The Perth Ensemble

Septet with repertoire firmly rooted in classical and romantic tradition of Beethoven's *Septet Opus 20*. Other works programmed include the Berwald and Kreutzer septets and some specially commissioned pieces which are not aggressively modern, all of which provides varied and approachable concert programmes.

Tigh-Na-Beithe, Birnam, Perthshire PH8 0EN
Tel: 01350 727371 / 0378 616151
Fax: 01350 727371
Contact: Graham Robb

Philip Greene and Friends

Philip Greene (clarinet), Peter Markham (violin), Alison Rushworth (violin), Simon Johnson (viola), Gillian Thomas (cello). Formed to take part in the Mozart double centenary celebrations during the Edinburgh Festival. Repertoire by Mozart and Carl Maria von Weber. Programmes can be varied for different combinations within the group.

16 Learmonth Terrace, Edinburgh EH4 1PG
Tel: 0131 332 0481
Contact: Philip Greene

SCO Brass

Formed 1985, affiliated to the Scottish Chamber Orchestra. Experienced in recitals and community and educational concerts. Can provide thematic concerts such as *A European Experience* and *American Images*, or offer a choice from a wide and varied repertoire.

29 West Bankton Place, Murieston West, Livingston, West Lothian EH54 9ED
Tel: 01506 415514
Contact: Peter Franks

Scottish Bach Consort

Based in Killearn Kirk, Stirlingshire. Takes classical music to rural audiences throughout Scotland. Artistic Director: John Doig.

66 Main Street, Killearn, Stirlingshire G63 9ND
Tel: 01360 550824 Fax: 01360 550588
Contact: Iain D Beattie (Manager) or Miss J R Stewart (Company Secretary)

The Scottish Brass Ensemble

Specialise in promoting the brass chamber music of Scottish composers. The Director, Nigel Boddice, was 1994 recipient of Society of Scottish Composers Award for the Ensemble's pioneering work. Plays extensively for Scottish music clubs, festivals, choirs, schools and colleges, in addition to recording regularly for radio and telelvision.

c/o 16 Lindsay Place, Kelvindale, Glasgow G12 0HX
Tel: 0141 357 1826 Fax: 0141 357 1826
Contact: Anne Cumberland

Sequoia

Chamber music ensemble, formed 1993. Instrumentation varies, having a core group of flute, violin, viola, cello, piano and harp. Given many recitals in the North East of Scotland - Aberdeen, Cowdray Hall, Haddo Hall, Monymusk Arts Trust etc. Can suit any recital situation because of its versatility in size and style of music.

Resthivet Cottage, Pitcaple, Inverurie AB51 5DT
Tel: 01467 681298 Fax: 01467 681298
Contact: Gillian Leonard (Leader)

Zoë Albamicum

Contemporary experimentalist group, formed to communicate the ideas of composer Cluny Strachan.

Flat 3/1, 69 Sinclair Drive, Langside G42 9PV
Tel: 0141 649 0467
Contact: Cluny Strachan

ARTISTS

CLASSICAL

VOCAL ENSEMBLES

Scottish Voices

Performs music for one or several women's voices, accompanied and unaccompanied. Repertoire: medieval to the present (including material in both cultivated and vernacular idioms). Special interest in Scottish composers. Graham Hair (director); Alice Dumas, Amanda Morrison, Taylor Wilson, Marie-Louise Edmondson (voices); Greta Mary Hair (research and development).

45 St Vincent Street, Glasgow G3 8NG
Tel: 0141 221 4933 Fax: 0141 307 8018
Contact: Graham Hair (Director) or Jane Mallinson (Administrator)
Tel: 0141 357 0243

55

Song Circle

Eight-piece *a cappella* group - two each SATB. Repertoire covers music past and present, early to contemporary, popular and classics. Available for functions, weddings and recitals.
35 Broomhill Drive, Glasgow G11 7AB
Tel: 0141 339 5931
Contact: Andrew Webb

![ARTISTS] **CLASSICAL**

MIXED ENSEMBLES

Intermezzo

Performs music written for the unconventional blend of two mezzo soprano voices and piano. Repertoire encompasses works from baroque through to the 20th c. including Montiverdi, Handel, Vivaldi, Rossi, Mozart, Brahms, Debussy, Satie, Britten, Kurt Weill and new commissions. Performs both solos and duets and often includes other instruments.
14 Cecil Street, Glasgow G12 8RQ
Tel: 0973 368363 (mobile)
Contact: Marie-Louise Edmondson

Mosaic

New contemporary music ensemble formed by young Scottish composer David Paul Jones. The ensemble will act not only as a vehicle for the composer's own work but aims to attract artists not usually associated with the classical medium. Début planned in Glasgow spring 1996.
7 Dunedin Street, Edinburgh EH7 4JB
Tel: 0131 556 6031
Contact: Fiona Graham (Administrator) Tel: 0141 357 4071 or David Paul Jones (Aritstic Director) Tel: 0131 556 6031

The Music Room

Formed 1995 for Argyll and Bute Concert Tours. Versatile group of singers all living and working in Scotland. Basic four singers and pianist, can be expanded to suit. Using simple props and some narration the group brings the excitement of the opera to music clubs. Also cabaret evening, Gershwin and Porter.
5 Little Road, Edinburgh EH16 6SH
Tel: 0131 467 3616
Contact: Fiona Mitchell

Note-Ability

Programmes are individually designed to suit various needs, can be built upon a theme and include colourful costumes.
88 Shawwood Crescent, Newton Mearns, Glasgow G77 5NB
Tel: 0141 639 5433
Contact: Lewis Allan Tel: 0585 423 214 (mobile)

Paragon Ensemble Scotland

Regularly performs new work in concerts, music theatre, opera, education and the community. With a flexible repertoire ranging from small chamber ensembles to music theatre productions, the company tours nationally and internationally, as well as promoting its own subscription series.
2 Port Dundas Place, Glasgow G3 3LB
Tel: 0141 332 9903 Fax: 0141 332 9904
Contact: Margaret Paterson (General Manager) or David Davies (Artistic Director)

The Quatrain

1995 is the group's 20th anniversary season. Wide assortment of programmes built up over the years.
4 Greenmount Road North, Burntisland, Fife KY3 9JQ
Tel: 01592 872424
Contact: Rhona White

Quern

Exists to help charities in their fundraising activities. Although offering concerts and taking part in festivals, the twelve strong group is best known for its 'musical journeys' on aspects of Scottish life: *Life of Burns/Hogg/Stevenson/Robert Service* and *Royal Mile, Fishing and Trawling*, and *Bothies, Bannocks and Brose*.
37 South Barnton Avenue, Edinburgh EH4 6JS
Tel: 01312 336 1807
Contact: Roy Benson or Amy Donaldson Tel: 01506 843854

Quernstane

Formed 1990. Programmes are researched and aim to recreate the atmosphere of 18th c. Scotland by performing songs and music of the period using harpsichord and baroque violin, and by using readings from contemporary letters, journals and newspapers.
5 St Mark's Lane, Portobello, Edinburgh EH15 2PX
Tel: 0131 669 3394
Contact: Lawrence Dunn

Uni-son

Glasgow University's student-run contemporary music ensemble, formed in June 1994 and dedicated to performing music by living composers. Provides platform for senior performance and composition students. Evening and lunchtime concerts during academic year. Forms an orchestra for final term concert.
Glasgow University, Music Department, 14 University Gardens, Glasgow G12 8QE
Tel: 0141 339 8855
Contact: Tommy Fowler (Artistic Director)

CELLO

Chahin, Myra

Programmes can be compiled to suit many tastes, from a full cello and piano recital to after dinner entertainment. Experienced teacher (at RSAMD), can also offer masterclasses before performing. Many concerts given with pianist Bernard King.
5 Chapelton Avenue, Bearsden, Glasgow G61 2RE
Tel: 0141 942 1356

Conway, William

Born Scotland. Appearances at Tivoli, Granada, Mayfest and Edinburgh festivals plus all the major halls in Scotland and London. Recorded with Claudio Abbado. Recorded Peter Maxwell Davies' cello concerto, which was specially written for him. Principal cellist of the Chamber Orchestra of Europe.
9 Sciennes Gardens, Edinburgh EH9 1NR
Tel: 0131 667 4630
Fax: 0131 667 4630

Irvine, Benedict

B.Mus. (Glasgow, 1995) in performance. Pupil of Alexander Volpov. Experience of traditional and light orchestral repertoire. Wide solo repertoire, from Renaissance to contemporary. Soloist with university orchestra. Founder member of student-run contemporary music ensemble Unison.
Music Department, University of Glasgow, 14 University Gardens, Glasgow G12 8QE
Tel: 0141 339 8855
Contact: PFJ Irvine Tel: 01904 707325 or Tommy Fowler Tel: 0141 353 0927

Norris, Philip

Active orchestral and chamber music player. Founder member Paragon Ensemble, former member Cantilena. Assistant principal cellist BBC SSO and teacher at RSAMD. Spent ten years in Germany first as student of the Torteliers and Mirko Dorner then at Essen and Wiesbaden as orchestral musician and teacher.
7 Clyth Drive, Giffnock G46 6NW
Tel: 0141 638 2698

ARTISTS

CLASSICAL

CLARINET

Lee, Dick

Plays a wide variety of musical styles, ranging from performances of the classical repertoire (baroque to contemporary) with the SCO and Schola Cantorum to folk and jazz with groups such as the Hamish Moore/Dick Lee Duo, Chamber Jazz, and Swing '95.
1 Cheyne Street, Edinburgh EH4 1JA
Tel: 0131 332 8083

Murdoch, Karen

Freelancing in orchestral, theatre and chamber music since graduation from the RSAMD in 1991. Work includes Royal Scottish National Orchestra, Scottish Chamber Orchestra, Scottish Opera, BBC Scottish Symphony Orchestra, Scottish Ballet, D'Oyly Carte, Tag Theatre, Theatre Theatrical, STV and BBC Radio.
Duncarnock Farm, Newton Mearns, Glasgow G77 6PH
Tel: 0141 880 5650

ELECTRO-ACOUSTIC MUSIC

Stollery, Pete

c/o Northern College, Aberdeen Campus, Hilton Place, Aberdeen AB9 1FA
Tel: 01224 283780 Fax: 01224 487046

FLUTE

Eliot, Rosemary

Born Dundee. Studied Guidhall and Paris Conservatoire. Principal flute BBC SSO. Regular soloist Hebrides Ensemble. Repertoire covers baroque to contemporary. Appeared as soloist with BBC SSO plus live recital on Radio Scotland.
25 Kelvinside Terrace South, Glasgow G20 6DW
Tel: 0141 946 0380
Contact: Rosemary Eliot

Evans, Anne

Performed with SCO, the original Scottish Baroque Ensemble, Dick Lee's Chamber Jazz and the North Winds wind quintet amongst others. Developed her piano playing, notably in partnership with violinist, the late Leonard Friedman, and with multi-instrumentalist Dick Lee.
1 Cheyne Street, Edinburgh EH4 1JA
Tel: 0131 332 8083

Hartley, Elaine

B.Mus. (Hons). Performer and teacher. Interested in variety of music, including contemporary classical, non-Western, electro-acoustic, improvisation and collaborative mixed media. Currently studying ethnomusicology as a post-graduate student at York University. Member of Women In Music.
c/o Scott, 51 Kirk Street, Prestwick KA9 1AU
Tel: 01292 474062
Contact: Margaret Scott

Leonard, Gillian

Graduated M.Mus. (in flute performance) 1984 from Northern Illinois University. Freelanced in Los Angeles until returning to Scotland in 1987. Performed with accompanists (Bob Howie and Barbara Payne), at various venues in north east scotland such as Northern College, Cowdray Hall, Monymusk Arts Trust and Haddo House.
Resthivet Cottage, Pitcaple, Inverurie AB51 5DT
Tel: 01467 681298 Fax: 01467 681298

MacIlwham, George

Born Glasgow 1926. Studied Glasgow and London. Freelance then joined SNO 1947, BBC SSO 1954 principal piccolo and flute (with BBC SSO for 34 years). Freelance composer, broadcaster. Member of chamber groups Trio Serenata, Syrinx Duo, The Lydian Ensemble. Regular concerts for the Council for Music in Hospitals. Also plays bagpipes in orchestral works.
25 Ravelston Road, Bearsden, Glasgow G61 1AW
Tel: 0141 942 6779

Mason, Camille

Studied Glasgow University (B.Mus., M.Mus.) and privately with Sheena Gordon. Featured soloist with Glasgow University Orchestra. Repertoire covers baroque to contemporary. Available as soloist or with small ensemble. Also teaches privately and in schools.
78 Arran Avenue, Motherwell ML1 3ND
Tel: 01698 261350

Mitchell, Alison Jane

Studied with Swiss flautist Peter-Lukas Graf. Appointed principal flute with the orchestra of Scottish Opera (1987-92). Performs as soloist since 1992 and appears regularly with orchestras and established musicians in various ensembles throughout Europe. Available for recitals, concertos, masterclasses and educational workshops.
28 Bellwood Street, Shawlands, Glasgow G41 3ES
Tel: 0141 649 9236

Morley, Ruth

Studied at RSAMD, Royal Northern College with David Nicholson, Peter Lloyd and Wissam Boustany. Performed concertos and recitals in the UK and abroad. Works with piano, guitar or harp. Member of Scottish Flute Trio and the Kilarney Quartet. Broadcast for BBC radio and Classic FM.
151 West Princes Street, Woodlands, Glasgow G4 9BZ
Tel: 0141 333 0828

Murray, Jean

Varied career including orchestral work (Heisenberg Ensemble, St Mary's Cathedral Edinburgh, Edinburgh Bach Society etc), chamber music (duos, trios and quartets at music clubs, festivals, dinners and receptions) as well as teaching at St Mary's Music School.
11 Melville Place, Edinburgh EH3 7PR
Tel: 0131 226 3392

Nicholson, David

Principal flute of the Scottish Chamber Orchestra since its inception. Teacher of flute at the RSAMD. Frequent soloist with the SCO. Founder member of the New Music Group of Scotland. Has given recitals and chamber concerts throughout the UK and Europe. Also masterclasses in the UK and abroad.
14 Nile Grove, Edinburgh
EH10 4RF
Tel: 0131 447 3398
Fax: 0131 447 3398

GUITAR

Argondizza, Peter

Performed solo and chamber music concerts throughout Britain and North America. Available for concert and recording work, as well as teaching/lecturing in various capacities. Holds a Doctor of Musical Arts degree from Yale University. Currently lectures at Strathclyde University.
26 Woodcroft Avenue (3/2), Broomhill,
Glasgow G11 7HY
Tel: 0141 357 1428

Chaurand, Anne

French by birth, Scottish by adoption. Trained at RSAMD then in Europe with Pepe Romero and Leo Brower. Solo recitals reflect the diversity of cultures and influences on the guitar's repertoire, with special highlights on Scotland's music old and new.
76 White Street, Glasgow G11 5BD
Tel: 0141 334 5691

Madeley, Selina

Solo programmes combine Renaissance music played on the lute as well as traditional guitar repertoire. The Scottish Guitar Duo with Phillip Thorne.
20 Baldoven Terrace (G/L), Stobswell,
Dundee DD4 6LT
Tel: 01382 451411

Neave, Allan

Prizewiner at many international competitions. Won the Maisie Lewis Young Artists Award (1993) resulting in a Purcell début. Regularly performs at guitar festivals worldwide. Recordings broadcast by BBC, Classic FM, ABC and Radio France.
29 Baldovan Terrace, Stobswell, Dundee
DD4 6NQ
Tel: 01382 453353

Thorne, Phillip

Promotes the work of contemporary Scottish composers, commissioning what is virtually a new repertoire for the guitar. PRS/Society of Composers Award for services to Scottish Music. He is guitar co-ordinator at the RSAMD
25 Brockwood Avenue, Penicuik,
Midlothian EH26 9AL
Tel: 01968 673470

HARP

Askew, Sophie

Studied with Sidonie Goossens and Sioned Williams at Guildhall and with Sancha Pielou at RSAMD. Solo performances as well as orchestral and chamber music. Repertoire ranges from classical to contemporary light music. Also plays clarsach, in a flute and harp duo (Harla), and is available for functions etc.
60 Airlie Street (G/L), Hyndland, Glasgow
G12 9SW
Tel: 0141 339 0634

Kennedy, Mary Ann

Studied piano at RSAMD but turned to concentrate on harp at RNCM. Works in both classical and traditional muisc; broadcast on BBC and ITV; premièred works for large and small harps; released a duo album and guested on many others; also presents Radio Scotland's Celtic/roots music programme *Celtic Connections*.
c/o 18 Glencairn Drive, Pollokshields,
Glasgow G41 4QN
Tel: 0141 423 6585 / 01808 521424

MacKay, Rhona

Former principal harp with SNO. Now freelances and enjoys a wide spectrum of music. Plays regularly with the RSNO, Scottish Opera and Scottish Ballet. Experienced in popular music, playing with the Glasgow Philharmonic Orchestra. Also experienced in recording work, adjucation and examination. Member of two trios.
Bridgeflat , Nr Bridge of Weir,
Renfrewshire PA11 3SJ
Tel: 01505 872595

Peacock, Judith

Performer and teacher of pedal harp and clarsach. Solo performances of classical and traditional Scottish music including Edinburgh Festival Fringe, Bute Folk Festival and the Highland Harp Festival. Also weddings, dinners etc. Special interest in Gaelic music and is a member of traditional group The Whistlebinkies.
11 Shaw Road, Milngavie, Glasgow
G62 6LU

Thuillier, Kate

Soprano and harpist offers song recitals with programmes ranging from Mozart to the 20th c., specialising in Fauré, Debussy, Richard Strauss, Delius and other composers of the Romantic era. Also background music for all occasions on concert harp or clarsach (Scottish harp).
11 Greenhill Terrace, Edinburgh
EH10 4BS
Tel: 0131 447 1601

Vickerman, Louise

Studied RSAMD. Principal harp NYOS. Played with BBC SSO, SCO, Scottish Ballet, Scottish Opera. Orchestral, ensemble and solo work throughout UK including radio and TV broadcasts and film music. Career moved to USA, first full performance of Paul Elwood's *Concerto for Harp and Percussion*. Now principal harp New World Symphony Orchestra, Miami.
16 Mirrlees Drive, Glasgow G12 0SH
Tel: 0141 334 2794

HORN

Hodson, Mark

Available for work in Aberdeen area, evenings and weekends. Experienced in ensemble and orchestral playing both classical and contemporary.
MLURI, Craigiebuckler, Aberdeen
AB9 2QJ
Tel: 01224 318611 Fax: 01224 311556

ARTISTS
CLASSICAL

ARTISTS

CLASSICAL

ORGAN

Erskine, Robin
B Mus (Hons), ARCO, organ scholar Glasgow University 1961-65. Studied with Douglas Gilles, Frederick Rimmer, Alexander Anderson and at Académie d'Orgue in Provence with Xavier Darasse and André Stricker. Recitals in UK and Germany. Broadcast as accompanist and church organist. Recording with GU Chapel Choir.
30 Gallowhill Road, Paisley PA3 4TE
Tel: 0141 889 9045

Hamilton, David
B.Mus. (Glasgow 1989); Organ, Harpsichord and Performance Practice study Germany and the Netherlands, 1989 -91 - UMus Zwolle 1991; FRCO 1992; 3rd prize European Organ Improvisation Competition 1990; finalist Paisley Organ Improvisation Competition 1992; recorded with Cappella Nova; performed throughout western Europe, Russia, Lithuania, Czech Republic; active teacher - all standards.
18 Orchard Street, Motherwell ML1 3JD
Tel: 01698 262728

Hindley, Mark
Organ and harpsichordist. Music degree in Cambridge. Organ scholar: studied with David Sanger. Postgraduate course in Oxford. Now Organist and Master of Choristers at St Paul's Episcopal Cathedral, Dundee. Performance diplomas: ARCM, ARCO. Soloist, accompanist and teacher, who has performed in many of the major national venues.
Binrock Lodge, 454A Perth Road, Dundee DD2 1NG
Tel: 01382 669331

Kitchen, John
Studied Universities of Glasgow and Cambridge. Lecturer in Music and University Organist at St Andrews 1976 - 88, currently Senior Lecturer and University Organist in Edinburgh. Researches 17th and 18th c. keyboard music. Performs with Scottish Early Music Consort, with other groups and as soloist. Recorded complete works of William Kinloch and broadcasts on BBC radio.
Faculty of Music, University of Edinburgh, Alison House, 12 Nicolson Square, Edinburgh EH8 9DF
Tel: 0131 447 3320

Massimo, Alberto
Born 1962. Organ recitals in Italy, Spain, Wales, France, Austria and Scotland. Award of Professional of the Year in Music 1991 by American Biographical Institute. Also conductor.
7/1 Windmill Place, Edinburgh EH8 9XQ
Tel: 0131 668 3390

Nickol, Christopher
Educated Ampleforth College, London University, RCM. Director of music at New Kilpatrick since 1993. Recitals in all major Scottish venues as well as throughout the UK, France, Italy and Denmark. Soloist with RSNO, Cappella Nova, BBC SSO, RSNO Chorus. Broadcast on Radio 3. Recording available.
New Kilpatrick Parish Church, 28 Kirk Place, Bearsden, Glasgow G61 3RT
Tel: 0141 558 6555

Stout, Alastair
Edina, Vidlin, Shetland ZE2 9QB
Tel: 01806 577257

PERCUSSION

Corbett, Heather
Percussion, timpani, cimbalon. Concerto soloist, orchestral soloist, chamber concerts and special education workshops. Section principal BBC SSO. Professor of percussion Napier University.
33 Faskally Avenue, Bishopbriggs, Glasgow G64 3PJ
Tel: 0141 772 3152 / 0860 234588 (mobile)
Contact: Heather Corbett or STR Music Tel: 0171 624 0177 / 0448 (fax)

Currie, Colin
Studied at RSAMD Junior Department (1990-94). Entrance scholar at RAM (1994) studying with Neil Percy and Kurt Hans Geodicke. Winner of Shell/LSO Scholarship (1992). Percussion finalist in BBC Young Musician of the Year (1994). Numerous concerto appearances include RSNO Prom. Large recital repertoire, including jazz.
35 Redford Avenue, Edinburgh EH13 0BX
Tel: 0131 441 2920
Contact: Kerry Nixon Tel: 0141 337 1299 or Robin Michael Tel: 01592 263087

Glennie, Evelyn
c/o Good Vibrations, Heritage House, Upton, Cambs PE17 5YF
Tel: 01480 891772 / 0831 847449 (mobile) Fax: 01480 891779

PIANO

Antonelli, Peter
Studied in Edinburgh and RCM then privately with Craig Sheppard. Performed at music societies and clubs throughout Scotland including Queen's Hall, Edinburgh. Has recorded various recitals for the BBC since his first in 1980.
11 Seton Place, Port Seton, East Lothian EH32 0DT
Tel: 01875 813840

Barnett, Michael
Performer/composer in contemporary and commercial fields. Classical commissions, jazz/contemporary dance and film/animation music. Performing ensembles include jazz trio/quartet, function band, Scottish cabaret party, Renaissance wind band and klezmer folk group. Employed by The Dance School of Scotland.
270 North Woodside Road, North Kelvinside, Glasgow G20 6LX
Tel: 0141 337 6867 Fax: 0141 638 0079

Beckles Willson, Rachel
Studied London, Glasgow and Liszt Academy of Music Budapest. Special interest Hungarian and contemporary music. Perfomed with Jane Manning, Scottish Voices, Inter Modulacio Contemporary Ensemble, Hungary. Regularly broadcasts on Radio Bartok. Performed in Park Lane Group recital in Purcell Room, London. Available for solo, ensemble and accompanying work.
c/o Cameron, 213 Wilton Street (1/R), Glasgow G20 6DE
Tel: 0141 946 9070

Brennand, Charlotte
Studied RSAMD and the Royal Academy of Music in London (prizewinner). Pursues recital and oratorio career throughout Britain with Intermezzo (a trio of 2 mezzos and a piano) which perform wide repertoire of works from baroque to contemporary including: Montiverdi, Handel, Vivaldi, Rossi, Debussy, Brahms, Britten, Kurt Weill and commissions.
14 Cecil Street, Glasgow G12 8RQ
Tel: 0141 339 1325

Cochrane, Lynda

Born Edinburgh. Studied piano and composition Manchester University, RNCM and Indiana University. Compositions performed at St Magnus Festival and by the RSNO. Frequently performs with Paragon Ensemble, Scottish Voices and the RSNO and enjoys a rich variety of chamber music.
Garden Flat, 11 Rosslyn Terrace, Glasgow G12 9NA
Tel: 0141 334 5607

Donald, George

Pianist/accompanist. Composer/Musical Director/performer - Scotland the What? Studied piano Nelly Akopian, London, and Aube Tzerko, Los Angeles. Numerous recitals both solo and with singers and instrumentalists in Britain, on the continent, and in America. 1986 and 1990 Edinburgh International Festivals. Worked extensively in radio and television.
12 Kincarrathie Crescent, Perth, Tayside PH2 7HH
Tel: 01738 622425

Evans, Peter

Varied career as solo pianist and chamber music performer, conductor and teacher. Studied Edinburgh University, Vienna Hochschule. Concerts throughout UK, Europe, USA, former USSR, Japan. Many recordings and broadcasts on radio and television. Featured as soloist with all Scottish orchestras. Artistic co-director Hebrides Ensemble. Principal conductor Edinburgh's Meadows Chamber Orchestra.
49 Spottiswoode Road, Edinburgh EH9 1DA
Tel: 0131 447 6414

Fenyo, Gusztáv

Recitalist and concerto soloist in three continents as well as throughout the UK. Performing highlights in Scotland have included Beethoven's complete sonata cycle in Glasgow and Edinburgh in 1990. Commercial recordings of works by Liszt, Chopin and Bartók. Repertoire ranges from the classics and romantics to contemporary music.
17 North Gardner Street, Hyndland, Glasgow G11 5BU
Tel: 0141 339 2708

Finlay, David

Fourteen years' experience as recital and rehearsal pianist. Worked with RSNO Chorus, Aberdeen International Youth Festival, Edinburgh Grand Opera, Glasgow Orpheus Club. Accompanist to solo singers and instrumentalists, plus piano duet work. Jazz experience on piano and other keyboards with soloist and in jazz group Between Friends.
85 East King Street, Helensburgh G84 7RG
Tel: 01436 672187 Fax: 01436 672187

Kingsley, Colin

B.Mus. (Cambridge 1946), D.Mus. (Edinburgh 1968). Senior lecturer at retirement in 1992. Throughout years on Edinburgh University Music Faculty teaching staff was active as concert pianist, introducing many new works, including Scottish composers William Sweeney and Edward Harper. Lectured Edinburgh Festival 1994, now concerned with guest lecturing, playing, and piano teaching.
236 Milton Road East, Edinburgh EH15 2PF
Tel: 0131 669 2070

McFarlane, Neil

Freelance accompanist, works regularly with Hector Scott of the BT Scottish Ensemble. Together they have released a CD *300 Years of Scottish Music*. Works in various other chamber groups and as official accompanist at music festivals. Broadcast for BBC, Classic FM and STV.
8 Garrioch Crescent (G/R), North Kelvinside, Glasgow G20 8RR
Tel: 0141 946 1848
Contact: Neil McFarlane

McLachlan, Murray

Born Dundee. Educated Aberdeen. Studied at Chetham's and Cambridge University. Wide reputation as a performing and recording artist. Radio broadcasts and numerous concerto performances with top orchestras. Also an active chamber musician. Pianist in residence at Strathclyde University.
Banrye Cottage, 5 Holburn Place, Aberdeen AB1 6HG
Tel: 01224 587610 Fax: 01224 587610
Contact: Murray McLachlan

Nicoll, Sheena

Studied Edinburgh/Vienna; scholarship/prize winner; lecture-recitalist; broadcasts/concerts in Britain, Europe and Africa; programmes include *Piano Music of European Countries* and *Women Composers*. Vast repertoire, rarely performed standard works. Many first performances at international conferences.
19 Rothesay Terrace, Edinburgh EH3 7RY
Tel: 0131 225 3393 / 01576 300357

Seivewright, Peter

Wide repertoire covering Bach, 19th and 20th c., Scandinavian and American music. Appeared as concerto soloist with many leading orchestras and has given recitals throughout UK, Ireland, Norway, Denmark, Belgium, Germany and Australia. CDs include *Contemporary Scottish Piano Music* (Merlin) and *Complete Piano Music of Carl Nielson* (Naxos). Also a jazz pianist.
The Old Joinery, Lintfieldbank, Coalburn, Lanarkshire ML11 0NJ
Tel: 01555 820369

Shur, Laura

Born in Glasgow, and studied at RSAMD. Gained Dip. (Mus. Ed.) RSAM, LRAM (piano teaching) and ARCM (piano performing). Recitals have included Royal Festival Hall and BBC.
c/o Sylvia Donne, 11/4 The Steils, Glenlockhart, Edinburgh EH10 5XD
Tel: 0131 447 2947

TROMBONE

Fernie, Alan

Studied at RSAMD (1977- 80). Working as trombonist, teacher, conductor and composer/arranger, mainly in the brass medium (band, quintet, ensemble and educational).
38 Hawthornvale, Edinburgh EH6 4JW
Tel: 0131 551 3887

Kenny, John

Repertoire stretches from the Renaissance to the avant garde. Over 80 pieces composed for him - solo, duos with organ, piano, percussion and electronics, string quartet and orchestra. He is also the first exponent of the reconstructed carnyx, Scotland's 2,000 year old war horn! Also performs jazz and composes.
69 Spottiswoode Street, Edinburgh EH9 1DL
Tel: 0131 447 3707 Fax: 0131 447 3707

ARTISTS

CLASSICAL

TROMBONE (CONTD)

Kirkwood, Derick

Former principal trombone with
Dalmellington Band. Currently leader/
musical director of the ensemble Glasgow
Computing Brass. Plays any type of music
but mainly classical, light and jazz. Can
improvise. Also composes for a variety of
groups.
*38 Harris Close, Newton Mearns,
Glasgow G77 6TU*
Tel: 0141 639 2504

VIOLA

Durrant, James

Lecture/recitals. Scottish and/or 20th c.
viola repertoire; orchestral coaching or
rehearsal; string specialist.
3 Victoria Circus, Glasgow G12 9LB
Tel: 0141 334 4867

King, Steve

Creative musician and educationalist.
Works in schools and centres for people
with learning disabilities, together with
staff training and development all over
Scotland. Has been pioneering new ideas
and methods for creating music in the
community with people of mixed abilities
and with no trained musical skill.
*89 Main Street, Aberdour, Fife
KY3 0VQ*
Tel: 01383 860226

McGillivray, Katherine

Viola, baroque and classical violas, viola
d'amore. Also contact person for
Ensemble Galant.
*20 Berryhill Drive, Glasgow
G46 7AA*
Tel: 0141 638 0838

VIOLIN

Cowan, Lucy

Studied at Vienna Hochschule. Worked in
London for three years. Returned to
Scotland 1973. Teaches at International
Cello Centre, Edrom House. Performed
with Scottish Ensemble and concerto
with SCO. Formed Merse Sinfonia.
Repertoire covers a range of musical styles
from classical to folk, early (especially
Scots) and jazz.
*Yarrow Records, The Forge, Yarrow
Valley TD7 5NE*
Tel: 01750 82254

Dixon, Alison

Born 1974. Studied St Mary's Music
School, Glasgow University and RSAMD.
Repertoire covers baroque to
contemporary. Performed with Scottish
Bach Consort, Scottish Opera, Uni-son.
Leader Kelvin Ensemble and Glasgow
University Orchestra. Solo recitals and
many premières.
*3 Papdale Crescent, Orkney
KW15 1JS*
Tel: 01856 874505

Doig, John

Born Helensburgh. 1972 first enrolled
pupil, St. Mary's Music School,
Edinburgh. 1979 Principal First Violin,
BBC Philharmonic Orchestra. 1986 Co-
Leader, later Soloist/Director, Scottish
Chamber Orchestra. 1991 Leader,
Orchestra of Scottish Opera. 1994 founder
and Artistic Director, Scottish Bach
Consort.
*Endrick Mews, Main Street, Killearn,
Stirlingshire G63 9ND*
Tel: 01360 550588
Fax: 01360 550588
Contact: Iain D Beattie (Manager)

Manson, Catherine

Appeared as soloist with many orchestras
in UK, USA and Canada as well as recitals
with her cellist brother Jonathan (with
whom she has recently formed The Manson
Quartet), pianists Paul Coker and Leslie
Howard, and organist Iain Quinn.
*48 Wester Row, Greenlaw, Berwickshire
TD10 6XE*
Tel: 01361 810 338
Fax: 01361 810 338

Paling, Edwin

Studied at the Royal Academy of Music.
Leader of the Royal Scottish National
Orchestra since 1975, appearing many
times as soloist performing a wide and
extensive repertoire. Also actively
involved in various chamber music groups
and regularly gives recitals.
*Royal Scottish National Orchestra,
73 Claremont Street, Glasgow
G3 7HA*
Tel: 0141 632 0567

Trabichoff, Geoffrey

Leader of the BBC Scottish Symphony
Orchestra, Salon Orchestra and Paragon
Ensemble. Available as leader/director/
soloist for chamber orchestra programmes.
Standard violin concerto repertoire plus the
concertos of Bloch, Vaughan Williams and
Boccherini, many of which he has recorded
for BBC Radio 3. Sample programmes are
available on request.
*40 Woodend Drive, Jordanhill, Glasgow
G13 1TQ*

SOPRANO

Drummond, Irene

Studied RSAMD, Britten-Pears School,
Munich. Performances include
Beethoven's *Mass in C*, Aldeburgh
Festival, Dvorak's *Te Deum* (TV, BBC
SSO), première of Edward McGuire's
Loonscapes. Much new music, often by
Scottish composers. Appeared with
Paragon Ensemble (including Radio 3
commission). Performances abroad
include Los Angeles, Reykjavik, Milan,
Canada and Germany.
*25 Coates Gardens, Edinburgh
EH12 5LG*
Tel: 0131 337 4705 Fax: 0131 337 4740
Contact: Frank Carroll (Manager)

Dumas, Alice

Brought up in north-west Scotland.
Studied RSAMD and The Hague. Wide
repertoire from early to contemporary as
well as music theatre and light music. Has
sung with Cappella Nova, the John Currie
Singers, the Scottish Early Music Consort
and Scottish Voices. Involved with many
premières.
14 Cecil Street, Glasgow G12 8RQ
Tel: 0141 339 1325

Mitchell, Fiona

Studied RSAMD. Sings throughout
Scotland. Oratorio, concert opera, lieder,
cabaret and Scots song. Soloist or with a
variety of chamber ensembles.
5 Little Road, Edinburgh EH16 6SH
Tel: 0131 467 3616
Contact: Fiona Mitchell

Tavener, Rebecca

Specialist in medieval, Renaissance and baroque solo repertoire. An exponent of contemporary music (has given a number of world premières); co-founder of Cappella Nova; ensemble singer and sight reader, currently studying vocal techinique with John Robertson.
172 Hyndland Road, Glasgow G12 9HZ
Tel: 0141 552 0634 / 357 0052
Fax: 0141 552 4053

MEZZO SOPRANO

Edmondson, Marie-Louise

Studied RSAMD. Pursues recital and oratorio career throughout Britain with Intermezzo and Scottish Voices, both of whom have a wide repertoire from baroque to 20th c. including Montiverdi, Handel, Vivaldi, Rossi, Debussy, Satie, Britten, Kurt Weill and new commissions. Also does TV and film soundtracks.
14 Cecil Street, Glasgow G12 8RQ
Tel: 0973 368363 (mobile)

Henriques, Kate

Studied RSAMD and the Royal Academy of Music in London (prizewinner). Pursues recital and oratorio career throughout Britain with Intermezzo (a trio of 2 mezzos and a piano) which perform wide repertoire of works from baroque to contemporary including: Montiverdi, Handel, Vivaldi, Rossi, Debussy, Brahms, Britten, Kurt Weill and commissions.
14 Cecil Street, Glasgow G12 8RQ
Tel: 0141 339 1325

McCafferty, Frances

Performs with the Chamber Group of Scotland, the Scottish Chamber Orchestra, the D'Oyly Carte Opera Company, Opera North, Buxton Festival Opera, Wexford Festival, Bournemouth Sinfonietta, Ulster Orchestra. World premières: William Sweeney, Alasdair Nicolson, Martin Dalby. Radio 3 broadcasts: opera and contemporary. Recordings: *Orpheus in the Underworld*, *Patience*, *Ivanhoe*.
8 The Latch, Cairney Hill, Dunfermline KY12 8UX
Tel: 01383 881835
Contact: Music International
Tel: 0171 359 5183

Ormiston, Linda

Sung throughout Europe, Scottish Opera - Salzburg Festival. Many engagements worldwide - Tokyo, Vancouver, New York. Début at ENO - December 1995. Part of The Music Box with Donald Maxwell. Several appearances at the RSNO Proms and Edinburgh Festival (1992 -95). Also appeared in BBC series *Hamish MacBeth* and regular presenter on Radio Scotland and BBC Radio 3.
Tel: 01357 29719 Fax: 01357 29719

Wilson, Taylor

Studied at the RSAMD then read languages at Strathclyde University. Currently postgraduate student at the Royal Northern College of Music, Manchester. Sings for Live Music Now, Cappella Nova and Scottish Voices. Recently won Caird Scholarship enabling her to study for a further year at the RNCM.
24 Regent Park Square, Glasgow G41 2AG
Tel: 0141 423 1437

Young, Alison

Specialises in oratorio, opera and recital work. Educated at Aberdeen University and Guildhall School of Music. National radio début on Classic FM, November 1994. Future engagements in London and Paris.
20 Broadstone Park, Inverness IV2 3LA
Contact: *A Young* Tel: *01525 383529 or M Young* Tel: *01463 232835*

TENOR

Boyd, James

Born and trained in Scotland. Established performer with music/choral societies in the UK, Scandanavia and United States. Numerous Edinburgh Festival appearances, recordings and broadcasts on radio and television. Repertoire covers oratorio, art song and the songs of Scotland. Also voice teacher and coach to professional and amateur performers.
57 Randolph Road, Glasgow G11 7JJ
Tel: 0141 339 0231 / 08500 69866 (mobile)

BARITONE

Maxwell, Donald

Début with Scottish Opera, 1976. Performed with Royal Opera House, Welsh National Opera, Vienna Sraatsoper, and in Buenos Aires, New York, Milan, Paris, Tokyo. Repertoire includes Wozzeck, *Flying Dutchman*, Falstaff, Rigoletto, Iago Goland. Televised operas and Prom concerts and many recordings. Performs as part of Music Box with Linda Ormiston.
c/o 6 Murray Crescent, Perth PH2 0HU
Tel: 01222 706504 Fax: 01222 706504

COMPOSERS & ARRANGERS

Achenbach, Chris

Born Belfast 1956. Studied Cheetham's and Leeds. Scots resident since 1985. Music therapy manager. With librettist Judy Steel writing opera trilogy based on local ballads. The second *Muckle Mou'd Meg*, (1995) performed by SCO.
1 Buckholm Mill Cottages, Galashiels TD1 2HA
Tel: 01896 757574

Adam, Stephen

Arranges for chamber ensembles, vocal and children's pieces, all customized for players' abilities. Manuscript or print: classical to pop.
35 Camphill Avenue, Langside, Glasgow G42
Tel: 01141 632 9115

Agnew, Elaine

Born N Ireland 1967. Music graduate Queens University, Belfast. Studied composition at RSAMD with James MacMillan. Postgraduate studies in Scotland 1990-93. Works performed by Paragon Ensemble, SCO, RSNO. Music reveals passion for folk elements, rhythm and modal harmony.
Flat 3, 6 Craighall Crescent, Trinity, Edinburgh EH6 1QY
Tel: 0131 552 4277

ARTISTS
CLASSICAL

63

ARTISTS

CLASSICAL

Armstrong, Craig

Studied composition RAM London. Written extensively for classical ensembles, theatre, film and television. Most recently RSC, Barbican; Tron Theatre, Glasgow. Films for BBC, STV. Chamber opera *Anna*, Edinburgh Festival. Arranged and composed for U2 (*Batman Forever*), Madonna, Future Sound of London, and Massive Attack. Orchestral commission Mayfest 1996.
19 Verona Avenue, Scotstoun, Glasgow G14 9DZ
Tel: 0141 959 4088 Fax: 0141 959 4088

Atkinson, Geoffrey

Educated Aberdeen University and ARCM. Compositions mostly church and choral music. Around 20 items in print published by Oecumuse, Bardic and in America by Hinshaw. Conductor of Queens Cross Orchestra and Chorus.
Beech Cottage, Drumoak, Banchory AB31 3AL
Tel: 01330 811363

Atkinson, Simon

Main composition work in electro-acoustic music. Has a keen interest in collaborative, multi-media work. Clarinettist and electro-acoustic music diffuser.
262 Gorgie Road (2F3), Edinburgh EH11 2PP
Tel: 0131 337 9033

Ball, Derek

Born 1949 Co. Donegal. Studied medicine then composition. Scots resident since 1978. Works as NHS consultant psychiatrist in North Glasgow. Secretary of Scottish Society of Composers.
Mazagon, 4 Glen Road, Lennoxtown, Glasgow G65 7JX
Tel: 01360 313217

Barker, Jennifer

Postgraduate study in piano and composition in USA. Doctorate from University of Pennsylvania studying with George Crumb. Now professor of theory and composition at Christopher Newport University, Virginia. Remains active as composer in Scotland. 1995 eight commissions from Scottish and American ensembles.
2 Kirkhouse Avenue, Blanefield, Glasgow G63 9BT
Tel: 01360 770362 Fax: 01360 770737

Barnett, Michael

Composer/performer in contemporary and commercial fields. Classical commissions, jazz/contemporary dance and film/ animation music. Performing ensembles include jazz trio/quartet, function band, Scottish cabaret party, Renaissance wind band and klezmer folk group. Employed by The Dance School of Scotland.
270 North Woodside Road, North Kelvinside, Glasgow G20 6LX
Tel: 0141 337 6867 Fax: 0141 638 0079

Barton, Peter

Born 1921. Studied composition under Dr R T Johnson and piano under Vivian Langrish and Ruth Harte. Major composition (35 years in preparation) *Scarlet and Black*, opera in three acts based on Stendahl's *Le Rouge et le Noir*. Also a painter.
Buchanan Cottage, Shieldaig, Strathcarron, Ross-shire IV54 8XN
Tel: 01520 755292

Beamish, Sally

Co-founder of the Chamber Group of Scotland. Extensive list of works including solo, chamber, vocal and orchestral music. Regularly performed in the UK and abroad with frequent broadcasts and television appearances. 1995 - broadcast premières of concertos for violin and viola, the latter in the London Proms.
Little Drumquharn Farm, Balfron, by Glasgow G63 0NL
Tel: 01360 440165 Fax: 01360 440208

Beat, Janet

Composes for conventional instruments (solo, chamber, orchestral), electronic music for tape alone and also for acoustic instruments with tape or computer. Written for concert hall, theatre and film. Featured composer at festivals in Germany, Greece, Australia and also performed in USA, Poland, Japan. Recordings available.
5 Letham Drive, Newlands, Glasgow G43 2SL
Tel: 0141 637 1952

Blunt, Marcus

English born but by choice resident in Scotland. Compositions mainly instrumental, from solo piano to large orchestra, and performed in at least ten countries, also on Radio 3 and Classic FM. Latest commission a piano concerto for Artur Pizarro.
Craigs Cottage, Lochmaben, Lockerbie, Dumfriesshire DG11 1RW
Tel: 01387 811949

Bragg, Glynn

Specialises in music for brass band, wind band, chorus and percussion ensemble as well as light orchestral arrangements. Publishers include Novello, Paxton, OUP, Belwin Mills. Recent work includes a march for wind band (available for brass band) and an extensive arrangement of Burns songs for male voice choir.
1 North Dumgoyne Avenue, Milngavie, Glasgow G62 7JT
Tel: 0141 956 2480

Butterworth, Neil

Born London 1934. Studied Nottingham, London and Guildhall School of Music. Specialised in conducting, horn and percussion. Lecturer Kingston College of Technology, 1960-68. Moved to Scotland - head of music at Napier College until going freelance as writer/lecturer from 1987. Over 300 compositions: orchestral, choral, vocal, and chamber.
The White House, Inveresk, Musselburgh EH21 7TG
Tel: 0131 665 3497

Carey, James Duncan

BA, B.Mus., FTCL. Freelance composer/ arranger and conductor. Formerly head of theory and composition Belfast School of Music and lecturer in music Moray House College. Compositions include much light-hearted music for recorder ensemble, choral works including church music, organ music, song cycles and a *Serenade for Strings*.
2 Mortonhall Park Way, Edinburgh EH17 8BW
Tel: 0131 664 6569

Clemson, Gareth

Born 1933. B.Mus. Auckland and Edinburgh. Member Composers' Guild and PRS. Contributor *Composers News* and freelance music critic. Recent compositions - *Pandura* and *Garb of Old Gaul Variations* (full orchestra); *Trumpet in the Dust* (song cycle); *Blackbird* (wind band); *Dunkeld Bridge* and *Lament*, freely realised for two violins. Commissions welcomed.
Tillywhally Cottage, Milnathort, Kinross-shire KY13 7RN
Tel: 01577 864297

Clennon, Ornette

Works in Edinburgh. Artistic Director of One Voice. Recent works include *Hidden Song* for string quartet, *Why?* for mixed ensemble and tape, and a new ECAT commission for voice and string quartet. Particularly interested in crossing stylistic boundaries.

45 Lorne Street (3/R), Leith , Edinburgh EH6 8QJ
Tel: 0131 554 1721

Coates, Leon

Born Wolverhampton 1937. Music lecturer Edinburgh University since 1965. Known both as performer and composer whose works include commissioned concertos for viola and harpsichord, songs including the recently published R. L. Stevenson cycle *North West Passage*, and music for choir and for chamber ensemble.

35 Comely Bank Place, Edinburgh EH4 1ER
Tel: 0131 332 4553

Cochrane, Lynda

Born Edinburgh. Studied piano and composition Manchester University, RNCM and Indiana University. Compositions performed at St Magnus Festival and by the RSNO. Frequently performs with Paragon Ensemble, Scottish Voices and the RSNO and enjoys a rich variety of chamber music.

Garden Flat, 11 Rosslyn Terrace, Glasgow G12 9NA
Tel: 0141 334 5607

Collins, Amanda

Born 1970. Composer in residence at St Andrew's College. Performed by various ensembles including SCO string quartet and wind ensemble, Scottish Brass Ensemble and Alain Trudel at Huddersfield Contemporary Music Festival, 1994. Worked on collaborative multi-media *River Clyde Project* for Art Machine 1995.

17 Bentinck Street, Kelvingrove, Glasgow G3 7TS
Tel: 0141 334 1558

Crawford, Robert

Born 1925. Studied privately with Hans Gal then Benjamin Franklin at Guildhall. Two quartets (1951, 1956) regularly performed. BBC Scotland music producer 1970-85. Commissions since then include an octet for Glasgow University and a sonata for the Scottish International Piano Competition. Many works performed 1995 to mark 70th birthday.

12 Inverleith Terrace, Edinburgh EH3 5NS
Tel: 0131 556 3600

Cresswell, Lyell

1994 events included: Asian Music Festival, Taipei (April); *Incontro con il compositore Lyell Cresswell* - L'Accademia di Belle Arti, Bologna (May); *Time of Music* - Viitasaari, Finland (July); *Lyell Cresswell is Fifty* - Tramway, Glasgow (November). CDs issued by Continuum, Linn Records, Tall Poppies. BBC commission for accordion and orchestra for 1995 Proms, London.

4 Leslie Place, Edinburgh EH4 1NQ
Tel: 0131 332 9181

Cribari, George Paul

Studied psychology and neuroscience in America before formal music education at California State University and RSAMD. SCO Hoy composers' course. First opera *Entre la piel y el alma* premièred in Glasgow 1992, followed by *Las Escondidas* in the Old Fruit Market, Glasgow, 1995.

262 Gorgie Road (2/3), Edinburgh EH11 2PP
Tel: 0131 337 9033
Contact: Anne Cumberland Tel: 0141 357 1826

Cull, Jeremy

Studying and working in Edinburgh. Musical director of One Voice. Recent performances include chamber works by Gemini at Sadlers Wells, One Voice in Edinburgh and the Hilliard Ensemble at Glasgow.

37 Royal Park Terrace, Edinburgh EH8 8JA
Tel: 0131 611 5377

Dalby, Martin

Born Aberdeen 1942. Studied composition and viola RCM. Two years' playing in Italy. 1965 BBC Radio 3 producer London. 1971 Cramb Research Fellow in composition Glasgow University. BBC Head of Music (Glasgow) until early retirement 1993. Works - symphony, viola concerto, choral, songs, song-cycles, brass and wind band pieces, chamber music. Chairman Composers' Guild of Great Britain.

23 Muirpark Way, Drymen, Glasgow G63 0DX
Tel: 01360 660427 Fax: 01360 660397

Davies, Peter Maxwell

Born Salford 1934. 1967 formed the Pierrot Players (later The Fires of London) with Harrison Birtwistle. 1970 moved to Hoy in the Orkneys and seven years later founded the St Magnus Festival there.

Judy Arnold Management, 50 Hogarth Road, London SW5 0PU
Tel: 0171 370 1477 Fax: 0171 373 6730

Dempster, Kenneth

Composition lecturer at Napier University, Edinburgh. Studied at Napier University, RAM, and Yale University. Commissions from the Hebrides Ensemble, Leda Trio, Emperor String Quartet, Pirasti Trio, English National Opera and the Edinburgh University Chamber Orchestra.

14 Marlborough Street (Top Flat), Edinburgh EH15 2BG
Tel: 0131 669 0601

Dillon, James

Born in Glasgow 1950. Works include: orchestral - *helle Nacht* (1987), *Ignis noster* (1992); ensemble - *Once upon a time* (1980), *Windows and Canopies* (1985), *La femme invisible* (1989), *Introitus* (1990), *L'évolution de vol cycle* (1993); choral - *Viriditas* (1994); solo - *Parjanya-Vata* (vc. 1981), *Del Cuarto Elemento* (vln. 1988), *Siorram* (vla. 1992); perc. - *East 11th St NY 10003* (1982).

c/o Peters Edition, 10-12 Baches Street, London N1 6DN
Tel: 0171 253 1638 Fax: 0171 490 4921

Dillon, Shaun

All kinds of music written including orchestral, choral, instrumental, vocal, Scottish tunes, arrangements and educational. Recent commissions include *Floreas!* for brass and percussion *The Land* for chorus and orchestra, *Lochaber* for strings and clarsachs.

34 Richmond Street, Aberdeen AB2 4TR
Tel: 01224 630954

Dixon, Martin J C

Born London 1969. Studied guitar and composition RSAMD. M.Mus. in Music Theory and Analysis; Computer Sound Synthesis Edinburgh University. Ph.D. Compositional Technique Cambridge University. Commissions Highland Chamber Orchestra, SCO Clarinet Quintet at Academy Now! festival. Current projects include Scottish Flute Trio, guitar music, cor anglais music and tape.

c/o Morley, 151 West Princes Street (2UL), Glasgow G4 9BZ
Tel: 0141 333 0828

65

ARTISTS

CLASSICAL

Dodd, Raymond

Studied composition at RAM then Oxford University with Edmund Rubbra and later privately with Matyas Seiber. Composition lecturer at Aberdeen University from 1956 until retirement in 1991. Now works as freelance composer.
14 Giffordgate, Haddington, East Lothian EH41 4AS
Tel: 01620 824618

Don, Nigel

Writes chamber and orchestral music - mainly concentrating on music which is accessible to and playable by amateur groups. Wrote a trumpet concerto premièred by John Wallace with the Perth Symphony Orchestra in February 1994, and a brass quintet played and broadcast by the BBC Scottish Brass Ensemble. Also arranges music.
12 Kelso Place, Dundee DD2 1SL
Tel: 01382 667251 Fax: 01382 640775

Dorward, David

Solo, chamber, vocal, choral, orchestral; incidental/commercial for radio, television, film, theatre.
10 Dean Park Crescent, Edinburgh EH4 1PH
Tel: 0131 332 3002

Douglas, James

Compositions: 9 symphonies, 20 orchestral works, 10 string quartets, over 200 songs, choral music, organ music, chamber and instrumental, operas: maskes; *The King*; *Polière*. Organ works recorded by Caritas Records. SAC commissions. Influences: the writings of George Steiner and Karl Popper.
28 Dalrymple Crescent, Edinburgh EH9 2NX
Tel: 0131 667 3633

Edwards, Alastair S

Educated at St Mary's Music School, Edinburgh. Graduated Mus.B.(Hons), University of Manchester. Ph.D (Composition), pending, University of Edinburgh. Performances by Lindsay Quartet, Edinburgh Quartet, Scottish Chamber Orchestra etc. Commissions from St Magnus Festival, Orkney, and Edinburgh Quartet. Avid Shetland fiddler. Seeks collaborative work with ensembles, poets, artists and film makers.
6 South Oxford Street, Edinburgh EH8 9QF
Tel: 0131 667 1265

Erskine, Robin

Orchestral: commissions - *Portrait of a Town* (Paisley Quincentenary), five others based on Scottish themes. Brass: schools ensembles, advanced ensembles (Christmas, Scottish, fanfares, hymns, carols, arrangements), brass and choir, brass band, solo. Organ: based on Scottish psalms, Celtic hymns, plainsong, free compositions. Choir: children's choir, adult choir, liturgical (masses).
30 Gallowhill Road, Paisley PA3 4TE
Tel: 0141 889 9045

Evans, Joseph

Born 1967, Kent. Began composing for tape and electronics 1983. Studied Electronics at Guildhall University until 1987. In 1991 he came to RSAMD to study with Janet Beat and John Maxwell Geddes. Written works include a saxophone sonata, a clarinet trio and a music theatre piece, *Beacon Burning*.
2 Grantley Gardens (Flat 2/R), Shawlands, Shawlands G41 3QA
Tel: 0141 636 1560

Fernie, Alan

Studied at RSAMD (1977-80). Working as trombonist, teacher, conductor and composer/arranger, mainly in the brass medium (band, quintet, ensemble and educational).
38 Hawthornvale, Edinburgh EH6 4JW
Tel: 0131 551 3887

Finlay, David

Works for piano solo *Sonata*; solo voice *White Guardians*, vocal groups *The Moon's a Balloon*, chamber groups *The Mad Gardener's Song*. Incidental music for theatre. Songwriter for jazz group Between Friends. Member of Scottish Society of Composers.
85 East King Street, Helensburgh G84 7RG
Tel: 01436 672187 Fax: 01436 672187

Finnerty, Adrian

Principal teacher of music education (Dip.T.Mus.) St Andrew's College; BA (Hons) OU; M. Mus. Edinburgh; ALCM (piano). Compositions include orchestral, choral, chamber, electro-acoustic works, two musicals plus a variety of arrangements mainly for educational use. Articles and reviews contributed to *Musical Times, British Journal of Music Education* and *Music Journal*.
10 Brandon Drive, Bearsden, Glasgow G61 3LN
Tel: 0141 943 1517

Fowler, Tommy

Born Aberdeenshire 1948. Journalist 20 years. B.Mus. (Hons) Glasgow University. Postgraduate composition research. Music performed by Uni-son, Cappella Nova (Christmas commission 1994), Hilliard Ensemble, SCO and RSNO (GRCH commission 1995). Won Sir William Baird Ross Trust organ writing competition - premièred by John Kitchen. Also theatre and film music. Commissions welcomed.
60 Maryhill Road, Glasgow G20 7QB
Tel: 0141 353 0927

Fraser, Bruce

Born India 1947. Studied RSAMD and Guildhall. Instrumental teacher and freelance trombonist. 1982 founded Lomond Music. Works include *The Three Perils of Man* for the Borders Festival, *The Visit* for Anstruther Philharmonic Society, *Panache* for the Royal Marines band, and *Magnificat* for soloists, choir and orchestra.
32 Bankton Park, Kingskettle, Fife KY15 7PY
Tel: 01337 830974 Fax: 01337 830653

Gardner, Jane

BA (Hons) York University; PG Stds, RSAMD. Studied Indonesian music in Java. Concert hall commissions include ECAT, SCO, RSAMD, Piano Circus, SSOT, Composers' Ensemble, Stirling Orchestra. Theatre/Dance: WPT, Dance Productions Ltd, Tron Theatre, Scottish Youth Theatre, Test Department. Outreach Projects: SCO, Paragon Ensemble, RSNO, ECAT, Scottish Ballet.
104 Comiston Drive, Edinburgh EH10 5QU
Tel: 0131 447 6859

Geddes, John Maxwell

Two symphonies, orchestral and chamber music, concert band, brass band, choral music, film scores, folk song settings. Commissions include BBC Connoisseur Concerts, RSAMD, ECAT, Paragon Ensemble, McEwan Bequest, McColl Arts Foundation. Premières in London Proms, Prokofiev Festival, St Petersburg Festival, Edinburgh Festival, Warsaw Autumn Festival.
21 Cleveden Road, Glasgow G12 0PQ
Tel: 0141 357 2941

Gordon, William

Born 1950. Developer of integrated composition system *Just Music* based on just intonation sets. Catalogue of sets and composition software for Psion 3a downloadable free from Compuserve Palmtop A Forum, Psion files section, filename JSTMUS.ZIP. Also on KOCH Media CD-ROM disk ECD000112. Generic name of compositions *Chronomorphs* available on tapes and scores from Esslin Music.
Esslin Music, Fraserford, Dunscore, Dumfries DG2 0UU
Tel: 01387 820271 Fax: 01387 820226

Gormley, John

Graduated Glasgow University 1995 with MA in music. Has had works performed at the University Lunch-hour Recitals. Had a piece performed by Cappella Nova September 1994. Plans to continue with composition at postgraduate level.
3 Hilary Drive, Garrowhill, Glasgow G69 6NP
Tel: 0141 773 0946

Gough-Cooper, Henry W

Born 1950. Farmer and company director, lives and works in Dumfriesshire. Output consists of original settings in traditional idiom of texts by Robert Burns and from traditional sources for voice (medium/low) and piano. Music distributed by Soar Valley Music, Leicestershire.
Esslin Music, Fraserford, Dunscore, Dumfries DG2 0UU
Tel: 01387 820271 Fax: 01387 820226

Gould, Janetta

Many pieces written for friends or special occasions using small forces and of individual nature. Several commissions for similar works. Most extensive work Burns Lieder (75 songs in twelve volumes, voice specified). Burns' original tunes and lyrics with composed piano accompaniments.
St Anne's, 14 Sandend Road, Glasgow G53 7DG
Tel: 0141 882 6127

Gray, John

Clarinet teacher, clarinettist and composer of music mainly for the theatre. Works include many devised productions for youth theatre groups and the score for the film *Blue Black Permanent*. Lectures in music theatre at Telford College, Edinburgh.
27 Oxford Street (3F/1), Edinburgh EH8 9PQ
Tel: 0131 667 0850

Hair, Graham

Born Australia1943, resident in Glasgow since 1990. Chamber works for female voice/s, with or without instrument/s, mostly written for Scottish Voices and Voiceworks, which he directs. *Setting of the Moon* (concert aria: voice, 11 instr.); *Songs of the Sibyls* (oratorio: 3 , 8 instr.); *Serenissima* (4 voices, hp.); also large pieces including *The Great Circle*.
45 St Vincent Crescent, Glasgow G3 8NG
Tel: 0141 221 4933 Fax: 0141 307 8018

Hallgrimsson, Haflidi

Born Iceland 1941, resident in Edinburgh. Teachers included Alan Bush and Peter Maxwell Davies (composition) and Derek Simpson (cello). 1977-83 principal cellist with SCO. Catalogue includes chamber, vocal and orchestral works. Principal publisher Chester Music Ltd.
5 Merchiston Bank Gardens, Edinburgh EH10 5EB

Hamilton, Eoin

Born in Glasgow. Specialises in arranging and composing for youth and amateur ensembles. To date his most popular works are *Three Scottish Sketches* and *Episodes for Percussion Ensemble and Orchestra*. Works for string orchestra published by Lomond Music.
St Ayles, 1 St Ayles Crescent, Anstruther, Fife KY10 3HE
Tel: 01333 310 793

Harper, Edward

Written in a wide range of genres with particular interest in opera: *Fanny Robin* (1975), *Hedda Gabler* (1985), *The Mellstock Quire* (1987). Other major works include the orchestral song cycles *Seven Poems by E. E. Cummings* (1977) and *Homage to Thomas Hardy* (1990). Published by Oxford University Press.
7 Morningside Park, Edinburgh EH10 5HD
Tel: 0131 447 5366

Hearne, John

Resident in Scotland since 1970 when he joined the music department of Aberdeen College of Education as lecturer and singing tutor. First chairman of Scottish Society of Composers when founded 1980. Compositions include chamber music, songs, choral and orchestral pieces. Spent some time teaching in Iceland and his music has northern influences.
Smidskot, Fawells, Keithhall, Inverurie AB5 0LN
Tel: 01651 882274 Fax: 01651 882274

Heath, Dave

Born Manchester 1956. Flute concerto *Free The Spirit* premièred by James Galway, Philharmonia, Slatkin. Violin concerto *Alone at the Frontier* premièred by Nigel Kennedy, Minnesota Symphony, De Waart. BT Scottish Ensemble composer in residence since 1993. *The Four Elements* and a violin concerto *The Celtic* written for and premièred by Clio Gould.
22 Hamilton Drive, Kelvinbridge, Glasgow
Tel: 0141 221 2222

Hill, Richard

Influences: Gaelic music, modes, chants, Rutter, Blake. Style: choral/vocal, instrumental, orchestral, church. Major works: *Gloria* (SATB, brass, percussion, organ); *Recorder Concerto*; *Ora Pro Nobis* (SATB); *Amhran Oidhche* (flute, oboe, strings); *Céo na Mara* (violin, piano). Commissions: *Toccata* for Kilmarnock Concert Brass Silver Anniversary. Future project: *A Sarajevo Requiem*.
24a North Tolsta, Isle of Lewis HS2 0NW
Tel: 01851 890382

Hind, Nicky

Currently engaged with developments at the forefront of computer music technology at the CCRMA Stanford University, California. In addition to electro-acoustic compositions, output includes combined media and dance projects, sound installations and purely acoustic works. Numerous international performances and Scottish based projects and commissions to date.
26 Pentland Crescent, Edinburgh EH10 6NP
Tel: 0131 445 2044

Horne, David

Up-to-date information available from the address below.
c/o Boosey and Hawkes Music Publishers Ltd, 295 Regent Street, London W1R 8JH
Tel: 0171 580 2060 Fax: 0171 637 3490
Contact: Publicity Department

Hutton, James

Classical/Jazz. Fascinated by the experiments of contemporary artists, but has little use for fashionable modes of expression for their own sake. His works are rather more concerned with the integration of form (i.e. sustained musical discourse) than with the disintegration of colour.
88 Warwick, East Kilbride, Glasgow G74 3PY
Tel: 013552 25895

ARTISTS

CLASSICAL

COMPOSERS AND ARRANGERS (CONTD)

ARTISTS

CLASSICAL

68

Inness, Peter

Composer of over 35 works, including music for orchestra, voice and piano/ chamber ensemble, piano, organ, choir and wind orchestra. Music of this output has been broadcast - some works are published by Novello and the *Symphonic Ode* for wind orchestra published by Neil Kjos (USA).
83 East Kilbride Road, Busby, Glasgow G76 8JE
Tel: 0141 644 1294

Jackson, William

Specialises in the combination of Scottish traditional music (including Gaelic) and classical music. Founder member of Ossian. Commissions include: *The Wellpark Suite* (1985), *St Mungo* (1990), *Gaidhealtachd* (1990) and *A Scottish Island* (SCO, 1995). Group and solo recordings (as harpist) on Iona, Greentrax and Linn Records.
1 New Road, Forfar, Angus DD8 2AE
Tel: 01307 463317

Jones, David Paul

Work performed by the SCO, the RSNO and Guildhall Contemporary Music Ensemble. Regularly performing as pianist with various ensembles. New ensemble Mosaic being formed.
Top Floor, 7 Dunedin Street, Edinburgh EH7 4JB
Tel: 0131 556 6031

King, Geoffrey

Commissions from Musica Nova, Edinburgh International Festival, St Magnus Festival and Lontano. Work performed at Almeida Festival and in 1989 the Aldeburgh Festival included a portrait concert of his work. 1990 London Sinfonietta premièred *Magritte Weather*, 1993 BBC SSO premiered orchestral piece *Man Dancing*. Founding member of ECAT.
c/o ECAT, 16 Clerwood Gardens, Edinburgh EH12 8PT
Tel: 0131 539 9877 Fax: 0131 539 2211

King, Steve

Writes both mainstream and popular music, much of which has been played on TV, radio and in concerts all over the UK.
89 Main Street, Aberdour, Fife KY3 0VQ
Tel: 01383 860226

Lee, Dick

Works include commissions from ECAT (*Sliding Scale* 1989), the Edinburgh Folk Festival (*Bagpipe Concerto* 1990), The Lemon Tree Trust (*Lemon Tree Samba*, 1993), and SAC, via a composer's bursary (*Mass Medium* 1995, for flute and computer-generated sounds). Film/TV scores and bagpipe music are specialities.
1 Cheyne Street, Edinburgh EH4 1JA
Tel: 0131 332 8083 Fax: 0131 332 8083

Leonard-Morgan, Paul

Born 1974. Studied Wellington College, Berkshire and RSAMD. Clarinet concerto, *The Awakening* won RSAMD Patrons Prize. Orchestral piece *Mohi-Jigg* won BT/NFMS Composing for Amateurs Competition and a commission *Mindscape*. Quintet *Eclipsed* premièred by SCO and Lichtzwang for choir and organ by Schola Cantorum at Edinburgh Festival 1994. Much music for television and radio.
Flat 10, 37 Glenfarg Street, Glasgow G20 7QE
Tel: 0141 333 0611

Liddell, Claire

Composer/Pianist/Accompanist/ Broadcaster: RSAMD; Royal College of Music, London, College Scholar. Main areas of composition: works for voice and piano and choral. Settings of Scots Folk Songs, Song Cycles. Commissions for choir. Author of book on harmony. Publishers; Stainer and Bell, Roberton, Barry Brunton.
15 Montpelier, Edinburgh EH10 4LZ
Tel: 0131 228 4001

Lunn, John

Born Glasgow 1956. Studied Glasgow University and RSAMD. Computer music at MIT. Active in writing for dance, theatre, film and television. *Le Voyage* BBC SSO 1992, work for Thames Brass at the 1994 Meltdown Festival and BBC commission for 1995 Edinburgh Festival. TV music for *Finney*, *The Last Machine*, *The Cormorant*, *The Gift*, and *Hamish MacBeth*.
37 The Paddock, Perceton, Irvine KA11 2AZ
Tel: 01294 214470

Lyall, Chick

Studied composition with Lyell Cresswell and Judith Weir at Glasgow University. Commissions include the electro-acoustic *Threads* (Musica Nova), *Voiceover* (Glasgow International Jazz Festival), *Rites* for SCO 1993, *The Eyes of Fire* for sax quartet and percussion for Academy Now!
171a Maryhill Road, Glasgow G20 7XL
Tel: 0141 332 9468

Lynch, Graham

Born London. Studied with Oliver Knussen, David Lumsdaine, Robert Saxton. Works include pieces for orchestra, chamber ensemble, string quartet, synthesiser, voices, and solo piano.
15 Custom House Street, Ullapool IV26 2XF
Tel: 01854 612837

McBain, Hugh

String quartet, brass quintet, ten piano pieces (*Nonogon, Decagon*), piano concerto *Tritergon*; two symphonies *Protergon, Deutergon*; three works for music theatre, *The Decagon, The Octagon, Amerol*. Essays published in *Composer and Stretto*: 'The Nature of Music', 'Edge of the Infinite'. Book publisher Jordan Books.
1 Munro Road, Glasgow G13 1SQ
Tel: 0141 959 1966

Macdonald, Hugh

Born Haddington 1948. Studied Edinburgh, Amsterdam, RCM. Edinburgh University postgraduate research in traditional Scots music. 1976 lecturer in Chinese University of Hong Kong. 1979 Stirling University. 1985 Music Producer (radio) BBC Scotland; 1990 Head of Music BBC Scotland. *Scotland's Winter* for piano, commissioned by Peter Evans and SAC, premièred at McEwan Memorial Concert Glasgow University.
Head of Music, BBC Scotland, Queen Margaret Drive, Glasgow G12 8DG
Tel: 0141 338 2489 Fax: 0141 357 1283

MacDonald, Iain

Works primarily written for secondary schoolchildren and include a cantata *Christmas Story*, instrumental/choral piece *American Suite*, instrumental *A Scottish March* and musicals *Indecision, Chess Game, Chances, Angel* and *Spy*. Vocal and instrumental parts at varying levels to allow greater participation.
8 Main Street, Chryston, Glasgow G69 9DH
Tel: 0141 779 1595

McGowan, Joe

Born Hamilton. Studied at Glasgow College of Building and Printing. Studied classical guitar and music theory at the same time. Began composing when studying music and art history with Open University. 1992 began guitar and composition studies at RSAMD. Works include pieces for solo guitar, piano, string quartet and *Fantasy for Brass and Percussion*.
53 County Avenue, Eastfield, Cambuslang G72 7DG
Tel: 0141 641 4225

McGuire, Edward

New opera in 1996 for RSNO Junior Chorus follows success of *The Loving of Etain* (Paragon Opera); *Peter Pan* (Scottish Ballet) and *Cullercoats Tommy* (Northern Stage). Recent CDs include *Calgacus* (BBCSSO); *Songs of New Beginnings* (Paragon); *Fast Peace III* (Alma Duo); *Divertimento, Martyr* (Durrant Viola Pieces).
13 Lawrence Street, Glasgow G11 5HH
Tel: 0141 334 8580

Macllwham, George

Born Glasgow 1926. Flautist, piper, composer. Studied Royal Academies Glasgow and London. Compositions in McCunn, McKenzie traditions: overtures, symphonic works, suites, choral, chamber, bagpipe (solo and with orchestra), songs and arrangements. Incidental music. Member of PRS, MCPS.
25 Ravelston Road, Bearsden, Glasgow G61 1AW
Tel: 0141 942 6779

McIntosh, John

Born Edinburgh 1944 . Studied Glasgow University. Has a particular interest in composing and arranging choral music and as an arranger recently completed a commission for Cappella Nova.
Stamford, 55 Royal Crescent, Dunoon, Argyll PA23 7AQ
Tel: 01369 703304

Mackie, James

Composer, teacher and arranger of classical, popular, light and jazz music. Studied at University College, Salford. Compositions include musical play *The World of Suzie Wong* and several suites for orchestra, brass, and big band, including *Childhood Memories* and the *Last Ferry from Hong Kong* suite.
190 Lee Crescent North, Aberdeen AB22 8FR
Tel: 01224 823256

McLeod, John

Performed and recorded by leading soloists and orchestras worldwide. Featured in London Proms and Edinburgh Festival. Guinness Prize for composition in 1979. Series of film and television scores. Director of the LCM postgrad course 'Composing for Film and Television'. CD issued in 1994 with Polish Radio and TV Symphony Orchestra.
9 Redford Crescent, Edinburgh EH13 0BS
Tel: 0131 441 3035 Fax: 0131 441 5218

MacMillan, James

Up-to-date information available from the address below.
c/o Boosey and Hawkes Music Publishers Ltd, 295 Regent Street, London W1R 8JH
Tel: 0171 580 2060 Fax: 0171 637 3490
Contact: Publicity Department

McMurdo, Stewart

Honours in composition from Glasgow University. Was principal violist of University Orchestra and Uni-son. Regular theatre musician. Recent compositions include setting Byron's poem 'To Anne' for baritone and orchestra. *String Quintet* and *Symphonic Movement for Orchestra* premièred 1995.
20 Moray Gardens, Uddingston, Glasgow G71 6EW
Tel: 01698 816181

McPherson, Gordon

Born Dundee 1965. Studied University of York (1983-86/1988-91). Composer, teacher and performer. Compositions - chamber, orchestral, solo from 1985. Recent works *On E* for orchestra; *Handguns: A Suite* for large ensemble.
8 Brantwood Avenue, Dundee, Tayside DD3 6EW
Tel: 01382 812265

McQuaid, John

Many settings of Old Testament texts for two voices (1994). Piano music, some published and much broadcast. Section winner Musica Nova 1984. Seventy-two *Little Waltzes and Preludes*, some broadcast or have won International competitions. Member of the New York Academy of Sciences.
St Annes, 8 Ardrossan Road, Saltcoats, Ayrshire KA21 5BW
Tel: 01294 463737

Mayo, Kevin

Born 1964. Studied composition at Edinburgh University and RCM. Most respected composers Mozart, Tchaikovsky, Debussy, Messiaen, Turnage. Works mainly (not exclusively) chamber and orchestral - various combinations and sizes. Music is often, in turn, rhythmically dynamic, melodic or expressive. Composes with musical considerations above all others. Self-published.
77 Bellevue Road (2/3), Edinburgh EH7 4DH
Tel: 0131 556 9964

Miranda, Eduardo Reck

Resident in Scotland since 1991. Music Ph.D. Edinburgh University. Joined Glasgow University staff 1995. Short-listed by SPNM 1994 with electro-acoustic pieces *Olivine Trees* and *Deep Resonance*. Electroacoustic Samba II second prize out of 107 in the ballet section of Grand Prix Internationaux de Musique Electroacoutique de Bourges 1994.
8 Mary's Place (2/R), Stockbridge, Edinburgh EH4 1JH
Tel: 0131 332 5569 Fax: 0131 332 5569

Mitchell, David C

Pied Piper children's cantata 1986. *The Tale of Mrundla the Rabbit*, African contemporary folk musical, part on Zimbabwe TV 1988, full première 1990. *Christmas Cantata* , part on Zimbabwe TV and Radio Scotland 1987, full première 1990. Church of Scotland project to re-set psalms (recordings available). Working on opera about Esther. Some instrumental pieces. Many songs.
27 Oxford Street (1/3), Edinburgh EH8 9PQ
Tel: 0131 667 0979

Morrison, Alan David

Born Paisley 1961. Composition self taught. Influenced by period 1850-1950 and modern film scores. Alternative to serial/dodecaphonic music in form of New Romanticism. Works include: orchestral - *Leningrad Suite, Singapore Suite, Waltz Fantasia, Waltz Triste, Wedding Intermezzo*; two piano sonatas; choral work *The Sons of Eos*.
41 Gillbank Avenue, Carluke ML8 5UW
Tel: 01555 751442

ARTISTS

CLASSICAL

69

Nelson, Peter

Works include vocal, chamber and orchestral music, some use recorded sound and/or interactive computer systems as well as electro-acoustic music. Commissioned and performed by BBC SSO, SCO, Vocem Electric Voice Theatre, Les Ateliers UPIC, Ensemble Exposé, Lontano Contemporary Chamber Orchestra.
16 Learmonth Grove, Edinburgh EH4 1BW
Tel: 0131 332 2960

Nicolson, Alasdair

Born Inverness 1961. Studied Edinburgh University. Works performed by RSNO, SCO, Chamber Group of Scotland, Philharmonia and EOS. 1991 founded Platform series of contemporary music festivals. 1995 winner of IBM Composers' Award. Has worked extensively in theatre and led many education projects. Conductor and pianist.
1 Harrison Road, Edinburgh EH11 1EG
Tel: 0131 337 0472

Norris, Michael

Professional bassoonist for many years. Now teaches academic studies at the RSAMD and at Douglas Academy Music School. He self-publishes several pieces (up to five performers) under the title Sirron Publications.
31 Hawthorn Avenue, Bearsden, Glasgow G61 3NG
Tel: 0141 942 5527

Norris, Philip

Studied composition Glasgow University (1966-70); later in Essen with W Hufschmidt. Output increased since returning to Scotland in 1981. Major works include *Scenes for Septet* (1984); *The Shipping Forecast* (clarinet, piano); *Trilogy* for strings (1986); *Brandenburg 90* (strings, harpsichord); *Cello Cantata* (1991) (available on Paragon Premières CD); *Horn Theatre* (1994).
7 Clyth Drive, Giffnock G46 6NW
Tel: 0141 638 2698

O'Brien, Garrett

Formerly of Southwark Cathedral. Founder/conductor of Exultate Singers (EMI, DECCA, VISTA - BBC, ITV, Belgian Radio) in London. Studied with Geoffrey Parson (piano), Michael Hurd (composition). Freelance composer/ conductor specialising in Scottish music from manuscripts - performances by SNO (Sir Alexander Gibson), Edinburgh Renaissance Band, Roxburgh Singers etc.
The Nest, Jedburgh TD8 6BG
Tel: 01835 862707
Contact: Ralph Kyte Tel: 01450 870 313 or Garrett O'Brien

Paterson, Wilma

Born Dundee. Studied RSAMD and later with Luigi Dallapiccola in Florence (Glasgow Educational Trust Travel Grant). Apart from BBC and Cheltenham Festival commissions for orchestral music has written mainly chamber music, music for theatre, radio drama and exhibitions. Editor of *Songs of Scotland* published by Mainstream (1995).
27 Hamilton Drive, Glasgow G12 8DN
Tel: 0141 339 2711 Fax: 0141 337 2754

Pert, Morris

B.Mus. Royal Philharmonic Award for first orchestral work. Symphonies premièred in Tokyo, Glasgow, Munich. Many chamber works, some recorded. 18 years as session percussionist/composer in London (Peter Gabriel, Kate Bush, Paul McCartney, Mike Oldfield etc). Five gold albums, ASCAP award, National Academy Washington nomination for recorded performances. Publisher - Josef Weinberger, London.
Clach Mhor, Blairmore, Kinlochbervie, Sutherland IV27 4RU
Tel: 01971 521369

Pettes, Marika de

Studied RSAMD and Craiglockhart C of E. Compositions for piano inspired by the Butterfly Kingdom; tenth piece in progress. Ballet story inspired by butterflies and Hungarian folklore. Received medal from Pope Paul VI after dedicating compositions to him. Carols broadcast on Radio Clyde and performed by Holyrood Choir in Paisley Abbey.
Sinfonia, 37 Busby Road, Eastwood, Glasgow G76 7BN
Tel: 0141 638 1417

Potter, Rick

Born Bournemouth 1956. Studied music and electronics Keele University and composition at Newcastle University. Set up contemporary music record label in London while composing part time. Then, recruitment consultancy work, Glasgow. Compositions include opera, orchestral, vocal, chamber and instrumental as well as music for film, theatre and rock groups. CDs available.
Flat 3, Solsgirth House, Langmuir Road, Kirkintilloch G66 3XN
Tel: 0141 777 8354

Purser, John

Composer, lecturer, broadcaster and consultant on Scottish music. Compositions cover most genres.
29 Banavie Road, Glasgow G11 5AW
Tel: 0141 339 5292

Randalls, Jeremy

Born 1959. Studied RSAMD (Frank Spedding), RCM (Philip Cannon). 4 SAC commissions; BBC recitals/broadcasts; Musica Nova; specialisation - flutes (all combinations), orchestra, chamber, wind band, educational. RSNO/IBM competition finalist 1993 *Scène de Naufrage*. RSNO commissioned *Ceilidh* (Scottish Proms 1994, 1995). Classical (contemporary), Scottish themes, folk, jazz, light music.
3 Luss Brae, Hamilton ML3 9UW
Tel: 01698 425471

Riddell, George S

Solo piano music (36 pieces). Funeral march performed on various occasions.
19 South Clunes, by Kirkhill, Inverness-shire IV5 7PT
Tel: 01463 831664

Robb, Magnus

Delphi (Nederlands Radio Kamerorkest, Amsterdam 1991); *Skyn*, solo viola (Scott Dickinson, Gaudeamus 1993). Works commissioned with SAC subsidy:*Veer-Erne* for Edinburgh Youth Orchestra, *Ancient Language of the Birds*, Linda Hirst (mezzo) and Chamber Group of Scotland. *Blood Foliage* (Yggdrasil Quartet of Aberdeen, Edinburgh Festival 1995) commissioned by BBC Radio Scotland.
13 Murrayfield Gardens, Edinburgh EH12 6DG
Tel: 0131 337 2930

Roddie, Matthew

Born Glasgow 1974 . Studies RSAMD horn and composition, composition with John Maxwell Geddes. Compositions for Academy Now and a horn concerto for BBC SSO co-principal Hugh Potts.
47 Danes Drive, Glasgow G14 9HY
Tel: 0141 959 2577

Rose, John

Born London 1928. Studied at Cape Town, RAM and OU under Edmund Rubbra. Lecturer in FE Glasgow 1964-78 and extra-mural tutor. Works include: *Psalm XLII* for chorus and orchestra (EMP); *Essay on DSCH* , piano; *Prelude and Fugue Op.8*, organ (EMP); *Scherzo - Intermezzo-Toccata Op.9*, organ (EMP).
42 Killermont Road, Bearsden, Glasgow G12 2JA
Tel: 0141 942 3089

Rowe, Rebecca

Works for orchestra, mixed ensembles, choral, voice with piano/ensemble, live video, string quartet, film soundtracks. Recent commissions/performances: *Shine Out, Fair Sun* (Cappella Nova), *There is nothing brighter than the sun; Lament* (Hilliard Ensemble); *Lightlines, Deltarhythms, The Anatomy of a Waterfall*. Influences - everything.
15 Chalmers Crescent, Marchmont, Edinburgh EH9 1TS
Tel: 0131 662 1851

Russell, Colin

Music for TV, ballet and film. Also works in popular music, electronic music and dance music. Three symphonies, piano concerto and much piano music.
112 Hamilton Avenue, Glasgow G41 4EX
Tel: 0141 427 1383

Shur, Laura

Born in Glasgow and studied at RSAMD. Gained Dip (Music Ed) RSAM, LRAM (piano teaching), and ARCM (piano performance). Compositions include piano solo, duet, six hands one piano, choral, cello and woodwind. Published by Novello, Universal, and Alry.
c/o Sylvia Donne, 11/4 The Steils, Glenlockhart, Edinburgh EH10 5XD
Tel: 0131 447 2947

Skene, Hugh Crawford

Two operas, two symphonies, concertos for flute, saxophone, double bass, violin and viola, percussion; cantata *Birthday of Jesus*, fanfare and other smaller works. Also conductor and teacher.
Crowhills, Chapelton Road, Quarter, by Hamilton, Lanarkshire ML3 7XP
Tel: 01357 300303

Smith, Tommy

Works include: *Unirsi in Matremio* and *Un Ecossais à Paris* (both tenor saxophone and strings), Scottish Ensemble; *Sonata No 1* and *Sonata No 2* (tenor saxophone and piano), Murray McLachlan. Currently working on a saxophone concerto for the Orchestra of St John Smith Square. Tommy Smith/Murray McLachlan duet available.
Tel: 0141 424 1026 Fax: 0141 423 5747

Spencer, Michael

Studying composition at Glasgow University. Works performed by Uni-son of which he is a founder member. Chamber works *Symbiont, L'ambience vingt-neuf, Bean Righean na Bruch, Grieve Not The Holy Spirit, My Patmos, Elegy*. All 1994-95.
27 Douglas Gardens, Uddingston, Glasgow G71 7HB
Tel: 01698 813355

Stevenson, Ronald

Born Blackburn of Scots and Welsh descent. Scots resident since 1952. Senior lecturer Cape Town University 1962-65; Hon. prof. Shanghai Conservatory 1985. Visiting prof. Julliard, New York 1987. *Piano Concerto No 1* premièred by SNO 1966. Many commissions since. *Violin Concerto* performed in 1992 by Hu Kun and BBC SSO under Yehudi Menuhin who commissioned it.
Townfoot House, West Linton, Peebles-shire EH46 7EE
Tel: 01968 660511

Stollery, Pete

Studied composition with Jonty Harrison at Birmingham University. Works primarily electro-acoustic, performed widely particularly throughout UK and Europe. Recent work for tape alone: *Sortstuff* (1993) awarded special prize in Musica Nova 1994, also selected for ISCM World Music Days 1995. Promoter of *Discoveries* concert series in Aberdeen.
c/o Northern College, Aberdeen Campus, Hilton Place, Aberdeen AB9 1FA
Tel: 01224 283601 Fax: 01224 487046

Stout, Alastair

Written up to 200 works for various ensembles (orchestra, chamber, vocal, instrumental) including many for organ (published by Oecumuse). Recent works: *Third String Quartet, The Language of the Unknown* (string orchestra), *The Agony and the Ecstasy* (organ, percussion and brass band), *Pentecostal Suite* (organ). Influences: Shetland, Messiaen, Ligeti.
Edina, Vidlin, Shetland ZE2 9QB
Tel: 01806 577257

Strachan, Cluny

Born 1969. Compositions mainly multi-media events, many in unconventional settings involving dance and film. 1989 formed ensemble Zoe Alambicum.
69 Sinclair Drive (3/1), Glasgow G42 9PV
Tel: 0141 649 0467

Strutt, Clive

Large repertoire unperformed: 6 symphonies; tone poems; unaccompanied choral (including 8 books, madrigals, many folksong arrangements); opera, *The Tragedy of Man*; church music includes *Litany of Dunkeld; Communion Service for St. Magnus Day*. Prizes include Manson (symphonic), Carolan (Celtic Harp) and Baird Ross (Scottish Church Music). Commissions accepted for all traditional concert genres.
Manse Bay, South Ronaldsay, Orkney Islands KW17 2TJ
Tel: 01856 831541

Sutherland, Hugh

Born 1930. Mature student of composition RSAMD (John Weeks). Works include: string quartets (3rd played by SCO 1994); *Wind Sextet* (SCO 1995); *Sinfonietta* (soprano, strings); *Comus* (piano); *Sonata Capricciosa* (organ); *Holiday Postcards* (four trombones); *Ten American Songs* (soprano, piano); *Three Legends* (oboe); *Oboe Concerto*.
23 Dunvegan Drive, Bishopbriggs, Glasgow G64 3LB
Tel: 0141 762 1008

Sweeney, William

Born Glasgow 1950. Studied clarinet and composition RSAMD, RAM. Written extensively for clarinet. Output, influenced by traditional Gaelic and jazz, covers wide range of instrumental, orchestral and vocal ensembles. Commissions include BBC, Glasgow University, Mayfest and Cappella Nova.
49 Lawrence Street, Glasgow G11 5HD
Tel: 0141 334 9987

ARTISTS

CLASSICAL

71

Theatre Songwriting Group

New group of mainly amateur songwriters hoping to provide any drama or musical theatre company with original songs and music for shows at minimal cost. The group does not as yet provide musicians. Contact for details or membership.

c/o 12a Prestonfield Crescent, Edinburgh
EH16 5EN
Tel: 0131 668 3211
Contact: Peter MacDiarmid (Group Coordinator)

Tocher, Gordon

Compositions include: *Five Poems of Gerard Manley Hopkins* (choir and orchestra, commissioned by Inverness Choral Society), *Four Satellites of Jupiter* (piano); *Chinese Paintings* (cello and piano); *September Evening* (four guitars, commissioned by Scottish International Guitar Festival, published 1995); other choral, chamber, piano and organ works.

54 Glenburn Drive, Inverness IV2 4NE
Tel: 01463 232345

Ward, David

Born 1941. Composer of operas (full length and chamber), orchestral (with and without soloist), vocal and chamber music. Various broadcasts on Radio 3, Radio Scotland, Radio New Zealand. Publisher Vanderbeek and Imrie Ltd.

St Olaf, Sellafirth, Yell, Shetland
ZE2 9DG
Tel: 01957 744307

Weeks, John R

Born Bath 1934. RCM 1952-7. Assistant Director of Music Dauntsey's School, Wilts. 1960-70. Lecturer RSAMD 1970-95. Flute and clarinet sonatas, *Wind Quintet* (Stroud Prize), songs, choral, organ - *Facets, Variations and Passacaglia* (Schnitger Prize, Zwolle). Commissions - *Oboe Sonatina* (Kilmardinney Music Club), *The Fire and the Rose* for organ (Gillian Weir).

120 Kylepark Drive, Uddingston,
Glasgow G71 7DE
Tel: 01698 813723

Weir, Judith

c/o Chester Music, 8/9 Frith Street,
London W1V 5TZ
Tel: 0171 434 0066 Fax: 0171 287 6329

Wiggins, Geraint

Musical interests range from church choral to electronic ambient. Particularly interested in interactive computer music. Works in sound recording and production through digital demos. Director of One Voice. Recent works *Elements* (flute, oboe, harp, cello), *Retrospective* (horn, piano), *Four Quartets* (strings).

99 Lothian Road, Edinburgh EH3 9AN
Tel: 0131 228 3706 Fax: 0131 650 6516

Williams, Roger Bevan

Born Swansea. Educated universities of Huddersfield, Cardiff, London, Cambridge. Director Chiswick Music Centre 1971-75. SNO chorusmaster 1984-88. Organist, Our Lady of Victories, Kensington since 1980. Director of Music, Aberdeen University. *Missa Brevis*, antiphons, introits, responsorial psalms, *Sonata for Piano, Sonata for Four Guitars, Cinq Chansons for Tenor and Harpsichord.* Recordings available.

University Music, Powis Gate, College Bounds, Old Aberdeen AB9 2UG
Tel: 01224 272570 Fax: 01224 272515

Wilson, Thomas

Scores, performing materials, durations and instrumentations for all works available from Queensgate Music at the above address.

120 Dowanhill Street, Glasgow G12 9DN
Tel: 0141 339 1699 Fax: 0141 339 1699

Yeats, Marc

Works include: duets (fl. clt.), (pno. fl.), (pno. clt.); trios (pno. clt. vla.), (clt. 2vl.); flute quartet; clarinet quintet, oboe, clarinet, bassoon, strings. String orchestra, chamber orchestra, flute concerto, symphony orchestra.

12 Loch Bay, Waternish, Isle of Skye
IV55 8GD
Tel: 01470 592253

CONDUCTORS & CHORAL DIRECTORS

Bell, Christopher

1987-89 Associate Conductor BBC SSO. From 1989 Chorusmaster RSNO Chorus. Works regularly with RSNO, SCO, Ulster Orchestra and abroad in Germany and Holland. Much work with youth ensembles especially Strathclyde Schools Orchestra and Chorus. Last four years Director Total Aberdeen Youth Choir.

143 Warrender Park Road, Edinburgh
EH9 1DT
Tel: 0131 229 9695 Fax: 0131 228 8624

Boddice, Nigel

Conducting début 1995, Ulster Orchestra, BBC SSO. Mayfest, Aberdeen International Youth Festival, Scandinavian tours. Appointed Conductor in Residence, Festival of Moss. Two CDs available. 1994 Scottish Society of Composers' award, pioneering work in contemporary music. 1995 inaugural winner Mortimer Medal, Worshipful Company of Musicians.

7 Orleans Avenue, Jordanhill, Glasgow
G14 9LA
Tel: 0141 959 1825 Fax: 0141 959 1825
Contact: Rostrum Promotions Tel: 01786 834449 / 833949 (fax)

Conway, William

Principal conductor of the NYOS Chamber Orchestra. Has a wide reputation as guest conductor and is artistic director of the Hebrides Ensemble.

9 Sciennes Gardens, Edinburgh EH9 1NR
Tel: 0131 667 4630 Fax: 0131 667 4630

Davies, David

Artistic Director, Paragon Ensemble Scotland. Has conducted BBCSSO, RSNO, SCO, Ulster Orchestra and Royal Liverpool Philharmonic Orchestra and in France, Germany, Iceland, Luxembourg and Switzerland. Commissioned and recorded many works (symphonic, concertos, opera, music-theatre, film music) and received PRS award for his services to music in Scotland.

Castle Semple House, Lochwinnoch,
Renfrewshire PA12 4HJ
Tel: 01505 843369 Fax: 01505 842389

ARTISTS

CLASSICAL

73

ARTISTS

CLASSICAL

Finlay, David
Conductor of Helensburgh Dorian Choir since September 1994. Rehearsal work with other amateur choirs and operatic groups.
85 East King Street, Helensburgh G84 7RG
Tel: 01436 672187 Fax: 01436 672187

Hamilton, David
B. Mus. (Glasgow 1989). Organist. Conductor of Strathhaven Choral Society, Glasgow Philharmonic Choir and St Mary's Episcopal Church Choir, Hamilton.
18 Orchard Street, Motherwell ML1 3JD
Tel: 01698 262728

Hearne, John
Resident in Scotland since 1970 when he joined the music department of Aberdeen College of Education as lecturer and singing tutor. Conductor of Stonehaven Chorus. Also composer.
Smidskot, Fawells, Keithhall, Inverurie AB5 0LN
Tel: 01651 882274 Fax: 01651 882274

MacAlindin, Paul
MD, conductor - orchestral, choral, stage musical, operatic, school, special needs and SCO education experience. Musical Director of Stirling Orchestra.
203 Onslow Drive, Glasgow G31 2QE
Tel: 0141 556 2829

Massimo, Alberto
Born 1962. Maestro di Cappella Basilica of Santa Cecilia Rome 1986-90. Conducted orchestra of Teatro dell'Opera di Roma in Church of Sant' Ignazio and the Cancelleria 1987-88. Musical Director of Edinburgh Chamber Orchestra and conductor of the Orchestra of the Auld Alliance. Also organist.
7/1 Windmill Place, Edinburgh EH8 9XQ
Tel: 0131 668 3390

Rowe, Rebecca
Work includes: rehearsals, recordings and performances of Mozart *Violin Concerto No.5*; Haydn *'The Clock' Symphony* ; Falla *El Amor Brujo*; R Strauss *Metamorphosen*; Rebecca Rowe *Lightlines* (and other works); Nigel Osborne *Esquisse II*; and Steve Reich *Electric Counterpoint*. Interested in music of all periods.
15 Chalmers Crescent, Marchmont, Edinburgh EH9 1TS
Tel: 0131 662 1851

Skene, Hugh Crawford
Has conducted soloists and youth orchestras. Also composer and teacher.
Crowhills, Chapelton Road, Quarter, by Hamilton, Lanarkshire ML3 7XP
Tel: 01357 300303

Smith, Marylin J
LRAM. Trained Royal Academy of Music, gained professional certificate in singing. Moved to Scotland 1973, worked with Scottish Opera, John Currie Singers and solo professional career. Lecturer St Andrews College of Education, singing teacher RSAMD. Conductor: Glasgow Phoenix Choir. Adjudicator at festivals and competitions.
16 Westbourne Crescent, Bearsden, Glasgow G61 4HD
Tel: 0141 943 0767

Tavener, Alan
Conducts Cappella Nova worldwide (early/contemporary concerts and broadcasts), and in the UK in CD recordings and world premières (John Tavener's *Resurrection* with SCO, James MacMlllan's *Seven Last Words* with BTSE); Strathclyde University orchestra and choirs; and various ad hoc and community choirs and orchestras around Scotland.
172 Hyndland Road, Glasgow G12 9HZ
Tel: 0141 552 0634 / 357 0052 Fax: 0141 552 4053

OTHER USEFUL CONTACTS

Alba
Formed early 1990s to promote Scottish music within Scotland. This has now evolved to promoting new works performed in unusual mediums by Scottish based performers, e.g. putting popular musical ideas into classical works; using actors and dancers alongside musicians.
11 Barrington Drive, Glasgow G4 9DS
Tel: 0141 337 3045
Contact: Christine Liddell (Administrator)

CHARM (Amateur Chamber Musicians Register)
The register exists so that members can contact each other to play chamber music in small groups. Informal concerts are held twice a year so that members can perform to each other. The audience is sympathetic and no-one minds mistakes!
1 Ramsay Garden, Edinburgh EH1 2NA
Tel: 0131 225 3292
Contact: Mrs Janet Sprinz

Contemporary Music Making for Amateurs
COMA founded 1992 to promote the composition of music suitable for amateur groups and the playing of quality contemporary music by amateur ensembles. Holds summer residential course and many smaller-scale regional events; commissions works from British composers. Members receive national and regional newsletters.
Flat 7, 85 Polwarth Terrace, Edinburgh EH11 1NW
Tel: 0131 455 4631 (day) Fax: 0131 455 4232
Contact: Colin Johnson (Scottish Co-Ordinator)

Federation of Recorded Music Societies - Scottish Group
Co-ordinator of 10 recorded music societies in Scotland. Each have regular meetings where members present programme of recorded music. Organises annual residential weekend at Bridge of Allan, which features guest speakers. Can provide list of affiliated societies and assist in setting up new ones.
11 Regent Place, Balfour St, Kirkcaldy, Fife KY2 5HE
Tel: 01592 262727
Contact: Miss I F Page (Secretary)

The Kenneth Leighton Trust

Established 1993 to promote British music in general and the music of Kenneth Leighton (1929-88) in particular, by providing funds for recordings, performances (especially by younger performers) and commissions. All information on Kenneth Leighton is available on the worldwide web: http://www.music.ed.ac.uk./pubs/composition/inded.html.

38 McLaren Road, Edinburgh EH9 2BN
Tel: 0131 667 3113
Contact: Mrs J A Leighton (Secretary) or Jeremy Upton (Treasurer) Tel: 0131 650 1000

National Association of Choirs Group 14 (Scotland West)

The National Association of Choirs was formed in 1920 and has over 430 choirs throughout Britain. These are arranged in 22 geographical groups. Choirs in Scotland are in Group 14 which is divided into West and East. Association holds annual Conference at different venue each year: Glasgow (1995), Grimsby (1996).

9 Ingleside, Lenzie, Glasgow G66 4HN
Tel: 0141 776 2665
Contact: Ian B Macpherson (Chairman) or Flo Allan (Secretary) Tel: 0141 772 3922

Ronald Stevenson Society

Founded to publicise and promote the music of Ronald Stevenson and to sponsor publication, performance and recording of his work. Quarterly newsletter and annual masterclass (piano and voice).

10 Chamberlain Road, Edinburgh EH10 4DL
Fax: 0131 229 9298
Contact: Michael Lister (Honorary Secretary) or Mrs Marjorie Stevenson (Archivist) Tel: 01968 660511

Scottish Bass Trust

Registered charity dedicated to organizing master classes, sponsoring performances and commissioning new music of all types. Members receive newsletter and discounts on CDs etc. Subscription: £10 per annum.

6 West Garleton, Haddington, East Lothian EH41 3SL
Tel: 0162 082 2532 Fax: 0162 082 2532
Contact: Jennifer Sharp

The Scottish Electro-Acoustic Music Association

Founded in late 1980s to support the performance of electro-acoustic music. Provides specialist equipment and technical support for concerts and educational projects. Promotes its own annual series of discoveries concerts in Glasgow, in conjunction with the series in Aberdeen. (e mail: s.arnold @ music.gla.ac.uk)

Music Department, University of Glasgow, 14 University Gardens, Glasgow G12 8QH
Tel: 0141 339 8855 ext 5509 Fax: 0141 307 8018
Contact: Steven Arnold (Chairman)

Scottish Society of Composers

Charitable organisation formed to promote wider knowledge and understanding of music, particularly modern Scottish music. Membership not restricted to composers. Makes annual awards to nominated professional and student musicians, produces a catalogue of members' compositions, and is currently planning to re-establish its tradition of making commercial recordings.

Mazagon, 4 Glen Road, Lennoxtown G65 4JX
Contact: Derek Ball (Secretary)

Society for the Promotion of New Music

Founded in 1943. The leading organisation in Britain dedicated to promoting new music and performances of new works by composers at the beginning of their careers. Promotes up to 50 new works each year at concerts, workshops, lectures and seminars nationwide. Publishes new notes, monthly guide to new music in the UK, free to members.

Francis House, Francis Street, London SW1P 1DE
Tel: 0171 828 9696 Fax: 0171 931 9928
Contact: Cathy Graham (Executive Director) or Elizabeth Webb (Administrator)

Sonic Arts Network

The national association of composers, performers, teachers and others interested in the application of technology to the composition and performance of music. Founded as EMAS in 1981, it acts as a concert, education and information resource and has over 400 members worldwide. Produces annual journal (edited by Pete Stollery) and bi-monthly Agenda; promotes and commissions new works, organises workshops for pupils and teachers. Its library consists of over 200 electro-acoustic works by more than 60 composers.

School of Music, Department of Aesthetic Education, Northern College, Hilton Place, Aberdeen AB9 1FA
Tel: 01224 283601 (day)
Contact: Pete Stollery (Scottish Representative)

Sounds Alive

Quarterly Magazine (founded 1989). Main circulation Perthshire and S.E. Scotland. Substantially pre-subscribed, plus retail sales. Principally covers classical music. Extensive forward diary of events (amateur and professional) and directory of performing groups, listeners' clubs, and related interest societies. Regular news, feature articles, competitions etc.

Kirkhall, Kirkall Road, Almondbank, by Perth PH1 3LD
Tel: 01738 583567
Contact: L MacGregor (Assistant Editor) Tel: 01738 710378 or S Scott (Editor) Tel: 01738 584567

ARTISTS

CLASSICAL

Country Music in Scotland ...??...!!

by Brigitte Strachan

Country music ... where and how does it fit in? When I was asked to write this piece I simply panicked. Even though I know that country music (the 'Western' style, not the 'Scottish', that is!) plays a very big part in the music scene in Scotland, I have not been involved with it as long as some people; in fact it's only been approximately ten years, though six of them have been very intense through working on the magazine.

I have always loved country music, but didn't realise that there were clubs where people could listen to their chosen music. Then one night I visited a club . . . and that was IT! I hardly missed a night. I believe it's like that for most people - you visit a club and go back again and again! Slowly getting into it doesn't work: you either love it or you hate it! It seems that country music lovers are a breed of their own. They are the kindest and most generous people around and any charity organisation will tell you this.

Even in the relatively short time that I have been involved with country music it has absolutely exploded up and down the country. There is hardly another word to describe it. Back then you could probably have counted the clubs on one hand; now look at the scene: I am sure there must be nearly 100 country music venues in Scotland.

I think part of the reason for its being so popular is that music lovers are fed up with some of the modern stuff of which nobody can make any sense and which is also aimed at the 17-and-under age group. In saying that, even the youngsters are getting fed up, and more and more of them are coming to the country clubs and enjoying the friendly atmosphere.

Country music has changed dramatically over the last few years. Out are the slow ballads which tell you the life stories of gunfighters who died in jail and in are very lively tunes and songs, some of which would do any good rock concert proud. With this 'New Country' music nobody needs to be bored, and if people say to me, 'I find country music boring,' I get very angry!

Unfortunately the media don't agree at this point that country music is as important as rock, folk, jazz, classical or pop. If they did then there would be better coverage. The reason? Nobody knows the right answer, but could it be 'money'? Also it could have something to do with the 'dressing up' side of things. Before I go any futher let me make it clear that nobody has to dress up, but if some people feel the need to escape their own lives for a while then at the end of the day what harm does it do?

One aspect we should not forget is the 'Western Dancing' which is sweeping the country at the moment and is suitable for people of all ages. Whether you are on your own or part of a couple, whether you are nine or ninety, there is something for you. Almost all clubs in Scotland do some western dancing, with a lot of them running classes.

The choice of country bands ten years ago was pretty limited; the choice of good bands today is practically limitless, with a lot of top bands coming out of Scotland. Unfortunately most professional bands struggle to make a decent living out of their chosen music, but I am a great believer in persistence, and I would like to predict that one day the most popular music around will be **COUNTRY!**

Brigitte Strachan is the editor of Country Music and Dance in Scotland.

77

Editorial Note

Brigitte Strachan has kindly provided the foregoing list of clubs and bands in Scotland. Unfortunately time didn't allow us to get the information necessary for the kind of listings with 50 word descriptions that we have in other sections, but contact telephone numbers are provided for each entry. This is one of the sections we would like to expand in future editions of the *Handbook* and in the SMIC database.

ARTISTS

COUNTRY
MUSIC

CLUBS

Alamo CWC (Alexandria)
Meets: Fri (monthly).
Tel: 01389 876204

Border CWC (Berwick)
Meets: Tue (monthly).
Tel: 01573 223368

Broken Spur CWC (Drumchapel)
Meets: Sat (monthly).
Tel: 0141 944 6439

Bronco's CWC (Clydebank)
Meets: Sat (monthly).
Tel: 01389 879505

Coldstream Country Nights (Coldstream)
Meets: Tue (monthly).
Tel: 01890 882235

Colorado CWC (West Calder)
Meets: Sundays.
Tel: 01506 873297

Country Nights in the Scotsman's Lounge (Dundee)
Meets: Tuesdays.
Tel: 01382 827159

Coupar Angus CWC
Meets: Fri (monthly).
Tel: 01828 627663

Dakota CWC (High Blantyre)
Meets: Fri (monthly).
Tel: 01698 426266

Denver CWC (Greenock)
Meets: every 3rd Fri.
Tel: 01475 726420

Double 'K' CMC (Dumfries)
Meets: Sun (monthly).
Tel: 01387 67451

Downtown USA (Inverness)
Meets: Tuesdays.
Tel: 01463 235023

Easter Ross CMC (Evanton)
Meets: Wed (fortnightly).
Tel: 01349 830888

EK Corral (East Kilbride)
Meets: Sundays.
Tel: 013552 20034

Elgin CMC
Meets: Thur (fortnightly).
Tel: 01343 544196

Ellon Country Nights
Meets: Sundays.
Tel: 01224 698044

Flag 'n Saddle CWC (Livingston)
Meets: Tuesdays.
Tel: 01506 763069

Forres CMC
Meets: Fri (monthly) + specials.
Tel: 01463 222729

Fort Wagner CWC (New Stevenson)
Meets: Fri (monthly).
Tel: 01236 754126

Fraserburgh CWC
Meets: Wed (monthly).
Tel: 01346 516445

Galloway Country and Western Spot (Markinch)
Meets: Thursdays.
Tel: 01592 759161

Glasgow Gunslingers Club
Meets: Tuesdays.
Tel: 0141 946 8864

Grand Ole Opry
Meets: Fri, Sat, Sun.
Tel: 0141 429 5396

Grantown-on-Spey CMC
Meets: Fri (monthly).
Tel: 01309 651259

Inverness CMC
Meets: Tuesdays.
Tel: 01463 221268

Jack Daniels CWC (Perth)
Meets: Fri (monthly).
Tel: 01738 630703

Jordan's Country Nights (Kirkcaldy)
Meets: Sun (monthly).
Tel: 01592 612114

JR's Country Music (Methilhill)
Meets: Sat (monthly).
Tel: 01592 591889

Kennoway CMC
Meets: Sun (monthly).
Tel: 01333 350294

Kentucky CWC (Bridge of Weir)
Meets: Sat (monthly).
Tel: 01505 690528

Lazy 'S' CWC (Springburn)
Meets: Fridays.
Tel: 0141 336 5395

Loanhead Country Crifters
Meets: Thur (fortnightly).
Tel: 0131 440 2408

Nairn CMC
Meets: Sun (monthly).
Tel: 01667 453941

North And South CWC (Larkhall)
Meets: Sat (monthly).
Tel: 01698 884569

Northern Nashville (Thurso)
Meets: Fri (monthly).
Tel: 01847 894734

Old 97 CWC (Kirkcaldy)
Meets: Sundays.
Tel: 01592 262838

Old No 7 Saloon (Paisley)
Meets: Sat (monthly).
Tel: 0141 889 7355

Orkney CMC (Kirkwall)
Meets: Sun (monthly).
Tel: 01856 761204

Panhandler's CWC (Kirkliston)
Meets: Sat (monthly).
Tel: 0131 442 4922

Pioneer CWC (Balloch)
Meets: Fri (monthly).
Tel: 01389 721811

Prairie Star CWC (Fishcross/Alloa)
Meets: Fri (monthly) + Sat specials.
Tel: 01259 724352

The Ranch (Addiewell)
Meets: Fri (monthly).
Tel: 01501 763468

The Ranchhouse (Dalkeith)
Meets: Fri (monthly).
Tel: 0131 654 2514

Rhinestone CWC (Hamilton)
Meets: Fri (monthly).
Tel: 01698 883880

Rocky Top CWC (Alexandria)
Meets: Sat (monthly).
Tel: 01389 753550

Rootes CWC (Allanton)
Meets: Saturdays.
Tel: 01501 821811

Scoutscroft CWC (Coldingham)
Meets: Fri or Sat (monthly).
Tel: 018907 71338

ARTISTS

COUNTRY
MUSIC

79

ARTISTS
COUNTRY
MUSIC

Silver Dollar CWC (Hawick)
Meets: Sun (fortnightly).
Tel: 01450 375866

Silver Dollar (Dunbar)
Meets: Fri (monthly).
Tel: 01368 862008

Silver Spur CWC (Linwood)
Meets: Sundays.
Tel: 0141 944 5289

Southern Comfort (Kilwinning)
Meets: Saturdays.
Tel: 01292 314016

Southern Star CWC (Ayr)
Meets: Wednesdays.
Tel: 01292 285842

Stagecoach CWC (Irvine)
Meets: Sat (monthly).
Tel: 01294 552094

Stars and Bars CWC (Dalkeith)
Meets: Fri (fortnightly).
Tel: 0131 663 3105

Stonehaven CMC
Meets: Saturdays.
Tel: 01569 740600

Texas Rangers CWC (Penicuik)
Meets: Thur (fortnightly).
Tel: 01968 676532

Texas Star CWC (Barrhead)
Meets: Tuesdays.
Tel: 0141 881 9455

Triple 'C' CMC (Caithness)
Meets: Fri (monthly).
Tel: 01955 604809

Tucson CMC (Edinburgh)
Meets: Mondays.
Tel: 0131 661 6886

Wells Fargo CWC (Grangemouth)
Meets: Sat (monthly).
Tel: 01324 718101

White Horse CWC (Saltcoats)
Meets: Fri (fortnightly).
Tel: 01294 552094

Winchester CWC (Clydebank)
Meets: Mondays.
Tel: 0141 959 8037

Yellow Rose CWC (Linwood)
Meets: Fri (fortnightly).
Tel: 01389 754711

SOLOISTS

Christie, P T
Tel: 01292 317090

Devine, Mike
Tel: 01862 4180

Ford, Gerry
Tel: 0131 445 1687

Roberts, Lennie
Tel: 01343 548143

Wesley, John
Tel: 01382 21754

DUOS

Bill Montana Duo
Tel: 01387 261536

Carol and Bobby Silver
Tel: 01563 535295

Duggan and Gibson
Tel: 01228 48939

Duke Boys Duo
Tel: 01847 83223

Frank Welshman Sound
Tel: 01292 286365

Jolene and Barry
Tel: 01324 815196

Western Rythm
Tel: 01573 410200

BANDS

Big City
Tel: 01592 744107

The Brothers
Tel: 01343 545714

Buffalo
Tel: 01374 147988

Buffalo River
Tel: 01292 671887

Buzzard Creek
Tel: 01324 713422

Charlie and the Moonshiners
Tel: 0131 660 3550

Cimarron
Tel: 01698 886091

Country Blues
Tel: 01294 463452

Country Flavour
Tel: 0131 669 0256

Del Rio
Tel: 01955 621261

Dez Walters Country Band
Tel: 01505 702849

Freight Train
Tel: 01555 751220

Gerry and Country Pride
Tel: 01563 821213

Handsome Hank
Tel: 01389 873765

Hogtied
Tel: 01505 504159

J C and Driftwood
Tel: 01555 665789

Janette Sommers
Tel: 01243 585545

Jefferson
Tel: 0141 554 8815

Kentucky Gamblers
Tel: 01968 678945

Nebraska
Tel: 01334 477603

Nevada
Tel: 01355 303226

Rambling Fever
Tel: 0141 637 1125

Rough Chaps
Tel: 0141 638 7563

Route 65
Tel: 01968 672563

Ruby Rendell
Tel: 01224 791765

Scott Stevens Band
Tel: 0141 641 5536

Shiloh
Tel: 0131 663 7127

Silver
Tel: 01847 63731

Silver Sun
Tel: 0131 669 3898

Springfield
Tel: 01506 856202

Steve James Country Band
Tel: 0141 944 4309

Texas Express
Tel: 0141 420 3039

Texas Gun
Tel: 01292 283899

Tommy Truesdale and the Sundowners
Tel: 01292 268822

Early Music in Scotland
by Rebecca Tavener

'The past is a foreign country - they do things differently there.' L P Hartley did not have any sort of music in mind when he penned this famous observation, but it is irresistibly apt when applied to historically informed performance. When we take a trip abroad we expect to find a language and culture that are different from our own, and the open-minded and intrepid traveller (having done a little background research) is always going to get the most from the experience.

Similarly, the time-travel adventure of early music in so-called 'authentic' performances demands a different level of forethought and commitment from both performers and audience than the regular concert repertoire.

You could say that hearing a J S Bach concerto performed by the instruments of today, with a technique which has evolved through the centuries since Bach's time, is like reading Goethe translated into English. It may be very lovely and exquisitely musical, but it is not what the composer heard. We can only hear something like the original 'language' by listening to a performance on baroque instruments at the appropriate pitch and played with techniques current in the early 1700s. This should also, of course, be a very lovely and exquisitely musical experience. In an ideal world the two equally valid approaches should be freely on offer as well as performances which come somewhere in between.

In Scotland we have been fortunate. We largely missed the excesses of the English early music boom in the 1970s. Instead, the considerable interest and expertise that now exists in Scotland has, by and large, grown thoughtfully and slowly. We have, perhaps, also avoided many of the more vituperative controversies. Our 'mainstream' musicians appear less frightened by the perceived Luddite tendencies of the early performer (and are less frequently shocked by their musical differences as time and hard work continue to foster higher standards). Peaceful co-existence with cross-fertilisation of ideas has become the norm and some practitioners successfully exist in both worlds.

Our specialist early musicians have grown in number and gained in expertise and confidence - particularly benefiting from contact and comparison, however challenging, with the world-class exponents who pass through Scotland with increasing frequency. Our audiences have broadened to the extent that a regular attender at the **Royal Scottish National Orchestra** or **Scottish Opera** may well also be a fan of the **Scottish Early Music Consort** or **Cappella Nova**. The rapidly growing number of people who actively seek to experience the different sound world of historically informed performance is evidence enough for its coming of age.

Looking back over the last 15 years we seem to have reached this stage due to a combination of scholarship; easier access to good published performing editions; performers, promoters and listeners all over Scotland who stubbornly refused to give up when times were hard; recording and broadcasting; and, last but not least, education - both in the formal sense in schools and colleges but also as a general learning process in the concert-going public. Some of the principal milestones in this journey include Dr Kenneth Elliott's formative work on Scotland's own rich early music repertoire; the steady audience-building achieved over many years by the **Scottish Early Music Consort**; the number of commercial recordings now available of Scottish early

81

music (including a growing series on the ASV *Gaudeamus* label by **Cappella Nova**); the dedicated work of specialist concert promoters such as Edinburgh's **Georgian Concert Society**; the willingness of the BBC to broadcast and discuss this repertoire - most notably John Purser's mould-breaking series *Scotland's Music*; the success of the imaginative biennial **Glasgow International Early Music Festival**; the creation of formal training opportunities at the **Royal Scottish Academy of Music and Drama**; and lastly, and highly significantly, the recent development of **the Early Music Forum for Scotland** with all its rich possibilities for education and general dissemination of information.

To return briefly to the foreign holiday analogy: it is still possible to attend early music events in Scotland which are the audible equivalent of the unscrupulous package tour operator with a half-constructed hotel, dodgy plumbing, and salmonella in the kitchen, but these experiences are becoming increasingly rare. In the following pages lies the evidence that a thriving, determined, innovatory, wide-ranging and exciting early music scene flourishes in Scotland. There is plenty of room aboard the time machine - bon voyage!

MAIN CONTACT

Early Music Forum of Scotland

Formed in 1992 to bring together those interested in any aspect of early music and dance: performers and listeners, amateurs and professionals. Quarterly newsletter with notices of events, contributions from throughout Scotland. Courses by leading professionals (concessions for members). Playing days. Register of members.
Kilquhanity House, Castle Douglas, Kirkcudbrightshire DG7 3DB
Tel: 01556 650504 Fax: 01556 650504
Contact: Richard Jones (Chairman)

DUOS

Lyrae Cambrenses

Robert Evans (voice/crwth), William Taylor (harp/lyre). Devoted to researching and performing Welsh medieval music, poetry and drama using period instruments. Primary source is the Ap Huw manuscript. Lecture/recital at World Harp Festival 1994; broadcast for S4C and BBC Radio Wales; British Council tour of Yemen 1995.
Orchard House, Castle Leod, Strathpeffer, Ross-shire IV14 9AA
Tel: 01997 421260
Contact: William Taylor

ENSEMBLES

The Banquet of Musick

Specialises in early baroque chamber music on period instruments including baroque violin, viola da gamba, baroque cello, violone and harpsichord. Contrasts national styles, explores neglected repertoire and plays folk music of 18th c. Scotland.
53 North Grange Road, Bearsden, Glasgow G61 3AG
Tel: 0141 942 6929
Contact: Gail Hobbs or Robert Lay
Tel: 01389 875996

Coronach

Specialising in 16th c. music. 20 concerts a year throughout Highlands, 5 commercial cassettes and CD on the market. Co-operate on a regular basis with Musick Fyne in concerts of music for voices and instruments and with the Kings Players in performances of 16th c. Scottish drama including *Ane Satyre of the Three Estates*.
Cullaggan, 18 Sunnyside, Culloden IV1 2EE
Tel: 01463 790666
Contact: James Ross (Director) or Gordon Tocher (Asst Director)
Tel: 01463 232345

Edinburgh Renaissance Band

Formed in 1973. 12 Edinburgh based musicians specialising in music from the period 1200 - 1600, including the important Scottish repertoire. The instruments used, from a selection of over 70, are all authentic replicas.
23 Queen's Crescent, Edinburgh EH9 2BB
Tel: 0131 667 4710
Contact: Peter Jones (Secretary)

Musick Fyne

16 strong vocal ensemble specialising in 16th c. choral music with particular emphasis on Scottish Renaissance music including the work of Robert Carver. Have commercially recorded Carver's *Mass à 4: Pater Creator Anniem*. Up to 10 concerts a year, some in conjunction with the early instrument consort Coronach.
Cullaggan, 18 Sunnyside, Culloden Moor, Inverness IV1 2EE
Tel: 01463 790666
Contact: James Ross (Director) or Gordon Tocher (Asst Director)
Tel: 01463 232345

Scottish Early Music Consort

Company of professional musicians with wide range of early instruments. Growing reputation for rediscovering and reviving early music masterpieces. Capacity subscription concerts in Edinburgh, Glasgow and Aberdeen in association with Glasgow University Music Department. Toured abroad in Israel, USA, Portugal, Poland, Germany, Belgium and Ireland. Recordings on the Chandos label.
2 Port Dundas Place, Glasgow G2 3LD
Tel: 0141 333 1178 Fax: 0141 333 1179
Contact: Warwick Edwards (Artistic Director) or Mary Carmichael (Administrator)

The Square Mile Consort of Viols

Based in Edinburgh/Glasgow, the consort is renowned for its performances of repertoire from the 16th and 17th c. Numbering from 2 to 7 players (with occasional voices or organ continuo), the consort enjoys performing regularly in museums, art galleries and churches all over central Scotland.
28 Mardale Crescent (3FR), Merchiston, Edinburgh E10 5AG
Tel: 0131 228 6929
Contact: David Heath

ARTISTS
EARLY MUSIC

LUTE

MacKillop, Robert

Specialist in the Scottish lute repertoire. Continuo and tuition. Publication (as Robert Phillips) *Music for the Lute in Scotland*, 20 pieces (tablature and transcription) with a ten page introductory essay on the history of the lute in Scotland (Kinmor Music). CD/cassette *Notes of Noy: Notes of Joy*, The Rowallan Consort (Temple Records).
14 Seaside Place, Aberdour, Fife KY3 0TX
Tel: 01383 860178

83

HARP

ARTISTS

EARLY MUSIC

Taylor, Bill
Recitals and lectures on historical harps. Specialist in fingernail technique on Highland and Irish wire-strung clarsach and Welsh bray harp. Performs internationally as soloist and with The Rowallan Consort (early Scottish music for lute and clarsach) and Lyrae Cambrenses (medieval Welsh music for harp, crwth and voice). Teaches all levels of harp.
Orchard House, Castle Leod, Strathpeffer, Ross-shire IV14 9AA
Tel: 01997 421260 Fax: 01997 421260

RECORDER

Burnett, Susan
Studied Napier University (LLCM) and Glasgow University (B.Mus.). Performed as soloist and with Napier Chamber Ensemble. Member of RSAMD Recorder Quartet. Repertoire from early through baroque to contemporary. Has played in cathedrals, kirks, castles and concert halls.
5 Derby Street (2FL), Glasgow G3 7TJ
Tel: 0141 337 1281

Traditional Music

by Sheena Wellington

Scotland has a rich, diverse and colourful heritage of music, song and dance, much of which is a total mystery to many native Scots. The very popularity of some aspects of our culture has hidden more than it reveals. The great Highland bagpipe is instantly recognisable and few have not thrilled to the sound of a pipe band in full marching order, but it is only in recent years that there has been a recognition that the Scottish small or cauld windpipes, with their gentle, haunting sound, are equally validly Scots. Indeed, in many parts of the country the Highland bagpipe was virtually unknown until the nineteenth century when it was introduced, usually by the British Army.

We are familiar with the exhilarating sound of a fiddle orchestra, setting the feet tapping with a fine selection, but how many know that every area of Scotland has its own distinctive style of bowing and phrasing? It is said that at one time a player from the Angus town of Kirriemuir could be distinguished from a player from Forfar, a few short miles away. In Shetland, the style carries the mark of a long acquaintance with Scandinavian neighbours, while the Border fiddle hints at the tones and intervals of the pipes of neighbouring Northumbria. The post Culloden banning of the Highland bagpipes has lent to the West Highland fiddle both the dignity of the Ceol Mor and the wild sweetness of the Ceol Beg. Although easier travel and access to recordings may threaten to blur some of the finer points, there is still a heartening and cherished difference between the playing of a fiddler from Skye and one from Sanquhar - and long may it be so.

Scotland is even more richly endowed with songs, in Scots, Gaelic and English. Nowhere does the great Indo-European narrative ballad heritage survive and flower more brilliantly than in Scotland's Muckle Sangs. These ancient tales spring from many sources: Greek legend, Norse sagas, the Southern European troubadour tradition and our colourful if troubled history. Their splendid use of Scots gives the lie to those who would dismiss it as a couthy but limited dialect, rather than the vigorous and expressive language that it is. With their wonderful tunes, and sung by a ballad singer of heart, soul and authentic voice, they are works of art the equal of any.

Romantic and funny songs also abound and the Scots speaker is as adept as his Gaelic speaking brother in creating nonsense rhymes and a mouth music, called diddling, to accompany the dance.

The Gaelic language sustains a song culture of world importance with the lyrical and profound *Oran Mor*, the rhythmic *puirt-a-beul*, the famous waulking songs, those gloriously improvised work songs of the women, sometimes with words indelicate to say the least. It has been estimated that there are some 10,000 Gaelic songs in existence!

The songs of Robert Burns are justly famous and most of us could name five or six - but he collected, improved and wrote new lyrics for over three hundred! He was not, of course, the only literary figure to become deeply involved in the songs of tradition. Lady Nairne, Walter Scott and others collected and rewrote, as Burns did, and their work, too, was seamlessly absorbed into the folk culture, a persistent feature of Scottish music but rare in other countries. This sense of shared musical Scottishness persists to this day, though it may only manifest itself before a rugby match or on a convivial Hogmanay or Burns night.

85

ARTISTS

FOLK &
TRADITIONAL

But what of today and what of the future of this precious gift? Traditional Scottish music is undergoing a revival of interest with more and more young people learning the traditional instruments; songwriters and composers as fine as we have ever had are creating new songs and music as part of a living vibrant tradition.

There are teaching progammes under way the length and breadth of the country, and a growing network of local and national organisations - the **Traditional Music and Song Association**, **Feisean nan Gaidheal**, **Commun na Clarsaich**, Edinburgh's **Adult Learning Project**, and until recently the **Glasgow Folk and Traditional Arts Trust** among them - taking on the responsibility of passing on the traditions.

But we must also honour and support the performers, those gifted enough (and brave enough) to make their living singing and playing in the clubs, festivals and concert halls. It is one of the ironies of music that it is more respected and better rewarded abroad than it is at home, and it is hard to avoid the conclusion that many of our musicians spend time working abroad as economic refugees as much as cultural ambassadors.

The traditional and folk artists listed here are talented, dedicated and worthy guardians of our great Scottish heritage of music and song.

Gaelic Music

by Eilidh MacKenzie

The term 'Gaelic Music' encompasses a wide variety of music styles - solo and ensemble; vocal and instrumental; traditional and contemporary; secular and sacred. The extant Gaelic song tradition itself boasts one of the richest stores of folk song in Western Europe. Until this century these songs belonged to a tradition that was almost exclusively oral. However, with the onset of mass literacy, and the increase in quantity and availability of published material, this tradition now exists with both oral and literary sources.

Gaelic song, in keeping with the situation found in music traditions of other indigenous peoples, reflects historical and social circumstance and was composed at all levels of society. From the twelfth to the eighteenth centuries bardic schools existed as a vehicle for classical poets. Alongside this, and indeed dominant throughout the past two centuries, songs were being sung and written by the ordinary folk. As a result the language employed by various poets is diverse in style and meaning.

The choice of subject within Gaelic song varies greatly. There are an abundance of love songs on different emotional levels: from the poet to his lover, frequently unrequited; from a mother to her child; songs of eulogy and elegy directed most commonly at clan chiefs and other poet patrons; and songs in praise of the land, this last category often directly relating to emigration.

Songs with an essential rhythmic element are equally popular and constitute a very large proportion of the tradition. These songs can be split into two groups - *puirt-a-beul* (mouth music) and work songs. *Puirt-a-beul* derived from social necessity when traditional instruments were banned in Gaelic speaking areas. The words themselves often have little meaning and today provide the performer with a chance to expose his vocal dexterity. The origins of work songs are more complex. This vast pool of Gaelic song is thought to have derived again out of social necessity, on this occasion to alleviate the monotony of various chores and create a sense of camaraderie among the workers who often took existing songs and moulded them to suit the task in hand. These work-songs provide us with one of the very few instances in traditional Gaelic song where performance requires more than the solo singer. However, the soloist still has a role to play, as the verses are sung by one who is then joined in the vocable chorus by a group of fellow workers.

Work songs were used in conjunction with a variety of tasks, most significantly that of fulling or waulking cloth. The term for such a song is *luadh* and, although rarely heard in conjunction with its specific task, the *luadh* is still a popular performance choice.

In parallel with this secular tradition there is a history of sacred Gaelic vocal music. Gaelic psalm-singing, specific to protestant Gaelic-speaking areas, takes the form of precentor and congregational response, embellishing popular post-reformation psalm tunes.

Although traditional song has retained a high profile within the Highland tradition, Gaelic song has developed to encompass other music types. Among these genres are choral and instrumental/vocal groups, both of which enjoy a certain popularity today. The choral tradition within the framework of Gaelic music began a hundred years ago as the result of the first National Mod. Groups using Gaelic songs and melodies take the form of folk, rock, jazz and classical.

87

ARTISTS

This leads us on to the instrumental tradition. Gaelic-speaking areas boast three indigenous forms - the harp, the bagpipe and the fiddle. These have been added to in more recent years and now include instruments such as guitar, whistle/flute, bodhran and keyboards, among others.

Until the latter half of the present century, Gaelic music was nurtured by the social structure of life in the Highlands and Islands, as well as in emigrant towns, cities and countries. However, with the loss of the ceilidh environment in its real sense, music-making within the tradition has been forced to look for other outlets. This in turn has encouraged the formation of several organisations, each concerned to some degree with the preservation and development of Gaelic music.

In 1891 **An Comunn Gaidhealach** (the Highland Society) was founded. This organisation's main public event is the National Mod, held annually in a different Scottish location. Today the Mod runs for a week and is a competitive music, literary and drama festival with partipants travelling from throughout Britain and further afield. Nearly a hundred years later, the **National Gaelic Arts Project** was founded in response to the need for the implementation of a structured Gaelic artistic environment. This organisation now looks to provide a support service for both the individual musician and his audience in addition to acting as a Gaelic music funding support, database and general catalyst for music both traditional and contemporary. Mirroring this, the rapid expansion of the *feis* (festival) movement throughout the Highlands and Islands within the 1980s demanded the creation of an umbrella body for the different festivals. And so **Feisean nan Gaidheal** (Highland Festivals) was born. The first *feis*, Barra 1981, has now mushroomed to include a further twenty-four such festivals of Gaelic arts, this number growing each year. These festivals are non-competitive, are aimed primarily but not exclusively at children, are normally residential and offer the highest quality of tutoring in song and instrumental music.

In the 1950s serious collecting work began in Gaelic-speaking areas of Scotland. Since then, field workers have been collecting songs and collating a variety of information under the banner of the **School of Scottish Studies**, attached to the University of Edinburgh. Today it is an vast archival resource of traditional Gaelic song.

Gaelic music, as illustrated above, enjoys a wealth of material and diversity of style. It is in large part due to this very fact that the tradition survives. With the aid of the aforementioned organisations and the enthusiasm of individual singers and instrumentalists the preservation and development of this part of Scotland's inherent music is limitless.

AGENTS

Bechhofer Agency

Organises, on a sole representation basis, tours for folk and blues musicians. Artists represented include Duck Baker and Molly Andrews, Andy Irvine, Lorraine Lee and Bennett Hammond, Billy Jackson and Tony Cuffe, Tim Lyons and Fintan Vallely, Magpie, Ed Miller, Rab Noakes, Tonny Sands, Hans Theesink (also with Jon Sass), Aileen Vance.

51 Barnton Park View, Edinburgh EH4 6HH
Tel: 0131 339 4083
Contact: Frank Bechhofer or Jean Bechhofer

Carrick Music Agency

Mainly deals with festivals, folk clubs and art centres. Represents Scottish artists and performers from further afield, especially in the Celtic tradition.

Whin Cottage, Dundas Street, Comrie, Perthshire PH6 2LN
Tel: 01764 679465 Fax: 01764 670990
Contact: Margaret Morgan or John Morgan

Macmeanmna

Gaelic music marketing, management, recording and promotion company, also involved in the promotion of live audio-visual shows. Management company for Arthur Cormack, Blair Douglas, Ishbel Macaskill, Mary Ann Kennedy and photographer/broadcaster Cailean MacLean.

Quay Brae, Portree, Isle of Skye IV51 9DB
Tel: 01478 612990 Fax: 01478 613263
Contact: Arthur Cormack (Partner) or Blair Douglas (Partner)

Nae Real (Scotland)

Agents for Bohinta; Drop the Box; Frank McLaughlin and Gillian MacDonald; Hardie, Marwick and Cattanach; The Journeymen; and Ross Kennedy and Archie McAllister.

11 Harling Drive, Troon KA10 6NF
Tel: 01292 31698
Contact: Peter Stott

Reel Good Agency

Ensures a lively and enjoyable experience with a wide range of experienced and professional musicians and entertainers i.e. pipers, disco, jazz, pop, swing, rhythm and blues, function, ceilidh bands, classical, Highland dancers, folk singers, musicians etc. All types of events i.e. weddings, balls, fundraisers, corporate entertainment, festivals etc.

6A Argyle Crescent, Joppa , Edinburgh EH15 2QG
Tel: 0131 657 2472 Fax: 0131 657 2472
Contact: Philip M Condie (Agent/ promoter)

Ross / Sutherland Scottish Music Group

Marketing group specialising in promoting semi-professional artists. Involved in traditional Scottish Highland music and dance. Bookings taken for country dance bands, dancers, pipers, singers (Scottish and Gaelic) and compères. No commission charged. Arrangement fee plus expenses.

33 Scotsburn Court, Tain, Ross-shire
Tel: 01862 893417 Fax: 01862 893417
Contact: Murray MacLeod

Stoneyport Agency

Has a list of well-known artists specialising in folk music, mostly from Scotland and Ireland. One act is a blues/jazz act (Tam White) and is available in different line-ups to suit different budget requirements. The accumulated experience within the agency allows for consultancy, and current/past clients include the Scottish Tourist Board and Tall Ships Race. Demo-cassettes usually available plus publicity material.

39 Shandon Crescent, Edinburgh EH11 1QF
Tel: 0131 346 8237 (24hr) Fax: 0131 313 2083
Contact: John Barrow Tel: 0131 654 2184 / 0385 255637 (mobile) Fax: 0131 660 2337 or Davy Steele

FIDDLE ORCHESTRAS

Edinburgh Highland Reel and Strathspey Society

Rehearsals: 7.30pm (October - March) at St George's West Church, Shandwick Place, Edinburgh. An ability to read music is required. Orchestra is for violin, cello and bass only. Two concerts per year in the Usher Hall, one for charity. Membership fee.

89 Colinton Mains Road, Edinburgh EH13 9DL
Tel: 0131 441 7100 / 650 4938
Contact: George Robertson (Secretary)

The Festival City Fiddlers

Professional players eligible. Rehearsal times and place as required. Entry by invitation.

101 Warrender Park Road, Edinburgh EH9 1EW
Tel: 0131 229 6439
Contact: Yla L Steven

Highland Strathspey and Reel Society

Formed 1903 by Alex Grant (Battan), fiddle maker, inventor of the rondello and close friend of Scott Skinner. Reformed in 1973 by the late Donald Riddell, whose tapes and a book of whose compositions, The Clunes Collection of Scots Fiddle Music, are available.

Hill House, Wardlaw Road, Kirkhill, Inverness
Contact: Elizabeth Smith Tel: 01463 831651 or Katie Summers Tel: 01463 242826

Inverness Fiddlers' Society

Formed 1977. Actively promotes traditional music by perfomances by large and small groups, tuition, recordings and exchanges with overseas groups. Its laid-back Highland style owes much to pipe music, but the repertoire is widely based. Visiting fiddlers are welcome to Monday evening practices.

Arras, Drumossie, Inverness IV1 2BB
Tel: 01463 230403 (H)
Contact: Eric Allan (Secretary) or Doug Stewart (Leader) Tel: 01381 620139

ARTISTS

FOLK &
TRADITIONAL

89

GAELIC CHOIRS

ARTISTS

FOLK & TRADITIONAL

Aberdeen Gaelic Choir

Formed 45 years ago and has around 35 members, both Gaelic and non-Gaelic speakers. The aim is to promote Gaelic song in the North East of Scotland. Meets weekly and performs at local venues as well as Mod competitions.
c/o Aberdeen Grammar School, Aberdeen
Tel: 01224 646530
Contact: Roddie MacLeod or Gay Slater Tel: 01569 764280

Coisir Chataibh

A vehicle for maintaining and promoting the Gaelic language in the counties of Sutherland and Caithness. Training in music and spoken aspects of Gaelic language provided. Available for performances (given ample notice) for local (North of Inverness) ceilidhs. Music and Gaelic verification services.
56 Sweyn Road, Thurso, Caithness
Contact: Dr Philip Page (Secretary)
Tel: 01847 893440 / 2121 x2852 or Myrtle Gillies Tel: 01847 802121 x2740

Coisir Ghaidhlig Inbhirnis

Membership is open to Gaelic-speaking or non-Gaelic speakers resident in Inverness district. Rehearsals are held in the music room, Millburn Academy, Tuesday 7.30pm. The choir participates at provincial and Royal National Mods.
34 Laggan Road, Inverness IV2 4EH
Tel: 01463 231169 (H)
Contact: Andrew MacKintosh

Coisir Ghaidhlig Loubhdaidh

Aims to promote Gaelic music and language. Competes at local and national Mods and sings by invitation at societies, charities etc. Meets weekly at Drummond Community School, Edinburgh, Thursdays 7.30-10pm. Conductor: Russell Day. Gaelic Tutor: Catriona MacKinnon.
1 Bilston Cotts, Roslyn, Midlothian EH25 9SQ
Contact: Margaret McVicar Tel: 0131 440 2603 / 453 6161 x220

Coisir Sgire a Bhac

95 North Tolsta, Isle of Lewis
Contact: Mairi MacLean (Secretary)

Dingwall Gaelic Choir

44 choristers. Repertoire: mainly Gaelic but also light classical and some sacred. Conductor: Hamish Menzies. Two concerts per year. Rehearsals Thursdays, 7.30pm, Dingwall Primary School.
Ceol na Mara, Muir of Ord, Ross-shire
Tel: 01463 870445
Contact: June Matheson (Hon Secretary)

Edinburgh Gaelic Choir

In existence for over 80 years and is the oldest established senior mixed voice Gaelic choir in Edinburgh. Anyone interested in joining is welcome to come along to rehearsals. Rehearsals: Wednesdays 7.30pm, Drummond Community High School, Cochran Terrace, Edinburgh. A little knowledge of music and/or Gaelic would be beneficial, but not essential.
12/3 Murrayburn Place, Edinburgh EH14 2RR
Tel: 0131 442 3792
Contact: Miss E MacDonald (President) or Susan Oswald Tel: 0131 445 3462

Glasgow Gaelic Musical Association

Founded 1893, the oldest Gaelic choir in Scotland. Includes many contemporary Gaelic works in its repertoire and has recently recorded with Rod Stewart. Annual concert second Friday in March, Partick Burgh Hall. Recordings: *Gaelic Galore* 1990 (LCOM 9037) and *Orain is Puirt-a-beul* 1993 (LCOM 5220).
14 Rosslyn Terrace, Glasgow G12 9NA
Tel: 01698 364120 / 0141 334 7773 (eve)
Fax: 01698 376671
Contact: Kenneth Thomson (Conductor) or Janette MacDonald (Secretary) Tel: 01236 732213

Inverness Gaelic Choir

Membership is open to all interested in furthering the Gaelic culture through songs. The choir has a musical director and a Gaelic tutor and welcomes learners of music and the Gaelic language. Participates at provincial mods, the Royal National Mod and similar festivals abroad.
34 Laggan Road, Inverness IV2 4EH
Tel: 01463 231169
Contact: A A Mackintosh (Secretary)

Isle of Mull Gaelic Choir

Choir with 30 members performing concerts of Gaelic songs about 4 times a year. Rehearsals: Thursdays 8- 10pm alternately at Salen Primary School and Tobermory Evangelical Church Hall.
Loch Frisa, By Tobermory, Isle of Mull
Tel: 01688 302168
Contact: Riona Whyte or Duncan MacGilp (Conductor)

Kintyre Ladies Choir

Choir of c. 20 meets in the Argyll Hotel, Campbeltown on Wednesdays at 7.30pm. Repertoire: Gaelic, Scottish and English, 5-6 concerts per year. Conductor: Mary Lang.
Contact: Jennifer McGrory (Secretary) Tel: 01586 552966

Lairg Gaelic Choir

12a Shore Street, Golspie, Sutherland
Contact: David Murray Tel: 01408 633592 or Evelyn Calder (Conductor)

Laxdale Gaelic Choir

27 Francis Street, Stornoway, Isle of Lewis HS1 2NF
Tel: 01851 705359 Fax: 01851 705359
Contact: John Young (Secretary)

Melvich Gaelic Choir

Unaccompanied 4 part singing in Gaelic. Competes at local and national Mods and gives concerts and appearances in aid of local charities. Rehearsals 7.30-9.30pm Tuesdays, Melvich Primary School.
175 Trantlemore, Forsinard, Sutherland
Tel: 01641 571246
Contact: Anne Cameron (Secretary) or Myrtle Gillies Tel: 01641 571241

Saltire Gaelic Choir (Edinburgh)

Gaelic choral music for SATB and SSA. Currently 20 members. 4 concerts per annum plus up to 4 in response to invitations from other organisations etc. Rehearsals: Wednesdays, 7.45-9.45pm, Lister Housing Co-operative, 36 Lauriston Place, Edinburgh.
11 North High Street, Musselburgh, Midlothian EH21 6JA
Tel: 0131 665 7500
Contact: Kenneth Mackenzie (Conductor)

Stornoway Gaelic Choir

Choir with 20 members meets Thursday evenings, 8pm in the Fortrose Lodge Hall, Stornoway. Extensive repertoire of Gaelic songs with a yearly concert.
14 Ripley Place, Stornaway, Isle of Lewis HS1 2LP
Tel: 01851 704511
Contact: Joy Ritchie (Secretary) or Christine McKee (Musical Director)

90

Strath Gaelic Choir

Present membership 36. Aim is to contribute to Skye and Lochalsh by learning and performing Gaelic and English choral music. Also individuals and groups within the choir. Attend local and national mods, and have also competed at Mod Vancouver and the Pan Celtic Festival.
Sanna Cnoc Terrace, Kyle, Ross-shire
Contact: Morag MacLeod (Secretary)
Tel: 0159953 4794

CEILIDH BANDS

Albanatchie

4-piece traditional and original Celtic folk ceilidh experience. Have ceilidh appeal for wide audience, especially those of energetic disposition and a taste for something rootsy. Fiddles, wooden flute, whistles, pipes, mandola, guitar, blues harp, mandolin, bodhran, vocals, global percussion and dance calling.
Soundfolk Music, 4 Chancellor Street, Glasgow G11 5RQ
Tel: 0141 334 5137
Contact: Stuart McCartney

An Teallach

In great demand for concerts and ceilidhs throughout Scotland and Ireland. Have appeared at many major traditional music festivals including Tønder in Denmark and the Fleadh Cheoil in Ireland. Repertoire is a broad mix of Scottish and Irish music and song. Albums available.
34 Alder Place, Kirkcaldy
Tel: 01592 265891
Contact: Bob Reid

Annasach Ceilidh Band

Two fiddles, flute, keyboard, guitar, bass guitar and caller. Plays at functions, weddings, ceilidhs etc.
Reel Good Music Agency, 6A Argyle Crescent, Joppa, Edinburgh EH15 2QG
Tel: 0131 657 2472 Fax: 0131 657 2472
Contact: Philip M Condie (Agent)

Back Ally Ceilidh Band

Played at Scotland's former rugby captain Gavin Hastings' wedding. Accordion, fiddle, guitar/caller, singer. Perform at weddings, graduation balls, ceilidhs, 21st parties, Scottish evenings.
Reel Good Music Agency, 6A Argyle Crescent, Joppa, Edinburgh EH15 2QG
Tel: 0131 657 2472 Fax: 0131 657 2472
Contact: Philip M Condie (Agent)

Bill Black Scottish Dance Band

Retired shepherd Bill Black leads the band on button box playing for festivals, ceilidhs and Scottish country dances from Northumberland to Shetland. Albums on Springthyme Records.
Leaside, Stanley, Perthshire PH1 4PN
Tel: 01738 828364
Contact: Bill Black

Celtic Spirit Folk and Ceilidh Band

Caller/male singer/drums, fiddle, flute, keyboards, double bass, bagpipes. Plays at festivals, weddings, ceilidhs etc. Finished 3rd in World Ceilidh Band Championships in Bute 1994.
Reel Good Music Agency, 6A Argyle Crescent, Joppa, Edinburgh EH15 2QG
Tel: 0131 657 2472 Fax: 0131 657 2472
Contact: Philip M Condie (Agent)

Dave Francis

34 Prince Regent Street, Edinburgh EH6 4AT
Tel: 0131 554 3092 Fax: 0131 554 3092
Contact: Dave Francis or Mairi Campbell

The Foundry Bar Band

Came together when they won the Ceilidh Band competition at the 1975 Kinross Festival. Thirty years down the line, some personnel changes, three albums on Springthyme Records.
12 Guthrie Street, Friockheim, by Arbroath DD11 4SY
Contact: Geordie Adamson or Springthyme Records Tel: 01337 830773

Gillean Ceilidh Band

Fiddle, male singer, guitar, bass, drums, caller. Performs at functions, events etc.
Reel Good Music Agency, 6A Argyle Crescent, Joppa, Edinburgh EH15 2QG
Tel: 0131 657 2472 Fax: 0131 657 2472
Contact: Philip M Condie (Agent)

Gordon Shand Ceilidh Band

Accordion, fiddle/mandolin, keyboards, drums and caller. Fife-based. Perform at functions, weddings, Scottish evenings.
Reel Good Music Agency, 6A Argyle Crescent, Joppa, Edinburgh EH15 2QG
Tel: 0131 657 2472 Fax: 0131 657 2472
Contact: Philip M Condie (Agent)

Islander Ceilidh Band

Line-up - fiddle, flute, keyboards, mandolin, drums and caller. Band plays at weddings, ceilidhs, functions etc.
Reel Good Music Agency, 6A Argyle Crescent, Joppa, Edinburgh EH15 2QG
Tel: 0131 657 2472 Fax: 0131 657 2472
Contact: Philip M Condie (Agent)

Jim MacLeod's Dance Band

A traditional Scottish Country Dance Band with a resident spot at the Dunblane Hydro. Toured throughout Scotland and released seven audio cassettes and four videos, including their newest release *The Road and Miles* (VITV583). Jim received a Gold Award in 1994 from the Scottish Record Industry Association in recognition of sales achieved by his *Hogmanay Party* video.
BGS Productions Ltd, Newtown Street, Kilsyth G65 0JX
Tel: 01236 821081 Fax: 01236 826900
Contact: Norman Scott (Marketing Manager)

The John Carmichael Ceilidh Band

Traditional style popular ceilidh band, also specialising in accompaniment for singing and traditional music shows. Toured extensively world wide and taken part in many radio and television broadcasts. Film appearances and numerous albums, the latest being *Carmichael's Ceilidh*.
2 Brora Drive, Giffnock, Glasgow G46 6NR
Tel: 0141 638 0344 Fax: 0141 638 0344
Contact: John Carmichael

The Kinlochard Ceilidh Band

Players in the true sense of the word. Will travel miles to play gigs, not only in Scotland, but in Portugal, Sweden and the Ukraine. Their first involvement in recording was as a support band to Bill McCue on *The Heart of Scotland* tape KITV552. From that, and rightly so, they have now released their own tape *Slainte!*
BGS Productions Ltd, Newtown Street, Kilsyth G65 0JX
Tel: 01236 821081 Fax: 01236 826900
Contact: Norman Scott (Marketing Manager)

The Loose Moose Ceilidh Band

Scottish dance music for ceilidhs or concerts, featuring the Scottish smallpipes and fiddle. Played at various folk festivals and dances throughout Scotland. CD/cassette available on Lomoco label from above address.
90b Riverside Road, Wormit, North Fife DD6 8LJ
Tel: 01382 541 457
Contact: Rosa Michaelson

ARTISTS

FOLK & TRADITIONAL

91

ARTISTS

FOLK &
TRADITIONAL

92

Norloch Ceilidh Band

Line up - 2 fiddles, keyboard, guitar, drums, percussion/caller. Performs at weddings, graduation balls, ceilidhs, festivals, Scottish evenings. Recorded by Lismor at Bute in 1992 in the International Ceilidh Band Championship.
Reel Good Music Agency, 6A Argyle Crescent, Joppa, Edinburgh EH15 2QG
Tel: 0131 657 2472 Fax: 0131 657 2472
Contact: Philip M Condie (Agent)

The Occasionals

Radio, TV, CD with 2nd to follow in 1995.
6 The Steils, Edinburgh EH10 5XD
Tel: 0131 447 0991 / 0831 779920 (mobile) Fax: 0131 447 0991
Contact: Freeland Barbour

Paddy Ryan's Dream

A ceilidh/session band with up to 18 musicians from Galloway, Leadhills, Edinburgh and Glasgow. All members of more rigid ceilidh bands - including Tapsalteerie, The Robert Fish Band and others - who like to get together once in a while. Fiddles, guitars, banjo, wooden flute, cello, percussion, pipes, accordion, piano, caller.
Bath Street Co-op, 9 Bath Street, Portobello, Edinburgh
Tel: 0131 669 3924
Contact: Robert Paul or Trevor (Fiddle Player) Tel: 016442 634

Robbie Shepherd's Nightmare

Charles MacLeod (accordion), Dougie Pincock (pipes, whistle, flute, sax), Fraser Neill (guitar, fiddle) and Graeme Barclay (drums).
313 Main Street, Renton G82 4PZ
Tel: 01389 759878
Contact: Dougie Pincock or Graeme Barclay Tel: 01360 860315

The Robert Fish Ceilidh Band

Experienced, contemporary up-beat ceilidh band. 6-piece with twin fiddles, button accordion, whistles and rhythm section featuring guitar, bass, drums and percussion producing a tight, driving sound. Call all the well known Scottish dances plus some older reels.
c/o 184 Dalry Road, Edinburgh EH11 2EP
Tel: 0131 337 5442
Contact: Stan Reeves

Scottish Blend Ceilidh Band

Started over 12 years ago with accordionist brothers David and Kevin Brown. Fiddle, drums, guitar/piano and caller now added to line-up. The band can be tailored to suit requirements. Repertoire consists of old and new music played in a traditional style but with modern upbeat arrangements.
Reel Good Music Agency, 6A Argyle Crescent, Joppa, Edinburgh EH15 2QG
Tel: 0131 657 2472 Fax: 0131 657 2472
Contact: Philip M Condie (Agent)

Steep The Feet

5-piece (or more) ceilidh band. All-round appeal. Music with a Glasgow flavour. Piper and caller available.
Soundfolk Music, 4 Chancellor Street, Glasgow G11 5RQ
Tel: 0141 334 5137
Contact: Charlie Saksena

Stepping Out Folk and Ceilidh Band

Line-up - guitar/banjo/caller, accordion, fiddle, drums. Band plays at weddings, functions, Scottish evenings, folk clubs etc.
Reel Good Music Agency, 6A Argyle Crescent, Joppa, Edinburgh EH15 2QG
Tel: 0131 657 2472 Fax: 0131 657 2472
Contact: Philip M Condie (Agent)

Sultans of Fling

Up-tempo ceilidh band with experienced players to suit most occasions.
Tel: 01764 670231
Contact: Rod Paul

Tattiehowkers Ceilidh Band

Seven musicians who have all previously been involved in the promotion of traditional music, playing mainly Scottish and Irish material, and a dance caller to help you with the foot work. After a Tattiehowkers ceilidh, everyone agrees with the band that ceilidhs are fun- and they want more.
2 Mairs Road, Darvel KA17 0LA
Tel: 01560 321102
Contact: Maggie Macrae

Wallochmor Ceilidh Band

Radio, TV, 5 CDs - a 6th in 1995.
6 The Steils, Edinburgh EH10 5XD
Tel: 0131 447 0991 / 0831 779920 (mobile) Fax: 0131 447 0991
Contact: Freeland Barbour

Wayne Robertson Band

Wayne Robertson (accordion) Nigel Jelks (guitars, mandolin, fiddle). Established 1990. BBC recording artists. Will play any music from 1600 to 1995. Basic calling available. Band can include caller, drums, piano, bass, singers. Listening music, Scottish ceilidh dance, Scandinavian, country dance, old-time etc.
32 Patrick Allen Fraser Street, Arbroath, Angus DD11 2LX
Tel: 01241 871964 Fax: 01575 572436
Contact: Wayne Robertson (Band Leader) or Nigel Jelks (Joint Band Leader) Tel: 01575 573 276

The Wild Cigarillos

Played together for 12 years at a wide variety of events including weddings, balls, charity fund raisers, folk festivals, corporate entertainments. This 5-piece has extended its repertoire so that Scottish dancing is now only a part offered alongside pop, twist, old-time and international folk dances (called if required).
c/o Stoneyport Agency, 39 Shandon Crescent, Edinburgh EH11 1QF
Tel: 0131 346 8237 (24hr) Fax: 0131 313 2083
Contact: John Barrow

Wild Geese Ceilidh Band

Fiddle, guitar/singer, bass guitar, drums, caller. Versatile folk/rock ceilidh band, performs at functions, pub/club circuit etc.
Reel Good Music Agency, 6A Argyle Crescent, Joppa, Edinburgh EH15 2QG
Tel: 0131 657 2472 Fax: 0131 657 2472
Contact: Philip M Condie (Agent)

GROUPS

Alive and Pickin'

First recording *Alive* released in September 1983 and has been reviewed throughout the UK and USA.
231 Mallard Crescent, Greenhills, East Kilbride G75 8UJ
Tel: 013552 63005
Contact: Gerry McCluskey or Steven McCluskey

Bachué Café

Formed to celebrate the Celtic Connections Second Gathering in Glasgow. Recorded a demo. Radio broadcasts include *Travelling Folk* with Archie Fisher. Band members: Corrina Hewat (small harp), David Milligan (piano, keyboards), Ken Fraser (fiddle, pipes, percussion).
8 Parkside Street, Flat 3, Edinburgh EH8 9RL
Tel: 0131 667 0249
Contact: Corrina Hewat

Battlefield Band

Bagpipes, flute, whistle / fiddle, cittern, accordion / keyboards / guitar, vocals. Under the banner *Forward With Scotland's Past*, Battlefield Band tour the world playing Scottish music, mixing old songs and tunes with new self-penned material, on a fusion of ancient and modern instruments.
c/o Temple Records, Shillinghill, Temple, Midlothian EH23 4SH
Tel: 01875 830 328 Fax: 01875 830 392
Contact: Robin Morton (Manager) or Joyce McMillan (Secretary)

Bohinta

Fronted by Martin and Aine Furey, combining original song writing with vocal harmonies, acoustic guitars, low whistles, uilleann pipes, keyboards and percussion. Band includes Carlene Anglim (champion fiddle player), Jill Hunter (keyboards) and Greg Stewart (drums).
11 Harling Drive, Troon KA10 6NF
Contact: Nae Real Tel: 01292 316968

Boys of the Lough

One of the first full-time Celtic bands. First tour in 1967. 17 group album/CD titles recorded; 45 tours of USA (at beginning of 1995); appeared widely in Europe, Asia and Australia. Fiddler Aly Bain awarded MBE in 1994 for services for folk music. Line-up: Aly Bain; Cathal McConnel; Dave Richardson; Christy O'Leary. Acoustic music with integrity and respect for the tradition.
31 Fountainhall Road, Edinburgh EH9 2LN
Tel: 0131 662 4992 Fax: 0131 662 0956
Contact: Dave Richardson (Administrator)

Burach

Experienced seven-piece electric/acoustic Celtic rock outfit playing own songs and instrumentals as well as a range of traditional material and occasional covers. Vocals, fiddle, accordion, guitars, bass and drums. Available for festivals, concerts, dances, functions, clubs, weddings etc.
1 Dublin Mews, Edinburgh EH3 6NW
Tel: 0131 558 1858
Contact: Iain Forbes

Calluna

A new Edinburgh-based trio of clarsach, cello and flute playing a mixture of Scottish traditional music and song and their own compositions. Charlotte Petersen (clarsach), Kath Campbell (cello/vocals) and Rebecca Knorr (simple-system flute, whistles).
22 Drummond Place, Edinburgh EH3 6PN
Tel: 0131 558 3102
Contact: Charlotte Petersen

Capercaillie

Gaelic roots/rock music. Seven albums and rapidly expanding international following due to consistent touring and exposure in various TV and film projects, the most recent being the MGM feature film *Rob Roy*, in which the band appeared as well as providing several tracks for the film score.
Chap Management, PO Box 1155, Glasgow G3 7TW
Contact: Lindsay Chapman

Ceol Alba

Quintet - flute, violin, harp, piano, double bass. Plays Scottish music from the infectious rhythm of the dance to the remote highland melancholy of the solo lament. Equally at home recording or performing live. Has broadcast many times on BBC Radio Scotland and Radio Two.
2 John Street Lane, Helensburgh, Dunbartonshire G84 9NA
Tel: 0143 667 4662
Contact: Walter Blair

Ceolbeg

Traditional Scottish music and song with wide modern influences. Line-up includes bagpipes, electric harp, percussion and vocals by Rod Paterson. Albums available. Toured USA and Canada. Used on film and video. Band members also do educational programmes in the Highlands.
c/o 133 Easter Road, Edinburgh EH7
Tel: 0131 661 7225 Fax: 0131 313 2083
Contact: Peter Boyd (Band Member) or John Barrow (Stoneyport Agency) Tel: 0131 346 8237

Clan Alba

Formed from well-known performing artists - including Dick Gaughan, Davy Steele, Sileas (also with The Poozies), Fred Morrison, Brian McNeill, Mike Travis (also with EH15 and the Cauld Blast Orchestra) and Dave Tulloch (percussion).
Stoneyport Agency, 39 Shandon Crescent, Edinburgh EH11 1QF
Tel: 0131 346 8237 (24hr) Fax: 0131 313 2083
Contact: John Barrow

The Clydesiders

Two fiddles, guitar, mandolin, keyboards, bass and vocal harmonies. More than two decades in the business.
19 Quarry Road, Fintry, by Glasgow G63 0XD
Tel: 01360 860444 Fax: 01577 382259
Contact: Sandy Kelso or Duncan McCrone Tel: 01877 382259

The Cutting Edge

Playing for concerts and ceilidh dances providing an exciting blend of accordion, fiddle, keyboards, drums, percussion, mandolin and guitar. Lively invigorating music with strong Scottish Celtic roots spiced with jazz, Latin and rock reflecting the wide ranging experience of the individual players. Début album - *Turning The Tide*.
35 Couper Angus Road, Dundee DD2 3HX
Tel: 01382 611256
Contact: George Carmichael

Drop The Box

Strong contemporary folk music drawing on the strong traditions of Shetland and Ireland. World music, reggae and indie grooves provide the base for most of the band's songs and tunes, making the sound difficult to pigeonhole.
11 Harling Drive, Troon KA10 6NF
Contact: Nae Real Tel: 01292 316968

Folk on the Water

Trio - female singer/fiddle, guitar, keyboards. Perform at Edinburgh pub circuit, played at Bute Folk Festival 1994 in the World Ceilidh Band Championships.
Reel Good Music Agency, 6A Argyle Crescent, Joppa, Edinburgh EH15 2QG
Tel: 0131 657 2472 Fax: 0131 657 2472
Contact: Philip M Condie (Agent)

ARTISTS

FOLK &
TRADITIONAL

Govan Gaelic Choir

Rehearsals: Mondays, 7.30-9.30pm, Woodside School, Glasgow. Repertoire is purely Gaelic. One main concert per year, others possible plus radio, TV broadcasts etc. Compete in National Mod. Choir has a Gaelic tutor.
289 Byres Road, Glasgow G12 8TL
Tel: 339 2817
Contact: Jean Gillon (Secretary) or Duncan G Robertson (Conductor)

Harvest Folk Band

Fiddle, guitar, bass guitar, banjo, vocals. Edinburgh based folk group, perform around the pub/club circuit, festivals etc.
Reel Good Music Agency, 6A Argyle Crescent, Joppa, Edinburgh EH15 2QG
Tel: 0131 657 2472 Fax: 0131 657 2472
Contact: Philip M Condie (Agent)

Highland Connection

Fiddle/guitar, Vocals/mandolin - Ian Hardie, Janice Clark and Dagger Gordon. Scots music and song with a northern flavour on fiddle, voice, guitar, mandolin, cittern, bass, Scottish small pipes. 1995 album *Gaining Ground* (CDTRAX 087).
Inchindown Farmhouse, by Invergordon, Ross-shire IV18 0XP
Tel: 01349 853118
Contact: David Gordon or Ian Hardie Tel: 01667 455948

The Iron Horse

Energetic and sensitive Scottish roots-inspired music 1991 MRA award for excellence. 3 CDs *The Iron Horse, Thro' Water, Earth and Stone* and *Five Hands High* (Lochshore). Regular TV and radio performances. Toured UK and abroad, including Europe, Poland and Egypt. Made sound track for BBC Scotland's documentary *The Gamekeeper* (1995).
PO Box 23, Comrie, Crieff, Perthshire PH6 2YE
Tel: 01764 679626 Fax: 01764 679626
Contact: Rod Paul or Peter Stott Tel: 01292 316968

James Malcolm Band

Guitars and harmonicas. Scottish traditional and contemporary folk/rock/pop. Début CD/Cassette *Sconeward* (Greentrax 1995). Concerts scheduled throughout Scotland and beyond. Available for workshops/festivals. Professional studio production and backing undertaken. Experienced compères (Edinburgh Folk Festival) and accompanists.
Ground Floor, 13 Spottiswoode Street, Edinburgh EH9 1EP
Tel: 0131 229 1071
Contact: James Malcolm

Jonny Hardie, Gavin Marwick and Davy Cattanach

Two young Scots fiddlers join forces with adventurous rhythm resulting in innovative interpretations of fiddle music the world over. Recording *Up in the Air.*
11 Harling Drive, Troon KA10 6NF
Contact: Nae Real Tel: 01292 316968

The Journeymen

Energetic 7 piece outfit. Interpret traditional standards alongside some original compositions which are provocative, passionate and powerful. Music is a blend of folk, rock and Celtic influences played with enthusiasm and feeling.
67 Viewmount Crescent, Strathaven
Tel: 01357 22967
Contact: Kevin Noon or Nae Real (Agency) Tel: 01292 316968

The McCalmans

Popular trio whose success has taken them worldwide. Their numerous recordings include *Peace and Plenty, Listen to the Heat, Ancestral Manoeuvres, Flames on the Water, Songs from Scotland, The Ettrick Shepherd* and *Honest Poverty* (all on Greentrax Records).
1 Kevock Road, Lasswade, Midlothian EH18 1HT
Tel: 0131 663 7943 Fax: 0131 663 7943

Mac-talla

Vocals, cello, clarsach, accordion and keyboards. Individually and collectively represent finest exponents of Gaelic music tradition with a freshness of approach which overcomes language barriers. Have toured throughout Europe. Won *Living Tradition's* 'Gaelic Album of the Year' award at the Glasgow Royal Concert Hall, 1995, with *Mairidh Gaol is Ceol* (Temple Records).
c/o Temple Records, Shillinghill, Temple, Midlothian EH23 4SH
Tel: 01875 830328 Fax: 01875 830392
Contact: Robin Morton (Manager) or Joyce McMillan (Secretary)

Macumba

Formed in Glasgow in 1988. Combine original and traditional Scottish pipe music with the street rhythms of Africa and Brazil. Numbering 10 people the group are costumed, mobile and available for street, stage or stadium performances.
Wardhill Cottage, Torrance, Glasgow G64 4EY
Tel: 013606 20379
Contact: John Beaver (Band Member)

Mouth Music

Albums include: *Mouth Music*, with singer Talitha MacKenzie: *Blue Door Green Sea*, with singer Mairi MacInnes; *Mo-Di* with singers Jackie Joyce and Michaela Rowan.
c/o PO Box 61, Welshpool, Powys SY21 7WF
Contact: John Reid Enterprises Tel: 0181 741 9933 or Free Trade Agency Tel: 0171 702 8111

Old Blind Dogs

Formed 1990. Ian Benzie (guitar/lead vocals), Buzzby MacMillan (banjo/cittern/electric bass/low D whistle/vocals), Jonny Hardie (fiddle/mandolin/block flute/guitar/ whistles/vocals) and Davy Cattanach (percussion/vocals). Several recordings (Lochshore). Toured USA.
Ibis Productions, East Balbridie, Crathes, Banchory AB31 3JB
Tel: 01330 844456 Fax: 01330 844435
Contact: Ian Middleton (Ibis Productions) or Marj Mitchell Tel: 01224 482400

The Poozies

Harps, guitar, fiddle and accordion with four part vocals. All-woman group, incorporating Patsy Seddon and Mary MacMaster from Sileas. A cross between Rabbie Burns and the Louisiana Rattlesnakes. The Poozies intelligently integrate contemporary with traditional while resisting trends and fads.
Stoneyport Agency, 39 Shandon Crescent, Edinburgh EH11 1QF
Tel: 0131 346 8237 (24hr) Fax: 0131 313 2083
Contact: John Barrow or Davy Steele Tel: 0131 654 2184 / 0385 255637 (mobile) Fax: 0131 660 2337

Runrig

Gaelic / rock band. 1991 played to 50,000 at Loch Lomond. 1994 televised Hogmanay celebrations in Edinburgh. Many hit singles and albums since the late 70s. Toured Britain and abroad and have headlined major shows at both Edinburgh and Stirling castles.
55 Wellington Street, Aberdeen, Grampian AB2 1BX
Tel: 01224 573100 Fax: 01224 572598
Contact: Marlene Ross (Manager) or Carol Morrice (PA to Marlene Ross)

Sangsters

An all-singing three-piece (Anne Combe, Fiona Forbes, and Scott Murray). TMSA singing competition winners. Perform traditional, contemporary and self-penned material. Most recent recording on Greentrax.
14 Poplar Crescent, Kirkcaldy KY2 5DU
Tel: 01592 200282
Contact: Sandy Forbes

Seannachie

4-piece combining vocals, clarsach, fiddle, guitar, percussion. A great deal of experience - recordings, numerous radio appearances, festival dates and folk club gigs.
3 Rockville Terrace, Bonnyrigg, Edinburgh EH19 2AG
Tel: 0131 663 7647 Fax: 0131 663 7647
Contact: Elspeth Cowie

Shooglenifty

Fiddles, mandolins, banjo, guitar, bass and percussion. Fast and furious 'hypofolkedelic' mix of traditional and original material, incorporating talents of ex-members of Kith and Kin, Mouth Music and Capercaillie. Fuse energies of current Scottish roots revival with upfront attitude of today's clubland grooves, creating dynamic new dance sound for the 90s.
c/o Greentrax Recordings, Cockenzie Business Centre, Edinburgh Road, Cockenzie, East Lothian EH32 0HL
Tel: 01875 814155 Fax: 01875 813545
Contact: Ian D Green

Simon Thoumire Three

Concertina/guitar/double bass. Simon Thoumire was winner of the BBC Radio 2 Young Tradition award in 1989. The band plays a fusion of traditional and jazz music.
Whirlie Management, Greenside House, 25 Greenside Place, Edinburgh EH1 3AA
Tel: 0131 557 9099 Fax: 0131 557 6519
Contact: Liz Wright (Managing Director) or George Thomson (Assistant)

Smalltalk

Comprising talented and well-experienced musicians: Fiddler Stuart Morrison and piper Iain MacInnes both played with The Tannahill Weavers in the late 80s; Billy Ross was a founder member of Ossian and sings both Scots and Gaelic songs. The band's music ranges from Gaelic song and instrumental music to North-East ballads.
Greentrax Recordings, Cockenzie Business Centre, Edinburgh Road, Cockenzie, East Lothian EH32 0HL
Tel: 01875 814155 Fax: 01875 813545
Contact: Ian Green or Iain MacInnes
Tel: 0131 336 3567

The Stars Band

An all-star line-up of Arthur Johnston, Brian Miller and Charlie Soane. Joined by George Carmichael for a recent tour of Denmark.
17 Brownlie Street, Mount Florida, Glasgow G42 9BT
Tel: 0141 632 7737
Contact: Rosetta Fitzpatrick

Stramash

Traditional Scottish and Irish songs from 5 singers: Anne Neilson, Bob Blair, John Eaglesham, Kevin Mitchell and Adam McNaughtan plus specialist accompanist Finlay Allison. Instruments can include fiddle, 2 concertinas, mandolin and 2 guitars. Also specialist programmes on Robert Burns, Matt McGinn, Glasgow and an A-Z song tour, plus educational programmes.
8 Melford Avenue, Giffnock, Glasgow G46 6NA
Tel: 0141 638 6589 Fax: 0141 638 6589
Contact: Bob Blair (Member of group) or Adam McNaughtan (Member of group)
Tel: 0141 632 3906

Stravaig

Women's *a capella* group. Toured USA, Canada, Ireland and UK. 1995/6 tours include France, Germany, Austria, Switzerland. Numerous broadcasts on BBC, local and American radio. Sing for children's concerts, collect traditional material and teach to schools. Three albums available.
Whin Cottage, Carrick Music Agency, Dundas Street, Comrie, Perthshire PH6 2LN
Tel: 01764 79465 Fax: 01764 670990
Contact: Margaret Morgan or John Morgan

Thulbion

Judi Nicolson (fiddle), Violet Tulloch (piano), Ian Nicolson (accordion), Andrew Tulloch (guitar). Music of Scotland, Shetland in particular, traditional and newly composed. Album *Twilight Bound*.
c/o Greentrax Recordings, Cockenzie Business Centre, Edinburgh Road, Cockenzie, East Lothian
Tel: 01875 814155 Fax: 01875 813545
Contact: Ian D Green

Tonight at Noon

Folk/rock - electro-acoustic original and traditional music for listening and dancing. Albums: *Tonight at Noon*, *Down to the Devils* and *Heart of the Lion*. Radio broadcasts and television appearances, including *Brag* and *Woolly Jumpers No More* (BBC Scotland). Toured USA, Russia, Holland, Poland, Galicia, Ireland.
1 Mortlach Court, Buccleuch Park, Glasgow G3 6NS
Tel: 0141 332 1087
Contact: Gavin Livingstone (Band Member) or Peter Livingstone (Band Member)

The Whistlebinkies

'Artists of the Week' BBC Radio 3, January 1995. Play and compose Scottish traditional music. Rab Wallace (small pipes), Judith Peacock (clarsach), Eddie McGuire (flute), Mark Hayward (fiddle), Stuart Eydmann (concertina), Peter Anderson (sidedrum). Several recordings available. New CD out January 1996 for US tour. Perform widely throughout Britain and abroad.
c/o Jester Management and Promotion Ltd., 41 Hamilton Drive, Glasgow G12 8DW
Tel: 0141 334 9245 / 0850 081119 (mobile)
Contact: Rick Standley

DUOS

Allan and Ingrid Henderson

Young fiddle and clarsach duo, also pipes and piano. Ingrid is youngest winner of Folk on Radio 2 Young Tradition. Two recordings *Light on the Mountain* and *Perpetual Horseshoe*. Allan available for freelance and band work. Both compose in traditional idiom.
Ashburn House, Achintore Road, Fort William PH33 6RQ
Tel: 0139 770 6000 Fax: 0139 770 6000
Contact: Allan Henderson or Ingrid Henderson

ARTISTS

FOLK & TRADITIONAL

95

ARTISTS

FOLK & TRADITIONAL

Andy Shanks and Jim Russell

Singer/songwriters. Songs covered by June Tabor, The Sangsters and others. Use a blend of guitars, melodeon, whistles, mandola and vocals. Available for clubs, festivals.
23 Moray Court, Auchtertool, Kirkcaldy, KY2 5XS
Tel: 01592 782485
Contact: Jim Russell or Andy Shanks Tel: 01356 647465

Arthur Cormack and Blair Douglas

Experienced Gaelic song and instrumental duo, available for concerts and dances, as well as workshops. Have each recorded solo, together, and with the Gaelic band Mac-talla, of which they are both members.
c/o Macmeanmna, Quay Brae, Portree, Isle of Skye IV51 9DB
Tel: 01478 612990 Fax: 01478 613263
Contact: Arthur Cormack (Partner) or Blair Douglas (Partner)

Bill Purves and Colin MacKenzie

2 male singers with guitar and banjo. Edinburgh based, perform around the pub and club circuit and festivals etc.
Reel Good Music Agency, 6A Argyle Crescent, Joppa, Edinburgh EH15 2QG
Tel: 0131 657 2472 Fax: 0131 657 2472
Contact: Philip M Condie (Agent)

Blackeyed Biddy

Scottish/Irish folk. Formed 1981. Toured Europe, Canada, USA, and Dubai, and numerous festival appearances in Scotland and Europe. Live TV and radio. 1993 performed with Tag Theatre Co. in *A Scots Quair* (including Glasgow Mayfest and Edinburgh Festival). Albums - *Guid Neibours* (BNK1), *High Spirits* (Dunkeld) and *Peace, Enjoyment, Love and Pleasure* (Greentrax).
7 Orchard Place, Hamilton ML3 6PG
Tel: 01698 459772
Contact: Kris Koren or Lionel McClelland Tel: 01683 220779

Brian Miller and Charlie Soane

Scottish traditional music and song, with fiddles, guitars and mandolins.
36 Greenhill Park, Penicuik, Midlothian EH26 9EX
Tel: 01968 678153
Contact: Brian Miller

Crooked Jack

Comic duo with original music. Well established on the folk circuit club scene. Recordings available.
16 Moray Court, Auchtertool, Kirkcaldy
Tel: 01592 781591
Contact: Dennis Alexander

The De'il's Trump

Lindsay Porteous and Duncan Williamson are two of Scotland's best known exponents of the jew's harp. Together they combine their talents in ballads, trump duets, and a wide assortment of other instruments. Duncan Williamson is also a very experienced and gifted storyteller.
Tron Workshop, Culross, Fife KY12 8JG
Tel: 01383 880271
Contact: Lindsay Porteous

Fiddle Harp and Voice

Repertoire of Scottish traditional music and Scottish dance music.
87 Swanston Avenue, Edinburgh EH10 7DA
Tel: 0131 445 2022 Fax: 0131 445 2022
Contact: Isobel Mieras or Jim Ferguson Tel: 0131 538 4777

Frank McLaughlin and Gillian MacDonald

Previously known as The Vital Spark. Perform a variety of traditional and original songs and music on guitars, small pipes, whistles and bodhran. Winners of the folk song competition at the National Folk Festival 1994. Have toured extensively throughout Britain, Europe and Canada. Début CD on Temple Records.
11 Harling Drive, Troon KA10 6NF
Contact: Nae Real Tel: 01292 316968

Ian Richard and Steve Rothero

Guitars, accordion, synthesizer. Traditional and contemporary music and song and original material. Resident artists at Aberdour Folk Club.
55 Morar Road, Crossford, Fife KY12 8XY
Tel: 01383 735023 Fax: 0131 316 4623
Contact: Ian Richard or Steve Rothero Tel: 01383 822141

John Eaglesham and Erlend Voy

Fiddle, concertina, vocals. Traditional Scottish music and humour.
32 Cardonald Gardens, Glasgow G52 3PG
Tel: 01592 781591
Contact: John Eaglesham Tel: 0141 883 2792 or Erlend Voy Tel: 0141 952 7237

John Martin and Billy Ross

Fiddle/guitar, vocals. Members of the famous ex-folk group 'Ossian'. Have performed as a duo at many festivals up and down the country.
4 Bernard Terrace, Edinburgh EH8 9NX
Tel: 0131 667 3268
Contact: John Martin

Mairi Campbell and Dave Francis

Concerts: traditional and self-penned songs. Highland/Cape Breton fiddling and step-dancing. Dances: a full evening of Scottish country dancing and older Scottish dances, called if required. Workshops: Scottish step-dancing; Highland/Cape Breton fiddling; ceilidh dancing; guitar.
34 Prince Regent Street (1f2), Edinburgh EH6 4AT
Tel: 0131 554 3092 Fax: 0131 554 3092
Contact: Dave Francis

Mouth Music

Traditional Gaelic song from a contemporary World Music perspective. The Mouth Music Project was taken forward by co-founder Talitha MacKenzie following the departure of Martin Swan. Albums: *Mouth Music* (Triple Earth) duo; *Sòlas* (Riverboat) solo - Talitha MacKenzie.
33 Millar Crescent, Edinburgh EH10 5HQ
Tel: 0131 447 0091
Contact: Talitha MacKenzie

North Sea Gas

Multi-instrumentalists. Toured Australia, USA, Arab Emirates and Europe extensively. Two silver discs for their albums *Caledonian Connections* (1993) and *Keltic Heritage* (1994). Latest album *Scottish Destiny*.
8 Loch Road, Blackhall, Edinburgh EH4 3PW
Tel: 0131 336 2864
Contact: Dave Gilfillan or Colin Ramage

Pete Shepheard and Tommy Bonnar

Traditional folk songs with melodeon and guitar. Pete Shepheard is a singer, musician, folk song collector and record producer. Tommy Bonnar founded the Howff Band in the sixties.
Balmalcolm House, Kingskettle House, Fife KY7 7TJ
Tel: 01337 830773
Contact: Pete Shepheard or Tommy Bonnar Tel: 01578 730247

Ross Kennedy and Archie McAllister

Ex-member of The Tannahill Weavers and The Iron Horse, Ross Kennedy (guitar and vocals) has played his original arrangements of songs across Britain and Europe. Archie McAllister has won several fiddle championships at senior level. Début recording *Twisted Fingers* is a mix of driving traditional tunes, songs with slow airs and ballads.
Contact: R Kennedy Tel: 01586 554709 or Nae Real Tel: 01292 316968

Russell and Kydd

Songs and vocal music from Scotland, performing *a cappella* and with guitar/ appalachian dulcimer, in 2 part harmony. Mix of traditional and contemporary material with emphasis on dance tunes and ballads. Run workshops in voice productions and songwriting. CDs on Greentrax *Janet Russell and Christine Kydd* (Trax011) and *Dancin' Chantin'* (Trax077).
32 Broughton Place, Edinburgh EH1 3RT
Tel: 0131 557 1334
Contact: Christine Kydd or Strathmartin Music Tel: 01535 656877

Sileas

World-travelled clarsach duo. Both members of Clan Alba folk 'supergroup' and The Poozies.
Stoneyport Agency, 39 Shandon Crescent, Edinburgh EH11 1QF
Tel: 0131 346 8237 (24hr) Fax: 0131 313 2083
Contact: John Barrow or Davy Steele Tel: 0131 654 2184 / 0385 255637 (mobile) Fax: 0131 660 2337

ACCORDION

Barbour, Freeland

Accordion player with The Occasionals ceilidh band and The Wallochmor Ceilidh Band. Has numerous recordings with these bands - has also released solo recordings and collections of published music.
6 The Steils, Edinburgh EH10 5XD
Tel: 0131 447 0991 Fax: 0131 447 8889
Contact: Freeland Barbour

Coupland, Gary

Musical Director and performer with The Singing Kettle, playing to over 200,000 people every year. Also specialises in keyboards, trombone and saxophone.
12 Stanley Street, Edinburgh EH15 1JJ
Tel: 0131 669 5278
Contact: Gary Coupland

Holmes, Ian

Scottish Dance Band leader. Recording and broadcasting artist since 1962. Composer.
11 Averill Crescent, Dumfriesshire DG2 7RY
Tel: 01387 254484

Jamieson, Alex

Piano accordionist. Scottish/Irish traditional, light classical, continental, standard pops. Experienced in clubs, summer seasons, cruise ships. Writes and performs own humourous songs, eg *The People's Palace, No Trident No, Living with a Healthy Heart.*
28 Cochrane Street, Kilbirnie, Ayrshire KA25 7AS
Tel: 01505 683430

BAGPIPES

Bennett, Martin

Bagpipes, flute and violin. Attended School for Musically Gifted Children in Edinburgh then RSAMD. Worked with groups such as Wolfstone and Mouth Music. Solo début album with Eclectic in October 1995. Commissions include work for BBC Scotland, Grampian, Traverse Theatre, Royal Lyceum and Edinburgh International Festival.
Braw Music Management, 78 Pentland Terrace, Edinburgh EH10 6HF
Tel: 0131 445 3317 Fax: 0131 445 4719
Contact: Kenny MacDonald (Manager) or Eclectic Records Tel: 0131 229 9299

Boyd, Ewan

Highland bagpipes.
Reel Good Music Agency, 6A Argyle Crescent, Joppa, Edinburgh EH15 2QG
Tel: 0131 657 2472 Fax: 0131 657 2472
Contact: Philip M Condie (Agent)

Davidson, Lindsay

Highland bagpipes and Scottish smallpipes. Toured widely abroad. Composer and teacher.
Reel Good Music Agency, 6A Argyle Crescent, Joppa, Edinburgh EH15 2QG
Tel: 0131 657 2472 Fax: 0131 657 2472
Contact: Philip M Condie (Agent)

Duncan, Gordon

In addition to solo and pipe-band playing, has also worked with The Tannahill Weavers, Wolfstone, The Dougie MacLean Band and other line-ups. Composer - some of his work has been recorded by other musicians. Solo album *Just For Seumas* contains traditional material, some of his own compositions, other contemporary pieces.
c/o Greentrax Recordings, Cockenzie Business Centre, Edinburgh Road, Cockenzie, East Lothian EH32 0HL
Tel: 01875 814155 Fax: 01875 813545
Contact: Ian D Green

Grace, Annie

Highland pipes, small pipes, whistles. Also vocals. Solid grounding in Celtic/ traditional music. Experienced in live performance (member of The Iron Horse), studio recording, TV and radio work, tutoring and composing. Influenced by whatever sounds good, but world music in general. Repertoire Celtic and eclectic.
92 Park Road (1/2), Kelvinbridge, Glasgow G4 9HB
Tel: 0141 357 4822

Moore, Hamish

Experienced player of Scottish small-pipes and Border pipes, also plays Highland pipes in the key of A using exciting step-dance rhythms, more often associated with Cape Breton fiddling. Solo, duo and ensemble - traditional or folk-jazz line-ups. 5 recordings to date, including *Stepping on the Bridge* and *Farewell to Decorum.*
Grianach, St Mary's Road, Birnam, Dunkeld, Perthshire PH8 0BJ
Tel: 01350 727 474 Fax: 01350 727 474

ARTISTS

FOLK & TRADITIONAL

97

ARTISTS

FOLK & TRADITIONAL

Morrison, Fred

Bagpipes. Whistles. Composer. Solo and group work - plays with Clan Alba and Capercaille. Involved in a lot of session and recording work. Composes in the Gaelic instrumental style.

141 Old Greenock Road, Bishopton, Paisley PA7 5DL
Tel: 01505 862275

Pincock, Dougie

Plays both Highland pipes and Scottish small pipes as well as whistles, flute and saxophone, and composes. Ex-Battlefield Band member, available for concerts, festivals, clubs and recording. Also experienced in TV and radio. First solo album *Something Blew* (Greentrax CDTRAX 080 - 1994).

313 Main Street, Renton G82 4PZ
Tel: 01389 759878
Contact: Dougie Pincock

Richard, Nigel

Developer of extended range chromatic bagpipes (see suppliers). Innovator in folk/jazz improvisation (bagpipes) with Dick Lee (sax), John Kenny (trombone), see *Maoin* on Watercourse records, also with group Inchcolm. Also plays cittern and guitar.

9 Beresford Avenue, Edinburgh EH5 3EU
Tel: 0131 551 1726

Wallace, Robert

Award winning solo piper and member of The Whistlebinkies. Available for traditional piping gigs and any other musical collaboration. Performed with Scottish Ensemble, RSNO. Taught at summer schools, USA and extensively throughout the world. Composer and compiler of *Glasgow Collection of Pipe Music*. Piping journalism another speciality.

32 Mount Harriet Drive, Stepps, Glasgow G33 6DW
Tel: 0141 779 1750 (24 hrs) Fax: 0141 779 1750
Contact: Robert Wallace or Rick Standley (Agent) Tel: 085 008 1119 (mobile)

CITTERN

Richard, Nigel

Cittern/bagpipes/guitar. Original background folk/blues guitar. Traditional accompanist on cittern. Developer of extended range chromatic bagpipes (see suppliers). Innovator in folk/jazz improvisation (bagpipes) with Dick Lee (sax), John Kenny (trombone), see Maoin on Watercourse records, also with group Inchcolm.

9 Beresford Avenue, Edinburgh EH5 3EU
Tel: 0131 551 1726

CLARSACH / SMALL HARP

Davidson, Fiona

Celtic harp/vocals (Gaelic, Scottish, Irish and some Welsh). Solo performances, inspired by the ancient 'Bards' as depicted in Celtic mythology, consist of traditional music, song and telling of legends. Also composes music and poetry and has collaborated for theatre, recordings and television. Recordings to date: *Uaithne* (Mull Recordings) cassette; *Fonsheen* (Watercolour Music) cassette and CD.

Duncauld Cottage, Cauldhame, Kippen FK8 3HL
Tel: 01786 870626
Contact: Julie Turner (Watercolour Music) (Agent) Tel: 01855 821513

Hewat, Corrina Dawn

1st class honours (with merit) degree in Jazz, Contemporary and Popular Music. Toured with Two Ring Ceilidh (combining solo performance and ceilidh dances). Radio broadcasts include *Travelling Folk*, *Young Musicians*, Moray Firth Radio. TV includes *Talla a' Bhaile*. Session musician for various recordings: Iain Fraser and Freeland Barbour, Dougie Pincock, Ross and Cromarty vol 2.

c/o Cullicudden Schoolhouse, Culbookie, The Black Isle IV7 8LL
Tel: 0131 558 3675

Jackson, William

Scottish harper/composer specialising in the combination of Scottish traditional, including Gaelic, and classical music. Founder member of Ossian. Commissions: *The Wellpark Suite* (1985); *St Mungo* (1990); *Gaidhealtachd* (1990); and *A Scottish Island* (1995) for SCO. 12 group and solo recordings on Iona, Greentrax and Linn Records. Also qualified music therapist.

1 New Road, Forfar, Angus DD8 2AE
Tel: 01307 463317

Kennedy, Mary Ann

Studied piano at RSAMD but turned to concentrate on harp at RNCM. Works in both classical and traditional music; broadcast on BBC and ITV; premièred works for large and small harps; released a duo album and guested on many others; also presents Radio Scotland's Celtic/ roots music programme *Celtic Connections*.

c/o Glencairn Drive, Pollokshields, Glasgow G41 4QN

Kinnaird, Alison

Gut-strung harp, wire-strung harp (clarsach), cello. Well-known exponent of traditional Scottish harp music and respected teacher. Also member of Gaelic group Mac-talla. Has travelled widely, from Hawaii to Kuala Lumpur, and has done many television and radio broadcasts. 4 albums and 3 books available

c/o Temple Records, Shillinghill, Temple, Midlothian EH23 4SH
Tel: 01875 830328 Fax: 01875 830392
Contact: Robin Morton (Manager) or Joyce McMillan (Secretary)

Macdearmid, Anne

Soprano and clarsach. Established performer with many television and radio performances, and theatre work. Has given recitals in Britain, Holland, America and Germany. Programmes include: *The Music and Songs of Scotland, The Music and Songs of Robert Burns and Lady Nairne* and *Traditional Music from round the World*.

10 Glenhome Avenue, Dyce, Aberdeen AB2 0FF
Tel: 01224 722633

MacKay, Rhona

Experienced singer and clarsach player taking her inspiration from Gaelic culture. Also accompanist and arranger. Enjoys working with other musicians. Experienced adjudicator and examiner.
Bridgeflat , Nr Bridge of Weir, Renfrewshire PA11 3SJ
Tel: 01505 872595

MacMaster, Mary

Scottish traditional clarsach player. Performs with Scottish clarsach duo Sileas, the 4-piece all women band The Poozies, and the 8-piece band Clan Alba. Currently embarking on a career in ambient music.
25 Liberton Drive, Edinburgh EH16 6NL
Tel: 0131 664 5211

Marshalsay, Karen

Scottish traditional and South American music on wire-strung clarsach and Paraguayan harp. Recently returned from Australia where she performed at Port Fairy Folk Festival, the Australian National Folk Festival, Geelong Celtfeis and others. Also taught Scottish harp workshops and schools/community music workshops using harp, marimbas, whistle and storytelling.
20 Stoneleigh Road, Greenock PA16 7TB
Tel: 01475 783249

Mieras, Isobel

Has performed a varied programme of Scottish music and song from Troon to Tokyo. Recitals suitable for music clubs, arts guilds, festivals, conferences, schools and colleges. Three recordings.
87 Swanston Avenue, Edinburgh EH10 7DA
Tel: 0131 445 2022 Fax: 0131 445 2022

Peacock, Judith

Performer and teacher of clarsach and pedal harp. Solo performances of traditional Scottish and classical music including Edinburgh Festival Fringe, Bute Folk Festival and the Highland Harp Festival. Also weddings, dinners etc. Special interest in Gaelic music and song. Member of traditional group The Whistlebinkies.
11 Shaw Road, Milngavie, Glasgow G62 6LU
Tel: 0141 956 3091

Petersen, Charlotte

Clarsach player and teacher. Performs with trio Calluna. Duo recording *Strings Attached* on Macmeanma.
22 Drummond Place, Edinburgh EH3 6PN

Seddon, Patsy

Scottish traditional clarsach player. Performs with Sileas (clarsach duo with Mary MacMaster), and The Poozies, a group of 4 women playing a variety of musical styles.
Midfield Lodge, Lasswade, Midlothian EH18 1ED
Tel: 0131 660 5559 Fax: 0131 660 2337

Smellie, Elspeth

Appeared on Edinburgh Fringe and main Festival (1991), Borders Festival. Toured in Scotland and abroad. Member of Wheelans for 4 years. Radio and TV broadcasts including *Weirs Way*, *About Britain*, *Highway*, and *Seventh Heaven*. Two recordings, *Keltswells* and *A Song for Yarrow*. Also plays at weddings, christenings, conferences and private functions.
No 3 Cottage, Easter Wooden Farm, Eckford, Kelso, Roxburghshire TF5 8ED
Tel: 01835 850729

Stevenson, Savourna

Experienced and versatile exponent of the Celtic harp. First album *Tickled Pink* (Springthyme); next three *Tweed Journey*, *Cutting the Chord*, and *Tusitala Teller of Tales* (Eclectic Records). Composition commissions include 4 productions for Edinburgh Royal Lyceum Theatre, works for Space Dance Theatre, Borders Youth Theatre, Borders Dance Festival and David Massingham Dance. Also TV commissions.
The Old School, Stobo, Peeblesshire EH45 8NU
Tel: 01721 760298 Fax: 01721 760298
Contact: Mark Norris (Manager)

Wycherley, Ellen

B.Mus. LRAM. In charge of music at Craiglockhart College. Produced many compositions for voice and clarsach, including words of Mary, Queen of Scots, R L Stevenson, *Carmina Gadelica* (in English and Gaelic), St John of the Cross and the Old Testament *Song of Songs*.
Tigh na Greine, 3 Auldgate, Kirkliston, West Lothian EH29 9HB

Yule, Heather

Performs solo and background on clarsach and pedal harp. Also a storyteller and teaches both instruments privately, in schools and at workshops. First studied clarsach with Savourna Stevenson and Isobel Mieras, later studied pedal harp with Sancha Pielou and Elunid Pierce. Has a B.Mus. in pedal harp performace from Texas Tech University.
Carnethy Cottage, Silverburn, Penicuik, Midlothian EH26 9LH
Tel: 01968 672877

CONCERTINA

Thoumire, Simon

Winner of BBC Radio 2 Young Tradition award in 1989. Plays a fusion of traditional and jazz on English concertina. Recordings include the traditional *Hootz* album with guitarist Ian Clark, 2 albums with Seannachie and his own *Waltzes for Playboys*. Numerous concerts, TV appearances etc.
Whirlie Management, Greenside House, 25 Greenside Place, Edinburgh EH1 3AA
Tel: 0131 557 9099 Fax: 0131 557 6519
Contact: Liz Wright (Managing Director) or George Thomson (Assistant)

FIDDLE

Bain, Aly

Born and raised on Shetland. Moved to mainland Scotland and formed the Boys of the Lough in 1967. Recorded numerous albums with the band, formed his own record label, produced two solo albums, presented six different TV programmes and is still touring, solo, with other artists and with the 'Boys', throughout the world.
c/o Whirlie Records, Greenside House, 25 Greenside Place, Edinburgh EH1 3AA
Tel: 0131 557 9099 Fax: 0131 557 6519
Contact: Liz Wright (Manager) or George Thomson (Admin Assistant)

ARTISTS

FOLK & TRADITIONAL

99

Edinburgh Highland Reel and Strathspey Society

Rehearsals: 7.30pm (October - March) at St George's West Church, Shandwick Place, Edinburgh. An ability to read music is required. Orchestra is for violin, cello and bass only. Two concerts per year in the Usher Hall, one for charity. Membership fee.
89 Colinton Mains Road, Edinburgh EH13 9DL
Tel: 0131 441 7100 / 650 4938
Contact: George Robertson (Secretary)

Fraser, Alasdair

Full time professional, now living in California. Tours extensively and performs throughout North America and Europe, frequently returning to Scotland. Particular interests include Scottish fiddle music of the 18th and early 19th c. Several recordings available on the Culburnie label.
c/o 2 Harestanes Gardens, Kirkintilloch
Tel: 0141 776 0113
Contact: Iain Fraser

The Festival City Fiddlers

Professional players eligible. Rehearsal times and place as required. Entry by invitation.
101 Warrender Park Road, Edinburgh EH9 1EW
Tel: 0131 229 6439
Contact: Yla L Steven

Fraser, Iain

Professional musician with an increasing commitment as a solo performer and fiddle teacher. Has played with amateur orchestras but now exclusively plays traditional music and performs with several different dance bands. Runs own recording company, Culburnie Records. Recordings include *Northlins* (Iona ~IRCD027).
2 Harestanes Gardens, Kirkintilloch G66 2BT
Tel: 0141 776 0113

Hardie, Ian

Scots fiddle - both traditional and original. Albums available. Miscellaneous broadcasts/sessions. Also plays string bass, electric bass, Scottish small pipes and viola.
Glebe End, Glebe Road, Nairn IV12 4ED
Tel: 01667 455948 Fax: 01667 455529

Highland Strathspey and Reel Society

Formed 1903 by Alex Grant (Battan), fiddle maker, inventor of the rondello and close friend of Scott Skinner. Reformed in 1973 by the late Donald Riddell, whose tapes and a book of whose compositions, *The Clunes Collection of Scots Fiddle Music*, are available.
Hill House, Wardlaw Road, Kirkhill, Inverness
Contact: Elizabeth Smith Tel: 01463 831651 or Katie Summers Tel: 01463 242826

Inverness Fiddlers' Society

Formed 1977. Actively promotes traditional music by perfomances by large and small groups, tuition, recordings and exchanges with overseas groups. Its laid-back Highland style owes much to pipe music, but the repertoire is widely based. Visiting fiddlers are welcome to Monday evening practices.
Arras, Drumossie, Inverness IV1 2BB
Tel: 01463 230403 (H)
Contact: Eric Allan (Secretary) or Doug Stewart (Leader) Tel: 01381 620139

Lawrence, Douglas

Native of Buckie. Received traditional Scottish fiddle tuition from Hector MacAndrew. Won many awards at the major festivals in addition to the 1977 National Competition at the Gathering of the Clans. Appeared frequently on radio and TV. Also traditional music teacher.
86 Deanston Drive, Glasgow G41 3LH
Tel: 0141 649 7666

Marwick, Gavin

Influences - everything and anything. Repertoire mainly but not exclusively Celtic; original compositions; bands and major recordings - The Iron Horse, trio with Johnny Hardie and Davie Cattanach, Burach; experienced in and available for TV, radio, soundtrack, session recording; dance and concert bands, trios, duos and solo live performances; teaching; composing commissions.
6 School Brae, Cramond, Edinburgh EH4 6JN
Tel: 0131 336 1115
Contact: Peter Stott Tel: 01292 316968 or Gavin Marwick

McNeill, Brian

Fiddler, multi-instrumentalist and singer. Ex-member and founder of the Battlefield Band. Solo recordings include *Monksgate*, and *The Back o' the North Wind*. Currently a member of Clan Alba. *Back o' the North Wind* is available as an audio-visual show (slides and songs). Sometimes accompanied by guitarist Tony McManus.
Stoneyport Agency, 39 Shandon Crescent, Edinburgh EH11 1QF
Tel: 0131 346 8237 / 313 2083 Fax: 0131 313 2083
Contact: John Barrow

GUITAR

MacArthur, Quee

Bass player, percussionist, composer. Member of Mouth Music. Interested in working in theatre, dance, session work. Soundtracks. Newly formed trio with Michaela Rowan and James MacKintosh.
Flat 6, 28 Rankeillor Street, Edinburgh EH8 9HY
Tel: 0131 667 6450

The Scottish
FIDDLE MUSIC
INDEX
The 18th & 19th Century
Printed Collections

First-ever systematic listing of over 12,000 traditional Scottish dance tune and song air titles (A-Z); where to obtain copies of the music. With tune-finder system for use where tune but not title is known. Details from:
The Amaising Publishing House Ltd., P.O.Box Musselburgh, EH21 7UJ SCOTLAND
Tel: 0131 665 8237
Fax: 0131 665 2582

MANDOLIN

MacKillop, Robert
Mandolin/guitar/lute.
*14 Seaside Place, Aberdour, Fife
KY3 0TX*
Tel: 01383 860178

MELODEON

Crawford, Jim
Over 80 years old and records albums of
melodeon playing for Springthyme
Records. Plays two row B/C Hohner
Double Ray as well as the single row
melodeon.
*Edentown, Ladybank, Cupar, Fife
KY7 7UH*
Tel: 01337 830444
Contact: Springthyme Records
Tel: 01337 830773

PERCUSSION

Bamford, Richard
Freelance percussionist. Played with The
Penguin Café Orchestra, Lost Jockey
Systems Orchestra. More recently played
with Hamish Moore and Dick Lee, and is
currently working with John Purser
recording pre-Christian ringing rocks
music, which will be available on CD.
*80/5 Craigentinny Road, Edinburgh
EH7 6ND*
Tel: 0131 669 1851

Logotse, Amu
Creative and performance artist currently
available for percussion sessions and
workshops on freelance basis.
*Flat 3/1, 4 Ancroft Street, Maryhill,
Glasgow G20 7HU*
Tel: 0141 333 1148

MacKintosh, James
Drummer, percussionist, composer.
Member of Mouth Music, Shooglenifty
and newly formed trio with Michaela
Rowan and Quee MacArthur. Interested
in working in theatre, dance,
sessionwork. Soundtracks. Recent
recording at Real World Studios with
various musicians following the Womad
Festival.
*87 Spottiswood Street, Edinburgh
EH9 1BZ*
Tel: 0131 447 5377

UILEANN PIPES

McNulty, Pat
Concerts, lectures and tuition given.
Music composition in folk and popular
idiom. Recorded 2 albums and 2 cassettes.
Video *The Singing Chanter* to be issued
soon. Fellow of Makers and Researchers
of Historic Instruments.
30 Parkhill Drive, Glasgow G73 2PW
Tel: 0141 647 5163

WHISTLE

Green, Alex
Highly experienced tin whistle player.
Member of duo Airs and Graces with
Madeline Millar (accordion) playing
mainly traditional music and ceilidh music.
15 University Road, Aberdeen AB2 3DQ
Tel: 01224 480549

FEMALE VOCAL

Bell, Hilary
Voice/guitar/flute. Studied Napier College
then RSAMD. Regular concert
performances and broadcasting. Member of
group Sangs and Clatter, bringing
musical performances and pupil
participation into the classroom. Recently
started to write music for The Rowan
Tree Company and involved in the
musical aspects of *The Travels of Mungo
Park*.
*c/o Yarrow Records, The Forge, Yarrow
Valley, Borders TD7 5NE*
Tel: 01750 82254

Bowman, Gill
Singer/songwriter. Traditional and
contemporary music. Has solo albums
City Love (1990 Fellside), *Perfect Lover*
(1994 Greentrax) and *Toasting the Lassies*
(1995 Greentrax), the latter being songs
from a one-woman show about the love-
life of Robert Burns.
*c/o The Stockbridge Music Business, 3
Leslie Place, Edinburgh EH4 1NG*
Tel: 0131 332 7067
*Contact: John Brown or Ian Green
(01875 814155)*

Carr, Romey
New album release on CD and cassette *A
Woman Knows* September 4 1995 on Alba
label. Tours include Scandinavia, South
Africa and Australia, including radio and
TV in all these countries. Formerly
EMI/Columbia recording artist.
*116 Albert Road, Gourock, Inverclyde
PA19 1NW*
Tel: 01475 631362 Fax: 0171 589 6233
*Contact: Michael Barrett (Manager)
Tel: 0171 589 7666*

Douglas, Sheila
Born 1932. Involved in 60s folk revival.
Won and judged TMSA festival
competitions. Visits schools as storyteller/
singer. Performed in many clubs, festivals
and concerts. Many radio broadcasts.
Songbook for schools *Sing a Song of
Scotland*. Other books: *Come Gie's a
Sang* and *The Sang's the Thing*. Cassette
on Scotsoun *The Sang in the Bluid*.
*Merlinwood, 12 Mansfield Road, Scone,
Perth PH2 6SA*
Tel: 01738 551588
*Contact: Scots Language Resource
Centre Tel: 01738 440199*

Fisher, Cilla
Solo singer (unaccompanied). Appears
often with members of her family, Ray
Fisher, and Archie Fisher who provides
guitar accompaniment. She also
performs with her husband Artie Trezize
and Gary Coupland as The Singing
Kettle.
Post House, Kingskettle, Fife KY7 7PN
Tel: 01337 831121 Fax: 01337 831544
Contact: Alan Garratt (General Manager)

Heywood, Heather
Traditional singer, performing largely
Scottish ballads and songs with some
contemporary material. Two albums
available on Greentrax Recordings.
Performs solo and with accompanying
musicians where required. Has done
several radio broadcasts, music for radio
education and one television broadcast.
*16 Annandale Gardens, Crosshouse,
Kilmarnock, Ayrshire KA2 0LE*
Tel: 01563 529902 Fax: 01563 544855
Contact: Peter Heywood (Manager)

Innes, Heather
Varied set of traditional and
contemporary songs reflected in her latest
CD *Caoineadh - Songs from the Heart*
(Fellside). Also sings songs in the early
Celtic Christian tradition. Performs solo
and with a variety of musicians.
*3 Cottage, West Longridge Farm,
Berwick-upon-Tweed TD15 2JX*
Tel: 01764 79465 Fax: 01764 670990

ARTISTS

**FOLK &
TRADITIONAL**

101

ARTISTS

FOLK & TRADITIONAL

Kydd, Christine

Songs from Scotland and beyond, both unaccompanied and plays guitar/piano. Mainly traditional including big ballads, but also contemporary and original material. Plays folk clubs and festivals, leads voice workshops and offers 1 to 1 tuition (holds advanced diploma from Central School of Speech and Drama). CD *Heading Home* (Fellside FECD093).
32 Broughton Place, Edinburgh EH1 3RT
Tel: 0131 557 1334

Macaskill, Ishbel

Traditional Gaelic singer. Solo performer and Gaelic singing tutor at feisean and workshops. Albums include *Sioda* on the Macmeanmna label. Available for concerts and workshops.
c/o MacMeanmna, Quay Brae, Portree, Isle of Skye IV51 9DB
Tel: 01478 612990 Fax: 01478 613263
Contact: Arthur Cormack (Partner) or Blair Douglas (Partner)

MacDougall, Wilma

Graduate of RSAMD (Masters); honours degree dissertation at Anglia University on *The Highland Bagpipes and Scottish Music*. Recently won *Voices of Discovery* competition. Sings at Burns' Nights, Scottish evenings etc. Repertoire also includes classical and modern Scottish music.
73 Finlay Drive (Flat 2/1), Glasgow G31 2QZ
Tel: 0141 554 5075

MacInnes, Mairi

1982, one of youngest winners of Gold Medal at Mod. 1984, winner in Pan Celtic Festival, Kilarney. Often heard on radio and TV, with two solo albums to date. Toured and recorded with Mouth Music. Recent album *This Feeling Inside* mixture of Gaelic and other songs with instrumental backing.
c/o Greentrax Recordings, Cockenzie Business Centre, Edinburgh Road, Cockenzie, East Lothian EH32 0HL
Tel: 01875 814155 Fax: 01875 813545
Contact: Ian D Green

MacKenzie, Talitha

Traditional singer, songwriter and vocal coach. Co-founder of duo Mouth Music, specialising in world music/Gaelic song. Performs solo or with semi-acoustic funk-rock band. Albums: *St James Gate* (Kells); *Shantyman!* (Islander); *Mouth Music* (Triple Earth); *Sòlas* (Riverboat).
33 Millar Crescent (Top Flat), Edinburgh EH10 5HQ
Tel: 0131 447 0091

MacPhee, Catherine-Ann

Gaelic singer from Barra. Played the part of Mairi Mhor nan Oran (Big Mary of the Songs) in John McGrath's play and film, from which the album *Catherine Ann MacPhee Sings Mairi Mhor* was produced (CDTRAX 038). She has also produced albums *Canan Nan Gaidheal* (CDTRAX009) and *Chi Mi'n Geamhradh* (CDTRAX 038).
c/o Greentrax Recordings, Cockenzie Business Centre, Edinburgh Road, Cockenzie, East Lothian EH32 0HL
Tel: 0141 353 1276 Fax: 01875 813545
Contact: Ian Green Tel: 01875 814155

Morrison, Frieda

c/o Dunkeld Records, Cathedral Street, Dunkeld, Perthshire PH8 0AW

Primrose, Christine

From Lewis. Has been winning prizes for Gaelic singing since a child. Has toured extensively. She is also a member of Gaelic group Mac-talla.
c/o Temple House, Shillinghill, Temple, Midlothian EH23 4SH
Tel: 01875 830328 Fax: 01875 830392
Contact: Robin Morton (Manager) or Joyce McMillan (Secretary)

Sandeman, Mary

National Mod Gold medalist. Number 1 hit record in 9 countries with song *Japanese Boy* in 1981. Appeared on radio, TV and in concert throughout the world. Scottish fiddle orchestra, National Trust for Scotland concerts, radio, TV, cabaret and recording work currently undertaken. Repertoire: anything from opera through Scots to comedy.
Croft Shennach, Ardeonaig, by Killin, Perthshire FK21 8SU
Tel: 01567 820481

Wellington, Sheena

Traditional singer and songwriter who has toured in Europe and North America. Broadcaster and radio presenter, television appearances. Albums *Kerelaw* and *Clearsong* on Dunkeld label. Dundee on Campus Radio (Radio Tay). New live album 1995.
6 St Andrews Road, Largoward, Leven, Fife KY9 1HZ
Tel: 01334 840297 Fax: 01334 840297
Contact: M H Wellington (Agent)

Williamson, Ann

Covers Irish, Country, Gospel and Scottish. Has recorded in Ireland and Scotland, and has toured Ireland, America, Canada, Australia and New Zealand and her native country Scotland. Video releases: *A Portrait of Scotland* (VITV574), *Flower of Scotland* (VITV590), and *Amazing Grace* (VITV574).
BGS Productions Ltd, Newtown Street, Kilsyth, Glasgow G65 0JX
Tel: 01236 821081 Fax: 01236 826900
Contact: Norman Scott (Marketing Manager)

MALE VOCAL

Aitken, Joe

Bothy ballads and folk songs from a singer and berryfield farmer. Cassette available on Springthyme Records.
The Cottage, Muirhead of Logie, Kirriemuir, Angus
Tel: 01575 572927
Contact: Springthyme Records Tel: 01773 830773

Blair, Bob

Traditional Scots songs and ballads, both unaccompanied and with concertina or guitar. Featured singer in Balnain House permanent exhibition and was used in John Purser's *Scotland's Music* (BBC Radio Scotland). TV and radio broadcasts. Recordings *McGinn of the Calton* (Greentrax) and *Voices* (Argo). Lectures on folksong and ballads.
8 Melford Avenue, Giffnock, Glasgow G46 6NA
Tel: 0141 638 6589 Fax: 0141 638 6589
Contact: Helen Blair (Agent) or Bob Blair

Bogle, Eric

Vocals/guitar. Scots born singer-songwriter now residing in Australia. UK tours enquiries handled by the Stoneyport Agency. Recordings include *The Eric Bogle Songbook* (Greentrax CTRAX 028). Next tour should be 1997 (approx. every three years).
Stoneyport Agency, 39 Shandon Crescent, Edinburgh EH11 1QF
Tel: 0131 346 8237 (24hr) Fax: 0131 313 2083
Contact: John Barrow

Bruce, Ian

Singer/songwriter and guitarist. Tours extensively in UK, USA and Europe. Live sets include contemporary songs and own compositions. Songwriting workshops offered. Recordings: *Too Far From She*; *Blodwen's Dream*; *Out of Office*; *Free Agent*.
c/o Carrick Music Agency, Whin Cottage, Dundas Street, Comrie, Perthshire PH6 2LN
Tel: 01764 679465 Fax: 01764 670990

Cormack, Arthur

Performer and tutor of Gaelic song. Also works with Blair Douglas and is a member of Mac-talla. Mod Gold medal winner and producer of albums. Has recorded solo albums on Temple Records. Development officer with Feisean nan Gaidheal.
c/o Macmeanma, Quay Brae, Portree, Isle of Skye IV51 9DB
Tel: 01478 612990 Fax: 01478 613263
Contact: Arthur Cormack (Partner) or Blair Douglas (Partner)

Cuffe, Tony

Formerly member of Glasgow based Scots group Ossian. Now lives in USA and visits UK. Vocals with guitar accompaniment.
Stoneyport Agency, 39 Shandon Crescent, Edinburgh EH11 1QF
Tel: 0131 346 8237 (24hr) Fax: 0131 313 2083
Contact: John Barrow

Davies, Bruce

Vocal with 6 and 12 string guitars. Contemporary and traditional songs for all ages. Venues: hotels (tours and business entertainment); theatres (variety shows and fiddlers' rallies); folk clubs; TV (ITV's Scotch and Irish); radio (presenter for Radio Tay). Albums available. Can work acoustically or amplified.
Rothes Recordings, PO Box 7, Glenrothes, Fife KY6 2TA
Tel: 01337 831116

Duncan, Jock

Traditional songs, bothy ballads and the classic ballads from the North East tradition. Records with Springthyme Records.
3b Tummel Crescent, Pitlochry, Perthshire
Tel: 01796 472984
Contact: Springthyme Records
Tel: 01337 830773

Gaughan, Dick

Vocal/guitar. Now a member of Clan Alba.
Stoneyport Agency, 39 Shandon Crescent, Edinburgh EH11 1QF
Tel: 0131 346 8237 Fax: 0131 313 2083
Contact: John Barrow

Hunter, Jim

Jim Hunter learned Highland pipes as a child but in his teens taught himself to play guitar. Songs range from forceful ballads to more rock orientated numbers. Albums available.
c/o Temple Records, Shillinghill, Temple, Midlothian EH23 4SH
Tel: 01875 830328 Fax: 01875 830392
Contact: Robin Morton (Manager) or Joyce McMillan (Secretary)

Johnstone, Arthur

Well-known figure in folk revival in the 60s. Lead singer Laggan, traditional and political band of 70s. Ran Star Folk club for 16 years.Toured Britain, Ireland, Canada and Europe. Currently sings with Star Band. Several albums, most recent solo albums : *North By North* and *Generations Of Change*.
17 Brownlie Street, Mount Florida, Glasgow G42 9BT
Tel: 0141 632 7737
Contact: Rosetta Fitzpatrick

Kyle, Danny

Singer, entertainer, compere. Well-known throughout the folk circuit, and famed for his bizarre choice in ties! Co-presents BBC Radio Scotland's *Travelling Folk* weekly programmes. Director of 4 festivals.
126 Renfrew Road, Paisley PA3 4BL
Tel: 0141 887 9991

Laing, Robin

Singer/songwriter. Spanish guitar. Scottish traditional songs and own compositions.
4 Clifton Hall Mains, Newbridge, Midlothian EH28 8LQ
Tel: 0131 333 2015

McDonald, Alastair

Experienced singer and guitarist, born Glasgow 1941. Many TV and radio appearances including *Songs of Scotland*. Also theatre and pantomime work. Numerous recordings from traditional folksong through Dixieland jazz to original material. Recent release of album *Velvet and Steel*.
Corban Records, PO Box 2, Glasgow G44 3LB

MacKintosh, Iain

Professional folk singer for over 25 years. Has toured widely in Europe and USA to the extent that he is less well-known in the UK (although not true for Scotland). Wide repertoire, good songs old and new with an unerring sense of presentation.
Stoneyport Agency, 39 Shandon Crescent, Edinburgh EH11 1QF
Tel: 0131 346 8237 (24hr) Fax: 0131 313 2083
Contact: John Barrow

Nardini, Peter

A singer/ songwriter whose style has been described as 'Tom Leonard meets Bob Dylan'. Previously performed with the likes of Billy Bragg and Louden Wainwright. His songs conjure up images of Scottish life - sometimes humorous, sometimes satirical, but mostly tender yet poignant. Also an artist and playwright.
c/o Eclectic Records, 3 Chamberlain Road, Edinburgh EH10 4DL
Tel: 0131 229 9299 Fax: 0131 229 9298
Contact: Carolyn Paterson

Noakes, Rab

Eight albums to his credit and several well-known artists have used his songs in performance and on record. Songs deal with many facets of human experience.
The Bechhofer Agency, 51 Barnton Park View, Edinburgh EH4 6HH
Tel: 0131 339 4083
Contact: Frank Bechhofer or Jean Bechhofer

Pearson, Graeme E

Edinburgh-based singer/songwriter. Released début demo *Blood on the Chip Shop Floor* a mix of 8 traditional and original pieces.
Reel Good Music Agency, 6A Argyle Crescent, Joppa, Edinburgh EH15 2QG
Tel: 0131 657 2472 Fax: 0131 657 2472
Contact: Philip M Condie (Agent)

Reid, Jim

Singer/songwriter, musician and former leader of the Foundry Bar Band. Accompanies songs on guitar, mouth-organ and concertina. Three albums with The Foundry Bar Band and two solo recordings including *I Saw the Wild Geese* on Springthyme Records.
c/o Collectables, Letham, Angus
Tel: 01307 818059
Contact: Springthyme Records
Tel: 01337 830773

ARTISTS

FOLK & TRADITIONAL

Scott, Tommy

Producer and songwriter, turned to performing popular traditional Scottish music 1989. Tours of Canada and Scotland in 1994, and South Africa in 1995. Albums and videos available.
BGS Productions Ltd, Newtown Street, Kilsyth, Glasgow G65 0JX
Tel: 01236 821081 Fax: 01236 826900
Contact: Norman Scott (Marketing Manager)

Thomson, Neil

Singer/guitarist performs around the Edinburgh pub/club circuit.
Reel Good Music Agency, 6A Argyle Crescent, Joppa, Edinburgh EH15 2QG
Tel: 0131 657 2472 Fax: 0131 657 2472
Contact: Philip M Condie (Agent)

ARTISTS

FOLK & TRADITIONAL

COMPOSERS & SONGWRITERS

Bamford, Richard

Scottish Arts Council commission saw composition of *Portraits of a Rain Forest*, written using digital recordings of sounds from rain forest of Borneo recorded while composer was visiting the country on educational trip. Performed in Japan, touring Europe 1996/97. Proposed composition based on current pre-Christian project. Also percussion, community music.
80/5 Craigentinny Road, Edinburgh EH7 6ND
Tel: 0131 669 1851

Barnes, David

Composer of Scottish bagpipe music, his tunes are played worldwide. First book published 1995. Also composed words and music for *Sands of Time*, a song reflecting the peace process in N Ireland, recorded by Dysart and Dundonald Pipe Band.
c/o 13 Golf View, Cardenden, Fife KY5 0NW

Cunningham, Phil

Composer, director, producer and performer whose work includes commissioned music for BBC, STV and Channel 4, music for film (20th Century Fox) and theatre. Record production credits include Wolfstone, Connie Dover, Dolores Keane, Altan. Music Director for 4 years on BBC *Hogmanay Live*. Annual concert tour with Aly Bain.
Craig Cottage, Crask of Aigas, Beauly, Inverness-shire IV4 7AD
Tel: 01463 782364 Fax: 01463 782525

Davidson, Lindsay

Pipe Major, B.Mus. (Hons.) P/M with Stockbridge Pipe Band, Edinburgh. Experienced composer of all varieties of pipe music. Presently producing first in series of canntaireachd pipe books. Also composing a ballet, an opera, and other orchestral and electro-acoustic works.
Ferniebank Cottage, Linlithgow, West Lothian EH49 6PL
Tel: 01506 843740

Douglas, Blair

A founder member of Runrig. Developed a solo career as a performer and composer. Responsible for many television theme tunes. Works with Arthur Cormack and the Gaelic band Mac-talla. Available for commissions, has recorded albums on MacMeanmna Records.
c/o Macmeanmna, Quay Brae, Portree, Isle of Skye IV51 9DB
Tel: 01478 612990 Fax: 01478 612990
Contact: Blair Douglas (Partner)

Douglas, Sheila

Involved 60s folk revival as performer, songwriter, organiser and editor. Won and judged TMSA festival competitions. Became full-time writer and performer after taking early retirement from teaching. Music published by Ossian. Cassette on Scotsoun *The Sang in the Bluid*.
Merlinwood, 12 Mansfield Road, Scone, Perth PH2 6SA
Tel: 01738 551588
Contact: Scots Language Resource Centre
Tel: 01738 440199

Hardie, Ian

Two published books of original compositions for fiddle.
Glebe End, Glebe Road, Nairn IV12 4ED
Tel: 01667 455948 Fax: 01667 455529

Hunter, Jim

Jim Hunter's songs range from forceful ballads to more rock orientated numbers. He has made two successful albums and is working on a third. (See also vocal soloists.)
c/o Temple Records, Shillinghill, Temple, Midlothian EH23 4SH
Tel: 01875 830328 Fax: 01875 830392
Contact: Robin Morton (Manager) or Joyce McMillan (Secretary)

Jordan, Lorraine

Singer, songwriter, musician. Contemporary songs with traditional influences. 2 CDs to date - *Inspiration* and *Crazy Guessing Games*. Available with her trio/ 4-piece line-up or as a solo performer.
51 Lorne Street, Edinburgh EH6 8QJ
Tel: 0131 554 1634 Fax: 0131 554 1634

Laing, Robin

Singer/songwriter. Spanish guitar.
4 Clifton Hall Mains, Newbridge, Midlothian EH28 8LQ
Tel: 0131 333 2015

MacLean, Dougie

Contemporary singer/songwriter, more 'Folk/Roots' than 'Folk and Traditional'. Best known for his song *Caledonia*, the music for the film *The Last of the Mohicans*, and the music for *A Scots Quair*. International performer (recently played Carnegie Hall in New York City).
Dunkeld Records, Cathedral Street, Dunkeld, Perthshire PH8 0AW
Tel: 01350 727 686 Fax: 01350 728 606
Contact: Jonathan Moses or Jenny MacLean

Mounsey, Paul

Composer working in commercial music. Has lectured in minimal music, electro-acoustic music and film music in Brazil and the USA, and written for many newspapers and journals on contemporary and Brazilian music. Album *Nahoo* combines traditional Scottish music with modern dance influences. Currently studying Celtic harp and Brazilian percussion.
c/o Iona Records, 27-29 Carnoustie Place, Scotland Street, Glasgow G5 8PH
Tel: 0141 420 1881 Fax: 0141 420 1892
Contact: Linda Mann or Ronnie Simpson

Pegg, Bob

Storytelling in song. Writer and performer on guitar and wind instruments, founder of seminal folk/rock band Mr Fox. Currently musician in residence in Ross and Cromarty. Composer of score for 1994 community production of *Macbeth*. New CD for Rhiannon label due late 1995.
1 Shore Street, Hilton, Tain, Ross and Cromarty IV20 1XD
Tel: 01862 832685

Sutherland, Jim

Experienced composer, producer and musician working across a a wide range of styles. Recorded with the Bhundu Boys, Jimmy Page and Robert Plant, Billy Bragg, and The Chieftains. Produced for Savourna Stevenson, Gordon Duncan, Shooglenifty etc. Composer for film and TV.
5B Union Street, Edinburgh EH1 3LT
Tel: 0131 556 9463

OTHER USEFUL CONTACTS

An Comunn Gaidhealach

Organises the Royal National Mod and coordinates local mods. Can provide information on Gaelic choirs, mod dates etc.
109 Church Street, Inverness

Balnain House: Home of Highland Music

Founded 1993 as a centre for the study and playing of Highland music. The building houses a permanent exhibition and rooms dedicated for performance, study and practice for individual musicians and groups; one of the exhibition spaces also doubles as performance/ceilidh venue. Organises instrumental tuition and workshops, hosts two major festivals, and is a major tour promoter in the region.
40 Huntly Street, Inverness IV3 5HR
Tel: 01463 715757 Fax: 01463 713611
Contact: Caroline Hewat (Asst Manager)

Banff and Buchan District Council

Traditional musician in residence (Tom McKean). Organise events, concerts, classes in instruments, singing, dance, schools workshops etc. Folklore archive in preparation. Series of cassettes and CDs released. Publishes arts magazine three times a year with a section on traditional music and featuring local tradition bearers.
1 Church Street, Macduff AB44 1UR
Tel: 01261 813384
Contact: Ian Macaulay (Arts Development Officer)

Feisean nan Gaidheal

Feisean nan Gaidheal (The National Association of Gaelic Arts Youth Tuition Festivals) is a limited company wholly owned and run by the community-Feisean throughout the country, with an elected Board of Directors, and is managed by the Development Officer. Originally set up to provide a wide range of advice and services to the Feisean there are now various projects for the 1993-97 period, including training for tutors and organisers, fund-raising, directories of tutors, regular newsletters, provision of follow-up tuition for Feis participants, the co-ordination of Feis activities as well as the provision of funding and lobbying of funding bodies. The Gaelic word feis (plural feisean) simply means festival but in the past few years it has been particularly associated with tuition-based festivals. Feisean are generally community based voluntary bodies where people over a wide age range, but primarily young people are offered training in skills in the Gaelic language and its associated traditional music, song and dance. 27 Feisean were held throughout Scotland in 1994. The list of feisean at time of printing was: Feis an Earraich; Feis Rois; Feis Ile; Feis Bharraigh; Feis Chataibh; Feis Strath Fharragaig; Feis na Hearadh; Feis na h-Oige; Feis nan Eilein; Feis Eilean an Fhraoch; Feis Tir an Eorna; Feis Oigridh Ile; Feis Thiriodh; Feis Tir a'Mhurain; Feis Spe; Feis nan Garbh Chriochan; Feis Muile; Feis Arainn; Feis Asainte; Feis Lochaber Beo; Feis Ealan na Hearadh; Feis Latharna; Feis Mhealainis; Feis Dhalriata; Feis nan Gleann; Feis a Bhaile. Contact Feisean nan Gaidheal for up to date details, dates etc.
5 Michell's Lane, Inverness IV2 3HQ
Tel: 01463 234138 Fax: 01463 237470
Contact: Arthur Cormack (Development Officer)

The Glasgow Fiddle Workshop

Established 1994 to offer a facility for people to increase their knowledge of Scottish traditional fiddle styles and learn more about fiddle music and its history. Organises workshops and group excursions. Tutors include Iain Fraser and Amy Mellor.
c/o 10 Sinclair Drive, Glasgow G42 9QE
Tel: 0141 636 1450
Contact: Brenda McCulloch (Secretary) or Iain Fraser Tel: 0141 776 0113

Glasgow Songwriters

Group of singer/songwriters provides an open platform for original live music every Tuesday. Musically and socially members encompass a broad range of backgrounds and influences. They now have their own record label and have released two compilation albums. Doors open to the public and possible new members at 9.30pm, Blackfriars, entrance is free.
c/o Blackfriars, 36 Bell Street, Glasgow G1 1LG
Tel: 0141 552 5924
Contact: Alex Osborne (Chairman) Tel: 0141 647 6406 or Brian McFarlane (Technical Coordinator) Tel: 0141 641 0646

The Living Tradition

Magazine founded 1993 to provide news, reviews and information from the world of traditional music. Circulation: around 10,000. 6 times a year; £2 per issue. Published by Inform (DATA) Ltd, a development agency for traditional arts, which organises concerts and workshops.
PO Box 1026, Kilmarnock, Ayrshire KA2 0LG
Tel: 01292 678277 Fax: 01563 544855
Contact: Pete Heywood (Editor)

Lowland and Border Pipers' Society

Founded 1981 to provide a focus for anyone interested in the lowland pipes and the Scottish small pipes, their history and music. Organizes meetings, recitals and annual conference. Produces a tutor (book) and a twice-yearly magazine, Common Stock.
6 Garrioch Crescent, North Kelvinside, Glasgow G20 8RR
Tel: 0141 946 8624 (eve)
Contact: Rona Macdonald (Publicity)

ARTISTS

FOLK & TRADITIONAL

105

ARTISTS

FOLK &
TRADITIONAL

National Association of Accordion and Fiddle Clubs

Founded early 1970s to promote accordion and fiddle music through its clubs. Publishes monthly newspaper, Box and Fiddle (seven times a year - not summer months) which includes directory of guest artists, news and reviews, and listings of forthcoming events. Available to members and general public on subscription.

63 Station Road, Thankerton, Biggar, Lanarkshire ML12 6NZ
Tel: 018993 08327
Contact: Charles Todd (Secretary) or Ron Ramsay (Editor, Box and Fiddle)
Tel: 01241 879487

North East Scotland Heritage Trust

Aims to develop the appreciation, preservation and promotion of the heritage of the North East. Hopes to act as a catalyst for the wide range of cultural activities and to provide a database of traditional writers, singers, musicians, artists and craftsmen currently at work in the area. Also run the Heritage Arts Regeneration Project (HARP).

Town House, The Square, Kintore, Inverurie, Aberdeenshire AB51 0US
Tel: 01467 633640 Fax: 01467 633640
Contact: Sandra Morrison (Development Officer) or Elaine McGregor (Secretary)

The Piobaireachd Society

Formed 1902 to promote the research and performance of piobaireachd. Publish music, and produce monthly magazine *The Piping Times*. Provide judges for piobaireachd competitions and organise annual conference (March/April).

16-24 Otago Street, Glasgow G12 8JH
Tel: 0141 334 3587 Fax: 0141 337 3024
Contact: Seumas MacNeill (Secretary)

The Royal Scottish Pipe Band Association

Founded 1920 to promote and organise pipe band competitions. Has 12 branches covering the whole of the UK and has 380 bands in membership. Publish a bi-monthly magazine, *The Pipe Band*, with world-wide readership. Branches run educational courses throughout UK and a week-long Summer School is held in Glasgow each year in July. Also publishes piping and drumming tuition books which are used as basis for examinations in various parts of the world.

45 Washington Street, Glasgow G3 8AZ
Tel: 0141 221 5414 Fax: 0141 221 1561
Contact: J Mitchell Hutcheson (Executive Officer) or Sandra Boyle (Admin Assistant)

The Royal Scottish Piper's Society

Formed 1881 to encourage the playing of the great highland bagpipe amongst gentlemen together with the study of its music. Private club for amateur pipers with both playing and non-playing members. Membership is by election. Sponsors recitals by leading professional players and provides prizes at some of the top competitions.

127 Rose St, South Lane, Edinburgh EH2 4BB
Contact: J J Burnet (Hon Secretary)
Tel: 0131 552 5231

Shetland Musical Heritage Trust

The Trust, created in 1985, is designed to protect and publish the unique archive of traditional fiddle music collected over 40 years by the late Dr. Tom Anderson M.B.E., augmented by the collections of other prominent researchers.

5 Burns Lane, Lerwick ZE1 0EJ
Tel: 01595 696349 Fax: 01595 696349
Contact: Mrs Judy Nicolson (Archivist)

Sounding Strings

The only European magazine dedicated to the non-pedal harp in all its various forms, from clarsach to Paraguayan. Published quarterly, it has an international readership of professional and amateur players of all standards. It incorporates a mail-order catalogue of music and recordings.

PO Box 12508, Bathgate, West Lothian EH48 3YA
Tel: 01501 731809 Fax: 01501 731809

Traditional Music and Song Association

The Traditional Music and Song Association (TMSA) of Scotland is the leading organisation in the promotion, preservation and presentation of Scotland's traditional music, song, story and dance.

Greenside House, 25 Greenside Place, Edinburgh EH1 3AA
Tel: 0131 557 8484
Contact: Lindsay Lewis (National Organiser)

106

Jazz in Scotland

by Kenny Mathieson

The situation of jazz in Scotland has improved radically in the past decade. The change reflects a general resurgence of interest in the music which began in the mid-1980s, following a relatively stagnant period during the 1970s, particularly for acoustic jazz. As the fusion decade departed, however, jazz began to bite back on both sides of the Atlantic, and Scotland benefited from that development in several ways.

Platform Jazz, the principal promoting organisation (which has now been superseded by **Assembly Direct**) began to feature bigger names from the international jazz scene, and it was soon augmented by an expanding **Edinburgh Jazz Festival**, and the arrival of the **Glasgow Jazz Festival** in 1987.

The presence of everyone from Miles Davis down on Scottish stages undoubtedly acted as a catalyst for the local scene, and as media interest - including a brief but useful flirtation with the style media - burgeoned, so more and more young musicians began to discover an interest in jazz, and, more importantly, increasing opportunities to develop that interest.

The much-publicised rise of saxophonist Tommy Smith was another important catalyst in all this, and a number of other young musicians have followed his path to the Berklee College in Boston, including pianist Steve Hamilton and drummer Paddy Flaherty, with saxophonists Laura MacDonald and Gail McArthur and trombonist Nicol Thompson currently taking up scholarships there.

Pianists Brian Kellock and Chick Lyall, guitarists Kevin MacKenzie and Nigel Clark, trumpeter Colin Steele, saxophonists Phil Bancroft and Russell Cowieson, and drummer Tom Bancroft have all made a significant mark, working in a wide variety of styles and idioms, from contemporary pop through to free improvisation.

An even newer wave of players working in the central jazz idioms, led by pianist David Milligan, now seems poised to join that list, while musicians from an older generation have also benefited from the general raising of both standards and interest, not to mention the increase in places to play.

There have been a number of exciting experiments at the intersection of jazz and folk or ethnic music as well, from the likes of the Cauld Blast Orchestra, Mike Travis's EH 15, Savourna Stevenson, Dick Lee and Hamish Moore, and Melanie O'Reilly, and it may be that this will prove to be one of the significant musical directions of the present decade.

A significant proportion of the new audience for jazz is being attracted to the music through the club scene, where jazz collides head-on with contemporary black dance music forms like rap and hip hop. There had been little evidence of that interest translating to the live music scene until the end of 1994, with the formation of the Edinburgh-based sextet Freshly Squeezed, which combines jazz musicians with rappers in performance.

There is arguably more jazz activity - and certainly more wide-ranging jazz activity - in Scotland now than at any time, but that expansion brings its own problems. The growth in jazz education may shortly present a quandary which would have seemed a remote possibility a decade ago, that of having more talented musicians emerging from organisations like the **Fife and Strathclyde Youth Orchestras** than the scene can comfortably absorb in its present form.

With a new National Jazz and Creative Music School due to be launched in

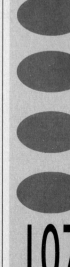

January at **Jordanhill College** to augment initiatives like the **Lothian and Aberdeen Jazz Schools**, the need to expand the infrastructure even further may become additionally pressing.

With the exception of Tommy Smith, almost none of the artists mentioned above has yet had the chance to make a significant recording, or to play with any degree of regularity outside Scotland. It would be a great shame if they had to take the traditional route of moving to London to achieve that exposure.

While it is difficult to foresee any considerable expansion of the domestic market from its present levels, **Assembly Direct**'s recent move to open touring circuits in France and Germany may help to find outlets for some of these musicians.

Nonetheless, there is now a talent pool of real depth and variety here, and many more opportunities to play on the club, concert and festival circuit, not only in the major cities, but also in less obvious places like Nairn, Bute, Girvan and Dunoon. The progress which that seems to represent is very real, but jazz remains conspicuously underfunded in relation to classical music, and nothing can be taken for granted in the drive to maintain that forward momentum.

ARTISTS

JAZZ

AGENTS

Glasgow Jazz Services

Jazz consultants, small venue promotion, co-operative band agency. All styles accommodated. Gigs available for MU members. Demos, tapes. Bookings accepted Greater Glasgow area. 'Sole agent' Pizza Express (Scotland).
Tel: 0141 649 4044 (afternoons only)
Contact: Mr Zigman

Ibis Productions

Represents Tommy Smith, Martin Taylor, Lammas, Dave O'Higgins Quartet, Bob Brozman.
East Balbridie, Crathes, Banchory, Aberdeen AB31 3JB
Tel: 01330 844456 Fax: 01330 844435
Contact: Ian Middleton

DUOS

Nigel Clarke and Dominic Ashworth

Guitar duo.
15 Seil Drive, Glasgow G44 5DU
Tel: 0141 637 0071
Contact: Nigel Clark or Dominic Ashworth

TRIOS

Green Room

Chick Lyall (keyboards/composer); David Baird (multi-instrumentalist); Dave Garrett (percussion). Instruments include piano, computer driven sound synthesis, samples, electric viol, Chapman stick and various originally built instruments, percussion and prepared piano frame.
171A Maryhill Road, Glasgow G20 7XL
Tel: 0141 332 9468
Contact: Chick Lyall

Hamish Moore, Dick Lee and Rick Bamford

Trio which twists and birls the wilder abundances of jazz and folk - not folk with a jazz tinge nor vice versa.
1 Cheyne Street, Edinburgh EH4 1JA
Tel: 0131 332 8083 Fax: 0131 332 8083
Contact: Dick Lee or Maggie Moore
Tel: 01350 727474

Savourna Stevenson Trio

The Old School, Stobo EH45 8NU
Tel: 01721 760298 Fax: 01721 760298
Contact: Mark Norris (Manager)

Suzanne Bonnar Trio

Top Left, 49 Peel Street, Partick, Glasgow G11 5LU
Tel: 0141 339 3457
Contact: Suzanne Bonnar

Tommy Smith's Forward Motion

Saxophone/bass/drums - Tommy Smith, Terje Gewelt, Ian Froman. International chamber jazz ensemble, originally formed at Berklee College in Boston as a quartet. The band later re-grouped as a trio. Their music brings together the diverse influences of contemporary jazz with music derived from European folk traditions. Recently released their first recording, *Reminiscence* (Linn Records, 1994).
Tel: 0141 424 1026 Fax: 0141 423 5747

GROUPS

The Alex Dalgleish All Stars

The All Stars are selected from a regular nucleus plus a pool of enthusiasts, equally at home with New Orleans, Kansas City, Chicago and Mainstream to Modern Jazz inspired by Armstrong, Bix, Hackett, Teagarden etc. Available for jazz clubs, concerts, formal occasions of every kind, small functions, house parties etc.
Tel: 0141 637 5334
Contact: Alex Dalgleish

Bobby Wishart Jazz Quintet

Performs music from BeBop and contemporary jazz repertoire. Have toured UK and performed on national TV and radio. Present clinics and workshops for schools, colleges and in-service courses. Bobby Wishart teaches jazz improvisation at RSAMD and the new National Jazz Institute at University of Strathclyde.
200 Greenock Road, Largs KA30 8SB
Tel: 01475 686993 Fax: 01475 675917
Contact: Bobby Wishart

The Cauld Blast Orchestra

Eight-piece band, jazz and folk sources using reeds, strings, brass, piano, concertina and drums. Two albums: *Savage Dance* (Eclectic 1990) and *Durga's Feast* (Eclectic 1994). Appearances include: WOMAD, TDK Round Midnight Jazz Festival, Celtic Connections etc.
c/o Eclectic Records, 3 Chamberlain Road, Edinburgh EH10 4DL
Tel: 0131 229 9299 Fax: 0131 229 9298
Contact: Carolyn Paterson or Mike Travis Tel: 0131 669 1389

Dick Lee's Chamber Jazz

Winners of BBC Radio 2 National Big Band Competition (1988). Ensemble of 15 players drawn from the worlds of classical, jazz and folk music. Repertoire consists mainly of original compositions for the group by Dick Lee. Featured soloists include John Kenny (trombone), William Sweeney (bass clarinet), Phil Bancroft (tenor saxophone) and Hamish Moore (bagpipes).
1 Cheyne Street, Edinburgh EH4 1JA
Tel: 0131 332 8083 Fax: 0131 332 8083
Contact: Dick Lee

The Easy Club

Jazz/folk. Rod Paterson, Jim Sutherland, Jack Evans and John Martin. Blend of Scottish rhythm and swing. Album *Essential* is on Eclectic Records.
c/o Eclectic Records, 3 Chamberlain Road, Edinburgh EH10 4DL
Tel: 0131 229 9299 Fax: 0131 229 9298
Contact: Carolyn Paterson or Jim Sutherland (Group Member) Tel: 0131 556 9463 0131 553 5429

Groove Juice Special

8 piece group (plus vocalist Kate McNab) - tuneful mainstream jazz. Over 6 appearances at Edinburgh and Glasgow Jazz Festivals, over 100 BBC Radio 2 broadcasts, and major billing throughout the Continent. Available for major events - either on its own, or in one of the several shows it mounts with the vocal trio Sweet Substitute and / or the dance company The Jiving Lindy Hoppers.
30 Royal Circus, Edinburgh EH3 6SS
Tel: 0131 226 3967
Contact: Ralph M Laing

Michael Marra and his Band

Blues-style band.
c/o Eclectic Records, 3 Chamberlain Road, Edinburgh EH10 4DL
Tel: 0131 229 9299 Fax: 0131 229 9298
Contact: Carolyn Paterson

ARTISTS

JAZZ

109

Mike Travis' EH15

Original music, jazz with world influences. *The View from Where* is available on Eclectic Records.
c/o Eclectic Records, 3 Chamberlain Road, Edinburgh EH10 4DL
Tel: 0131 229 9299 Fax: 0131 229 9298
Contact: Carolyn Paterson or Mike Travis Tel: 0131 669 1389

Nigel Clark Quintet

Guitar/saxophone/piano/bass guitar/drums - Nigel Clark, Tim Garland, Brian Kellock, Andy Mitchell, Mike Bradley. One of the most popular electric jazz bands in the UK.
15 Seil Drive, Glasgow G44 5DU
Tel: 0141 637 0071
Contact: Nigel Clarke

Northern College Swing Band

Ensemble made up of staff and students at the Northern College - music ranging from Ellington and Basie to Bacharach and Grusin.
Northern College Aberdeen Campus, Hilton Place, Aberdeen AB9 1FA
Tel: 01224 283500 Fax: 01224 283576
Contact: Pete Stollery (Performance Co-ordinator) or Dundee Campus Tel: 01382 464000

Phil Mason's New Orleans All Stars

Formed in 1993. Together with their black gospel/blues singer Christine Tyrrell are a popular traditional jazz band playing festivals and clubs in Europe.
Shalunt, Isle of Bute PA20 0QL
Tel: 0170084 1283 Fax: 0170050 5313
Contact: Phil Mason

Ralph Laing Quartet

Ralph Laing is a pianist, and a visiting lecturer in jazz improvisation and jazz history at the University of Warwick. His quartet plays tuneful night-club jazz - piano, bass, drums and tenor saxophone, and is suitable for relaxed, convivial events.
30 Royal Circus, Edinburgh EH3 6SS
Tel: 0131 226 3967
Contact: Ralph M Laing

Sophie Bancroft and Gina Rae

Contemporary music with jazz, folk, soul and world music influences. All original material. Work as a duo but also as a six-piece band.
Rock House, 26 Caltonhill, Edinburgh EH1 3BJ
Tel: 0131 558 3586

Spirits of Rhythm Jazz Band

New Orleans Dixieland traditional jazz band based in Edinburgh. Plays at jazz festivals both home and abroad, and at local jazz scene in Edinburgh. Line up - drums, piano, bass, banjo, trumpet, trombone, reeds, alto sax.
Reel Good Music Agency, 6A Argyle Crescent, Joppa, Edinburgh EH15 2QG
Tel: 0131 657 2472 Fax: 0131 657 2472
Contact: Philip M Condie (Agent)

Sweet Substitute

Close harmony vocal jazz group, with a host of TV and radio appearances, and concert performances on 4 continents. The group normally appears backed by Groove Juice Special, but in more intimate locations works with a smaller band.
30 Royal Circus, Edinburgh EH3 6SS
Tel: 0131 226 3967
Contact: Ralph M Laing

Swing 95

Formed 15 years ago to play small group swing jazz. Dick Lee (sax/recorder), John Russell (acoustic rhythm guitar), Phil Adams (electric solo guitar) and Roy Percy (double bass). Varied programme, with the music of Django Reinhardt, Stephane Grapelli and the Quintette of the Hot Club of France at its core.
1 Cheyne Street, Edinburgh EH4 1JA
Tel: 0131 332 8083 Fax: 0131 332 8083
Contact: Dick Lee or Roy Percy Tel: 0131 652 1131

Tam White Shoestring Band; Tam White Eco Drive; Tam White Big Bonus.

Tam White fills halls almost anywhere in Scotland. A past-master entertainer, Tam sings the blues like he has known it (and he has - ask him!). The Shoestring Band is an acoustic trio; The 5-piece Eco Drive includes Jim Mullen on lead guitar and involves a Hammond organ; Big Bonus is the cookingest, funkiest 8-piece band and deserves wider recognition.
Stoneyport Agency, 39 Shandon Crescent, Edinburgh EH11 1QF
Tel: 0131 346 8237 Fax: 0131 313 2083
Contact: John Barrow

Tommy Smith Quartet

Tommy Smith / Kenny Wheeler / Lars Damielsson / Jon Christensen.
Tel: 0141 424 1026 Fax: 0141 423 5747

Tommy Smith Sextet

10 Belmont Street, Aberdeen AB1 1JE
Tel: 0131 621188 Fax: 0131 621218
Contact: Ian Middleton / D Hendry

Uptown Shufflers

Known throughout Strathclyde Region and beyond, playing mainly acoustic performances at such venues as the Hamilton and Ayr race courses, on a regular basis. Other open air events include garden parties, regattas, jazz festivals, flower shows and parades.
19 Kensington Gate, Glasgow G12 9LQ
Tel: 0141 334 1790
Contact: Dave Wilson

BIG BANDS

Bob Peter Big Band

Available for commercial work i.e. dance promotional etc. with video and tape. Third place in BBC Radio 2 Big Band competition. Under the Bob Peter name there are bands from 9-17 piece 'Beatles', 'Miller', 'Basie' etc.
12 Nether, Craigour, Edinburgh EH17 7SB
Tel: 0131 477 1872
Contact: Bob Peter or Davie Swanson Tel: 0131 554 1924

Edinburgh Jazz Orchestra

Band of 15-21 musicians, play EIJF and others. Play charts by Monk, M Davis, Rob McConnell etc. A modern style of big band, available for work in jazz clubs and festivals etc.
12 Nether, Craigour, Edinburgh EH17 7SB
Tel: 0131 477 1872
Contact: Bob Peter

Edinburgh University Jazz Orchestra

Rehearsals: 6.30-9.30pm Thursdays, Reid Concert Hall.
c/o Faculty of Music, Alison House, Nicolson Square, Edinburgh EH8 9DF

George Ogilvie's Dixieland Band

Been around for a long time and been around the country too, from Inverness to Carlisle and Dunbar to Oban, playing at all types of functions from jazz clubs to weddings and concerts. Also shared the bill with Kenny Ball, Acker Bilk, Dutch Swing College and Joe Loss.
59 Netherhill Avenue, Netherlee G44 3XF
Tel: 0141 637 1633
Contact: George Ogilvie

ARTISTS

JAZZ

Glasgow University Big Band

Repertoire from Ellington to the present. Auditions held at beginning of October. Rehearsals: Wednesdays, 5.30 - 7pm, Concert Hall. Termly subscription.
c/o The Concerts Organiser, University Concerts Office, 14 University Gardens, Glasgow G12 8QE
Tel: 0141 330 4092 Fax: 0141 307 8018
Contact: Concerts Organiser or Graham Hair (Director)

Napier University Big Band

A 19-piece jazz ensemble, largely made up of students on the two-year Music Diploma/HND course at Napier University. The band performs regularly in public; their repertoire is eclectic, covering everything from old favourites to specially-written new compositions.
21 Sloan Street, Edinburgh EH6 8PN
Tel: 0131 554 9245 Fax: 0131 455 3515
Contact: J Simon van der Walt (Director)

Strathclyde University Big Band

24 piece band performing adaptations of pieces played by leading American big bands (such as Count Basie, Buddy Rich, Stan Kenton and Woody Herman) as well as arrangements designed for the developing jazz ensemble. Rehearsals: Mondays, 6.30-8.30pm. Annual membership fee, concession for students.
Director of Music, University of Strathclyde, Livingstone Tower, Richmond St, Glasgow G1 1XH
Tel: 0141 552 4400 x3444 Fax: 0141 552 4053
Contact: Alan Tavener (Director of Music)

BASS

Cooper, Lindsay L

Bass player, tubaist, composer and occasional bandleader. Main influences: New Orleans jazz, Japanese folk music and Thelonious Monk. Many recordings with traditional and free improvisers, also *Tubular Bells*. Last album *All* (1993), 4 Stars *Downbeat* magazine. Recognises no boundaries in music.
50 King's Road, Potobello, Edinburgh EH15 1DX
Tel: 0131 669 8097

Ronnie, Rae

Experienced bass player - played with just about everybody including many visiting American artist. Radio, TV broadcasts etc.
The Nest, Portincaple, Dumbartonshire G84 0EU
Tel: 01436 810752

CLARINET

Lee, Dick

Plays a wide variety of musical styles, ranging from performances of the classical repertoire (baroque to contemporary) with the SCO and Schola Cantorum to folk and jazz with groups such as the Hamish Moore/Dick Lee Duo, Chamber Jazz, and Swing 95.
1 Cheyne Street, Edinburgh EH4 1JA
Tel: 0131 332 8083

GUITAR

Cowan, Francis

Performs at Jazz Festivals and Art venues both as a soloist, and with his own ensembles, with arrangements for various numbers of up to 10 players.
23 Gillespie Crescent, Edinburgh EH10 4HU
Tel: 0131 229 8131
Contact: Francis Cowan

Mackenzie, Kevin

Played with Strathclyde Youth Jazz Orchestra, John Rae Collective, and Tom Bancroft Orchestra. Received SAC Jazz Project grant in 1993. Currently working with Simon Thoumire 3. Composes also and runs own projects involving various band. Also folk and funk.
22 Belmont Gardens, Edinburgh EH12 6JH
Tel: 0131 337 4571

HARP

Hewat, Corrina Dawn

Studied with Sanchia Pielou, Savourna Stevenson and Máiri ní Chathasaigh and has a 1st class honours degree in Jazz (City of Leeds College of Music). Plays with Bachué Café, a folk/jazz quintet and Seannachie, a folk based band.
c/o Cullicudden Schoolhouse, Culbokie, The Black Isle IV7 8LL
Tel: 0134 9877434

Stevenson, Savourna

Experienced and versatile exponent of the Celtic harp. First album *Tickled Pink* (Springthyme); next three *Tweed Journey*, *Cutting the Chord*, and *Tusitala Teller of Tales* (Eclectic Records). Composition commissions include 4 productions for Edinburgh Royal Lyceum Theatre, works for Space Dance Theatre, Borders Youth Theatre, Borders Dance Festival and David Massingham Dance. Also TV commissions.
The Old School, Stobo, Peebleshire EH45 8NU
Tel: 01721 760298 Fax: 01721 760298
Contact: Mark Norris (Manager)

PERCUSSION

Bancroft, Tom

The leading influence behind the Tom Bancroft Band and the French-Scottish band Kiltcouture. Keen session musician.
Birkhedges Cottage, Spittalrig, Nr Haddington EH41 3SU
Tel: 0162 0826613 Fax: 0162 0826613

Travis, Mike

Experienced musician. London: Jon Hedrix, Hugh Hopper, Stomu Yamashta. Scotland: own band EH15, Cauld Blast Orchestra, Clan Alba, Savourna Stevenson, and many jazz and blues greats. Theatre: Lyceum, Communicado, Bill Bryden's *The Ship*, *The Big Picnic*. TV, radio, recordings with most of above. Experienced workshop leader jazz and acoustic.
3 Woodside Terrace, Edinburgh EH15 2JB
Tel: 0131 669 1389

PIANO

James, Ken

Mainly solo work, some duo. Music of McLaughlan, Weather Report era. Jazz/ Indian/Arabic/Flamenco fusion.
1/1 Avrilhill, Kilbirnie, Ayrshire KA25 6BN
Tel: 01505 684746

ARTISTS

JAZZ

111

ARTISTS

JAZZ

Michael, Richard
Specialises in jazz improvisation. Directs Fife Youth Jazz Orchestra and is Director of the National Youth Orchestra of Scotland's Jazz Course. Publications: *Jazz Beginnings* (Lomond Music) and *Creative Jazz Education* (Stainer and Bell - with Scott Stroman). Has given solo concerts throughout Scotland. Will improvise on themes suggested by the audience in any of 12 keys.
6 Dronachy Road, Kirkcaldy, Fife KY2 5QL
Tel: 01592 263087

Milligan, David
Studied 4 years at City of Leeds College of Music, on the Jazz and Contemporary Music course (piano and keyboards). Currently based in Edinburgh, doing a variety of work ranging from writing and arranging to performing with local musicians and visiting artists (including various tours and radio broadcasts). Works solo/duo/trio/quartet or ensemble.
6A Regent Terrace, Edinburgh EH7 5BN
Tel: 0131 558 3675

Paterson, Foss
Piano/keyboards. Toured five years with John Martyn, also toured and recorded with Fish, Julia Fordham and Any Trouble, among others.
101 Lothian Street, Bonnyrigg, Midlothian EH19 3AG
Tel: 0131 663 9323
Contact: Foss Paterson

SAXOPHONE

Bancroft, Phil
Has the Phil Bancroft Octet and the Big Chebang. Also involved in the trio AAB.
26 Caltonhill, Edinburgh EH1 3BJ
Tel: 0131 556 9448

Smith, Tommy
Saxophone/flute/clarinet. Worked with Chick Corea and Gary Burton. Has recorded, over the last decade, 15 albums. Several albums on Bluenote: *Step by Step, Peeping Tom, Standards* and *Paris.* Currently signed with Linn Records.
Tel: 0141 424 1026

TROMBONE

Kirkwood, Derick
Former principal trombone with Dalmellington Band. Currently leader/musical director of the ensemble Glasgow Computing Brass. Plays any type of music, but mainly classical, light and jazz. Can improvise. Also composes for a variety of groups.
38 Harris Close, Newton Mearns, Glasgow G77 6TU
Tel: 0141 639 2504

TRUMPET

Dalgleish, Alex
Jazz trumpet player and peripatetic teacher. Previously played with Terry Lightfoot. Has also worked with Louis Armstrong, Bobby Hackett, Peanuts Hucko, Yank Lawson, Red Allen, Zutty Singleton, Kenny Baker, Chris Barber, Humphrey Littleton, Kenny Ball, Acker Bilk, Alex Welsh - to name just a few!
86 Alyth Crescent, Clarkston, Glasgow G76 8PB
Tel: 0141 637 5334

FEMALE VOCAL

Bancroft, Sophie
Performs own music. Previous career as a jazz singer, mainstream to modern. Also takes vocal workshops.
Rock House, 26 Caltonhill, Edinburgh EH1 3BJ
Tel: 0131 558 3586

Bonnar, Suzanne
Two TV documentaries - *Fly Me To Dunoon* and *The Blacksburg Connection.* Also broadcast on Radio 2 with the BBC Big Band and Midweek on Radio 4. Various broadcasts on Radio Scotland.
Top Left, 49 Peel Street, Partick, Glasgow G11 5LU
Tel: 0141 339 3457

Duncan, Fionna
40 years of professional experience. Runs the late night Jazz Club at the Glasgow festival as well as vocal jazz workshops. Busy touring schedule, radio and TV broadcasts etc.
The Nest, Portincaple, Dumbartonshire G84 0EU
Tel: 01436 810752

Kidd, Carol
Sings covers of Porter, Gershwin, Berlin etc. Supported Frank Sinatra at his 1990 Ibrox appearance. Albums (Linn Records) include *The Night We Called it a Day* (1990). Best Vocalist: Edinburgh Festival Critics Award 1990 and 1991; Cannes European Jazz Awards 1991; British Jazz Awards 1992 and 1994.
c/o Mackay, 45 Milton Avenue, St Neot's, Cambridgeshire PE19 3LH
Tel: 01480 76325 Fax: 01480 215969
Contact: John Mackay

O'Reilly, Melanie
A native of Dublin based in Scotland, Melanie has appeared with : Benny Waters, Martin Taylor, Alec Dankworth and others. Best known as jazz singer. Studied with vocalist Sheila Jordan in New York. Latest project brings together jazz influences and Celtic roots resulting in début CD *Tir na Mara/ The Sea Kingdom.* Self-penned new material drawn from Irish myth, poetry and history.
19 Briarbank Terrace, Shandon, Edinburgh EH11 1SU
Tel: 0131 337 3251 Fax: 0131 337 3251

Rae, Sylvia
Member of the Rae clan, Sylvia has been singing since the age of 14. Equally at home singing a country ballad and a hard driving jazz tune. Currently working with The Brian Kellock Trio (jazz), Someotherland (folk/groove/jazz),The Pink Oblong Club(country). Recent Edinburgh Festival Fringe début.
35 Eastfield, Joppa, Edinburgh EH15 2PN
Tel: 0131 669 3819

MALE VOCAL

McMurdo, Craig

Blend of crooning vocals, tongue in cheek humour and music supplied by backing band That Swing Thing. Available for corporate entertainment, theatre dates, festivals, television and radio.
5/5 Glenogle Road, Edinburgh EH3 5HW
Tel: 0131 557 5767

Marra, Michael

Vocals/piano, singer/songwriter, with his own brand of Scottish soul. Solo or with his blues band. Has shared the stage with Deacon Blue (UK and European tour), Gallagher and Lyle, Hue and Cry, Gary Clark and The Cauld Blast Orchestra.
c/o Eclectic Records, 3 Chamberlain Road, Edinburgh EH10 4DL
Tel: 0131 229 9299

COMPOSERS & SONGWRITERS

Bancroft, Phil

Writes all the music for the Phil Bancroft Octet and the Big Chebang. Has received regular commissions.
26 Caltonhill, Edinburgh EH1 3BJ
Tel: 0131 556 9448

Bancroft, Sophie

Writes songs with jazz, folk, soul and world music influences.
Rock House, 26 Caltonhill, Edinburgh EH1 3BJ
Tel: 0131 558 3586

Bancroft, Tom

Composes original contemporary jazz, and is regularly commissioned. Leading influence behind the Tom Bancroft Band.
Birkhedges Cottage, Spittalrig, nr Haddington EH41 3SU
Tel: 0162 0826613 Fax: 0162 0826613

Beauvoisin, Allon

Composer/arranger and saxophonist, plays with Hung Drawn Quartet whose CD includes some of his work. Recent commissions include music for the *Harris Weaving Project* promotional video and big band music for Strathclyde Arts Centre jazz Band. (Final year B.Mus. student, Glasgow University.)
38 Clarinda Court, Harestanes, Kirkintilloch G66 2SD

Lee, Dick

Recent works include commissions from ECAT (*Sliding Scale* 1989), the Edinburgh Folk Festival (*Bagpipe Concerto* 1990), The Lemon Tree Trust (Lemon Tree Samba, 1993), and the SAC (via a composer's bursary) (Mass Medium 1995, for flute and computer-generated sounds). Film/TV scores and bagpipe music are specialities.
1 Cheyne Street, Edinburgh EH4 1JA
Tel: 0131 332 8083

Michael, Richard

Born Stonehaven. Educated Mackie Academy, graduated RSAMD 1971. Currently Head of Music at Beath High School, Cowdenbeath; Director of Fife Youth Jazz Orchestra; Director of the National Youth Orchestra of Scotland's Jazz Course; and a freelance composer and jazz educator. Writing a jazz piano syllabus for the Associated Board.
6 Dronachy Road, Kirkcaldy, Fife KY2 5QL
Tel: 01592 263087

Paterson, Foss

Film score *Double X* (for Virgin Films) as well as numerous TV and corporate work.
101 Lothian Street, Bonnyrigg, Midlothian EH19 3AG
Tel: 0131 663 9323
Contact: Foss Paterson

Robb, Graham

Jazz and commercial music. 1970s - recording / broadcast by Head, Windjammer, SAC commission *Above The Hill*. TV series *The Standard*. Theatre projects. 1980s - Dundee Rep. *How Handsome To Be Seen, The Tempest.* TV series *Education Extra*. 1990s - Radio commercials. Jazz education music published, Faber Music. Commercial music, DSM Producers, New York. Projects for the internet.
Tigh-na-Beithe, Birnam Glen, Birnam, Dunkeld, Perthshire PH8 0BW
Tel: 01350 727371 / 0378 616151 (mobile) Fax: 01350 727371

Smith, Tommy

Born Edinburgh 1967. Saxophonist/composer. Commissions include: suites for sextet *Misty Morning* and *No Time*, *Tribute* for brass quartet and *Scotland's Winter* for big band.
Glasgow,
Tel: 0141 424 1026 Fax: 0141 423 5747

Wells, Bill

Bandleader, composer, arranger. The Bill Wells Octet, Quartet and Big Band. Plays electric bass, guitar and keyboards. May 1995 set up his own record label, Loathsome Reels. First release *The Bill Wells Octet Live* 1993-94. Compositions combine wide ranging influences with freedom for improvisation/ interaction. *Loathesome Reels, PO Box 14864, Falkirk FK1 1ZA*
Tel: 01324 624120

ARTISTS
JAZZ

Light Music in Scotland

by Iain Sutherland

I am delighted to contribute an introductory article on Light Music for this new and welcome Handbook. Having been involved with most aspects of light music throughout my professional life, I have decided to present my overview of the subject in a subjective way.

All categorical appellations are ill-defined at their outer limits, but perhaps 'light' music, as opposed to 'classical', 'rock', 'pop', or 'country' is the most difficult of all to pin down in that it will, inevitably, being popular, touch upon them all. It is also the only name which, when applied to the substantial area of 'classical' music which it overlaps, is used as a pejorative. However, such usage usually denotes in the user an inability to distinguish between a developed opinion and an innate prejudice.

So, what is 'light music'?

For the purposes of this article, light music will include orchestral compositions, songs, opera, operetta, musicals, and orchestrations and arrangements of vocal and instrumental music prepared for performance by and for every conceivable combination of voices and instruments, from an unaccompanied fiddle to a full symphony orchestra. All compositions otherwise classified as 'classical' could be referred to as light music, in which the emotions of the listener are engaged directly, without requiring to appreciate the intellectual arguments and architectural forms employed by the composer. Rather like looking upon Loch Lomond in the sunset and being moved by the beauty, without rehearsing the geological and meteorological reasons for the beauty. Apply this yardstick, and much, if not all, of the most beloved of the 'classical' repertoire would belong to the 'light' category. Even Tovey, comparing the symphonies of Brahms and Tchaikovsky, remarked that the former were eclipsed by the latter in their day, and concludes, 'Of course they were, for they were not light music.'

The categorisation of light music as something separate from the mainstream is surely a recent development; reference to concert programmes up to the First World War, at least, will attest to that. Like the Queens Hall Orchestra in London, all around the UK, particularly during the summer months, orchestras were engaged at the fashionable spas and seaside resorts, and in the grander hotels, to perform concerts of light music and play for the grand ball or the 'Thé Dansant'. Gleneagles Hotel in Perthshire earned a place for Scotland in the early history of the broadcasting of popular music in this way. Henry Hall, the popular dance band leader at Gleneagles during the 1920s so impressed the managers of John Reith's early **British Broadcasting Corporation** (**BBC**) that he was invited to London to form the first BBC Dance Orchestra, at a time when the burgeoning new national broadcasting system was setting up new orchestras for studio broadcasting, as opposed to 'outside broadcasting', throughout the country. In Scotland, the BBC were to found two orchestras operating from their Glasgow studios, a symphony orchestra and a light orchestra.

The BBC Scottish Variety Orchestra, as the light orchestra was eventually named, had many famous conductors, musicians, artists and producers connected with it, and, despite being disbanded in 1982, has had an influence on musical activity in Scotland lasting to the present day. Among the conductors were Kemlo Stephen and Jack Leon; then in 1966, I was appointed Principal Conductor. I changed the

ARTISTS

name to the BBC Scottish Radio Orchestra to widen its musical horizons for the greater demands of the expanding radio networks and also for TV.

Eventually, under Brian Fahey, the SRO changed its format to Big Band and Strings. Among many well-known musicians associated with it were leaders Ian Tyre and Dennis McConnell, and arrangers Ian Gourlay and Robert Docker, and among the many famous artists whose careers were established on radio and TV with the SRO are Moira Anderson, Kenneth McKellar, Bill McCue and Peter Morrison. The SRO took part in the great Light Entertainment tradition established in Scottish broadcasting under producers like Eddie Fraser and Iain MacFadyen, with Sir Harry Lauder, Jimmy Logan, Stanley Baxter, Andy Stewart and the White Heather Club, among countless radio and TV shows including the annual 'live' transmission to the nation every Hogmany. The BBC SRO and I also appeared regularly at the Edinburgh Festival.

Light music performances were not, of course, exclusive to the BBC. The Scottish Orchestra (now the **Royal Scottish National Orchestra**) established a highly popular Sunday afternoon series of concerts at Glasgow's plushest picture palace, Green's Play House, which concentrated on the more popular aspects of the symphonic repertoire. This tradition continues in the **RSNO**'s annual Proms series each June. In the field of choral music Glasgow's name in particular, and therefore Scotland's, was to become internationally famous in the light music genre, through the popular recordings and concerts of the Glasgow Orpheus Choir and Sir Hugh S. Roberton. 'All in the April Evening', 'The Dashing White Sergeant' and the 'Crimond' setting of the 23rd psalm, all either composed or arranged by Hugh S. Roberton, became best sellers, constantly requested on the radio.

As we approach the millennium, light music in Scotland must be considered in its British and world-wide contexts. With the demise of all the famous BBC regional light orchestras over the past 15 years, a roll call of their names and their conductors is now redolent of nostalgia for the days when their names became familiar to us in our homes on 'Home' and 'Light' programmes, the forerunners of the cold numbers by which they are now identified: the BBC Welsh Orchestra (Rae Jenkins); West of England (Frank Cantell); Midland Light Orchestra (Gilbert Vinter); Northern Dance Orchestra (Alyn Ainsworth); Northern Ireland Light Orchestra (Stanley Black); and the BBC Radio Orchestra in London, of which I was Principal Conductor, which was itself the amalgamation of the Variety Orchestra (Paul FenLoulet) and the Revue Orchestra (Malcolm Lockyer), as well as the SRO. This leaves the BBC Concert Orchestra, Principal Conductor Barry Wordsworth, as the only dedicated light music orchestra in the BBC, one of the only two such orchestras in the UK; the other is the **City of Glasgow Philharmonic Orchestra (CGPO).**

You will recall that I said that even although the SRO had been disbanded in 1982 it continued to have an influence on light music in Scotland to the present day. I was determined to fill the gap in music making left by the loss of the SRO, and in 1989 I became Founder-Conductor of the **City of Glasgow Philharmonic Orchestra**. Many of the musicians who had played in the SRO joined with the cream of Scottish freelance players to re-establish a light music orchestra in Scotland, administered initially by Jenny Wales, who had been the orchestral manager of the SRO. The new orchestra became a firm favourite with Glasgow audiences during 1990 City of European Culture Year and the opening of the **Glasgow Royal Concert Hall** gave added impetus to our efforts. The **CGPO**, (Leader: Clive Thomas), is modelled on its famous counterparts in America: the Boston Pops Orchestra, the Hollywood Bowl, Cleveland Pops and New York Pops. It plays the same wide-ranging repertoire touching on all aspects of music from Bach to the Beatles; from Stravinsky to strathspeys and reels.

However, there the similarity ends. Despite grants and sponsorships from the public and private sectors, it is hopelessly under-funded and relies for its existence on the box-office. State subsidised and state broadcasting orchestras play light music in every major European city, but Glasgow is the only city where a top professional light music dedicated orchestra exists on the will and goodwill of its patrons, its players, and legions of voluntary helpers. Nevertheless, it has drawn within its orbit such excellent and dedicated music makers as the **City of Glasgow Chorus;** the **Bearsden Burgh Choir**; the **Glasgow Wind Band;** the **Glasgow Jewish Choral Society**; and the **City of Glasgow Pipes and Drums.** Its concerts provide a platform for Scottish performers already famous and for those who are up and coming, and guest performers come from the rest of the UK, Europe and America. It is also my hope that the success of the **CGPO** will inspire light operatic companies and professional freelance orchestras as well as amateur orchestras to perform and dip into light music in all its myriad manifestations: Brass Bands, Wind Bands, Choirs, Strathspey and Reel Societies, Pipe Bands and Big Bands.

Sir Thomas Beecham loved to conduct his 'lollipops'; the New Year's Day Concerts from Vienna have made the music of the Strauss family world-famous; then there is film music, and the work of the unsung orchestras and arrangers, whom we hear on radio, TV and records every day. Light music? Well, it's all music! As Sir Edward Elgar said, 'Music is in the air - you simply take as much of it as you want.'

ARTISTS

117

MUSIC FROM OTHER CULTURES

Glasgow 1990 Steel Band

Set up in the same year as Glasgow's nomination as City of Culture to create the first Scottish Steel Band. This is a multi-cultural and multi-racial project. Organises workshops teaching steel band music to people of all ages, groups and backgrounds. Successfully pioneered the first Scottish Steel Band Carnival in Glasgow.
33 Cleveden Place, Kelvindale, Glasgow G12 0HG
Tel: 0141 334 8866
Contact: J E Squire (Director)

James, Ken

Involved with various ethnic/world music projects eg Japanese drumming; identifying the roots of Flamenco (Arabic and Indian roots); teaches world music at Strathclyde University (BA Applied Music course). Involved in using new technology in world music.
1/1 Avrilhill, Kilbirnie, Ayrshire KA25 6BN
Tel: 01505 684746

Kangutkar, Vijay

Tabla player, over 30 years experience. Played with various visiting artists and two bands: Looking East (cross cultural) and Keltz (cross cultural folk). Teaches tabla in school for Strathclyde Region, weekend classes for Asian Artists Association and private work.
121 Yokermill Road, Glasgow G13 4HL
Tel: 0141 952 6628

Mambojam

Ensemble made up from staff and students at Northern College performing samba and salsa music from Latin America.
Northern College Aberdeen Campus, Hilton Place, Aberdeen AB9 1FA
Tel: 01224 283500 Fax: 01224 283576
Contact: Pete Stollery (Performance Co-ordinator) or Dundee Campus
Tel: 01382 464000

Naga Mas (The Glasgow Gamelan Group)

A community based group formed in 1991 playing Javanese music. The gamelan consists of tuned metallic instruments resembling xylophones, plus gongs and a small set of hand drums. The group has performed at a number of venues from the Kelvingrove Art Gallery to the Perth Museum and French Embassy. The music itself is a haunting and otherwordly, using cyclic melodies to combine interlocking patterns which produce a distinctive, entrancing sound.
Tel: 0141 339 0440
Contact: Mary Anne Carroll

Northern Gamelan

Ensemble made up from students at the Northern College, performing authentic gamelan music. One of only 4 Balinese Gamelans in the UK. Led by Gordon Jones, co-ordinator of the World Music Centre at Northern College.
Northern College Aberdeen Campus, Hilton Place, Aberdeen AB9 1FA
Tel: 01224 283500 Fax: 01224 283576
Contact: Pete Stollery (Performance Co-ordinator) or Dundee Campus
Tel: 01382 464000

Northern Steel

Popular steel pan ensemble, comprising students at the Northern College, regularly in demand throughout the NE performing arrangements of well known music.
Northern College Aberdeen Campus, Hilton Place, Aberdeen AB9 1FA
Tel: 01224 283500 Fax: 01224 283576
Contact: Pete Stollery (Performance Co-ordinator) or Dundee Campus
Tel: 01382 464000

Pachakum: Music from the Andes

Peruvian musicians who play traditional and contemporary music from the Andes on panpipes, Andean flute, charango, ronroco, drum and other indigenous instruments. Based in Edinburgh and available for concerts, schools, workshops or fiestas anywhere in the UK.
9 Watson Crescent, Polwarth, Edinburgh EH11 1HB
Tel: 0131 229 2183 Fax: 0131 229 2183
Contact: Sandra Thomson

Sedenka

Women's vocal ensemble, performing music and dance from around the world. Specialising in Eastern European, African and Celtic styles. Albums: featured on Sòlas, by Talitha Mackenzie (Riverboat).
33 Millar Crescent, Edinburgh EH10 5HQ
Tel: 0131 447 0091
Contact: Talitha MacKenzie or Sally Freedman Tel: 0131 555 1410

OTHER USEFUL CONTACTS

Asian Artistes Association

Aims to bring together Asian artists for the promotion of Asian arts, to encourage and promote a greater knowledge and understanding of the Asian arts, particularly in a religious and ethnic context by the teaching of dances, songs and other arts. Promotes performances, workshops, training-courses and educational schemes.
Dowanhill Primary School, 30 Havelock Street, Glasgow G11 5JE
Contact: Dr L Prasad (President) Tel: 0141 943 0009

Bengali Performing Arts

Formed 1992 to promote Bengali culture. Organises year-round programme of Bengali celebrity performances reflecting all aspects of music - vocal, instrumental and dance. Maintains close links with other similar organisations throughout Scotland.
127 Woodhill Road, Bishopbriggs, Glasgow G64 1BB
Tel: 0141 762 0021
Contact: Dr P Ghosh

Foundation for African Cultural Exchange (F.A.C.E.)

A new organisation aiming to stimulate and promote interest in African arts, music and dance. Currently planning concerts, international events and exhibitions.
3/1 4 Ancroft Street, Maryhill, Glasgow G20 7HX
Tel: 0141 333 1148
Contact: Gift Amu-Logotse or Vicky Davidson Tel: 0141 339 1212

ARTISTS

MUSIC FROM OTHER CULTURES

119

Rock and Pop in Scotland
by John Williamson

Any discussion of the rock and pop industry in Scotland is dogged by the i-word. 'There is no infrastructure,' whinge many in the business, before they either pack their bags and head for London or retire for a career in banking.

In some cases this is a genuine complaint, in others a simple excuse for lack of talent on either the musical or business side. Sure, Scotland does not have the breadth of facilities that you may find in London or New York, but there certainly is no shortage of musical, business and studio talent north of the border.

Scotland has venues that are well established on the touring circuit (from **Barrowland** via **The Garage** to **King Tut's** in Glasgow alone), internationally respected promoters in **Regular Music** and **DF Concerts**, a nationally respected festival in **T in the Park**, studios (Funny Farm, Ca Va, Castlesound, Park Lane, Waterfront) which are as good as anything offered anywhere in Britain and of course bands as varied as **Wet Wet Wet**, **Texas**, **Del Amitri**, **Teenage Fanclub**, **The Proclaimers** and **The Nightcrawlers**, who all sell decent quantities of records while still living and working in Scotland.

For a nation of five million it is probably well represented. It is possible to work in the music business, be based in Scotland and make a living. There are plenty of us doing it, and it may not always be the easiest option, but talent usually finds a way of rising to the surface. Making your own infrastructure is the best option - there

are always like minded and independently minded people working in Scotland.

Independence is the key. Scotland suffered more than most from the recession of the late eighties, and perhaps even more from the economic boom which preceded it. Major record companies swamped Scotland by the shuttle-load, signing half developed bands and dumping them almost as soon as they could get rid of them when purse strings were tightened. Whatever happened to **Slide**, **Slice**, **Win**, **The River Detectives**, **Botany 500** or any one of the other Scottish next big things? And more importantly, did any of the thousands of pounds in advances given to them make its way back into the Scottish music economy?

Did it hell. Pony-tailed American producers, high powered English PR companies, recording studios scattered all over the world were the main beneficiaries. Even bands who made some attempts to maintain a Scottish base (namely **Wet Wet Wet**,

Deacon Blue, **Hue and Cry**) could not alter the fact that although the talent may be in Scotland, the banks (i.e. record companies) were very much in London.

OK, so having blamed London for some of the ills of the Scottish music scene, it is also important to take a long and hard look at ourselves. We hardly came out of it dignity intact. A series of talking shops, of which the long forgotten Scottish Record Industry Association was the most notorious and least effective sponge for public funding, highlighted the disunity that characterised the varying factions that made up the body: folkies versus rock, promoters versus studios, managers against just about everybody, the successful against the unsuccessful. At best the SRIA was a misguided attempt to focus Scottish music, at worst it was an embarrassingly public forum for shooting ourselves in the foot.

So, chewed up and spat out by the London 'biz', only able to kick ourselves when down - what happened next? Well, bizarrely

things have slowly begun to come together: Scotland has more pockets of genuine potential, both in terms of musical talent and small businesses, than ever before.

ARTISTS

Pleasing our selves has become more important than pleasing accountants, and everyone seems to be prospering: the bigger bands who have survived the recession are now more successful than ever, and the artistic achievements of even the smallest bedroom labels are often equally staggering.

Education has provided Scotland with more talented individuals to ensure that musical talent is now backed up by business acumen. If the first and most high profile course of music industry education at **West Lothian College** seems to act primarily as a (highly successful) recruiting ground for London record companies, then other courses like those at **Perth**, **North Glasgow** and **Stow Colleges** have provided more budding managers, studio entrepreneurs and sound engineers all living in Scotland than ever before.

Organisations like the **Music in Scotland Trust**, **The Musicians' Union**, **Mechanical Copyright Protection Society** and **Ten Day Weekend** have also put on a number of seminars, talks and smaller informal workshops over the last few years, which, if nothing else, have allowed access for the uninitiated to some of the most important

people in the Scottish and even British music scenes.

Even with all the business know-how going, there are still obstacles to getting a new Scottish band out of, firstly, the bedroom and thereafter, Scotland.

There may not be a lack of venues, but there is certainly a lack of good venues in Scotland. Gone are the days of shady promoters willing to take the odd chance; the nineties gig promoting ethos is 'Will it make money?' rather than 'Is it any good?' As promoters become more business-like, the options for new bands tend to be either to lose money playing half decent gigs, or to fall into the pub-rock cover versions circuit, from which there is no escape. Outwith **King Tut's** (Glasgow), **The Lemon Tree** (Aberdeen), **Lucifer's Mill** (Dundee) and **La Belle Angele** (Edinburgh), quality small venues are few and far between. If you live outside the aforementioned cities, the chances of your succeeding are even smaller.

The other option, if you cannot raise awareness of your act through playing live, is to look for support through the media. It was this after all, as much as enthusiastic audiences, that brought the likes of **Wet Wet Wet** to the attention of the record companies back in the mid eighties. Scotland had enthusiastic and respected 'stringers' on all the major music papers, and a number of new music champions on local radio, notably Billy Sloan,

Mark Goodier, Bryan Burnett and Colin Somerville.

Constant play on specialist radio shows undoubtedly helped bands to build a live following - now there are still pockets of support. Radio Scotland's *Beat Patrol* seems to have ploughed a lone furrow for a long number of years, while Mark Findlay (Forth FM), Ward McGaughrin (Radio Tay) and Jim Galletly (North Sound) all regularly feature new bands. Unfortunately their shows tend to be marginalised, while bigger stations like Clyde and Scot FM prefer to choose playlist material only. The **Nectarine No 9** are unlikely ever to trouble the playlist compilers.

These are the problems - but there are many ways to overcome them. Many acts whose music is either unsuitable for corporate consumption or which have been ignored by the major labels, have found doors opening on the formation of their own labels. **Postcard** has re-established itself, Glasgow band **The Delgados** have successfully released both their own and **BIS**'s singles on their bedroom run Chemikal Underground label, selling more copies in the process than many major label flop releases.

Glasgow acts have also benefited from releases by Creeping Bent Records (home of **The Leopards**, **Secret Goldfish** and **Spacehopper**) and dance labels like Soma, Melon and Limbo, the latter selling 5000 copies of **Melonhaus**' 'Dopamine' single. Dundee's **Spare Snare** have sold well in America on their own Chute Records. Others have found outlets with small London labels: **Urusei Yatsura** (on Che Records), **Coast** (on Sugar Records), **Shriek** (Deceptive Records), and a whole host of Scottish bands (most recently **The Diggers**) on Alan McGee's Creation Records.

Support for the above has tended to come from the music papers and Radio 1's *John Peel* and *Evening Session*, meaning that a number of these bands sell more records outside their home country than they do in it. Though not the fault of individual music writers, the Scottish press is too centred on selling advertising and papers to give more than cursory attention to anything less than well established Scottish bands.

The conclusions? Don't be dispirited about operating in the Scottish music scene. There is no escape from talent - it invariably finds its way (often slowly) into the media, the venues and the record shops. In some instances it may even end up in the charts. **BUT!** Don't expect anyone to do it all for you. Don't expect any great favours or support. And, in particular, don't trust anybody who tells you that 'what Scotland really needs is an infrastructure'.

If enough bands and entrepreneurs opt for a DIY approach then the infrastructure for releasing and promoting records will exist in Scotland - and several stratospheres' worth of hot air will have been saved in the process.

ARTISTS

123

COMMUNITY

Bamford, Richard

Senior tutor Drake Music Project, Project Organiser Hands on Technology Group (for people with special needs), involved with Light Opera Project (multi-media performance programme for people with special needs), founder of Edinburgh Samba School, member of several organisations including Art Link.
80/5 Craigentinny Road, Edinburgh
EH7 6ND
Tel: 0131 669 1851

James, Ken

One of two Scottish reps on Sound Sense. Teaches community music at Strathclyde University. Works as programme designer/consultant for community music projects.
1/1 Avrilhill, Kilbirnie, Ayrshire
KA25 6BN
Tel: 01505 684746

Lochwinnoch People's Carnival Orchestra

Community based orchestra currently comprising 9/10 percussion players and 4/5 piece brass section. Perform Latin American rhythms and African based music. Set line-up meeting Thursday and Sunday nights. Performed at several festivals in 1st year of existence. Organisers looking for funding to expand idea into other communities.
Braeview, Kilmacolm, Lochwinnoch
PA12 4LA
Tel: 01505 842103
Contact: Joseph Pieraccini

McVicar, Ewan

Songwriter. Community Music Worker.
187 Wilton Street, Glasgow G20 6DF
Tel: 0141 946 2817

O'Neill, Lynne

Energetic, fun voice workshops exploring the use of the voice through the breath, movement, rhythms, games, songs and improvisation within a supportive and relaxed environment. Suitable for all ages and abilities. Group size to be discussed. Professional singer/teacher happy to work on projects with other artists.
18 Oakfield Avenue (Top Right),
Glasgow G12 8JT
Tel: 0141 357 0089

Trouton, David

Composer and performer. Composed for Dance: Saorsa dance company, Lillian Bayliff; Theatre: Dundee Repertory Theatre, Edinburgh Festival Society. Also music for commercial video and student film. Use of sequencers and computers for composition. Piano, guitar, percussion. Work with special needs groups including the Drake Music Project and Strathclyde Orchestral Productions.
25 Montpellier Park, Edinburgh
EH10 4LX
Tel: 0131 229 2136

OTHER USEFUL CONTACTS

East End Arts

Funded through the East End Management Committee, the aim of the project is to develop the various art forms in the East End of Glasgow for the benefit of the people of that area. Promotes workshops in visual arts, dance, theatre and music at certain times of the year. Also some touring theatre/music which East End Arts brings to the area whenever possible.
Budhill Hall, Hallhill Road, Springboig,
Glasgow G32 0PR
Tel: 0141 774 0261 Fax: 0141 774 0263
Contact: Angela Hogg (Arts Officer) or Elaine McSorley (Assistant)

Impact Arts Management

Formed in May 1994. Agency specialising in projects and workshops based in the community. A team of music, drama and art specialists with extensive experience in the community can deliver workshops in various areas.
124 Dumbarton Road, Glasgow
G11 6NY
Tel: 0141 334 1520
Contact: Susan White (Coordinator)

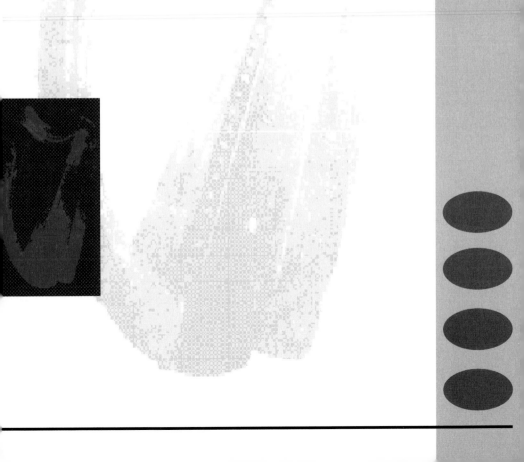

YOUNG PEOPLE'S
MUSIC

Editorial Notes

This chapter is divided into sections according to the type of music, e.g. classical, folk and traditional etc. The CLASSICAL section is further subdivided so that all orchestras, bands, and choirs are grouped together. The FOLK AND TRADITIONAL section has three headings: FEISEAN, which are tuition based festivals for young people in the Gaelic tradition, FIDDLE ORCHESTRAS and GAELIC CHOIRS. The entries for feisean and Gaelic choirs give a general overview of what is available and it is recommended that the organising bodies FEISEAN NAN GAIDHEAL and AN COMUNN GAIDHEALACH are contacted for more details of individual events or choirs.

Several children's festivals and children's entertainers are also listed in this chapter. The intention is to have all listings relating directly to opportunities available for young people in one place rather than scattered throughout the *Handbook*, and it is hoped to develop this in future editions. The term 'Young People' is used loosely, going up to about 25 years in some cases. Age ranges or limits are often noted in the listings.

CLASSICAL

CONTACTS

Ayrshire Voices

Exists to develop voice as an instrument through an education programme offering training to young singers at all stages of development and incorporating group and individual tuition, and a performance programme of concerts and musical theatre supported by the professional resources of Opera West.
14 Ashgrove Street, Ayr KA7 3AQ
Tel: 01292 264489 Fax: 01292 282424
Contact: Raymond Bramwell (Artistic Director) or Marilyn de Blieck (Artistic Director)

British Federation of Young Choirs

The British Federation of Young Choirs exists to further youth choral singing by promoting singing days, weekends and weeks, developing choral skills through courses and conferences for singers, conductors, teachers and schools. It also supports established choirs and choral groups.
38 Swanston Avenue, Edinburgh EH10 7BY
Tel: 0131 445 3114
Contact: John Roberston (Scottish Agent)

The Children's Music Foundation

Promotes classical concerts specially designed for children. All concerts have an educational input and are suitable for children (and adults) of all ages. The aim is to present classical music as being accessible to all. Concerts are held throughout Scotland in major Concert Halls from October till March.
537 Sauchiehall Street, Glasgow G3 7PQ
Tel: 0141 248 1611 Fax: 0141 248 1989
Contact: Louise Naftalin

National Association of Youth Orchestras

Formed in 1961 to represent youth orchestras in UK. Members include chamber, symphonic, wind and jazz orchestras. Also run the Edinburgh and Glasgow Festival of British Youth Orchestras, the Anglo-German Youth Music Week and various awards. Their newsletter *Full Orchestras* is published 3 times a year.
Ainslie House, 11 St Colme Street, Edinburgh EH3 6AG
Tel: 0131 225 4606 Fax: 0131 225 3568
Contact: Carol Main (Director) or Jenny Brockie (Administrator)

St Mary's Saturday Morning Music School

Offers classes in musical play, workshop, recorder, violin, cello, chamber music, choir and orchestra, for ages 3 to 17. Waiting list for play and workshop classes; eligibility for recorder, violin and cello dependent on completing workshop. Vacancies in chamber music, choirs and orchestras.
Rosebery Crescent, Edinburgh EH12
Tel: 0131 538 7766
Contact: Jean Murray

BANDS

Kirkintilloch Kelvin Brass

Junior section of Kirkintilloch Brass Band.
62 Fellsview Avenue, Kirkintilloch, Glasgow G66 2LX
Tel: 0141 776 3395 (H) / 248 5811(W)
Contact: Peter Fraser MBE (Secretary)

MacTaggart Scott Loanhead Silver Band

Runs a junior training band with tuition for beginners. New members always welcome.
Mansfield Villa, 23 Polton Road, Loanhead, Midlothian EH20 9BU
Tel: 0131 440 3830 Fax: 0131 452 8272
Contact: Alan MacLaren (Secretary)

North Ayrshire Youth

Formed in 1975 to give brass players in North Ayrshire schools an opportunity to play together. Performs at local events, gives own concerts and competes in 3rd sections (4th section winners 1994). Previously won youth section. UK finalists 3 times since 1975. Band tours include Germany and Switzerland.
84 Auldlea Road, Beith, Ayrshire KA15 2JU
Contact: Paul Stonelake Tel: 01505 503113 or Hugh Brennan Tel: 01505 683766

Stranraer Youth Band

7 Millfield Avenue, Stranraer, Wigtownshire DG9 0EG
Tel: 01776 703726
Contact: Donald Walls (Secretary)

Whitburn Burgh Junior

4th section Scottish Champions (1995). Play at galas, fêtes, fund raising events, concerts and church services.
33 Bridgeside Avenue, Whitburn, West Lothian EH47
Tel: 01501 741659
Contact: Elma Stockman (Secretary)

CHOIRS

Glasgow Youth Choir

Founded 1957. Boys and girls from 6 years to young ladies in their twenties who love singing. Wide range of music is taught by a conductor dedicated to the 'joy of music'. Interested young people should contact Miss Hoey or the Secretary.
30 Haggswood Avenue, Pollokshields, Glasgow, Glasgow G41 4RH
Contact: Agnes Hoey (Conductor) or Isobel McInnes (Secretary) Tel: 0141 563 6699

Inverness Junior Singers

Junior Choir for children of 7 years and upwards. Takes part in two public concerts per year with its parent choir The Inverness Singers. Also sings for charity, at Old Folks' Homes etc.
20 Broadstone Park, Inverness IV2 3LA
Tel: 01463 232835 (H)
Contact: Margaret Young or Doris Blair Tel: 01463 230233

YOUNG PEOPLE'S MUSIC

131

RSNO Junior Chorus and Training Choir

Founded in 1978 by Jean Kidd and now trained by Christopher Bell. Works with the RSNO and other major orchestras. Supported financially by the Gannochy Trust, it recruits members from all over Glasgow. The Training Choir prepares young children for entry to the Junior Chorus.

73 Claremont Street, Glasgow G3 7HA
Tel: 0141 226 3868 Fax: 0141 221 4317
Contact: Eleanor Owen (Administrator) or Christopher Bell (Musical Director)

Waverley Singers

For girls aged 7 - 18 years. Rehearsals: Saturdays, 11.15 - 11.45am (7-11yrs) and 11.45 - 12.45pm (11-18yrs). Standards: 6-week trial to assess suitability. Membership fee flexible, depending on age. No auditions, but new members should join in September/October. January 1995 performed Britten's *Ceremony of Carols.*

6 Netherby Road, Edinburgh EH5 3NA
Tel: 0131 552 3925
Contact: Pamela Duncan (Music Director)

ORCHESTRAS

Bearsden and Milngavie Youth Orchestra

Cater from beginners to Grade 8 in three groups. Rehearsals: Thursdays, September - March at Milngavie Primary School. Annual membership.

c/o Kilmardinny House, 50 Kilmardinny Avenue, Bearsden, Glasgow G61 3NN
Tel: 0141 956 3829
Contact: Mrs S Sutherland (Secretary)

Camerata Scotland

The chamber orchestra of NYOS. This pre-professional group of senior and recent past members of the National Youth Orchestra of Scotland performs with international conductors and soloists. Available for concerts in April and August/September.

The National Youth Orchestra of Scotland, 13 Somerset Place, Glasgow G3 7PT
Tel: 0141 332 8311 Fax: 0141 332 3915
Contact: Trevor Marshall or Eva Flannery

Edinburgh Secondary Schools Orchestra

Rehearsals: 6.15 - 8.00pm, Mondays, September - March, St Oswald's Hall, Montpelier Park, Edinburgh. Standard: Grade 6 and above. Auditions held early September, during rehearsals (7.00pm). Concert dates in November and March, at Usher Hall and Central Hall, Tollcross, Edinburgh.

Westwood House, 498 Gorgie Road, Edinburgh EH11 3AF
Tel: 0131 469 5783
Contact: Dr Colin O'Riordan (Head of Instrumental Music (Strings))

Edinburgh Youth Orchestra

Founded in 1963, The Edinburgh Youth Orchestra meets at Easter for a week's course leading to two concerts, one of which takes place in the Usher Hall. Standard: Grade 7 upwards. The EYO has undertaken three overseas tours to Germany, California and Central and Eastern Europe. Members between the ages of 13 and 21 are selected by audition.

92 St Alban's Road, Edinburgh EH9 2PG
Tel: 0131 667 4648 Fax: 0131 662 9169
Contact: Marjory Dougal (Administrator) or Neil Butterworth (Vice-Chairman)

Hillhead Strings

Directed by Elaine Fernandez. Consists of two youth string orchestras (age 6-18) and chamber groups, involving over 100 young people. Entry by audition. Senior orchestra (Hillhead Strings) minimum Grade 5. Training Orchestra (Hillhead Juniors) Grade 2 - 4. Senior orchestra members of NAYO.

3 Bolton Drive, Glasgow G42 9DX
Contact: Elaine Fernandez Tel: 0141 649 4218 or Brian Nixon Tel: 0141 337 1299

The National Youth Orchestra of Scotland

Provides orchestral training for young musicians aged 12 to 21. Tuition with professionals on residential courses is followed by concert tours with international conductors and soloists. Other activities include Easter courses in string repertoire, wind and brass training groups and schools workshops.

13 Somerset Place, Glasgow G3 7JT
Tel: 0141 332 8311 Fax: 0141 332 3915
Contact: Richard Chester or Lesley Paterson

Peebles Orchestra

Youth Orchestra rehearses Wednesday, 6.30 - 7.30pm, at Priorsford School, Peebles.

c/o Claire Garnett, Glenternie Lodge , Manor Valley, Peebles EH45 9JN
Tel: 01721 740256
Contact: Claire Garnett or Malcolm Porteous Tel: 0131 447 0539

Spectrum Junior String Orchestra

Preparatory group (7-11 yrs) meets on Saturdays 10am - noon; Senior Orchestra (11-18 yrs) meets on Mondays 6.30 - 8.30pm. Founded by the musical director, who trained at the National Conservatoire in France and taught strings in Highland schools for 25 years. Orchestra tours abroad and gives fundraising concerts.

2 Aldourie Road, Inverness IV2 4RL
Tel: 01463 238134
Contact: A Sieczkarek (Musical Director) or M Sieczkarek (Secretary)

EARLY MUSIC

Flat Pavan

The group has performed in the old USSR, Germany, Italy and at international conferences in the UK and USA. Specialises in 400 year old popular music, part songs and dances. Age ranges mainly teenage to early twenties.

8 Florida Crescent, Glasgow G69 6LP
Tel: 0141 771 7078
Contact: Richard Tedstone (Musical Director)

FOLK & TRADITIONAL

Feisean nan Gaidheal

Feisean nan Gaidheal (The National Association of Gaelic Arts Youth Tuition Festivals) is a limited company wholly owned and run by the community-Feisean throughout the country, with an elected Board of Directors, and is managed by the Development Officer. Originally set up to provide a wide range of advice and services to the Feisean, it now has various projects for the 1993-97 period, including training for tutors and organisers, fund-raising, directories of tutors, regular newsletters, provision of follow-up tuition for Feis participants, the co-ordination of Feis activities as well as the provision of funding and lobbying of funding bodies. The Gaelic word feis (plural feisean) simply means festival but in the past few years it has been particularly associated with tuition-based festivals. Feisean are generally community based voluntary bodies where people over a wide age range, but primarily young people, are offered training in skills in the Gaelic language and its associated traditional music, song and dance. 27 Feisean were held throughout Scotland in 1994. They are of great importance educationally, culturally, socially and economically. The list of feisean at time of printing was:Feis an Earraich, Feis Rois, Feis Ile, Feis Bharraigh, Feis Chataibh, Feis Strath Fharragaig, Feis na Hearadh, Feis na h-Oige, Feis nan Eilein, Feis Eilean an Fhraoch, Feis Tir an Eorna, Feis Oigridh Ile, Feis Thiriodh, Feis Tir a'Mhurain, Feis Spe, Feis nan Garbh Chriochan, Feis Muile, Feis Arainn, Feis Asainte, Feis Lochaber Beo, Feis Ealan na Hearadh, Feis Latharna, Feis Mhealainis, Feis Dhalriata, Feis nan Gleann, Feis a Bhaile. Contact Feisean nan Gaidheal for up to date details, dates etc.
5 Mitchell's Lane, Inverness IV2 3HQ
Tel: 01463 234138 Fax: 01463 237470
Contact: Arthur Cormack (Development Officer)

Gaelic Choirs

There are over 30 junior choirs in Scotland, some affiliated to senior choirs and some attached to schools. Choirs compete in local and national mods and often perform in annual concerts or other events. Choirs include: Bowmore Primary School, Burghead Primary School, Bute Primary Schools, Coisir Ard Sgoil an Obain, Coisir Ard Sgoil Phortrigh, Coisir Loch a Tuath, Coisir Og Srughlea, Coisir Og a Bhac, Coisir Og Cille Bhrighde an Ear, Coisir Og Eilean Bharraigh, Coisir Og Inbhir-Narunn, Coisir Og Phortrigh, Dingwall Primary School Gaelic Choir, Dunbeg Primary School, Falkirk Junior Gaelic Choir, Glasgow Islay Junior Gaelic Choir, Islay High School, Lochaber High School Gaelic Choir, Lochgilphead Primary School, Lochinver Primary School, Moorfoot Primary School, Nairn Junior Gaelic Choir, Nicolson Institute Girls Choir, Park (Oban) Primary School, Port Ellen Village Choir, Rockfield Gaelic Choir, Sir E Scott School, St Columba's School, Tiree High School, Tiree Primary School, Tobermory High School, Tobermory Primary School. Contact details for individual choirs can be obtained from An Comunn Gaidhealach.
An Comunn Gaidhealach, 109 Church Street, Inverness IV1
Tel: 01463 231226

Lothian Schools Strathspey and Reel Society

10 - 18 year olds eligible if resident within Lothian Region. Entry by audition. Contact Yla Steven for further information. Performed at the Edinburgh Military Tattoo. Toured Canada and Argentina.
101 Warrender Park Road, Edinburgh EH9 1EW
Tel: 0131 229 6439
Contact: Yla L Steven (Conductor)

JAZZ

Strathclyde Youth Jazz Orchestra

Funded by Strathclyde Regional Council. Provides an opportunity for 14 - 25 year olds to learn and perform big band charts, study improvisation and be involved in schools workshops and performances. Has links with European Network of Jazz Education and the Glasgow International Jazz Festival, working with the composer in residence.
200 Greenock Road, Largs KA30 8SB
Tel: 01475 686993
Contact: Bobby Wishart

MUSIC FROM OTHER CULTURES

Naga Mas (The Glasgow Gamelan Group)

Children's classes on Sundays 11am - 12.30pm, at Strathclyde Arts Centre, Washington Street. Annual membership £1 and 50p per session. The Javanese gamelan consists of a group of tuned metallic instruments resembling xylophones, plus gongs and a small set of hand drums, and the simplicity of technique makes the music accessible to all.
Tel: 0141 339 0440
Contact: Mary Anne Carroll

ROCK/POP

Jewish Youth Singers

Children aged 12 - 17 years. Wide repertoire of lively and upbeat music ranging from Hebrew and liturgical to pop is performed in 3 part harmony. Aims to encourage children musically in every dimension, including instrumental as accompaniment or solo spots. Voice training provided. Performers are Jewish but keen to perform to all audiences.
7 Broomstone Avenue, Newton Mearns, Glasgow G77 5LA
Tel: 0141 639 5114
Contact: Edward Binnie (Musical Director) or Lesley Ross (Secretary)

YOUNG PEOPLE'S MUSIC

133

National Youth Music Theatre

Performs in Edinburgh during the Festival and provides workshops for local children. Opportunities for 11 - 19 year olds to become involved in all aspects of the performing arts. Auditions are held at various centres throughout the UK in October/November with 2nd auditions in London in December.
2 Bow Street, London WC2E 7BA
Tel: 0171 836 9791 Fax: 0171 240 7949

COMMUNITY

Balornoch Youth Centre

Ages 5 - 25, free to all residents of the area, 6.30 - 9.45pm. Tuesday, Wednesday, Thursday: acoustic guitar lessons divided into groups by age. Tuesday, Thursday: use of sequencing equipment available to over 12's. Fridays 6 - 8pm: drum lessons for primary age members. All groups will be extended to meet demand.
285 Wallacewell Road, Balornoch, Glasgow G21 3RP
Tel: 0141 558 1387
Contact: Scott Douglas

Bandwagon

Community music forum for under 25 year olds. Yearly membership £3. Cheap equipment rental. Organise gigs in centre and elsewhere.
Terminal One, Logan Street, Blantyre G72 0NT
Tel: 01698 829455
Contact: Fiona Robertson

Castlemilk Youth Complex

Only open to 12 - 25 year olds from Castlemilk. Membership £1 a year. Range of workshops led by young people's interests: singing; tuition on bass, drums, guitar; technical, in the recording studio (4-track recording, engineering); DJ and programming in the internal radio station; Techno DJ skills at the complex disco; karaoke.
39 Ardencraig Road, Castlemilk, Glasgow G45 0EU
Tel: 0141 630 0000
Contact: Ronan Bresslan (Music Development Worker)

Music and Drama Creative Workshops

Community project offering creative workshops in expressive arts to children, using the skills of musicians, music teachers etc. in the local community.
12 Lochbay, Waternish, Dunvegan, Isle of Skye IV55 8GB
Tel: 01470 592253
Contact: Jane Yeats

Music Development Project

Project financed by social work for 12 - 19 year olds. Sampling workshops, computer based music workshops. In schools use songs to approach social issues. Combine with other arts for multi-media work. Moving in to work with people with special needs - proposed sampling workshops for special needs groups.
The Mearns Centre, Mearns Street, Greenock
Tel: 01475 729121
Contact: Jim Reid

Petersburn Youth Project

13 - 26 year olds . All facilities free of charge. Scotvec modules in 4-track and stereo sound recording. Introduction to video production. Drop in guitar, bass and drum tuition. Occasional workshops on other instruments. Recording studio and rehearsal room for local residents. Acoustic guitars lent with library card. Two local CDs.
Petersburn Library, Varnsdorf Way, Petersburn, Airdrie ML6
Tel: 01236 760315
Contact: George Williamson or Stewart MacLeod

Terminal One

Open to 13 - 25 year olds, Tuesdays: sound engineer course. Hands on experience. 2 hour sessions at £2, all day and evening. Also classes for the blind: Wednesdays and Thursdays: guitar tuition (vocal and keyboard tuition to start soon). Also, open to all - rehearsal space and the recording of groups demos.
Logan Street, Blantyre G72 0NT
Tel: 01698 829455
Contact: Robert Getty

West Johnstone Music Workshops

A group of around 12 young people specialising in techno/dance have learned basic techniques in songwriting and mixing having attended various workshop sessions. A Scotvec module (Hi Tech Pop Comp) will run from October 1995. The group was set up by Community Education.
Tel: 01505 329219
Contact: Donald Howard

Woodhead CE Centre

12 - 16 year olds. Wednesday evening workshops tutoring bands in all aspects of playing and recording.
Woodhead Park, Kirkintilloch, Glasgow G66 3DD
Tel: 0141 775 2483
Contact: Bill Craig

FESTIVALS

International Children's Festival

Combined arts festival with international and British companies producing works for 3 - 13 year olds. Takes place in a tented village in Inverleith Park, Edinburgh. Music from around the world. 1995 featured African musicians, opera from Australia and Taiko drumming.
22 Laurie Street, Edinburgh EH6 7AB
Tel: 0131 554 6297 Fax: 0131 555 1304
Contact: Katie Stuart (Administrator)

CHILDREN'S ENTERTAINERS

Crooked Jack's Giant Jeely Piece Show

Non-stop songs, comedy and fun for kids. Features *Sam the Skull*, the *Glasgow Cat*, lots of audience participation, children's comedy etc. Ideal for theatres, holiday venues, folk festivals, community events. Stage set, lights, publicity, merchandise, full length video, cassette.
16 Moray Court, Auchtertool, Kirkcaldy KY2 5XS
Tel: 01592 781591
Contact: Dennis Alexander

Pegg, Bob

Singer, songwriter and multi-instrumentalist with over 20 years' experience working in schools, libraries, book weeks and festivals with both pupils and teachers. Special show *A Brief History of Sound* combines story and song with dozens of unusual musical instruments. Hands-on music-making and songwriting workshops.
1 Shore Street, Hilton, Tain, Ross and Cromarty IV20 IXD
Tel: 01862 832685

The Singing Kettle

Scotland's most successful children's entertainers. Several series for BBC. Seven videos on BBC on *Polygram*. Cast of three: Cilla Fisher, Artie Trezise, Gary Coupland. 3 tours annually - Easter, Summer, October, plus a Christmas season (normally Glasgow). BAFTA award winners.
Post House, Kingskettle, Fife KY7 7PN
Tel: 01337 831121 Fax: 01337 831544
Contact: Alan Garratt (General Manager)

YOUNG PEOPLE'S MUSIC

135

EDUCATION

Editorial Notes

This chapter is divided into various sections, mainly by the type of music, e.g. classical, jazz etc. Courses listed in the CLASSICAL and ROCK/POP sections are further subdivided under the headings FULL TIME and PART TIME & OCCASIONAL.

Courses in the COMMUNITY section are generally of a part time or occasional workshop nature, often requiring no previous experience or ability, and cover various musical genres as well as recording techniques etc.

SPECIALIST SCHOOLS are state schools with special music provision, while the schools listed under MUSIC SCHOLARSHIPS are private schools offering scholarships to musically talented children.

CONTACTS

Arts and Entertainment Training Council

Develops courses across the UK for the arts and entertainment industry.
Glyde House, Glydegate, Bradford BD5 0BQ
Tel: 01274 738800 Fax: 01274 391566

Scottish Community Education Council (SCEC)

Each region has a community education office where there is information on informal music courses. Argyll and Bute - 01369 6918; Ayr - 01292 612241; Borders - 01835 23301; Central - 01786 442335; Dumfries and Galloway - 01387 260406; Dunbarton - 01389 727349; Fife - 01592 267905; Glasgow - 0141 227 6753; Grampian - 01224 664695; Highland - 01349 864962; Lanark - 01698 454466; Lothian - 0131 229 9166; Orkney - 01856 873535; Renfrew - 0141 842 5631; Shetland - 01595 696606; Tayside - 01382 227129; Western Isles - 01851 703773
West Coates House, 90 Haymarket Terrace, Edinburgh EH12 5LQ
Tel: 0131 313 2488 Fax: 0131 313 2477
Contact: Irene Clark (Development Officer)

Scottish Council for Educational Technology (SCET)

Provides educational resources for teachers. Music CD Rom staff development resource for implementing the 5-14 music guidelines. Beyond the Edge video, non-technical explanation of the benefits of multi-media. Software package *Discovering Multi-media.* Also supply of BBC software free to schools including *Music, Aesthetics, Exploring musical composition.*
74 Victoria Crescent Road, Glasgow G12 9JN
Tel: 0141 337 5000 Fax: 0141 337 5050

Scottish Music Education Forum

Established May 1995 for everyone involved in Scottish music education with a three-day programme of talks and debates. Met in a North Berwick hotel. Aims include enhancing Scottish music strengths, information exchange, promoting good practice.
Summerhill Education Centre, Stronsay Drive, Aberdeen AB2 6JA
Tel: 01224 208205
Contact: Lloyd Davies (Music Adviser)

SCOTVEC

National body responsible for vocational qualifications. Responds to the needs of industry and the economy in partnership with education, industry and government. Provides qualifications relevant to employers' needs; flexible to response change and recognised nationally and internationally.
Hanover House, 24 Douglas Street, Glasgow G2 7NQ
Tel: 0141 248 7900 Fax: 0141 242 2244

TAP/Scottish Training Information Service

A Scotland-wide information service for people who want to know about training. The service in each region has comprehensive details of local training provision and information on nearly 30,000 Scottish training opportunities. This information is available on computerised database and it will tell you when and where courses are run, if they lead to a recognised qualification, whom to contact and details of course content and entry requirements. Contact your local TAP agency. Borders - 01896 758991; Central - 01786 446150; Dumfries and Galloway - 01671 403530; Fife - 01592 611231; Grampian - 01224 210300; Highland - 01463 710019; Lothian - 0131 557 5822; Moray - 01343 551858; Strathclyde - 0141 357 1774; Tayside - 01382 206116

EDUCATIONAL ADVISORS/ REGIONS

Association of Music Advisers In Scotland

The association holds annual conferences to discuss music education and related issues. Most regions have a music adviser who can give information on courses. (See regional entries). Each adviser will also be able to tell you which secondary schools in your area take adults into day and/or evening music classes - many do.
Summerhill Education Centre, Stronsay Drive, Summerhill, Aberdeen AB2 6JA
Tel: 01224 208205 Fax: 01224 208845
Contact: LLoyd Davies (Adviser Grampian) or Andrew Kerr (Adviser Lothian)

Borders

Support to schools especially in relation to staff and curriculum development. Regional music activities - wind orchestra, reserve band, training band, percussion ensemble, stage band, chamber orchestra, chamber ensembles (string, wind), guitar ensemble, recorder ensemble.
Regional HQ, Newton St Boswells, Melrose TD6 0SA
Tel: 01835 823301 Fax: 01835 822145
Contact: Alistair Salmond (Adviser in Arts)

Fife

Regional music activities - Youth Orchestra, Youth String Orchestra, Youth Concert Band, Youth Choir, Youth Percussion Group, Youth Guitar Ensemble, Junior Singers, Wind Bands, String Orchestras. Weekly activities and residential music camps.
Auchterderran Centre, Woodend Road, Cardenden KY5 0NE
Tel: 01592 414699 Fax: 01592 721937
Contact: R W Tait (Assistant Adviser in Music)

EDUCATION

Grampian

Music centres in Aberdeen, Elgin and Fraserburgh which operate bands, orchestras, ensemble and choral groups catering for 2,000 pupils at a variety of levels. Grampian Region Schools Orchestra - annual course with concerts in Aberdeen and Elgin. Promotion of curriculum initiatives in schools; links with SCET, SCO, RSNO etc. (1994/95 PRS Composer in Education Award). Instrumental music provision in schools. Financial support - NYOS/NE Scotland School of Music.
Summerhill Education Centre, Stronsay Drive, Summerhill, Aberdeen AB2 6JA
Tel: 01224 208205 Fax: 01224 208845
Contact: Lloyd Davies (Adviser in Music)

Highland

Visits to schools to provide advice on curriculum content, methodology etc. Training in all aspects of the music curriculum, for class teachers, instrumental tutors and visiting specialists. Curriculum support materials. Co-ordination of instrumental tuition and ensemble activities (e.g. bands, choirs, orchestras). Liaison with professional and amateur bodies. Provision of weekend and vacation courses in band and orchestral playing and choral singing as well as opportunities for public performance. Organisation of foreign performing tours.
Education Centre, Castle Street, Dingwall, Ross-shire IV15 9HW
Tel: 01349 863441 Fax: 01349 65637
Contact: H C Richardson (Adviser in Music)

Lothian

1993/94 Premier Award for UK schools music provision. Staff: adviser, 2 heads of instr. music, 112 inst. staff, 123 secondary staff, 42 primary specialists, 4 special education staff, Lothian Specialist School, extensive in-service. 11,000 pupils having instruction (highest percentage in UK). Full adult provision. 'Music For All' policy.
Quality Assurance Division, Westwood House, 498 Gorgie Road, Edinburgh EH11 3AF
Tel: 0131 469 5781 Fax: 0131 469 5757
Contact: Andrew Kerr (Adviser in Music)

Strathclyde (Ayr)

Responsible for curricular development and in-service provision in secondary and primary schools in Ayr, part of Lanark and part of Dunbarton.
Greenwood Centre, Dreghorn, Irvine KA811 4HL
Tel: 01294 212716 Fax: 01294 222430
Contact: Lorna Graham (Education Development Officer (Music))

Strathclyde (Lanark)

Information available on courses mainly targetted at teachers in schools.
Education Development Service, Regional Offices, Almada Street, Hamilton ML3 0AE
Tel: 01698 454218 Fax: 01698 454469
Contact: June Fearns (Adviser)

Tayside

Education Development Section, Floor D, Gardyne Road, Dundee DD4 1NY
Tel: 01382 462857 Fax: 01382 462862
Contact: Fiona McIntosh (Adviser in Music) or Roz Brown

Western Isles

Curriculum development, advisory support, in-service training, liaison with colleges of education and universities in Scotland.
Haldane Curriculum Centre, Church Street, Stornoway HS1 2LS
Tel: 01851 703564 Fax: 01851 704709
Contact: R A Barr (Principal Adviser) or Neil Galbraith (Director of Education)

SPECIALIST SCHOOLS

Lothian Specialist Music School

In Flora Stevenson Primary School and Broughton High. All instruments and voice catered for. Primary age pupils spend majority of time in a normal mixed ability class with c. 2 hours a day devoted to music. At secondary level additional time is available for music by opting out of other subjects. Pupils study English, maths, a modern language plus a further 3 or 4 subjects, including music. No fees. Applications welcome from any area.
Broughton High School, Carrington Road, Edinburgh EH4 1EG
Tel: 0131 332 7805 Fax: 0131 343 3296

The Music School of Douglas Academy

Strathclyde Region's specialist school for musically gifted children of secondary age. Allows pupils to continue a general education while receiving instrumental tuition and additional time for musical study. Boarding facilities available.
Mains Estate, Milngavie, Glasgow G62 7HL
Tel: 0141 956 2281
Contact: The Head Teacher

MUSIC SCHOLARSHIPS

Fettes College

A large number of scholarships available at any age from 10 to 16 at this co-educational day and boarding school with 4 full time staff, 25 visiting teachers, 4 orchestras, 5 choirs and various ensembles and special events.
Tel: 0131 332 2281 Fax: 0131 332 3081
Contact: David Thomas (Director of Music)

Loretto

Music scholarships and bursaries, including the Major Organ Scholarship (awarded annually) available at this independent co-educational boarding school for ages 8 to 13 in the Junior School and 13 to 18 in the Upper School.
Musselburgh, Midlothian EH21 7RE
Tel: 0131 653 2618 Fax: 0131 653 2773
Contact: The Admissions Secretary

St Leonard's Music School

The music school opened in 1987. Prepares pupils for the Royal School of Music examinations. Junior and Senior wind bands, string and full orchestras, junior, senior and recital choirs, ceilidh band and jazz band. Tuition available on orchestral instruments plus piano, voice, harp, guitar and bagpipes. Music scholarships awarded on entry at any age.
St Andrews, Fife KY16 9QU
Tel: 01334 76345

EDUCATION

St Mary's Music School

Co-educational day and boarding school combining musical and academic education in small, friendly classes. The schools's 53 pupils aged 9 - 18 are supported by the Governmnent's Aided Places scheme or by scholarships. Entry is by audition at any stage. Prospectus available. Also runs Saturday morning classes (see Young People's chapter).
Coates Hall, 9 Roseberry Cescent, Edinburgh EH12 5JP
Tel: 0131 538 7766
Contact: J P S Alison (Headmaster) or Nigel Murray (Director of Music)

CLASSICAL

FULL TIME COURSES

Aberdeen College

Offers a two-year music teaching diploma.
School of Arts and Business Studies, Ruthrieston Centre, Holburn Street, Aberdeen AB9 2YT
Tel: 01224 640366 Fax: 01224 573758
Contact: Aileen Kelly (Senior Music Lecturer)

Jewel and Esk Valley College

The college offers a one-year full-time HNC and two-year full-time HND in Modern Musicianship and an evening class in guitar tuition.
Milton Road Centre, 24 Milton Road East, Edinburgh EH15 2PP
Tel: 0131 669 8461 Fax: 0131 657 2276
Contact: Adam Armit (Music course contact)

Langside College

A Music Diploma class prepares students for the written papers of all external diploma examinations and includes harmony, counterpoint, history, form, analysis and aural perception.
50 Prospecthill Road, Glasgow G42 9LB
Tel: 0141 649 4991 Fax: 0141 632 5252
Contact: Lois Emanuel (Head of School)

HND IN MUSIC STUDIES

This course consists of 2 years full-time study covering the following areas:

 ## PERFORMANCE/COMPOSITION STUDIES

First and second study individual lessons in all standard orchestral and band instruments, piano, organ, guitar, lute, voice, composition (electric keyboard, guitar and home entertainment organ are not taught).

 ## ACADEMIC STUDIES

Lectures and classes in history, notation, harmony, aural perception, music technology and keyboard or fretboard skills.

There is a BMus course planned to commence in 1996, subject to validation.

The Department of Music, currently located at our Sighthill campus, has excellent facilities which include extensive music technology equipment, a practice organ, a well-stocked library with listening facilities, and well-equipped teaching and practice rooms. It has 7 full-time members of staff and 20 part-time staff, many from the major Scottish orchestras and ensembles and is home to the only Scottish music research fellowship in the UK. The Head of Department is Philip Sawyer. The Senior Lecturers are Anna Butterworth (academic) and Margaret Murray McLeod (performance). In 1996 the department will be moving to Napier's new campus at Craighouse, which will provide the university with extensive teaching accommodation set in pleasant grounds overlooking the city.

For further information, contact: The Information Office, Napier University, 219 Colinton Road, Edinburgh EH14 1DJ. Tel: 0131-455 4330.

NAPIER UNIVERSITY
EDINBURGH
Investing in teaching and research to serve the community

RSAMD
Royal Scottish Academy of Music and Drama

The **RSAMD** now has degree-awarding powers and its new performance degrees (validated by the RSAMD) are professionally focused towards a performing career.

In an exciting building with state of the art facilities, students enjoy regular and ensemble work and specially structured coaching in chamber music. Instruction is given by international consultants, conductors, directors and instrumental specialists. The Academy's many orchestras and ensembles cover a broad repertoire from early to contemporary music.

The Courses
BA (Musical Studies) with Honours
BEd (Music) with Honours
BMus (Performance) with Honours
MMus (Performance/Opera/Composition/ Conducting)

Entrance is by competitive audition to be held in Glasgow in November 1995 and March 1996 and applications should be lodged by 15 October 1995 and 31 January 1996 respectively.

Full details of all courses, qualifications awarded
and entrance scholarships are obtainable on application to:
The Registrar, Royal Scottish Academy of Music and Drama,
100 Renfrew Street, Glasgow G2 3DB.
Telephone 041-332 4101

Napier University

The HND in Music Studies consists of two years' full-time study comprising first and second study instrument/voice, composition, history, notation, harmony, aural perception, music technology, keyboard or fretboard skills. A B.Mus. course is planned to commence in 1996 subject to validation.
Department of Music, Sighthill Court, Edinburgh EH11 4BN
Tel: 0131 444 2266 Fax: 0131 455 3515
Contact: Philip Sawyer (Head of Department)

Northern College

Four-year B.Ed. course in music teaching.
Hilton Place, Aberdeen AB9 1FA
Tel: 01224 283500 Fax: 01224 487046
Contact: Admissions Office

Royal Scottish Academy of Music and Drama

BA (Musical Studies) and B. Mus. (Performance) are both four year courses with Honours. Postgrad M.Mus. in opera, advanced opera, concert singing, instrumental studies, composition and conducting. Four-year B.Ed. with Honours in music teaching offered in conjunction with St Andrews College (see college entry). BA in Scottish Music starts in 1996. (See Folk & Traditional). Certificate of Postgraduate Studies involves one year of advanced training.
100 Renfrew Street, Glasgow G2 3DB
Tel: 0141 332 4101 Fax: 0141 332 8901
Contact: Philip Ledger (Principal) or Rita McAllister (Director of Music)

St Andrews College

The four-year B.Ed. course is for those wishing to become music teachers. All aspects of the course recognise the changes which have taken place in music teaching. Music studies covers performing, composition and history. Education studies covers preparation for teaching, the development of the individual, assessment and the curriculum.
Duntocher Road, Bearsden, Glasgow G61 4QA
Tel: 0141 943 1424 Fax: 0141 943 0106

Stevenson College

The college offers the SCE Higher and GCE A Level music courses as well as courses in piano servicing, stringed keyboard instrument technology and orchestral instrument repair.
Carrickvale Annexe, Stenhouse Street West, Edinburgh EH11 3EP
Tel: 0131 443 8888 Fax: 0131 455 765

University of Aberdeen

Although the university no longer offers a music degree, students taking other courses may take first level standard music courses in History and Repertoire or Form and Structure.
Powis Gate, College Bounds, Old Aberdeen AB9 2UG
Tel: 01224 272571 Fax: 01224 272515

University of Edinburgh

B.Mus., B.Mus. (music technology) or an MA in music. Postgrad courses are M.Mus., M.Phil. or Ph.D.
Faculty of Music, Alison House, Nicolson Square, Edinburgh EH8 9DF
Tel: 0131 650 2422 / 1011
Contact: C D S Field (Head of Department)

University of Glasgow

The university offers a B.Mus. with an honours option and MA students can take single honours on music or joint honours with another arts subject. There is also a B.Eng. degree in Electronics with Music. Postgrad courses are M.Mus., M.Litt. and Ph.D.
Department of Music, 14 University Gardens, Glasgow G12 8QH
Tel: 0141 339 8855
Contact: Marjorie Rycroft (Head of Department) or Sybille Samuels (Department Secretary)

University of Strathclyde

The university offers a four-year BA single or joint degree in Applied Music aimed at those wishing to become professional performers, administrators or music technologists.
Jordanhill Campus, 76 Southbrae Drive, Glasgow G13 1PP
Tel: 0141 950 3242 / 3246

PART TIME & OCCASIONAL COURSES

Aberdeen College

The college offers part-time courses in music, drumming, guitar and solo keyboarding. The Basic Musicianship course lasts for a year and offers grade music theory exams from the London Guildhall School of Music.
School of Arts and Business Studies, Ruthrieston Centre, Holburn Street, Aberdeen AB9 2YT
Tel: 01224 640366 Fax: 01224 573758

Anglo/German Youth Music Week

Held alternately in Germany and the UK. There is an orchestra and chamber groups with a bias towards 20th century music.
NAYO, Ainslie House, 11 St Colme Street, Edinburgh EH3 6AG
Tel: 0131 225 4606 Fax: 0131 225 3568
Contact: Carol Main (Director)

Carnegie Hall Music Institute

Individual teachers hire rooms in the institute for private tuition. A wide range of instruments is covered.
East Port, Dunfermline KY12 7BA
Tel: 01383 720108 Fax: 01383 622633

Edinburgh Teachers' Co-operative

Courses are open to all, lead to an SCE Standard Grade or Higher in music and can be held in either the student's or the teacher's home. Individual or group tuition available. Cost is £10-£16 per hour, shared with others in the group; 25% reduction for OAPs and unemployed.
3 Hayfield, Edinburgh EH12 8UJ
Tel: 0131 339 5374

The Guitar School

Classical guitar tuition is available.
Illyria, Tower Brae North, Westhill, Inverness IV1 2BW
Tel: 01463 793717
Contact: Alan Bolger

Kenneth van Barthold Piano Workshop Course

During Edinburgh Festival workshops in association with Edinburgh University Music Faculty and Centre for Continuing Education.
Arvensis, Stour Lane, Stour Row, Shaftesbury, Dorset SP7 0QJ
Tel: 01747 838318
Contact: Kenneth van Barthold

Kilmardinny House Arts Centre

A strings chamber music summer workshop open to individuals and groups of any age and standard. Covers all aspects of string playing, rehearsal and chamber music coaching. There is individual help and advice, a string orchestra and advice on the basic care of the instruments etc.
50 Kilmardinny Avenue, Bearsden G61 3NN
Tel: 0141 943 0312

Lochaber Music School

Musical instruction for stringed instruments including the small harp. Tuition given at weekly music centre or weekend workshops (three or four times a year). These are open to all ages and abilities and include orchestral, chamber and traditional music. At the centre there are two orchestras, a Suzuki group and musicianship classes.
Finnisgaig, Bunroy, Roybridge PH33 4AE
Tel: 01397 712557 Fax: 01397 712557
Contact: Patricia Hoole (Administrator) or Audrey Scott (Director)

Music at Oxenfoord

Opera and master classes for voice, accompaniment and harpsichord.
Easter Haining, Ormiston Hall, Tranent EH35 5NJ
Tel: 01875 340512
Contact: Joan Busby

Open College of the Arts

Understanding Opera is a year long course outlining the skills involved in making an opera. It is run in conjunction with the Royal Opera House. The course combines home study of the music, words, design and staging of opera with group practical work, probably over four weekends, at Covent Garden.
44 Fir Park, Tillicoultry, Clackmannanshire FK13 6PJ
Tel: 01259 752485
Contact: Lewis Waugh (Scottish Rep) Tel: 01259 752485

Open University in Scotland

Home study courses available: Understanding Music; Beethoven; From Baroque to Romantic; Introducing Music; Principles of Orchestration.
10 Drumsheugh Gardens, Edinburgh EH3 7QJ
Tel: 0131 225 2889

The Pipers' Guild (Edinburgh Branch)

Members make their own bamboo pipes, simple whistle-type instruments in all consort sizes. Fortnightly meetings. Play original and broadly classical music.
8 Dell Road, Edinburgh EH13 0JR
Tel: 0131 441 7114
Contact: Angela Hopkinson

The Rehearsal Orchestra (Edinburgh)

Meets for one week during the Edinburgh Festival at the Craiglockhart Campus of Napier University and attendance can be residential. Music included in the festival programme and other works are studied and there is an informal concert on the last day. Players are expected to be at least Grade VIII.
London College of Music, Thames Valley University, St Mary's Road, London W5 5RF
Tel: 0181 231 2643
Contact: Jean Shannon (Administrator)

Royal Scottish Academy of Music and Drama

A postgrad M.Mus in concert singing, instrumental studies, composition and conducting can be done over two years. Also the Department of Continuing Education offers performance, practical, compositional and other part-time musical study units at four levels.
100 Renfrew Street, Glasgow G2 3DB
Tel: 0141 332 4101 Fax: 0141 332 8901
Contact: Philip Ledger (Principal) or Rita McAllister (Director of Music)

St Andrews International Singing Weeks

Choral workshops and three concert performances open to choirs and/or individuals.
37 Frederick Street, Loughborough, Leicester LE11 3BH
Tel: 01509 211664 Fax: 01509 233749
Contact: Susan Lansdale (Director) or Andrew Fairbairn (Hon Sec)

Scottish Amateur Music Association

Runs courses for brass, wind and string orchestras, chamber music, church organ and recorder.
18 Craigton Crescent, Alva, Clackmannanshire FK12 5DS
Tel: 01259 760249
Contact: Margaret Simpson (Hon Sec)

Scottish Chamber Orchestra

The SCO runs an annual course for composers on the Orkney island of Hoy. Music composed during the course will be performed in Hoy and immediately after in Edinburgh.
4 Royal Terrace, Edinburgh EH7 5AB
Tel: 0131 557 6802 Fax: 0131 557 6933
(Development Manager)

EDUCATION

147

The Shell Expro Music School

The Shell Expro Music School is run as part of the Aberdeen International Youth Festival and there are courses for instrumentalists and singers. All students can also compete for cash awards.

Nutborn House, Clifton Road, London SW19 4QT
Tel: 0181 946 2995 Fax: 0181 944 6507

Stevenson College

Elements of Music is aimed at those with little or no theoretical knowledge and provides an understanding in the basic musical techniques of pitch, rhythm, keys and chords. Listening for Pleasure is a ten-week course to understand and appreciate old favourites from Bach to Shostakovich. Both courses run twice a year from September and January.

Carrickvale Annexe, Stenhouse Street West, Edinburgh EH11 3EP
Tel: 0131 443 8888 Fax: 0131 455 7656

Workers Educational Association

On offer is an eight-week evening course on reading music aimed at those who have a basic knowledge of musical terms. Also occasional courses on a variety of musical aspects often related to current events such as an introductory course on opera centred around the Scottish Opera and BBC Radio 3 seasons.

Riddle's Court, 322 Lawnmarket, Edinburgh EH1 2PG
Tel: 0131 226 3456 Fax: 0131 220 0306
Contact: Joyce Connon

EARLY MUSIC

Scottish Early Music Consort

Committed to taking early music into the community with workshops in schools and adult training centres. In 1993 won the Sainsbury's Arts Education Award for music-theatre workshop project 'Opera from Scratch' in remote areas of Scotland. Also promotes workshops in connection with their biennial Glasgow International Early Music Festival.

2 Port Dundas Place, Glasgow G2 3LD
Tel: 0141 333 1178 Fax: 0141 333 1179
Contact: Warwick Edwards (Artistic Director) or Mary Carmichael (Administrator)

Society of Recorder Players Edinburgh Branch

Meets weekly. Leisure rather than performance based. Repertoire - lots of early music. Also original compositions and 20th c. Adults.

14 Bruntsfield Gardens, Edinburgh EH10 4EA
Tel: 0131 229 8081
Contact: Eileen Finlayson

FOLK & TRADITIONAL

Adult Learning Project

The ALP Scots Music Group run participative learning classes from which have emerged bands and ensembles who can perform at festivals and community events.

Scots Music Group, 184 Dalry Road, Edinburgh EH11 2EP
Tel: 0131 337 5442
Contact: Stan Reeves Tel: 0131 337 5442

Ardival Harps

Four-day courses for complete beginners and specialised courses for experienced players. Beginners' courses explore traditional and early harp music using gut-strung harps, wire-strung clarsachs and buzzing bray harps. Specialist courses on wire technique, traditional style and early music. Harps are provided. Courses taught by Bill Taylor.

Orchard House, Castle Leod, Strathpeffer, Ross-shire IV14 9AA
Tel: 01997 421260 Fax: 01997 421260

Balnain House

A variety of workshops and classes in a wide range of traditional instruments, singing and songwriting.

40 Huntly Street, Inverness IV3 5HR
Tel: 01463 715757 Fax: 01463 713611
Contact: Caroline Hewat (Asst Manager)

College of Piping

Courses leading to certificates and diplomas cover playing, maintenance, notation, theory, history, adjudication and Highland dress.

16-24 Otago Street, Glasgow G12 8JH
Tel: 0141 334 3587 Fax: 0141 337 3024

Community Education Service

Volunteers from the Gaelic adult education classes organise occasional master classes in Gaelic music and dance.

Area Office No. 14, Battlefield Primary School, 44 Carmichael Place, Glasgow G42 9SY
Tel: 0141 649 6124

Easterhouse Arts Traditional Music Project

Adult and junior classes and group practice sessions running weekly for all abilities led by experienced musicians. Schools programme including related special drama and creative writing and in-service courses. Summer school in August.

32 Aberdalgie Road, Glasgow G34 9HT
Tel: 0141 771 9368
Contact: Jim Cathcart or Paul McKinlay

Feis Rois

Year-round tuition for all ages on a weekly and monthly basis in harp, fiddle, accordion, tin whistle and guitar. Also Ross-shire piping school. Special events include Gaelic singing, piping and groupwork. Summer entertainments programme includes ceilidhs and recitals.

Ross House, High Street, Dingwall IV15 9QN
Tel: 01349 862600
Contact: Rita Hunter (Feis Rois Administrator)

Feis Rois Inbhich

3 day festival at end of April based around tuition in traditional instruments and gaelic song open to anyone over 17 (with priority going to those working or living in Ross and Cromarty). Tuition offered in fiddle, accordion, gaelic song, harp, guitar, tin whistle and groupwork as well as informal evening sessions and ceilidhs.

Ross House, High Street, Dingwall IV15 9QN
Contact: Rita Hunter (Feis Rois Administrator)

EDUCATION

Glasgow Fiddle Workshop

A non-profit making group committed to increasing the understanding and awareness of Scottish traditional fiddle music. Weekly workshops offering tuition on Scottish and Cape Breton fiddle styles. Players of all levels welcome.

10 Sinclair Drive, Langside, Glasgow
G42 9QE
Tel: 0141 636 1450
Contact: Brenda McCulloch
(Administrator)

H.A.R.P.

Heritage Arts Regeneration Project (H.A.R.P.) in association with the Traditional Music and Song Association of Scotland, aims to promote the traditional arts in the North East by working with young people under 25. Educational pack available, as well as tailor made workshops.

North East Scotland Heritage Trust, Town
House, The Square, Kintore, Inverurie
AB51 0US
Tel: 01647 6133640 Fax: 01647 6133640
Contact: Sandra Morrison (Development
Officer)

Lochaber Music School

Provides musical instruction for stringed instruments including the small harp. Tuition given at weekly music centre or at weekend workshops three or four times a year, subjects including Scottish fiddle and traditional music. Open to all ages and abilities. Also covers classical with two orchestras, a Suzuki group and musicianship classes.

Finnisgaig, Bunroy, Roybridge
PH33 4AE
Tel: 01397 712557 Fax: 01397 712557
Contact: Patricia Hoole (Administrator)
or Audrey Scott (Director)

Queen Margaret College

Two seminar schools. Clarsach - August with Anne Macdearmid. Accordion - July with Douglas Muir. All standards welcome. Specialising in Scottish traditional music.

Clerwood Terrace, Edinburgh EH12 8TS
Tel: 0131 317 3000 Fax: 0131 317 3256

Royal Scottish Academy of Music and Drama

BA in Scottish Music starts in 1996. Four year course offers traditional music for performers to further skills and explore Scots heritage. Practical studies with supporting academic subjects and business studies. Principal studies include accordion, bagpipes, Scottish harp, fiddle and voice.

100 Renfrew Street, Glasgow G2 3DB
Tel: 0141 332 4101 Fax: 0141 332 8901
Contact: Philip Ledger (Principal) or
Rita McAllister (Director of Music)

Royal Scottish Pipe Band Association College

The various branches of the association run courses during the winter and a week-long summer school is held in the Glasgow college.

45 Washington Street, Glasgow G3 8AZ
Tel: 0141 221 5414 Fax: 0141 221 1561
Contact: J Mitchell Hutcheson (Executive
Officer)

Sabhal Mor Ostaig

Courses are available on fiddle, piping and drumming, Cape Breton step dance, tin whistle, clarsach and Gaelic song.

Teangue, Sleat, Isle of Skye IV44 8RQ
Tel: 01471 844373

The Scots Fiddle School

Summer school run by the Scottish Amateur Music Association and held in St Andrews University. Caters for players of all ages and standards though Grade 3 is recommended. Deals with fiddle techniques, bowing and ornamentation, and provides an insight into the lives of famous fiddlers. Tuition is on both individual and group basis.

c/o Hillpark Education Centre, Benview,
Bannockburn FK7 0JY
Tel: 01786 816205 Fax: 01786 815451
Contact: Iain White (Director)

University of Stirling (Summer School)

The summer school has five-day courses on the accordion, clarsach, highland bagpipe, Scots fiddle and Shetland fiddle.

The Summer School Office, Airthrey
Castle FK9 4LA
Tel: 01786 467951 Fax: 01786 463398

Wallace Clan Trust

Aims to promote Scottish and Irish traditional music by providing reasonable cost group tuition in c.15-20 different instruments and singing. Tuition provided by experienced tutors and professional musicians in Glasgow city centre location. More information from Bob Copeland.
Tel: 0141 429 6968
Contact: Bob Copeland Tel: 0141 429
0994

JAZZ

The Arts in Fife

The Fife Summer Jazz Course includes sessions for beginners and teachers and attracts enthusiasts from all over the country. In an intensive series of morning, afternoon and evening workshops participants will work with some of the best known jazz tutors in the country to develop playing standards, public performance and improvisation.

The Tower Block, ASDARC, Woodend
Road, Cardenden
Tel: 01592 720594 Fax: 01592 414641
Contact: Bridget McConnell (Principal
Arts Officer)

Enjoy Jazz!

Series of talks, discussions and optional concerts designed to illuminate the many aspects of jazz music. Evening classes held during the winter months.

Aberdeen University Centre for
Continuing Education, c/o Assembly
Direct, 89 Giles Street, Edinburgh
EH6 6BZ
Tel: 0131 553 4000 Fax: 0131 554 0454
Contact: Suzy Melhuish

Enjoying Jazz!

Series of talks, discussions and optional concerts designed to illuminate the many aspects of jazz music. Evening classes held during the winter months.

Stirling University Open Studies Course,
c/o Assembly Direct, 89 Giles Street,
Edinburgh EH6 6BZ
Tel: 0131 553 4000 Fax: 0131 554 0454
Contact: Suzy Melhuish

EDUCATION

The Grampian Jazz School - Aberdeen

Practical jazz tuition for students of all ages and abilities covering a wide range of instruments. Led by a team of professional jazz musicians, the school is run on five Saturdays throughout the year.
c/o Assembly Direct, 89 Giles Street, Edinburgh EH6 6BZ
Tel: 0131 553 4000 Fax: 0131 554 0454
Contact: Suzy Melhuish

Lothian Jazz School

Practical jazz tuition for students of all ages and abilities covering a wide range of instruments. Led by a team of professional jazz musicians. Sessions held during weekends.
c/o Assembly Direct, 89 Giles Street, Edinburgh EH6 6BZ
Tel: 0131 553 4000 Fax: 0131 554 0454
Contact: Suzy Melhuish

National Jazz Institute

Course launched 1995. Two-year certificate or four-year diploma part-time courses meet 24 times a year. Applicants submit a cassette recording assessed for entry. Instruction by experienced jazz educators including Tommy Smith and Bobby Wishart. Course includes harmony, history, piano, ensembles, ear training and technology.
University of Strathclyde, Jordanhill Campus, 76 Southbrae Drive, Glasgow G13 1PP
Tel: 0141 950 3476 Fax: 0141 950 3314
Contact: Tommy Smith (Director of Music) or Mark Sheridan (Head of Music Division)

LIGHT MUSIC

Aberdeen College

The college offers part-time courses in music, drumming, guitar and solo keyboarding.
School of Arts and Business Studies, Ruthrieston Centre, Holburn Street, Aberdeen AB9 2YT
Tel: 01224 640366 Fax: 01224 573758

Aberdeen Guitar Institute

Courses for all standards from beginners. One to one tuition available. Courses can be designed to suit personal needs.
67 The Green, Aberdeen AB1 2NY
Tel: 01224 210121 Fax: 01224 585553
Contact: Andy Watson

Billy McEwen Organs

Tuition is available in organ, piano and keyboards. There is another branch at 4-6 Earl Grey Street, Mauchline (tel 01292 550187). The Technics Music Academy is housed in the Ayr branch.
31-35 Fort Street, Ayr KA7 1DG
Tel: 01292 269667 Fax: 01292 289597

Henderson Organ Tuition

The course is described as tuition for organ and keyboard 'the fun way'.
23 Stewart Street, Milgavie
Tel: 0141 956 4517

Langside College

Music Keyboarding course available.
50 Prospecthill Road, Glasgow G42 9LB
Tel: 0141 649 4991 Fax: 0141 632 5252
Contact: Lois Emanuel (Head of School)

Motherwell College

A course on keyboard studies covers a variety of popular ballads arranged to suit either the beginner or more advanced student.
Dalzell Drive, Motherwell ML1 2DD
Tel: 01698 259641 x2204

Open College of the Arts

Singing is a course for all who would like to sing well, and is aimed at choral and solo singers. Ability to read music is not essential as all the exercises are sung on tapes included with the course manual. Students send their work on tape to their tutor.
44 Fir Park, Tillicoultry, Clackmannanshire FK13 6PJ
Tel: 01259 752485
Contact: Lewis Waugh (Scottish Rep)
Tel: 01259 752485

Rolston Accordians

Tuition is available on accordion and keyboards.
62 Windmill Hill Street, Motherwell ML1 1TA
Tel: 01698 265350 Fax: 01698 265350

Wilkie's Music House

Tuition is available on accordion, piano, keyboards, sax and flute.
2/4 Canal Crescent, Perth PH2 8HZ
Tel: 01738 23041

Yamaha Music School

Keyboard and guitar tuition at all levels.
141 West Nile Street, Glasgow G1 2RN
Tel: 0141 332 6474

Yamaha Music School

Class and individual tuition is available and there are facilities for the disabled.
35 Sciennes Road, Edinburgh
Tel: 0131 667 8477

MUSIC FROM OTHER CULTURES

Drumstruck

Drumstruck has been developed both as a performance and a workshop activity to offer people the chance to experience the music of the drumming traditions of the Far Ear and in particular, the Japanese TAIKO. The group can be booked to perform pieces by Kodo, Wadaiken, Yamashta and their own compositions. The workshops are open to all ages and abilities and provide a chance to find your own rhythm and synchronicity with others. Lots of noise, lots of fun!
Impact Arts Management, 124 Dumbarton Road, Glasgow G11 6NY
Tel: 0141 334 1520
Contact: Susan White (Co-ordinator)

Edinburgh Samba School

Workshops of 25-30 people held on Fridays (7-9.30pm) at Tollcross Primary School Edinburgh. Beginners are welcome on the first Friday of each month. The workshops cover many styles including batucada, maracatu, samba, reggae, timbalada and other Brazilian styles. The workshops are free of charge.
26 Shore Street, Leith, Edinburgh
Tel: 0131 555 0290
Contact: Lynn Wotherspoon

The Glasgow Gamelan Group (Naga Mas)

A community group formed in 1991 to learn and perform Javanese music. The gamelan consists of tuned metallic instruments and a small set of hand drums. The music is very accessible and ranges from the use of simple striking techniques to complex drum patterns. Weekly meetings Sundays 2-4pm and Wednesdays 7-9pm, Strathclyde Arts Centre, Washington Street, Glasgow. Will do workshops before or after performances. Schools workshops also possible. Also have an improvisation group and children's classes on Sundays (11am - 12.30pm). Yearly membership £1, and each session costs 50p.
Tel: 0141 339 0440
Contact: Mary Anne Carroll

EDUCATION

150

Logotse, Amu
Travelling African music, dance, art and drama workshops available to schools, colleges, community groups and individuals for one day, one week or longer periods. Instruction by Ghanaian born, qualified and experienced folklorist, artist and tutor.
Flat 3/1, 4 Ancroft Street, Maryhill, Glasgow G20 7HU
Tel: 0141 333 1148

ROCK / POP

FULL TIME COURSES

Jewel and Esk Valley College
HNC or HND courses in Modern Musicianship are available covering performance on keyboard, guitar or vocals and involving marketing, sound engineering and recording.
Milton Road Centre, 24 Milton Road East, Edinburgh EH15 2PP
Tel: 0131 669 8461 Fax: 0131 657 2276
Contact: Adam Armit

Perth College of Further Education
A Scotvec course leading to a National Certificate in Rock Music is available as are HNC and HND courses in Rock Music (Performer). Courses are one year full-time.
Crieff Road, Perth PH1 2NX
Tel: 01738 530802 Fax: 01738 531364
Contact: Pamela McLean (Head of Music and Media)

PART TIME & OCCASIONAL COURSES

Aberdeen Drum Centre
Snare and full drum set tuition.
148 Hutcheon Street, Aberdeen AB2 3RX
Tel: 01224 620300
Contact: Mike Kidd

Axis Guitars
Tuition is available on the guitar.
3 East Fountainbridge, Edinburgh EH3 9BH
Tel: 0131 229 5092
Contact: David May

Ayrplay Music
In-house guitar and bass tuition is available.
Wellington Square, Ayr KA7 1EH
Tel: 01292 266889 Fax: 01292 288399

Bandwagon
Guitar tuition is available.
9 St Paul's Square, Perth PH1 5QW
Tel: 01738 37714

Billy McEwen Organs
Tuition is available in organ, piano and keyboards. There is another branch at 4-6 Earl Grey Street, Mauchline (Tel. 01292 550187). The Technics Music Academy is housed in the Ayr branch.
31-35 Fort Street, Ayr KA7 1DG
Tel: 01292 269667 Fax: 01292 289597

Fonn Music Shop
There is in-house tuition for guitar and keyboard.
19 Bayhead Street, Stornoway HS1 2DU
Tel: 01851 704632

Music Corner
Organ and guitar tuition.
88 Mary Square, Laurieston, Falkirk FK2 9PP
Tel: 01324 27100

Varsity Music
Guitar tuition is available.
8a-10a Nicholson Street, Edinburgh EH8 9DH
Tel: 0131 556 3273 Fax: 0131 556 3273

COMMUNITY

Borders College
Courses are available on guitar and keyboard playing.
Duns Building, Newtown Street, Duns TD11 3AE
Tel: 01361 883738 Fax: 01361 883686
Contact: Jennifer Brown (Evening Class Supervisor)

Community Music Project Alloa
Free one-to-one tuition for unemployed people aged 16+ in Clackmannan District. Also recording equipment workshops.
Alloa Community Arts Centre, Top Floor, Alloa Town Hall, Marshill, Alloa FK10 1AB
Tel: 01259 215237
Contact: Norman Shackleton

Dundee Rep Theatre
A community musician works with an Urban Aid funded dance team in community education centres and other education and care settings in areas of multi-deprivation in Dundee. The team involves local musicians in dance projects with original music.
Tay Square, Dundee DD1 1PB
Tel: 01382 224877
Contact: Michael Duke (Associate Director Dundee Rep)

Gorbals Music Project
Free individual lessons on guitar, keyboard and percussion, primarily for the unemployed. Open 9am-5pm. Contact centre to sign up.
Gorbals UC, 52 Waddle Street, Glasgow G5 0LU
Tel: 0141 429 3905
Contact: John Hynes or Ann Marie Murray

Jewel and Esk Valley College
There is a guitar tuition evening class.
Milton Road Centre, 24 Milton Road East, Edinburgh EH15 2PP
Tel: 0131 669 8461 Fax: 0131 657 2276
Contact: Adam Armit

Kilmardinny House Arts Centre
The centre has daytime classes in guitar and electronic keyboard playing and also a range of art, music and drama activities for children. It is also home to the Berkley Guitar School which holds classes on Wednesdays for children and adults.
50 Kilmardinny Avenue, Bearsden G61 3NN
Tel: 0141 943 0312

MacRobert Arts Centre
Community music occurs regularly on a project by project basis as part of the centre's education outreach.
University of Stirling, Stirling FK9 4LA
Tel: 01786 67160
Contact: Sylvia Dow (Arts Education Officer)

Musicworks in Wishaw
This musical resource centre offers instrumental classes and musical activities in a range of instruments for all ages and abilities. The centre can also provide information on music as a career.
Motherwell District Council, PO Box 14, Civic Centre, Motherwell ML1 1TW
Tel: 01698 266166 Fax: 01698 275125
Contact: N Turner (Director of Motherwell Leisure)

EDUCATION

151

New Argo Centre

The centre runs courses for young people in keyboard and guitar playing. There is also a 16-track recording studio for community use.

8 Halgreen Avenue, Drumchapel
Tel: 0141 944 8332
Contact: May Benson (Manager) or Nicky McElhill

Paragon Ensemble

Offer an education programme related to the main concert programme. Single workshops and individual projects, normally four weeks long, involve three groups of up to 15 people each. Aim is to stimulate musical invention, ensemble playing and performance technique by helping each group create their own music. Also offer consultancy and advice on composition, workshops available.

2 Port Dundas Place, Glasgow G2 3LB
Tel: 0141 332 9903
Contact: Ninian Perri (Education Director)

Peebles Players

An opportunity for less able people to take part in music and drama activities with other members of the community.

Glentermie Lodge, Kirkon Manor, Peeblesshire EH45 9JN
Tel: 01721 4256
Contact: C R Garnett (Leader)

Random Rhythms

Workshops held in the recording studio for community groups, special needs groups, school groups, university and college groups. Special rates for concessions. Open weekdays 10am-10pm and weekends 12-9pm.

Bridgehaugh Road, Stirling FK9 5AP
Tel: 01786 479082
Contact: Guy Dadge

Ross and Cromarty District Council

Leisure Services department offer a music programme which includes Early Music, community productions, a Junior folk orchestra and the midsummer Rock Week. Some concerts, but the majority of events are participatory, for musicians and singers of all ages and abilities.

Ross House, Dingwall, Ross and Cromarty IV15 9RY
Tel: 01349 863381
Contact: Bob Pegg (Music Development Co-ordinator)

Scottish Chamber Orchestra

The SCO runs an extensive programme of education projects with schools and community groups throughout Scotland. Specialist ensembles have evolved within the SCO to develop specific programmes for these venues.

4 Royal Terrace, Edinburgh EH7 5AB
Tel: 0131 557 6802 Fax: 0131 557 6933
(Development Manager)

Streetsounds

Take recording studio equipment to unemployed clubs and youth clubs to give people a taste of how techno/dance music is produced. Teach how to programme, and tape work produced at workshops. Stewart also gives guitar lessons(Castlemilk and Govan), Ian singing lessons.

24 Gairbraid Avenue, Maryhill, Glasgow G20 8YE
Tel: 0141 883 2877 / (mobile) 0589 953033
Contact: Stewart Robertson or Ian Donaldson

Valley Arc

Basic lessons available in drumming, keyboard skills and guitar. There are also percussion workshops specialising in ethnic styles.

10 Garnockside, Glengarnock, Beith, Ayrshire G2 3LB
Tel: 01505 684225
Contact: Susan Maxwell (Community Drama and Music Worker)

Wallace Clan Trust

Community Action and Training for Work courses available for those unemployed 6 months or more. Training in all aspects of the music industry e.g. use of 8 track recording studio, rehearsal facilities, bands' showcase etc. Folk and blues especially welcome. Glasgow city centre location.

Tel: 0141 429 6968
Contact: Bob Copeland Tel: 0141 429 0994

EDUCATION

PERCUSSION

Aberdeen College
The college offers part-time courses in drumming as well as guitar and solo keyboarding. Rudiments of Drumming is mostly for kit drummers and has beginners and advanced classes.
School of Arts and Business Studies, Ruthrieston Centre, Holburn Street, Aberdeen AB9 2YT
Tel: 01224 640366 Fax: 01224 573758

Drum Shop
Part-time in-house tuition is available.
15 Blackie Street, Glasgow G3 8TN
Tel: 0141 339 4497

Logotse, Amu
Workshops offered by Ghanaian-born professional percussionist. Uses drums, voice and percussion to help musical creativity, no matter what type of music. Also offers workshops on African art, dance, drama and music.
Flat 3/1, 4 Ancroft Street, Maryhill, Glasgow G20 7HU
Tel: 0141 333 1148

Partickbeat
Drum music for adults and children. Processional events include a parade at Partick Fair. The group meets on Saturday mornings (10.30am) at Dowanhill Primary School. Membership costs £1 and sessions 50p.
43 Peel Street, Partick, Glasgow G11 5LU
Tel: 0141 334 6298
Contact: Crawford McCallum (Tutor)

Valley Arc
Percussion workshops specialising in ethnic styles. Also basic lessons available in drumming, keyboard skills and guitar.
10 Garnockside, Glengarnock, Beith, Ayrshire G2 3LB
Tel: 01505 684225
Contact: Susan Maxwell (Community Drama and Music Worker)

MUSIC & OTHER ARTS

Open College of the Arts
The course Music and Sculpture is available with face-to-face tuition at the college's study centres only.
44 Fir Park, Tillicoultry, Clackmannanshire FK13 6PJ
Tel: 01259 752485
Contact: Lewis Waugh (Scottish Rep)

MUSIC & BUSINESS

North Glasgow College
The college has a one-year course 'Performance with Promotion'.
110 Flemington Street, Springburn, Glasgow G21 4BX
Tel: 0141 558 9001 Fax: 0141 558 9905

School of Audio Engineering
A five-day introductory course 'Music Business' covers recording contracts, publishing deals, artist management, tours, staging copyright and so on aimed at those who want to work in the audio or broadcasting industries.
33 Coatbank Street, Coatbridge ML5 3SP
Tel: 01236 436561
Contact: Gordon McMillan

Stow College
HNC in Music Business Administration.
43 Shamrock Street, Glasgow G4 9LD
Tel: 0141 332 1786

West Lothian College
The college offers an HNC in Music Business Administration specifically geared towards preparing for a job in music management. The course has a practical emphasis with students running the in-house record label. One and two day consultancy programmes are also available.
Marjoriebanks Street, Bathgate, Edinburgh EH48 1QJ
Tel: 01506 634300 Fax: 01506 654860

MUSIC & TECHNOLOGY

Clydebank College
The college offers an SNC in Electronic Music and Recording which is intended for those who wish to pursue a career in the music recording industry but its main aim is to enhance the skills of self-employed musicians.
Kilbowie Road, Clydebank G81 2AA
Tel: 0141 952 7771
Contact: Caroline Bain x2151

Falkirk College of Technology
The college offers an SNC in Music Technology and Electronics.
Grangemouth Road, Falkirk FK2 9AD
Tel: 01324 624981

Jewel and Esk Valley College
HNC or HND courses in Modern Musicianship are available covering performance on keyboard, guitar or vocals and involving marketing, sound engineering and recording. There are also advanced diplomas in Composing, Arranging and Producing Audio for Video as well as Music Management and Marketing.
Milton Road Centre, 24 Milton Road East, Edinburgh EH15 2PP
Tel: 0131 669 8461 Fax: 0131 657 2276
Contact: Adam Armit

North Glasgow College
The college has full-time courses in Sound and Video Recording and Performance with Promotion.
110 Flemington Street, Springburn, Glasgow G21 4BX
Tel: 0141 558 9001 Fax: 0141 558 9905

Perth College of Further Education
Courses are available in Sound Engineering and Modern Audio Engineering.
Crieff Road, Perth PH1 2NX
Tel: 01738 530802 Fax: 01738 531364
Contact: Pamela McLean (Head of Music and Media)

EDUCATION

153

Stow College

Ten-week course in Music Technology for Music Teachers which is designed to provide training and support for music teachers who wish to incorporate the use of hi-tech equipment in their instruction. Also SNC, HNC and HND in Music Technology and Electronics.
43 Shamrock Street, Glasgow G4 9LD
Tel: 0141 332 1786

INSTRUMENT MAKING & REPAIR

Anniesland College

The college offers an SNC in Stringed Instrument Repair and an HNC in Musical Instrument Technology.
Hatfield Drive, Glasgow G12 0YE
Tel: 0141 357 3969

The Centre for Historical Harp and Clarsach Research

Harp-making and kit assembly, supervised by one of the resident harpmakers. Historical harps available for study or performance hire. Playing tuition with associated teachers. Workshops arranged for schools and community groups. Build A Small Harp In A Day. Instruments and kits from several makers. Enquiries for information and advice welcome.
Harpmakers' Workshop, 1103 Argyle Street, Glasgow G3 8NQ
Tel: 0774 005061 (tel messagepoint)
Contact: Tim Hobrough

Stevenson College

The college offers courses in piano servicing, stringed keyboard instrument technology and orchestral instrument repair as well as the SCE Higher and GCE A-Level music courses.
Carrickvale Annexe, Stenhouse Street West, Edinburgh EH11 3EP
Tel: 0131 443 8888 Fax: 0131 455 7656

SOURCES OF FUNDING

Editorial Notes

E ntries are listed alphabetically. While many of these bodies are located outwith Scotland the information is still valuable and relevant to people in Scotland as they are eligible to apply for funding, providing they meet any specific requirements. The entries all relate directly to music. We have not included information on funding for academic courses for example, as this information is the same for music courses as it would be for other subjects. We would recommend obtaining up to date information on grants etc. from the academic institute concerned.

Alfreda Hodgson Bursary

For singers under 30 who would benefit from additional financial support towards specific training, coaching and development needs. Biennial bursary - 1995 male voice, 1997 female voice.
c/o NFMS, Francis House, Francis Street, London SW1P 1DE
Contact: Kate Fearnley

Allied Domecq

No individuals - organisations only.
24 Portland Place, London W1N 4BB
Tel: 0171 323 9000
Contact: Clive Burns (Asst Comp Secretary)

Belmont Trust

Annual award by competitive auditions to violinists, violists, cellists, singers and pianists training to become performers. 1994 sum was £1,500.
c/o Helen E F Corbett, Solicitors, 3 Grasmere Close, Merrow, Guildford GU1 2TG
Contact: The Trustees

Benslow Musical Instrument Loan Scheme

For promising young students who cannot afford (mainly) orchestral string instruments. Borrowers selected on the basis of musical promise and financial need, by letter of recommendation from teacher and audition at Scheme's centre. Instruments generally lent for initial period of three years or until end of a recognised course of study.
Little Benslow Hills, Benslow Lane, Hitchin, Herts SG4 9RB
Tel: 01462 420748
Contact: The Secretary

Boise Foundation

For performers of either sex, under 30, who show outstanding promise. Candidates should be nominated by heads of musical colleges, etc. by the first week in March each year. Auditions held biennially in April. Awards for advanced studies either abroad or in UK. Next competition in 1997. List of nominations available.
c/o The Department of Music, King's College London, The Strand, London WC2R 2LS
Contact: Hon Secretary

British Federation of Women Graduates

Makes a number of awards to women for graduate research. All disciplines are considered except where a specific award states otherwise. Candidates must have completed at least one year of academic graduate research. Entry fee £12.
4 Mandeville Courtyard, 142 Battersea Park Road, London SW11 4NB
Tel: 0171 498 8037
Contact: The Secretary

The British Reserve Insurance Youth Orchestra Awards

Ten awards of £250 to orchestras which are members of NAYOS to encourage further development of youth orchestras at all levels. 1995 application deadline April for projects to be completed by the end of May 1996.
National Association of Youth Orchestras, Ainslie House, 11 Colme Street, Edinburgh EH3 6AG
Tel: 0131 225 4606 Fax: 0131 225 3568
Contact: The Director

The Britten-Pears Foundation

Established 1986 by executors of both Britten and Pears. Major charitable objects centred at Aldeburgh, plus limited funds towards new works and educational projects involving Britten's music and contemporary works. Excludes grants for music festivals, promotional literature or individuals for tuition fees or instrument purchase.
The Red House, Aldeburgh, Suffolk 1P15 5PZ
Tel: 01728 452615 Fax: 01728 453076
Contact: The Administrator

The Commonweal Fund

No projects requiring funding for a number of years. No political, municipal or ecclesiastical purposes. No distribution among members and members' families.
The Trades House of Glasgow, 310 St Vincent Street, Glasgow G2 5QR
Tel: 0141 228 8000 Fax: 0141 228 8310
Contact: G M Wyllie (Writer to the Signet)

Countess of Munster Musical Trust

For outstanding music students (instrumentalists, singers, composers) between 18 and 25 or under 27 for female singers or 28 for male singers on 1 September in the relevant year of study. Loans only for instrument purchase. Applications for assistance for the academic year commencing in September should be submitted between the preceding November and January.
Wormley Hill, Godalming, Surrey GU8 5SG
Contact: The Secretary

Courtauld Trust

Devoted to string quartet work. Policy still being formulated.
16 Ogle Street, London W1P 7LG
Contact: The Administrator

Craigmillar Opportunities Trust Ltd

Deals mainly with property, business development and training. Individuals or organisations must apply with an actual business proposal.
Peffer Place , Edinburgh EH16 4BB
Tel: 0131 661 8888
Contact: Susan Carr (Admin Manager)

Craxton Memorial Trust

For individual young pianists and instrumentalists (excluding organists, harpsichordists and percussionists). 1995 deadline 31 January. Send sae for application form and further details.
50 Hatherleigh Road, Ruislip, Middlesex HA4 6AU
Contact: The Secretary

The David Cohen Family Charitable Trust

33A Elsworthy Road, London NW3 3BT
Tel: 0171 586 3192 Fax: 0171 722 7134
Contact: Dr David Cohen (Chairman of the Trustees) or Duncan Haldane (Administrator)

Edward Boyle Memorial Trust

Competitive biennial award - £1500 - given to an outstanding performer under 30 for advanced tuition. The prize may include a London recital. 1996 is for strings. Applications should be made after May 1996.
18 Park Crescent, Leeds LS8 1DH
Contact: Professor P L Marsden

SOURCES OF FUNDING

Eric Thompson Trust

Offers aspiring professional organists assistance with special studies, or other incidental costs incurred in their work. Applicants should send full details of their needs, together with confirmation of their training and career, references etc. Applications received by 31 December will be decided upon by the end of February.
c/o The Royal Philharmonic Society, 10 Stratford Place, London W1N 9AE
Contact: Clerk to the Trustees

The Esmée Fairbairn Charitable Trust

Prospective applicants should first of all obtain a copy of the Trust's guide lines before submitting an application.
1 Birdcage Walk, London SW1H 9JJ
Tel: 0171 222 7041 Fax: 0171 223 0421
Contact: Margaret Hyde (Director) or Judith Dunworth (Secretary)

Guilhermina Suggia Gift

For exceptionally talented cello students under 21 with potential to become first class solo performers. 1995 closing date 16 February, auditions in March. Application forms from November. Entry fee £10.
16 Ogle Street, London W1P 7LG
Contact: Awards Administrator

Harriet Cohen Memorial Music Awards Trust

Annual awards to professional musicians up to 30 years old having shown outstanding promise in their careers. Nominations invited from principal music institutions in rotation. No individual applications.
2 Raymond Buildings, Gray's Inn, London WC1R 5BZ

Harris Kaufman Trust

Specifically for applicants with one Jewish parent and one non-Jewish parent, who are unable through poverty to become efficient in their chosen fields. Provides payment for educational or instructional fees, travelling costs and other necessary expenses.
c/o Bishop and Robertson Chalmers, 2 Blythswood Square, Glasgow G2 4AD
Tel: 0141 248 4672 Fax: 0141 221 9270

Hattori Foundation

Assists solo instrumentalists (18-26) or ensembles (average age not over 26) of exceptional talent with potential to pursue international careers. No instrumental purchase. No post/undergraduate study unless combined with ongoing concert career. 1995 deadline 21 May. Auditions to follow.
72D Leopold Road, London SW19 7JQ
Tel: 0181 944 5319 Fax: 0181 946 6970
Contact: Noel L Masters

Hinrichsen Foundation

Promotion of music concentrating on contemporary composition and research including production of performance materials, public performance, research projects and their publication. No grants for recording costs, funding of commissions, degree or other study courses or instrumental/equipment purchase. Trustees meet quarterly. 1995 deadline October 1994.
c/o 27 Kingscroft Road, Leatherhead, Surrey KT22 7BU
Contact: The Secretary

Holst Awards

For individual composers and pianists. Applications should be made on behalf of the composer by the pianist who wishes to commission substantial new works for piano. (Preferred duration of 7-15 minutes). Four or more awards of up to £2,000. 1995 deadline 25 March.
43 Alderbrook Road, London SW12 8AD
Tel: 0181 673 7129 Fax: 0171 228 2358
Contact: Anna Cuddon (Administrator)

Hope Scott Trust

Promotion of visual arts and music in Scotland. Applicants should be able to show that they qualify for the Scottish element of this requirement. Unable to assist with applications for course fees.
Murray, Beith and Murray WS, 39 Castle Street, Edinburgh EH2 3BH

Ian Fleming Charitable Trust Music Education Awards

For first class singers (under 30) and instrumentalists (under 26) at the start of performing careers. May be put towards study, special projects or musical instrument provision. Application forms given. Entry fee £10.
16 Ogle Street, London W1P 7LG
Contact: Awards Administrator

Ida Carroll Double Bass Award

For players under 19 (by 1 April) who wish to study the double bass. Award may be used for any reasonable purpose. Deadline for return of application forms 1 March. Auditions to follow. Workshops also arranged.
c/o School of Strings, Royal Northern College of Music, 124 Oxford Road, Manchester M13 9RD
Contact: The Trustees

The Idlewild Trust

Supports registered charities - not normally individuals. Grants normally non-recurrent. Open to applicants within the UK only. Grants given to beneficiaries residing within the applicant's immediate locality.
54/56 Knatchbull Road, London SE5 9QY
Tel: 0171 274 2266
Contact: Lyn Roberts (Secretary)

The Inverforth Charitable Trust

The Farm, Northington, Alvesford SO24 9TH
Tel: 01962 5024974
Contact: E A M Lee (Secretary and Treasurer)

The John Ellerman Foundation

Funds not normally given to youth causes or education except (limited) to handicapped. Prefer to give to control bodies rather than local groups. Registered charities only. No individuals. No religious causes. Applications by letter.
Suite 10, Aria House, 23 Craven Street, London WC2N 5NT
Tel: 0171 930 8566 Fax: 0171 839 3654
Contact: P C Pratt (Director and Secretary)

The John S Cohen Foundation

33A Elsworthy Road, London NW3 3BT
Tel: 0171 586 3192 Fax: 0171 722 7134
Contact: Dr David Cohen (Chairman of the Trustees) or Duncan Haldane (Administrator)

KPMG / Martin Musical Scholarship Fund

The Philharmonia Orchestra assists talent up to age 25 with specialist and advanced study. Does not currently support organists, singers, conductors, composers, academic students or piano accompanists. Two types of award made for tuition fees and/or maintenance grants while studying. Selection by audition. Closing date 1 October. Entry fee £5.
76 Great Portland Street, London
W1N 5AL
Contact: The Administrator

Loan Fund for Musical Instruments

Helps young musicians (having already started professional careers) to buy instruments they could not otherwise afford, of a quality appropriate to their needs. Loans at nominal rates of interest, paid over a maximum period of five years. Application forms given.
16 Ogle Street, London W1P 7LG
Tel: 0171 436 4816
Contact: Marjorie Dickinson (Secretary)

Ludgate Trust

Open to registered charities and other organisations involved with performance schemes for advanced students. Apply by letter.
c/o Musicians Benevolent Trust, 16 Ogle Street, London W1P 7LG
Contact: Awards Administrator

Manoug Parikian Award

For exceptionally talented violin students under 21 having potential to become first class soloists. 1995 closing date 16 February, auditions in March. Entry fee £10.
16 Ogle Street, London W1P 7LG

Mario Lanza Educational Foundation

Awards made nationally throughout the year. No age limit but students expected to be engaged in the advanced study of classical singing.
7 Lionfields Avenue, Allesley Village, Coventry CV5 9GN
Contact: Hon Secretary

Michael Tippett Musical Foundation

Gives priority to live and contemporary music through performance and education, especially in areas of social/ economic deprivation. Donations generally not more than £1,000. Commissions, music copying and recording projects are not priorities. Student tuition, travel or living expenses rarely given. Trustees meet three times per year. No application forms.
1 Dean Farrar Street, London
SW1H 0DY
Contact: Gwyn Rhydderch (Secretary)

Music in Scotland Trust

Secures funding in the form of grants and low interest loans to people between 18 and 25 who are setting up new music-related businesses in Scotland. Also runs an annual awards competition.
PO Box 183, Glasgow G3 8DG
Tel: 0141 204 3520
Contact: John Dingwall

Oppenheim John Downs Memorial Trust

Annual awards in December to deserving artists of any kind over 30 (parents are UK subjects and grandparents born in UK) who are unable to pursue their vocation by reason of poverty. Awards vary depending upon need and number of applications to between £50 and £1000. Larger awards for exceptional applicants.
Reference 13, 36 Whitefriars Street, London EC4Y 8BH

Park Lane Group Composer Award

Annual £2,000 award. Further details from organisers.
Park Lane Group, Russell Chambers, Covent Garden Piazza, London WC2E 8AA

Peter Whittingham Award

Promotes composition and performance in the field of jazz and popular music. Offered to projects in creation, performance, teaching or research. £3,000 available for 1995. Award may be divided between more than one applicant. Application form available July with interviews in October.
16 Ogle Street, London W1P 7LG
Contact: Awards Administrator

Pierre Fournier Award

The Philharmonia Orchestra grants this biennial award to a promising postgraduate cellist to help with costs of a début recital. Upper age limit 28.
76 Great Portland Street, London W1N 5AL
Contact: The Administrator

Prince's Trust

Has a number of different schemes and programmes to encourage groups and individuals aged 14 to 25 to develop their talents. Particular emphasis is placed on the disadvantaged and projects which help the community.
National Office, 8 Bedford Row, London WC1R 4BA
Contact: Director of Finance and Administration

Professor Charles Leggat Trust

For brass players over 18 but under 26 by closing date. 1995 for French horn, 1996 trombone and 1997 tuba. Closing date November, auditions January. Entry fee £10.
Leggat Awards, 16 Ogle Street, London W1P 7LG
Contact: Awards Administrator

Ralph Vaughan Williams Trust

Concerned with assisting young composers and promoting works by neglected past composers. Funds available for copying parts for scheduled performances, for extra rehearsals of new works and to offset costs of small societies in concerts or festivals where British music is a feature. Write for further details, including restrictions.
7th Floor, Manfield House, 376-379 Strand, London WC2R 0LR
Contact: Bernard Benoleil (Administrator)

Sascha Lasserson Memorial Prize

The trust has decided to terminate its biennial competition in favour of offering assistance for study in the form of grants to violinists under 18. At time of printing this was under review by the trustees. Send sae for details.
Sascha Lasserson Memorial Trust, 127 Lynton Road, London SE1 5QX
Contact: Hon Secretary

SOURCES OF FUNDING

Scottish Arts Council

Training and travel bursaries. Will consider applications from professional musicians, based in Scotland, who wish to develop skills or to diversify into new areas. Applications are considered annually.
12 Manor Place, Edinburgh EH3 7DD
Tel: 0131 226 6051
Contact: Music Officer

Sir Henry Richardson Award

Alternately for accompanists and repetiteurs at postgraduate level with considerable talent and the intention to make careers in their respective fields. 1995 - accompanists. 1995 closing date April, auditions May. Application forms. Entry fee £10.
16 Ogle Street, London W1P 7LG
Contact: Awards Administrator

Stephen Arlen Award

For individuals pursuing a professional career intending to initiate an imaginative programme of further study, removed from academy or university training. 1995 deadline 28 February. Up to £3,000 awarded periodically. Application forms given.
London Coliseum, St Martin's Lane, London WC2N 4ES
Contact: The Secretary

Sybil Tutton Awards

For operatic students under 30 at advanced level of training (postgraduate). Two awards offered up to £7,500 mainly to cover maintenance costs. 1995 closing date 16 February, auditions in March. Application forms available from November. Entry fee £10.
16 Ogle Street, London W1P 7LG
Contact: Awards Administrator

Trevor Snoad Award

Awarded by the Philharmonia Orchestra. Full particulars and application forms given.
76 Great Portland Street, London W1N 5AL
Contact: The Administrator

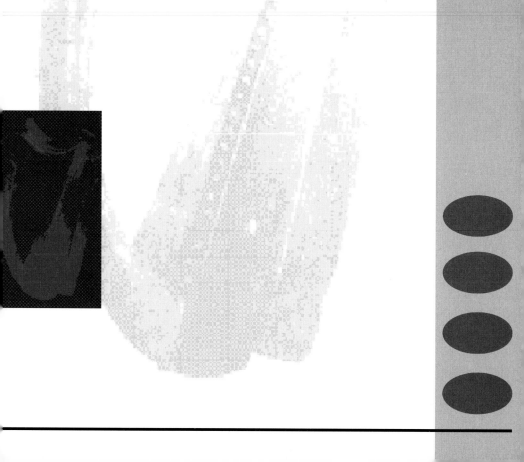

PUBLICITY AND MARKETING

Marketing Music in Scotland

by Ian Bone

Successful marketing requires the employment of a number of fundamental practices. However, it is important to realise that marketing is not an exact science and that all the methodology discussed may be adapted to suit particular circumstances. The four main areas of the marketing mix that must be addressed when structuring a marketing plan are *product*, *price*, *place* and *promotion*.

In order to deal with these areas effectively market research must be carried out. As the market place becomes increasingly competitive and consumers are given more purchasing options, organisations and individuals must become more sophisticated in their approach to the provision of services. In the past flair and initiative were in many cases sufficient to ensure success. In the present market, flair and initiative are still valuable commodities, but research can provide vital information that will aid the making of informed management decisions. Research must be viewed as an on-going process and be monitored throughout the lifecycle of the marketing plan. The market information gained before a plan is implemented may change radically over the period of a few months, and as a result those involved in the marketing must constantly monitor changes in circumstances, and be ready to adapt strategies accordingly. Whenever possible accurate records should also be maintained, so that details of both the successes and failures of the campaign will be available to aid the planning of future marketing initiatives. The accumulation of market research through traditional methods may be prohibitively expensive, but other options are available. The most cost-effective means is to talk to as many individuals already operating in the market as possible. In most cases, unless the event would represent direct competition, most promoters will be willing to share information and observations on current market trends.

The final piece of preparation required before the marketing plan is constructed is some self analysis of the resources available to the individual or organisation. A popular and effective method of gaining this information is to carry out a SWOT analysis, this abbreviation standing for Strengths, Weaknesses, Opportunities and Threats. Due to the lack of space a detailed discussion of SWOT analysis is not possible, but a number of publications are available on the subject. Once carried out, the SWOT analysis should give a clear picture of where the organisation or individual is at present and what they trying to achieve. The marketing plan is the method by which the gap between these two points can be traversed.

When considering music as a *product* it is vital that it is viewed in the context of the market place. Music is a service and must be viewed as such in order to be marketed properly. What the promoter is selling to the audience is not purely music, but a musical experience which must provide satisfaction if further ticket sales are to be achieved. The music being played may be technically brilliant, but if the surroundings and atmosphere are not conducive to a pleasurable experience for the audience then service is devalued. When decisions are being made about the type of music or event to be staged due consideration must be given to its uniqueness, or any unique selling points it may have in relation to other products being offered by other promoters or venues. The consumer must be convinced that the product you are offering can not be obtained elsewhere. The form the unique selling point takes is not important, but the fact that it exists is vital. Caution should be exercised with new projects as evidence shows that many new ventures or services fail despite the fact that the concept is unique. Research has shown that the most common reasons for failure include: not giving enough management time to the new venture, not ensuring that adequate

165

demand exists and not ensuring sufficient financial support for the project. Market segmentation must also be given consideration.

The promoter must decide if the event is to be aimed at a large cross section of the market place, or at a smaller, specialist audience. Factors to be taken into account while making this decision include the demographics of the potential consumers with income, age, social status and geographical location all influencing the rest of the marketing mix.

The *pricing* of any concept or event is a difficult task because of the number of factors which have to be taken into account. The prices set must obviously cover the overheads incurred. Research must be done to establish the cost of similar products within the chosen field. In the past the music business has been guilty of ignoring other forms of entertainment. This can no longer be tolerated as consumers have an ever growing choice of leisure time activities on which to spend their disposable income. Pricing must be sensitive to the target market in terms of demographic factors such as age and social profile of the potential consumers. Due consideration must also be given to concessionary pricing, with discounted tickets available for special interest groups, such as the disabled and the unemployed, whenever possible. The failure to

provide concessionary tickets may well lead to the alienation of a significant market, and in many cases to a great deal of adverse publicity.

Once the pricing of tickets has been established there are a number of techniques that can be implemented to help sales. If the cost of tickets for an event seems to be higher than the consumer is used to paying, emphasis must be placed on the quality of the product or the uniqueness of the event. Research has shown that one of the most powerful ways to overcome consumer concern about price is to establish the belief that the product or service has a quality not available elsewhere in the market. When possible, consumers should be given the opportunity to spread the cost of payments, for example through direct debit mandates or bankers' orders, both of which are well established in the market place and benefit both promoter and consumer. As a final general comment on pricing, every effort should be made to have tickets on sale for an event at the earliest opportunity.

The consideration of *place* in the marketing mix is more limited within the music field than it would be under competitive commercial conditions. As well as the consideration of cost, seating capacity and acoustics, other factors must be taken into account. The most important of these is access in its broadest sense. The

geographic location of the potential market must be taken into account when deciding on the venue. The frequency of public transport and the availability of parking play a significant role in the ticket purchasing decisions of consumers. As has been stressed elsewhere, the removal of potential obstacles from the path of potential consumers must be of paramount importance. Attention must be given to special needs groups; access for the disabled must meet current legislative standards. In the context of music, *place* also encompasses the locations at which tickets are to be sold. The box office facilities available at venues should also be a contributory factor in the choice of venue, and the links the venue box office has with other venues must also be taken into consideration. For example the benefits of a city-wide box office link system means that the public not only has a wide variety of purchase points to choose from, making it easier to buy tickets for all performances and events, but also has more access to information on all aspects of arts related events.

The importance of *promotion* within the marketing mix can not be over-emphasised. Within the area of promotion there are two distinct sub-divisions: the first is promotion that is paid for, in all of its various guises, and the second is Public Relations.

Within the overall budget for any event advertising plays a significant role. The choice of advertising media is one that should be given a great deal of consideration. Due to the significant costs involved, advertising through television is an option which in most instances can be discounted. However, television networks are aware of the need to attract potential advertising revenue and frequently offer competitive short-term package deals. Music events particularly benefit from the aural and visual impact of television advertising. Advertising through the national press offers the best opportunity to reach large sections of the population. While the cost of press advertising is significant it does offer the chance for greater target marketing, in that any reputable publication will be able to provide an in-depth analysis of its readers profiles. As with other areas of research every effort should be made to contact other promoters who have advertised similar events in similar publications. In terms of target marketing consideration should be given to specialist publications. The advantage that such publications offer is that in terms of cost they give greater value, because they give advertisers direct access to consumers who have shown commitment to specific goods or services by the very act of purchasing the publication.

If the greatest proportion of the promotional budget is to be spent on advertising then consideration should be given to the employment of an advertising agency. While there are some associated costs, in most instances the cost is offset by the expertise, advice and support given. When buying advertising either direct or through an agency never pay the rate card price; all prices quoted for advertising are negotiable.

The next area of promotion to be considered is that of leaflets and posters. In general for the promotion of music events, leaflets and flyers should be considered as essential. As with advertising this can be a difficult area for the uninitiated, as printing tends to have a language of its own. There are, however, a number of print brokers and designers who will be willing to handle the whole production process from design to print, for a fee. If cost saving is of premium importance the buying of design, reproduction and print can be done direct at significant savings, but detailed quotes should always be obtained. The novice should also be aware that any alterations or mistakes to the final printed material can be extremely costly.

Once the printed material has been produced the problems of distribution must be addressed. The advantage of leaflets is that the promoter is able to influence exactly where the material will be displayed.

A number of distribution companies exist that can offer services tailored to the needs of clients. The distribution of leaflets to patrons leaving other venues or performances similar to your own can represent a very effective marketing tool. It should be noted, however, that as a matter of protocol it is good practice to ask the permission of the other venue before distributing material outside their building. In many cases other promoters may be willing to allow leaflets to be placed on the seats of their performance for a small fee, a practice which offers a very cost effective means of reaching a target market.

The use of direct marketing can also be considered. This form of promotion has increased significantly over the past few years. There are many people who despise what is often called 'junk mail', but prestigious companies such as American Express use it to great effect. To be effective it is vital to use up-to-date mailing lists, which can often be purchased from other promoters or venues. The greatest asset of such mailing lists is that they are specifically targeted at consumers that have shown an interest in the product. If direct mail is to be considered it should be noted that professionals in the industry feel that a response rate of 10% should be considered a success. With the response rate at such a low level direct mail can only be considered as a supplement to the main promotional activities.

Public Relations used effectively can gain an organisation or event a great deal of publicity without the inherent costs of advertising. It would-be misleading to state, however, that PR is free advertising, as a great deal of time application is often required to ensure effective PR. The basis of PR is the establishment of contacts with publications in your area of interest, in addition to the local and national press. Many individuals and organisations seem intimidated by contacting the press; however, this apprehension is unfounded as most publications will welcome information. It should be borne in mind that editors and journalists are fighting a constant battle to fill pages with relevant and interesting articles. The problems that some organisations face when it comes to getting press coverage is not that the information they are trying to provide is not newsworthy, but rather that it is not presented in the right form. Space does not permit a detailed discussion of the writing of press releases, but there are a good number of very good publications available on the subject which would represent a sound investment for any organisation. As well as writing press releases, publicity can be gained through the use of photocalls. When

considering photocalls it is important that the planning is done with the publications in mind. In order to convince a picture editor to send a photographer you must be offering the chance of a photograph which is unique. The more unusual the potential picture opportunity the better the chance there is of it appearing in print.

In conclusion, it should be noted that the information given here is of a basic nature and that further study of marketing techniques is recommended. As has already been stated, marketing is not an exact science, but through constant monitoring and adaptation, marketing plans can be a significant management tool and greatly improve the profitability of ventures.

Ian Bone is the Press and Public Relations Manager of the Glasgow Royal Concert Hall.

Editorial Notes

The chapter provides basic information and contact details for radio, television and the Scottish press, as well as several video production companies. Radio and television companies based outwith Scotland have been included if their broadcasts cover Scotland, e.g. Radio 1, Channel 4 etc. It should be noted that several of the entries in the Scottish press section are listed as newspaper groups and may well publish several local papers.

169

THE MEDIA

RADIO

All Edinburgh Radio
Covering Edinburgh and immediate environs.
PO Box 1111, Edinburgh EH7 5JN
Contact: Jeff Ruderham

BBC Highland
7 Culduthel Road, Inverness IV2 4AD
Tel: 01463 720720 Fax: 01463 236125
Contact: Alisdair MacKinnon (Music Producer)

BBC Radio Orkney
Commercial Union House, Castle Street, Kirkwall, Orkney KW15 1DF
Tel: 01856 873939 Fax: 01856 872908
Contact: John Ferguson (Senior Producer)

BBC Radio Scotland
Classical music output for Radio 3 and Radio Scotland. BBC Scottish Symphony Orchestra.
Broadcasting House, Queen Margaret Drive, Glasgow G12 8DG
Tel: 0141 339 8844 Fax: 0141 357 1283
Contact: Hugh Macdonald (Head of Music (Music Department)) Tel: 0141 338 2489

BBC Radio Scotland
Entertainment Department: folk, rock, jazz, roots, etc. Programmes such as Celtic Connections, Travelling Folk, Country, plus Radio 1 Rock Show and piping programmes.
Broadcasting House, Queen Margaret Drive, Glasgow G12 8DG
Tel: 0141 339 8844 Fax: 0141 338 2657
Contact: Stewart Cruickshank (Senior Producer (Light Entertainment Department)) or Helen Munro or Angus Lyon (Senior Producers)

BBC Radio Scotland
Usual Suspects - arts based programme.
5 Queen Street, Edinburgh EH2 1NN
Tel: 0131 469 4214 Fax: 0131 469 4220
Contact: Jane Fowler (Senior Producer)

BBC Radio Shetland
Brentharn House, Lerwick, Shetland ZE1 0LR
Tel: 01595 694747 Fax: 01595 694747
Contact: Mary Blake (Senior Producer)

BBC Solway
Elmbank, Lovers' Walk, Dumfries DG1 1NZ
Tel: 01387 268008 Fax: 01387 252568
Contact: Glenn Cooksley (Senior Producer)

BBC World Service
Bush House, Strand , London WC2B 4PH
Tel: 0171 240 3456 Fax: 0171 379 3984
Contact: Jenny Bild (Executive Producer (Classical Music)) or Dave Tate (Executive Producer (Popular Music))

Classic FM
Academic House, 24-28 Oval Road, London NW1 7DQ
Tel: 0171 284 3000 Fax: 0171 713 2630
Contact: Anna Gregory (Head of Music)

Forth FM
Top 40, new releases. Daytime station with specialist programmes in dance, soul and indie.
Forth House, Forth Street, Edinburgh EH1 3LF
Tel: 0131 556 9255 Fax: 0131 556 1991
Contact: Jay Crawford (Head of Music), Tom Wilson (Music Co-ordinator) or John Collins (Programme Co-ordinator)

Heartland FM
Weekly two-hour programmes, alternating under the titles Classical Concert Hall and Journeys through Music. Features include a widespread concert events guide of 'live' music, new CD releases, the Top Ten classical 'hits' (monthly), 'building a library', and interviews with musicians, composers, festival directors, instrument makers, etc. Programmes cover mainstream and cross-over music.
Lower Oakfield, Pitlochry, Perthshire PH16 5DS
Tel: 01796 474040 Fax: 01796 474007
Contact: John D MacGregor (Producer/ Presenter) Tel: 01738 710378

Max AM
Night station featuring classic hits.
Forth House, Forth Street, Edinburgh EH1 3LF
Fax: 0131 556 1991
Contact: Jay Crawford (Head of Music) or Donny Hughes (Music Co-ordinator)

North Sound Radio
Split into 2 stations: North Sound 1 (FM) - top 40, current popular music. North Sound 2 (AM): wider range of music and interviews for 30s+.
45 Kings Gate, Aberdeen AB2 6BL
Tel: 01224 632234 Fax: 01224 637289
Contact: John Martin (Managing Director) or Neil McLeod (Head of Music)

Radio 1
BBC Broadcasting House, London W1A 1AA
Tel: 0171 580 4468 Fax: 0171 436 1636
Contact: Matthew Bannister (Controller of Radio 1)

Radio 2
BBC Broadcasting House, London W1A 1AA
Tel: 0171 580 4468 Fax: 0171 765 3373
Contact: Ms Francis Line (Controller of Radio 2)

Radio 3
BBC Broadcasting House, London W1A 1AA
Tel: 0171 580 4468 Fax: 0171 323 9620
Contact: Nicholas Kenyon (Controller of Radio 3)

Radio 4
BBC Broadcasting House, London W1A 1AA
Tel: 0171 580 4468 Fax: 0171 765 3822
Contact: Michael Green (Controller of Radio 4)

Radio 5
BBC Broadcasting House, London W1A 1AA
Tel: 0171 580 4468 Fax: 0171 765 3751
Contact: Jenny Abransky (Controller of Radio 5)

Radio Clyde
Broad range of popular light music for 30s+.
Clydebank Business Park, Clydebank, Glasgow G81 2RX
Tel: 0141 306 2200 Fax: 0141 951 1122
Contact: Mike Riddoch (Head of Clyde 2 (MW))

Radio Clyde
Current music: top 40.
Clydebank Business Park, Clydebank, Glasgow G81 2RX
Tel: 0141 306 2200 Fax: 0141 951 1122
Contact: Bobby Hain (Head of Clyde 1 (FM))

PUBLICITY & MARKETING

171

Radio Nan Gaidheal

Folk, fiddle, piping, etc music is broadcast.

Church Street, Stornoway, Isle of Lewis HS1 2LS
Tel: 01851 705000 Fax: 01851 704633
Contact: Mairead MacLennan

Radio Tay AM

Broadcast to over 35s. Jazz, country and folk.

6 North Isla Street, Dundee DD3 7JQ
Tel: 01382 200800 Fax: 01382 224549
Contact: Alex J Wilkie (Managing Director) or Richard Allan (Programme Co-ordinator)

Radio Tay FM

Broadcast to under 35s. Popular, rock, dance music.

6 North Isla Street, Dundee DD3 7JQ
Tel: 01382 200800 Fax: 01382 224549
Contact: Alex J Wilkie (Managing Director), Ally Ballingall (Programme Director) or John Darroch (Programme Co-ordinator)

Scot FM

Classics, rock, pop. New Scottish artists. American country. 25-44 age groups.

No 1 Shed, Albert Quay, Leith, Edinburgh EH6 7DN
Tel: 0131 554 6677 Fax: 0131 554 2266
Contact: Tom Hunter (Managing Director) or James Curran (Head of Music)

South West Sound

Same output as West Sound Radio. Broad range of programmes for all tastes. Age group 25+.

Campbell House, Bankend Road, Dumfries DG1 4TH
Tel: 01387 250999 Fax: 01387 265629
Contact: Gordon McArthur (Programme Director)

Virgin Radio

1 Golden Square, London W1R 4DJ
Tel: 0171 434 1215 Fax: 0171 434 1197
Contact: Suzy Mayzel (Head of Music)

West Sound Radio

Daytime - broad range of programmes. Age group 25+. Specialist programmes: dance, classic, country and western, rock, folk.

Radio House, 54 Holmston Road, Ayr KA7 3BE
Tel: 01292 283662 Fax: 01292 262607
Contact: Gordon McArthur (Programme Director)

TELEVISION

AVC Enterprises

Concerts. Outside broadcasts of music.

Greenbank Crescent, East Tullos, Aberdeen AB1 4BG
Tel: 01224 248007 Fax: 01224 248407
Contact: Neil Gordon (Business Manager) or Susan Wallace (Productions and Facilties Manager)

BBC Aberdeen

Produce programmes for BBC Radio Scotland: Take the Floor and Reel Blend.

Beechgrove Terrace, Aberdeen AB9 2ZT
Tel: 01224 625233 Fax: 01224 624888
Contact: Ken Mutche (Producer) Tel: x207 or 208

BBC Scotland

Broadcasting House, Queen Margaret Drive, Glasgow G12 8DE
Tel: 0141 339 8844 Fax: 0141 330 2527
Contact: John Archer (Head of Music and Arts) Tel: x2454 or May Miller (Senior Producer) Tel: x2455

BBC1 (Television)

BBC Television Centre, Wood Lane, Shepherd's Bush, London W12 7RS
Tel: 0181 743 8000 Fax: 0181 740 7965
Contact: Alan Yentob (Controller of BBC1)

BBC2 (Television)

BBC Television Centre, Wood Lane, Shepherd's Bush, London W12 7RJ
Tel: 0181 740 8000 Fax: 0181 740 7965
Contact: Michael Jackson (Controller of BBC2)

Border TV PLC

Television Centre, Carlisle, Cumbria CA1 3NT
Tel: 01228 25101 Fax: 01228 41384
Contact: Gwynne Challenger (Music Services)

C5TVC Ltd

Range of film and video production - including pop videos. Also Worldbeat Music, recording and production company.

Bridgend House, Lasswade EH18 1NA
Tel: 0131 654 2372 Fax: 0131 654 0816
Contact: Paul Blythe (Managing Director)

Channel Four Television

124 Horseferry Road, London SW1P 2TX
Tel: 0171 396 4444 Fax: 0171 306 8347
Contact: Waldemer Januszczak (Commissioning Editor for Arts and Music)

Edit 1, 2, 3

Post production: editing, graphics and other music related products. Sister company to Scope Picture Production Ltd.

123 Blythswood Street, Glasgow G2 4EN
Tel: 0141 248 3123 Fax: 0141 248 3423
Contact: Colin Seeley (Facilities Manager)

Eolas Productions Ltd

Wide range of documentaries in Gaelic and English. Arts and music programming.

7 James Street, Stornoway, Isle of Lewis HS1 2QN
Tel: 01851 705638 Fax: 01851 706577
Contact: Sam Maynard or Ann Morrison

Fields and Frames Production Ltd

Experimental TV/creative TV and the arts. Pop promos.

Corshellach, Brigend, Dunning PH2 0RS
Tel: 01764 684200 Fax: 01764 684200
Contact: Jane Rigby

Full Moon Productions

Documentaries, music video, corporate and broadcast.

16 Westbourne Gardens Lane, Glasgow G12 9PB
Tel: 0141 334 3591 Fax: 0141 334 3591
Contact: Barry Paton

Garfield Kennedy Company

Range of programming including the arts.

420 Sauchiehall Street, Glasgow G3 3JD
Tel: 0141 353 0456 Fax: 0141 353 1012
Contact: Garfield Kennedy (Producer)

Grampian Television PLC

Queen's Cross, Aberdeen AB9 2XJ
Tel: 01224 646464 Fax: 01224 635127
Contact: George Mitchell (Director of Programmes)

Hand Pict Independent Productions

Specialising in music and arts programmes.

4 Picardy Place, Edinburgh EH1 3JT
Tel: 0131 558 1543 Fax: 0131 556 0792
Contact: George Cathro (Director)

Ideal World Productions Ltd

Documentaries, drama, arts programming and magazine programme.

St Georges Studios, 93-97 St Georges Road, Glasgow G3 6JA
Contact: Zad Rogers (Managing Director)

Lomond Television

Arts and education programming.
40 Carlton Place, Glasgow G5 9TW
Tel: 0141 420 3132 Fax: 0141 420 3134
Contact: Alistair Scott (Producer)

Mirage Video

Range of music videos, general
promotional work.
*53 Newington Road, Edinburgh
EH9 1QW*
Tel: 0131 668 2010 Fax: 0131 668 2243
*Contact: Douglas Grey (Creative
Director)*

MNE Television (Media Nan Eilean Ltd)

An independent TV company covering
Gaelic, documentary, light entertainment/
music programmes.
24 Park Circus, Glasgow G3 6BE
Tel: 0141 353 3135 Fax: 0141 353 3105
*Contact: Alan MacDonald (Managing
Director) or John Carmichael
(Producer)*

Move On Up

Broad range of productions relating to
music: documentaries, film scores etc.
Laurel House, Cromarty IV11 8YR
Tel: 01381 600777 Fax: 01381 600778
Contact: Don Coutts or Lindy Cameron

Over The Moon Productions

Music and arts programming. Freelance.
*Maureen White, c/o Burngill Cottage,
Shore Road, Kilmun, Argyll PA23 8SB*
Tel: 01369 840625
*Contact: Maureen White (Television
Producer/Director)*

Pelicula Films Ltd

Music films for TV, drama and
documentaries.
*7 Queen Margaret Road, Glasgow
G20 6DP*
Tel: 0141 945 3333 Fax: 0141 946 8345
*Contact: Mike Alexander (Director/
Producer)*

REL Studios Ltd

Post production, sound effects, CD
library, voice and music production for
film, TV and radio. Also REL Film
Production and REL Records.
40 Sciennes, Edinburgh EH9 1NH
Tel: 0131 668 3366 Fax: 0131 662 4463
*Contact: Alasdair George (Managing
Director) or Bel Emslie (Studio
Manager)*

Scope Picture Production Ltd

Large independent production company
covering wide spectrum of music
programmes/video.
*Keppie House, 147 Blythswood Street,
Glasgow G2 4EN*
Tel: 0141 332 7720 Fax: 0141 332 1049
Contact: David Turner (Senior Producer)

Scottish Television PLC

Arts programmes include Don't Look
Down and NB. The present producer is
Ken Neil.
Cowcaddens, Glasgow G2 3PR
Tel: 0141 332 9999 Fax: 0141 332 6982
*Contact: Blair Jenkins (Director of
Broadcasting (Regional Programming))
or Alistair Moffat (Chief Executive for
STV Enterprises (Network
Programming))*

Skyline Film and Television Productions Ltd

Range of TV programmes including
music and arts.
10 Scotland Street, Edinburgh EH3 6PS
Tel: 0131 557 4580 Fax: 0131 556 4377
*Contact: Trevor Davies (Company
Director) or Leslie Hills (Company
Director)*

Wall to Wall

Range of programmes, including the arts.
*St Georges Studios, 93-97 St Georges
Road, Glasgow G3 6JA*
Tel: 0141 333 9822 Fax: 0141 353 1735
*Contact: Marie Divine (Development
Manager) or Fiona White (Producer)*

Wark Clements and Company

Wide range of programmes including arts
programmes.
*The Production Centre, The Tollgate,
Marine Crescent, Glasgow G51 1HD*
Tel: 0141 429 1750 Fax: 0141 429 1751
*Contact: Alan Clements (Producer) or
Judy Brown (Office Manager)*

THE SCOTTISH PRESS

The Courier

Daily newspaper.
80 Kingsway East, Dundee DD4 8SL
Tel: 01382 223131 Fax: 01382 454599

Dumfriesshire Newspapers

Newspaper group.
*96-98 High Street, Annan, Dumfries and
Galloway DG12 6DW*
Tel: 01461 202417 Fax: 01461 205659

Dunfermline Press Group

Newspaper group.
*Pitreavie Business Park, Dunfermline,
Fife KY11 5QS*
Tel: 01383 728201 Fax: 01383 739040

Evening Express

Daily newspaper.
*PO Box 43, Lang Stracht, Mastrick,
Aberdeen AB9 8AF*
Tel: 01224 690222 Fax: 01224 694613

Evening News

Daily newspaper.
20 North Bridge, Edinburgh EH1 1YT
Tel: 0131 225 2468 Fax: 0131 220 3714

Evening Times

Daily newspaper.
195 Albion Street, Glasgow G1 1QP
Tel: 0141 552 6255 Fax: 0141 552 1344

Fife Free Press

Newspaper group.
*22-25 Kirk Wynd, Kirkcaldy, Fife
KY1 1EP*
Tel: 01592 261451 Fax: 01592 204180

Glaswegian Publications

Newspaper group.
40 Anderston Quay, Glasgow G3 8DA
Tel: 0141 221 2121 Fax: 0141 242 3222

The Herald

Daily newspaper.
195 Albion Street, Glasgow G1 1QP
Tel: 0141 552 6255 Fax: 0141 552 1344

Highland News Group

Newspaper group.
*Henderson Road, Longman Industrial
Estate, Inverness IV1 1SN*
Tel: 01463 710999 Fax: 01463 221251

The List

Fortnightly.
14 High Street, Edinburgh EH1 1TE
Tel: 0131 558 1191 Fax: 0131 557 8500

PUBLICITY & MARKETING

173

Moray and Nairn Newspapers
Newspaper group.
175-177 High Street, Elgin IV30 1DP
Tel: 01343 548777 Fax: 01343 545629

Moray Firth Radio
PO Box 271, Inverness IV3 6SF
Tel: 01463 224433 Fax: 01463 713318
Contact: Thomas Prag (Managing Director) or Dave Cochrane (Head of Music)

Oban Times
Weekly newspaper.
PO Box 1 , Oban, Argyll PA34 5PY
Tel: 01631 63058 Fax: 01631 65470

The Orcadian
Weekly newspaper.
9 Victoria Street, Kirkwall, Orkney KW15 1DW
Tel: 01856 873249 Fax: 01856 873978

The Press and Journal
Daily newspaper.
PO Box 43, Lang Stracht, Mastrick, Aberdeen AB9 8AF
Tel: 01224 690222 Fax: 01224 694613

Scotland on Sunday
Weekly newspaper.
20 North Bridge, Edinburgh EH1 1YT
Tel: 0131 225 2468 Fax: 0131 220 3714

The Scotsman
Daily newspaper.
20 North Bridge, Edinburgh EH1 1YT
Tel: 0131 225 2468 Fax: 0131 220 3714

Scotsman Communications
Newspaper group.
38 Gardners Crescent, Edinburgh EH3 8DQ
Tel: 0131 228 5042 Fax: 0131 228 5580

Scottish and Universal Newspapers
Newspaper group.
Press Buildings, Campbell Street, Hamilton ML3 6AX
Tel: 01698 283200 Fax: 01698 891151

Shetland Times
Weekly newspaper.
Prince Alfred Street, Lerwick, Shetland ZE1 0EP
Tel: 01595 693622 Fax: 01595 694637

Stornoway Gazette
Weekly newspaper.
10 Francis Street, Stornoway, Isle of Lewis PA87 2XE
Tel: 01851 702678 Fax: 01851 706424

The Sunday Post
Weekly newspaper.
144 Port Dundas Road, Glasgow G4 0HZ
Tel: 0141 332 9933

Tweedale Press Group
Newspaper group.
90 Marygate, Berwick on Tweed TD15 1BW
Tel: 01289 306677 Fax: 01289 306677

West Highland Free Press
Newspaper group.
Industrial Estate, Broadford, Skye IV49 9AP
Tel: 01471 822464 Fax: 01471 822694

VIDEO

BGS Productions Ltd
Specialise in videos for traditional, Scottish and country music.
Newtown Street, Kilsyth, Glasgow G65 0JX
Tel: 01236 821081 Fax: 01236 826900
Contact: Douglas Stevenson (Managing Director)

Tonn-mor Visual Arts
Produce a variety of music videos, and music for films. Connected to Temple Records and Kinmor Music (publishers).
Shillinghill, Temple, Midlothian EH23 4SH
Tel: 01875 830328 Fax: 01875 830392
Contact: Robin Morton (Managing Director)

VIP
Social issue programming and community arts. Pop videos. Lothian Region funding.
30 Ferry Road Avenue, Edinburgh EH4 4BA
Tel: 0131 343 1151 Fax: 0131 343 2820
Contact: Joel Vennet or Hugh Farrell

PUBLICITY & MARKETING

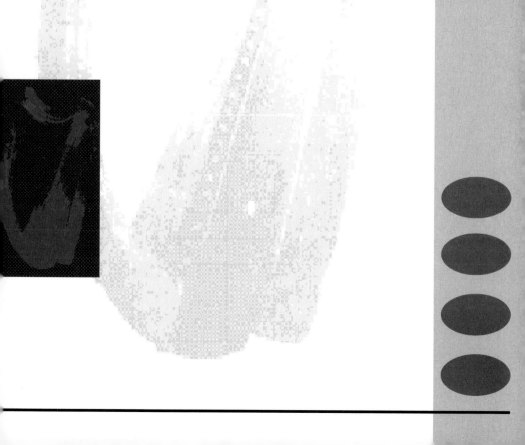

SUPPLIERS AND SERVICES

Editorial Notes

The chapter is divided into six main areas. Two of these, namely **PUBLISHERS** and **LIBRARIES AND MUSEUMS**, have no further subdivisions and entries are listed alphabetically. **PA AND LIGHTING** is arranged by region in the first instance and then alphabetically. The **COPYISTS** section is divided into two categories, HAND and COMPUTER, with alphabetical listings for each category.

The **RECORDING** section has been divided into four categories: RECORD COMPANIES, RECORDING STUDIOS, REHEARSAL STUDIOS, and RECORDING SERVICES. In this section it is inevitable that there will be some overlap between the categories, with some companies providing several different services. In general, if the recording studio is available for hire it is listed under RECORDING STUDIOS, but if it is a studio attached to a company which produces albums then it would be found under RECORD COMPANIES. Many RECORDING STUDIOS also have practice rooms and facilities but to save space these details have been included in the one entry rather than repeating entries in the REHEARSAL STUDIOS category. If you are looking for rehearsal space therefore, it would be worthwhile to look through both STUDIOS sections. RECORDING SERVICES deals mainly with companies offering tape and CD duplication.

The **INSTRUMENTAL** section is divided into eleven categories, two of which, GENERAL MUSIC STORE and PIANO TUNERS, are arranged by region. The sections BAGPIPES, BRASS AND WOODWIND, CLARSACH/SMALL HARP, ELECTRONIC, KEYBOARDS, PERCUSSION, and STRINGS cover makers, repairers, retailers, and hirers. Often, of course, one company will perform several of these functions, and this is detailed in the entry itself. GENERAL MUSIC STORE may also have hire schemes as well as selling instruments and sheet music, and many stores can arrange for repairs to be done.

Entries are listed alphabetically. However, it should be noted that an individual (usually an instrument maker) is listed by surname while a company is listed by the first word of its title, even if that title incorporates an individual's name. For example in the BAGPIPES category we have 'Daily, Jim' but 'David and Hamish Moore'. This should not be a problem as categories rarely fill more than one page and the *Handbook* is indexed. So, if you know exactly whom you are looking for the index could be the quickest way to find them.

INSTRUMENTAL

BAGPIPES

Anderson, Jas
Maker, repairer. Scottish small pipes, Borders pipes and mouth blown pipes.
5 Dundarroch Street, Larbert FK5 3AA
Tel: 01324 557991

The Bagpipe Centre
Retailer, repairer. All types of pipes sold and accessories. Also Blackfriars Publishers.
49 Blackfriars Street, Edinburgh EH1 1NB
Tel: 0131 557 3090 Fax: 0131 557 3090

Bagpipes of Caledonia
Maker, repairer, retailer. Bagpipes. Also tuition products, music publications, cassettes and accessories.
Lorn House, Links Garden Lane, Leith, Edinburgh EH6 7JQ
Tel: 0131 553 5503 Fax: 0131 553 5550
Contact: Jane Lawson

Begg, James
Retailer. Maker of bagpipe bags. Supplier of bagpipe accessories.
85 Renfield Street, Glasgow G2 1LP
Tel: 0141 333 0639

Clan Bagpipes
Maker, repairer. Scottish Highland bagpipes. All hand crafted. Practice chanter starter kit, reeds and accessories.
13a James Court, Lawnmarket, Edinburgh EH1 2PB
Tel: 0131 225 2415

Daily, Jim
Maker, repairer. Uilleann pipes, pastoral pipes and lowland pipes. Also wooden flutes.
29 Clouston Street, Maryhill, Glasgow G20 8QR
Tel: 0141 946 3711

David and Hamish Moore
Maker. Established 1986, specialise in individually hand-crafted Scottish small pipes and Border pipes. Each set is meticulously reeded, tuned and played in by Hamish Moore, resulting in a rich, well-balanced tone and ease of playing. Also available, 'A' Highland pipes, copied from the 1785 Black Set of Kintail.
Grianach, St Mary's Road, Birnam, Perthshire PH8 0BJ
Tel: 01350 727474 Fax: 01350 727474
Contact: Hamish Moore or David Moore

Discount Highland Supply
Retailer, repairer. Bagpipe and practice chanters, sale and repair. Bagpipe accessories. Hire of Highland dress.
Main Street, Gordon TD3 6JN
Tel: 01573 410385 Fax: 01573 410385

Gillanders and McLeod Ltd
Maker, retailer. Bagpipes. Supplier of band uniforms and accessories.
103 Whitehouse Loan, Edinburgh EH9 1AT
Tel: 0131 447 8863 Fax: 0131 452 8709
Contact: Stuart MacKay Tel: 01307 463156

Goodacre, Julian
Maker, retailer. Lowland and Scottish small pipes from museum examples. English, Welsh, Cornish, Italian bagpipes in British hardwoods. Books, prints, accessories.
4 Elcho Street, Peebles EH45 8LQ
Tel: 01721 722539 Fax: 01721 729514

Hugh McPherson (Scotland) Ltd
Retailer, repairer. Bagpipes and accessories. Pipe band centre, pipe band music books.
17 West Maitland Street, Edinburgh EH12 5EA
Tel: 0131 225 4008 Fax: 0131 225 9823
Contact: Alison Ross

Inveran House
Maker, repairer. Bagpipes.
10 Dean Street, Edinburgh EH4 1LW
Tel: 0131 332 8115

Kilberry Bagpipes Edinburgh
Maker, repairer, retailer. Manufacturer of own make of Highland, Scottish small, and chamber pipes with retail outlet. Repairs, replacements and refurbishment of pipes - can tackle any job concerning pipes. Piping accessories such as reeds, hemp, covers, cords, music books, cases, CDs, cassettes, etc.
38 Lochrin Buildings, Gilmore Place, Edinburgh EH3 9ND
Tel: 0131 221 9925 Fax: 0131 221 9925
Contact: Neil Manderson (Proprietor) Tel: 0131 557 0256

Kintail Bagpipes
Maker, repairer, retailer. Bagpipes, Scottish small pipes and practice chanters. Manufacturer of bagpipes by Drumran, David Glen and J and R Glen. All accessories. Restoration work. Brochure available.
The Old Telephone Exchange, Fountain Road, Bridge of Allan FK9 4ET
Tel: 01786 834454 Fax: 01786 834454
Contact: Greig Sharp

McLeod Highland Supplies
Retailer. Retail and wholesale of bagpipes and accessories.
136 Bridgegate, Glasgow G1 5HZ
Tel: 0141 553 1513

McNulty, Pat
Maker, repairer. Uilleann pipes.
30 Parkhill Drive, Rutherglen, Glasgow G73 2PW
Tel: 0141 647 5163

Piob Mhor
Maker, repairer, retailer. Bagpipes. Practice chanters and accessories.
39-43 High Street, Blairgowrie PH10 6DA
Tel: 01250 872131 Fax: 01250 874741
Contact: Ruthven Milne or Gwen Milne

R G Hardie and Co
Maker, repairer, retailer. Bagpipes.
24 Renfrew Street, Glasgow G2 3BN
Tel: 0141 332 3021 Fax: 0141 332 8381
Contact: Mr Weatherston.

R T Shepherd and Son
Maker, retailer. Bagpipe and bagpipe reed manufacturers. Developers of the world's first all plastic drone reed. Instruments played by pipe band world champions Shotts and Dykehead Pipe Band under P/M Robert Mathieson.
164 Jamphlars Road, Cardenden, Fife KY5 0ND
Tel: 01592 720130 Fax: 01592 721857

SUPPLIERS & SERVICES

179

Richard Bagpipes

Maker, repairer. Maker specialising in Scottish Lowland (or Border) bagpipes and keyed bagpipe chanters (extended range to fully chromatic - Highland and Lowland). Keywork made in classical style (as oboe etc). Also Scottish small pipes, and instrument repairs (woodwind and strings).
9 Beresford Avenue, Edinburgh EH5 3EU
Tel: 0131 551 1726

Rutzen, John

Maker of Scottish small pipes. Bellows blown. Keys of A, B flat, C, D.
Sunshine Cottage, Kirkton Road, Rattray, Blairgowrie, Perth PH10 7DZ
Tel: 01250 87831

Thistle Bagpipe Works

Maker, repairer and retailer. Bagpipes. Kiltmaker and Highland dress hire. Accessories.
Luss, Loch Lomond G83 8NX
Tel: 01436 860250
Contact: James Kirkpatrick (Proprietor)

Weston, John

Maker, repairer. Bagpipes.
44 Borestone Place, St Ninians, Stirling FK7 0PL
Tel: 01786 475406

William Sinclair and Son

Maker, retailer. Bagpipes.
1 Madeira Street, Edinburgh EH6 4AJ
Tel: 0131 554 3489 Fax: 0131 554 3489
Contact: Alistair Sinclair

BRASS & WOODWIND

Band Supplies

Retailer, repairer. Woodwind and brass sales. Music, books and accessories.
5 Old Dumbarton Road, Glasgow G3 8QY
Tel: 0141 339 9400 Fax: 0141 334 8157

Cameron, Rod

Maker of historic woodwinds, especially baroque flutes, for c.20 years. Also has workshop in California and divides his time between Scotland and USA.
39 Union Street, Nairn IV12 4PR
Tel: 01667 455584 Fax: 01667 455584

Clydesdale Music

Maker, repairer. Hand made 18th and 19th c. simple system and baroque flutes.
82 Crosswood Terrace, Tarbrax, West Calder EH55 8XE
Tel: 01501 785416
Contact: George Ormiston

Daily, Jim

Maker, repairer. Wooden flutes, uilleann pipes, pastoral pipes and lowland pipes.
29 Clouston Street, Maryhill, Glasgow G20 8QR
Tel: 0141 946 3711

Foster, Charles

Maker. Renaissance woodwind instruments.
Glen Cottage, 63 Holburn Street, Aberdeen AB1 6BS
Tel: 01224 580024

Just Music

Retailer. Brass and woodwind music, books and exam pieces.
246 Auldhouse Road, East Kilbride G75 9DX
Tel: 013552 45674 Fax: 013552 31020

Kirkpatricks Musical Instrument Repair

Repairer. Brass and woodwind.
The Studio, Burnfoot Lane, Falkirk FK1 5BH
Tel: 01324 612258

Martin Neale Musical Instrument Repairs

Repairer. Professionally qualified in repair and servicing of woodwind, brass and strings. (Member of the National Association of Musical Instrument Repairers).
24 Obsdale Park, Alness, Ross-shire IV17 0TP
Tel: 01349 883347
Contact: Martin Neale

Musical Instrument Services

Repairer, hirer. Brass and woodwind.
Front Row, Aberargie, Perth PH2 9NB
Tel: 01738 850700
Contact: Stewart Benzie

Normans Musical Instruments Ltd

Retailer. Brass and woodwind.
The Studio, Burnfoot Lane, Falkirk FK1 5BH
Tel: 01324 611895 Fax: 01324 634611

Richard Bagpipes

Repairer. Woodwind repairs. (Also bagpipe maker and string repairs).
9 Beresford Avenue, Edinburgh EH5 3EU
Tel: 0131 551 1726

Rutzen, John

Maker. Keyless Irish flutes in D for traditional music.
Sunshine Cottage, Kirkton Road, Rattray, Blairgowrie, Perth PH10 7DZ
Tel: 01250 873831

Sanderson and Taylor Ltd

Retailer, repairer. Sale of Fox bassoons and oboes plus accessories.
6 Barclay Terrace, Bruntsfield, Edinburgh EH10 4HP
Tel: 0131 229 2051
Contact: Laurence Taylor

CLARSACH / SMALL HARP

Ardival Harps

Maker. Modern clarsachs and historical Scottish harps. Range includes triangular gut-strung pictish harps, brass-strung clarsachs with hollowed-out soundboxes and harps with buzzing bray pins. 34 string modern clarsachs come standard with brass levers or deluxe with Loveland levers and coopered soundbox.
Orchard House, Castle Leod, Strathpeffer, Ross-shire IV14 9AA
Tel: 01997 421260 Fax: 01997 421260

Brown and Bruce

Maker. Hand-made clarsachs to order.
29 Grange Road, Edinburgh EH9 1UQ
Tel: 0131 667 6533
Contact: R G Bruce

Forbes, Hugh

Maker, repairer. Makes and sells own instruments. Also works on sub-contract basis. Paraguayan harps, clarsachs and older style harps. Hammer and Appalachian dulcimers.
20 Pritchard Crescent, Beauly, Inverness IV4 7EU
Tel: 01463 782750

Fountain Harps

Maker, repairer, hirer. Supplier of strings, hardware, hard/soft cases. Beginners' workshops. One day introductory tuition with harps provided. No experience necessary.
Borthaugh, Hawick, Roxburghshire TD9 7LN
Tel: 01450 377477 Fax: 01450 371080
Contact: James Maybury

Hobrough, Tim

Maker. One of the founders of the movement towards 'authentic' construction of medieval, renaissance and baroque harps. Full-time professional since 1972. Historical harps made to appropriate structural and aesthetic criteria. Also supplies the 'Widsith' brand of low-cost harps, northern lyres and medieval vielles and crowdes.
The Harpmakers' Workshop, 1103 Argyle Street, Glasgow G3 8NQ
Tel: 0774 005061 (messagepoint)

Norris, Mark

Maker of small harps.
The Old School, Stobo, Peebles EH45 8NU
Tel: 01721 760298 Fax: 01721 760298

Starfish Designs

Maker, repairer. Range of seven instruments including knee harp. 26 to 34 strings. Folk or concert stringing.
Unit Four, Old Ferry Road, North Ballachulish, By Fort William, Inverness-shire PH33 6SA
Tel: 01855 821429 Fax: 01855 821577
Contact: Mike Anderson or Gay Anderson

Wall, Steve

Maker, repairer. Beginners' clarsachs.
Burnfoot Lodge, Barskimming, Mauchline, Ayrshire KA5 5TB
Tel: 01290 Fax: 552020

Yule, John

Maker. Clarsachs.
Carnethie Cottage, Silverburn, Penicuik, Midlothian EH16 9LQ
Tel: 01968 672877

ELECTRONIC

Asimov Electro

Maker, repairer. Custom built amplifiers, electronic equipment. Repairs to all electronic equipment including keyboards, guitars, PA and amplifiers. Repair and modification to accordions.
Barntimpin House, St Anns, Lockerbie, Dumfries DG11 1HL
Tel: 01576 470222
Contact: Matthew Grant

Gurney, Kevin

Repairer. Amplifier, electronic and string repairs.
2 Jamaica Lane, Greenock PA15 1XY
Tel: 01475 888694 Fax: 01475 888694

West End TV and Video

Repairer. Amplifier and electronic equipment repairs.
74 Norse Road, Scotstoun, Glasgow G14 9EF
Tel: 0141 959 2797

KEYBOARDS

Aeolian

Retailer, repairer, tuner. Pianos bought and sold. Specialises in pianolas etc. Restoration and tuning.
4 Chapel Street, Galashiels TD1 1BU
Tel: 01896 752308
Contact: Malcolm Beattie (Proprietor)

Allan Makin and Sons

Retailer, hirer, repairer, tuner. Acoustic piano. Valuations.
4 and 5 Summer Place, Inverleith Row, Edinburgh EH3 5NR
Tel: 0131 556 1287 Fax: 0131 557 1287
Contact: Colin Makin

Barnes, John

Maker, repairer. Maker of harpsichords and clavichords. Repair and restoration of old keyboard instruments. Sale of keyboard kits.
3 East Castle Road, Edinburgh EH10 5AP
Tel: 0131 229 8018

Billy McEwen Organs

Retailer, repairer. Organ, keyboard, synthesiser, piano, PA and keyboard amplifier sales. Repairs to instruments sold from shop. Technics Music Academy housed. In-house tuition.
31-35 Fort Street, Ayr KA7 1DG
Tel: 01292 269667 Fax: 01292 289597

SUPPLIERS & SERVICES

EINE KLEINE NACHTMUSIK

Whatever time the muse takes you, a Yamaha Silent Piano will always strike the right chord.

By day it's a fine, resonant, traditional piano.

But at night, or when necessary, practice can be perfectly quiet.

Using an ingenious third pedal mechanism, the strings are silenced and the Silent Piano's alter ego takes over.

A digitally sampled Yamaha grand responds note for note to your every touch.... through headphones.

It feels the same, looks the same, but your neighbours will think you moved out.

Don't sleep on it, call 01908 366700 today for a free brochure.

Yamaha-Kemble Music (UK) Ltd. Acoustic Division

Edinburgh Organ Studio

Retailer, repairer. Electric keyboards, organs, digital pianos. Repair workshop including full-time engineer.
98 Canongate, Royal Mile, Edinburgh EH8 8DD
Tel: 0131 556 3005 Fax: 0131 556 8445
Contact: William McIntosh

The Edinburgh Piano Company

Retailer, hirer, repairer, piano tuner, piano removal. New and second hand pianos.
Edgar Hall, Chesser Avenue, Edinburgh EH14 1TA
Tel: 0131 443 5999
Contact: James Cameron

Edmonstone, Alexander

Maker, repairer. Pipe organ builders. All acoustic keyboard repairs.
The Workshop, Forteviot, Perth PH2 9BT
Tel: 01764 684451

Henry Willis and Sons Ltd

Maker, restorer, tuner. Organs.
50 The Oval, Clarkston, Glasgow G76 8LZ
Tel: 0141 637 8275
Contact: John McCarron (Scottish Representative) or Head Office Tel:01730 263141

Hill Norman and Beard

Repairer. Tuning, maintenance, surveys of pipe organs. Advice given on new organs and rebuilding/restoration.
81 Thorncroft Drive, Condorrat, Cumbernauld G67 4JT
Tel: 01236 723136
Contact: Mr H Tomlinson (Scottish Representative) or Head Office Tel: 01371 830338

Jones H G and Son

Maker, repairer, hirer. Organs.
Alderburn, Kippford, Dalbeattie DG5 4LL
Tel: 01556 620282
Contact: Herbert Granville Jones

Keyboard Repair Services

Repairer. Electronic keyboard and accordion repair. Midi installations.
Unit Six, Waukrigg Mill, Galashiels TD1 1QD
Tel: 01896 752025
Contact: Keith Robinson

Keyboard Services Scotland

Repairer. Electronic musical instrument repair.
9 Kingswood Road, Kingswells, Aberdeen AB1 8TD
Tel: 01224 744585
Contact: Allan Morrison

L G Harpsichords

Maker. Early keyboards. Also string instruments and early bows. 23 years' experience. Recipient of SDA fellowship in 1983.
The Cartshed, Pencaitland, East Lothian EH34 5BE
Tel: 01875 340057
Contact: Lionel Gliori

Lammermuir Pipe Organs

Maker, repairer. Make church, house and practice organs to order. Maintain and restore own organs.
Old Schoolhouse, Oldhamstocks, East Lothian TD13 5XN
Tel: 01368 830411
Contact: Neil Richerby

Macdonald, Michael

Repairer. Restores, maintains and tunes pipe organs.
39 Rockall Drive, Sunshill, Glasgow G44 5ES
Tel: 0141 637 1014

Malcolm Smith Pianos

Retailer, repairer. Piano technicians - tuning, repairs. Retailer - new and second hand, sales throughout Scotland.
35a Stenhouse Road, Edinburgh EH11 3LJ
Tel: 0131 443 6224
Contact: Perth Office Tel: 01738 440204 or Inverness Office Tel: 01463 711062

Martin, Darryl

Maker, repairer. Early keyboards.
3 East Castle Road, Edinburgh EH10 5AP
Tel: 0131 229 8018

Moray Firth Pianos

Retailer, repairer, tuner. Sale of new and second hand grand and upright pianos.
Milton Brodie, Forres IV36 0UA
Tel: 01343 850686 Fax: 01343 850686

Musicmakers

Retailer, repairer. Specialise in keyboards and digital piano. Also some guitars, music and accessories.
22 Chapelwell Street, Saltcoats, Ayrshire KA21 5EB
Tel: 01294 469807

Organ Stop

Retailer. Organs, keyboards, music and accessory sales. Tuition.
23 Stewart Street, Milngavie, Glasgow G62 6DW
Tel: 0141 956 4517

P S Pianos

Retailer, repairer, tuner. New and second hand pianos, transport and insurance arranged.
9 Canal Street, Paisley PA1 2HD
Tel: 0141 848 6500
Contact: Peter Smith

Peter Smith and Sons

Retailer, hirer, repairer, tuner, remover. New and second hand pianos.
The Piano Warehouse, 60 Back Sneddon Street, Paisley PA3 2BY
Tel: 0141 887 6160
Contact: Peter Smith

The Piano Workshop

Retailer, repairer. Also valuations and harpsichord hire.
1103 Argyle Street, Glasgow G3 8ND
Tel: 0141 221 1829

Rolston Accordians

Retailer, repairer. Accordions and accessories. Midi specialists.
61 Windmill Hill Street, Motherwell ML1 1TA
Tel: 01698 265350 Fax: 01698 265350
Contact: George Rolston or David Rolston

Smith, Ronald

Maker, repairer of organs.
Strathardle, Cockairney Fues, Cleish, Kinross KY13 7LQ
Tel: 01577 850298

PERCUSSION

Aberdeen Drum Centre

Retailer, repairer. Drum sales and accessories.
148 Hutcheon Street, Aberdeen AB2 3RX
Tel: 01224 620300
Contact: Mike Kidd

The Drum Shop

Retailer, repairer, hirer. Sale of percussion instruments and accessories.
15 Blackie Street, Glasgow G3 8TN
Tel: 0141 339 4497
Contact: Bob Kerr

SUPPLIERS &
SERVICES

183

Murray Seaton's Drum Centre

Retailer, repairer, hirer. Percussion.
66 South Clerk Street, Edinburgh
EH8 9PS
Tel: 0131 667 3844 Fax: 0131 688 4231

Porteous, Lindsay

Maker, repairer, retailer. Hand made goatskin bodhrans, wooden bones, dulcimers, harps, mouthbows and other folk instruments. Also minor repairs to instruments. Jew's harp and other instruments supplied.
Tron Workshop, Culross, Fife KY12 8JG
Tel: 01383 880271

STRINGS

Allan, Ian

Maker and repairer. Violins, violas, cellos and bows. Early music instruments including viola da gamba and medieval fiddles.
6 Grove Road, Broughty Ferry, Dundee
DD5 1JL
Tel: 01382 776043

Axis Guitars

Retailer, repairer. Specialist guitar shop. Amplifiers, music and accessories.
3 East Fountainbridge, Edinburgh
EH3 9BH
Tel: 0131 229 5092
Contact: David May

Beavitt, Alan

Maker of violins and violas in baroque and modern style.
Scorraig, Dundonnell, Ross-shire
IV23 2RE
Tel: 01854 633293

Bridge Music

Maker, repairer. Stringed instruments including violins, mandolins, banjos and guitars.
34 Pitfirriane Park, Crossford, Fife
KY12 8NU
Tel: 01383 720755
Contact: David Grant

C C Music

Retailer, hirer, repairer. Acoustic and electric, guitar sales, sheet music, books and accessories. PA and 4 track hire. Guitar and electronic repair.
33 Otago Street, Glasgow G12 8JJ
Tel: 0141 339 0566 Fax: 0141 339 7467
Contact: Steve Caban

Chalmers V and E Guitar Centre

Retailer, repairer. Specialists in guitars, particularly jazz. Amplifiers, guitar music. Tuition services.
9 Albert Street, Dundee DD4 6NS
Tel: 01382 457642

Dow, Marshall

Maker, repairer. Variety of stringed instruments, guitars, etc. Violins and violas custom built. Repair and restoration of all stringed instruments. Currently part time.
20 Gladstone Place, Woodside, Aberdeen
AB2 2RP
Tel: 01224 491365

Edwards, Aidan

Maker, repairer. Classical and steel string guitars. Psalteries made to order.
The Neuk, Strontian, Acharacle, Argyll
PH36 4HY
Tel: 01967 402194

Fay, Grant

Maker, repairer. Bow maker, repairer and rehairer.
The Old School, Ardgay, Sutherland
IV24 3BG
Tel: 01863 766483

The Fiddle and Guitar Shop

Maker, repairer. Maker of guitars, violins, mandolins. Restoration. Instruments bought and sold. Suppliers of hardwoods, veneers and instrument fittings.
The Old Schoolhouse, The Clachan, Campsie Glen, Glasgow G65 7AB
Tel: 01360 313004
Contact: Neil Baird

The Fiddle Gallery

Repairer, retailer. String instruments bought and sold. Bow rehairing. Valuation.
158 Queen Margaret Drive, Glasgow
G20 8NY
Tel: 0141 945 3113
Contact: Robert Nelson

Fyffe, Neil

Maker, repairer. Mandolins, octave mandolins and bouzouki.
The Old Carpenter's Workshop, Ballindalloch Castle, Ballindalloch, Aberlour AB37 9AX
Tel: 01340 831358 (H)

The Guitar Centre

Retailer. Vintage and jazz guitars and amplification.
21 Stonelaw Road, Rutherglen, Glasgow G73 3TW
Tel: 0141 613 3833

The Guitar Store

Retailer, repairer. Instruments, books and accessories.
185 Hope Street, Glasgow G2 2UN
Tel: 0141 331 2211 Fax: 0141 332 9521
Contact: Jim Cleland

Gurney, Kevin

Repairer. Guitars, violins, mandolins. General repairs, including electronic.
2 Jamaica Lane, Greenock PA15 1XY
Tel: 01475 888694 Fax: 01475 888694

Holton, Norrie

Maker, repairer. Violins, violas, cellos, double basses, guitars, mandolins, etc. Bow rehairing and repair. Instruments and bows bought and sold.
Cumbernauld
Tel: 01236 721032

L G Harpsichords

Maker of stringed instruments, early bows and early keyboards for 23 years. Recipient of SDA fellowship in 1983.
The Cartshed, Pencaitland, East Lothian EH34 5BE
Tel: 01875 340057
Contact: Lionel Gliori

Live Music

Retailer, repairer. Guitar and amplifier sales plus some accessories.
48 Elm Row, Edinburgh EH7 4AH
Tel: 0131 556 9956 Fax: 0131 556 9956

M J Vanden Guitars and Mandolins

Maker. Jazz and acoustic guitars. Mandolins (electric and acoustic) custom made to order. Range of active mimesis pick-ups for acoustic instruments.
The Old School, Strontian, Acharacle, Argyle PH36 4JA
Tel: 01967 402114
Contact: Mike Vanden

MacArther, Neil

Experimental electric stringed instrument maker.
26 Rankeillor Street, Edinburgh EH8 9HY
Tel: 0131 667 6450

MacMillan, Hector

Maker of violin and violas for serious music students and performers. Occasionally has second-hand instruments. Awarded certificate of distinction for tone in the *Facta Britannia* competition 1985.
59 Springfield View, South Queensferry EH30 9RZ
Tel: 0131 331 4000

Margerum, Alice C

Maker. Trained in Boston, London and Newark. Makes hand-carved medieval stringed instruments, vielles, rebecs, harps, citoles and gitterns, individually crafted from native European timbers. Commissions for decorative carving etc. welcome.
The Harpmakers' Workshop, 1103 Argyle Street, Glasgow G3 8NQ
Tel: 0774 005171 (messagepoint)

Martin Neale Musical Instrument Repairs

Repairer. Professionally qualified in repair and servicing of woodwind, brass and strings. (Member of the National Association of Musical Instrument Repairers).
24 Obsdale Park, Alness, Ross-shire IV17 0TP
Tel: 01349 883347
Contact: Martin Neale

Martins Music

Maker, repairer, retailer. Dulcylyn - 3 and 4 stringed instrument based on dulcimer fretting. Music, book and instrument sales.
16 Ferry Brae, Dunoon PA23 7DT
Tel: 01369 704985
Contact: Martin Morren

SUPPLIERS & SERVICES

Maynard, Brian

Maker, repairer. Modern and historical violins, violas and cellos. 25 years' experience in the restoration of instruments back to baroque and classical forms. Visitors welcome by appointment.
Teviot House, Fishers Brae, Coldingham, Eyemouth, Berwickshire TD14 5NJ
Tel: 01890 771235

Moon Guitars

Maker, repairer and retailer. Custom built acoustic and electric guitars. Second hand instrument sales.
974 Pollokshaws Road, Glasgow G41 2EU
Tel: 0141 632 9526 Fax: 0141 632 9526

Pollock, Helen

Maker and repairer. Violin maker and restorer. Buys and sells instruments.
The Old School, Ardgay, Sutherland IV24 3BG
Tel: 01863 766483

Rattray, Brian

Maker, repairer. Violin and viola maker for over 25 years. Also repairs all bowed instruments. Rehairs bows.
34 Spylaw Street, Edinburgh EH13 0JJ
Tel: 0131 441 1098

Richard Bagpipes

Repairer. String repairs. (Also bagpipe maker and woodwind repairs).
9 Beresford Avenue, Edinburgh EH5 3EU
Tel: 0131 551 1726

Semitone Musical Instruments

Make c.22 different stringed instruments, distributed to over 17,000 shops in USA, Japan, Germany and France. Make for Gremlin and Hobgoblin (Sherwood and Soar Valley ranges). Also make under the Freshwater name and do dulcimer and clarsach. Will do repairs. The company Precision Woodworking and Finishing also operates from same address.
Dave Freshwater, Stroma, Croyard Road, Beauly IV4 7EX
Tel: 01463 782459 Fax: 01463 782459

Serenade for Strings

Retailer. Specialist mail-order suppliers of music for strings (violin, viola, cello, double bass).
South Teavarran Enterprises, Foxhole, Kiltarlity IV4 7HT
Tel: 01463 741651 Fax: 01463 741651

Simpsons Guitars and Things

Retailer, repairer, hirer. Specialise in guitars and strings. Hire of woodwind. All repairs, book music and accessory sales.
6A Stafford Street, Edinburgh EH3 7AY
Tel: 0131 225 6305 Fax: 0131 226 5340
Contact: Rebecca Simpson or Clifford Simpson

Sinton Guitars

Maker, repairer. Guitars.
Dave Binton, Balnaferry Farm Cottage, Forres IV36 0SJ
Tel: 01309 675119

Soundfolk Music

Maker, retailer, repairer. Folk instruments made to order, especially strings. Specialise in traditional music, selling instruments, cassettes, books and accessories.
4 Chancellor Street, Glasgow G11 5RG
Tel: 0141 334 5137
Contact: Charles Saksena

Starfish Designs

Maker, repairer. Electric violins, skeletal instruments - 4, 5 and 6 strings plus bass violins; 4 and 5 string cellos; 4 and 5 string bowed bass guitars. Also make harps.
Unit Four, Old Ferry Road, North Ballachulish, By Fort William, Inverness-shire PH33 6SA
Tel: 01855 821429 Fax: 01855 821577
Contact: Mike Anderson or Gay Anderson

Stevenson, Gordon

Retailer, repairer. Violin restoration, bow rehairing. Instruments purchased. Insurance arranged. Strings, cases and accessories.
6 Barclay Terrace, Bruntsfield, Edinburgh EH10 4HP
Tel: 0131 229 2051 Fax: 0131 229 9298

Stringers Musical Instruments

Retailer, repairer. String instruments. Repair and restoration. Accessories also.
55/57 Causewayside, Edinburgh EH9 1QF
Tel: 0131 662 1862 Fax: 0131 667 8911
Contact: Maureen Morrison

Thomson, Ewen

Maker and repairer. Also does basic bow repairs. Trained at Newark School of Violin Making (youngest student ever taken in). Has been professional maker for 4 years.
Taft, Fair Isle ZE2 9JU
Tel: 01595 760276

Violin Shop

Retailer, repairer. Sale of new and second hand violins, violas, cellos, double basses, bows, cases and accessories. Instruments purchased, valuation and insurance arranged.
11 Blackie Street, Glasgow G3 8TN
Tel: 0141 339 8078
Contact: Ray Daniel

The Violin Shop

Repairer, retailer. Violins.
High Street, Falkland, Fife KY15 7BU
Tel: 01337 858181
Contact: Robert Beveridge

Wright and Schrijver

Maker, repairer, retailer. Violins and bows. Rehairing.
20 Renfrew Street, Glasgow G2 3BW
Tel: 0141 332 4513 Fax: 0141 779 3792
Contact: Graham Wright or Corrie Schrijver

FLIGHT CASES

Black Box

Custom built flight cases.
4 Colinton Road, Edinburgh EH10 5DS
Tel: 0131 447 6217
Contact: Jim Condy

Clark Cases

Custom built flight cases for any instrument.
Cuminestown, Aberdeenshire AB53 7XG
Tel: 01888 544535
Contact: Alan Clark

Fountain Harps

Tailor made flight cases for all instruments.
Borthaugh, Hawick, Roxburghshire TD9 7LN
Tel: 01450 377477 Fax: 01450 371080
Contact: James Maybury

G B Professional Audio

Custom made flight cases.
Unit D, 51 Brunswick Road, Edinburgh EH7 5PD
Tel: 0131 661 0022 Fax: 0131 661 0022

The Justin Case Company

Custom built flight cases for instruments and PA systems.
23 Water Street, Leith, Edinburgh EG6 6SU
Tel: 0131 555 4466 Fax: 0131 555 6901

Protex Flight Case Company

Custom built flight cases for any instrument.
13 Lingerwood Walk, Newtongrange, Midlothian EH22 4QW
Tel: 0131 660 5459 Fax: 0131 660 5459

GENERAL MUSIC STORE

BORDERS

Jimmy Clinkscale Music Station

Retailer, repairer. Sale of accordions, guitars, amplifiers, keyboards, drums, cassettes, CDs, videos, books and accessories.
50-52 Island Street, Galashiels TD1 1NU
Tel: 01896 750588 Fax: 01896 750469
Contact: Neil Turnbull

Spence's Music Shop

Retailer. Violins, guitars, keyboards, accessories, CDs, cassettes, records, hi-fi. All musical instruments can be ordered.
3 Buccleuch Street, Hawick GD9 0HW
Tel: 01450 372115

CENTRAL

Hay J M (Stirling) Ltd

Retailer, repairer, piano tuner. Instruments, books, music and accessories. Instrument repairs (not keyboards or PA).
29 Friars Street, Stirling FK8 1HE
Tel: 01786 473573

Music City

Retailer, hirer, repairer. General instrument sales (second hand brass and woodwind), music, books and accessories. PA and amplifier sales, installation, PA hire.
3 Cow Wynd, Falkirk FK1 1PL
Tel: 01324 627008 Fax: 01324 627008

Music Corner

Retailer, repairer. Range of instruments, music and accessories. Tuition on keyboard, organ and accordion.
88 Mary Square, Laurieston, Falkirk FK2 9PP
Tel: 01324 627100
Contact: Morag Robertson

Ochil Music

Retailer, repairer. Range of instruments sold and repaired. Music and accessories.
3 Baker Street, Stirling FK8 1BJ
Tel: 01786 474438 Fax: 01786 474438
Contact: Martin Jones

Roadshow Music

Retailer, hirer, repairer. Sale of guitars, electric and acoustic bass, amplifiers, percussion and accessories (new and second hand). Vocal PA and lighting hire. Disco hire.
64 Upper Craigs, Stirling FK8 2DF
Tel: 01786 471323 Fax: 01786 471323

DUMFRIES & GALLOWAY

Ian Holmes

Retailer, repairer. General music store with noticeboard, music and accessories. Repairs - guitar and fiddle. Index of tutors and musicians.
1-7 Glasgow Street, Dumfries DG2 9AF
Tel: 01387 262063

John Douglas

Retailer, repairer. Instruments, books, music and accessory sales. Accordion repairs.
9 Great King Street, Dumfries DG1 1BA
Tel: 01387 256479 Fax: 01387 256479

FIFE

Mentiplay Music Store

Retailer, repairer. General instrument sales, music, books and accessories. Some repairs, index of local tutors and musicians.
12 Olympia Arcade, Kirkcaldy KY1 1QF
Tel: 01592 260557

Musicmongers

Retailer. Sheet music, CDs and cassettes, strings, reeds and other accessories.
151 South Street, St Andrews KY16 9UN
Tel: 01334 478625
Contact: Angela Bell

Sound Control

Retailer. Sale of keyboards, guitars, amplifiers, PA systems etc. Music, books and accessories.
63 Dunnikier Road, Kirkcaldy KY1 2RL
Tel: 01592 260293
Contact: Head Office Fax: 01383 725733

Sound Control

Retailer, repairer. Sale of keyboards, guitars, amplifiers, PA systems, etc. Music books and accessories. Guitar workshop and engineer.
73 Elgin Street, Dunfermline KY12 7SD
Tel: 01383 733353 Fax: 01383 725733

GRAMPIAN

Bruce Millers

Retailer, hirer, repairer, piano tuning. Sale of instruments, CDs and tapes, sheet music, books and accessories. Second hand and ex-rental instruments.
363 Union Street, Aberdeen AB9 1EN
Tel: 01224 592211 Fax: 01224 580085
Contact: Alan Duthie

Leonard's Music

Retailer, repairer. Instrument sales, music and accessories. Mail order service available. Also 'browser box' service for schools, choirs, orchestras; can look at music for a week then order when boxes picked up.
3 Ross Lane, Market Place, Inverurie, Aberdeenshire AB51 3PN
Tel: 01467 624629 Fax: 01467 625404
Contact: Joe Leonard (Owner) or Gillian Leonard

Music Matters

Retailer, repairer. General instrument sales (no woodwind, brass or percussion). CDs, cassettes, videos. Range of country and western.
42 East Church Street, Buckie, Banffshire AB56 1AB
Tel: 01542 832020 Fax: 01542 832020

R and B Music

Retailer, hirer, repairer. Guitar, keyboards, percussion, amplifier, and brass sales. Repairs (not brass). Books, music and accessories. PA hire. Guitar tuition.
67 The Green, Aberdeen AB1 2NY
Tel: 01224 210121 Fax: 01224 585553
Contact: Ross Donald or Bill Sinclair

SUPPLIERS & SERVICES

187

Sound and Vision

Retailer, hirer, repairer. Sale of instruments, amplifiers, PA, disco equipment, music, books and accessories, CDs and cassettes. Hire of PA and disco equipment.
14 and 18 South Street, Elgin IV30 1LE
Tel: 01343 543778 Fax: 01343 543778
Contact: Vic Flett

Top Note Music Shop

Retailer, hirer. Brass, string and woodwind instruments sold and some hire available. Accessories, music, CDs. Bow rehairing service available.
123 Crown Street, Aberdeen AB1 2HN
Tel: 01224 210259

HIGHLAND

Eisd Music Shop

Retailer, hirer, repairer. Sales range from penny whistles to guitars and keyboards. Music, books, and accessories. Vocal PA hire. Specialise in Gaelic and Scottish folk recordings.
Quae Brae, Portree, Isle of Skye IV51 9DB
Tel: 01478 612990 Fax: 01478 613263

Maitland Music

Retailer, repairer. General instrument sales (new and second hand). Music, books, and accessories. Index of tutors.
George Street, Dingwall IV15 9SA
Tel: 01349 863191

The Music Shop

Retailer, hirer, repairer. General instrument sales, plus locally made folk instruments. Music, accessories.
27 Church Street, Inverness IV1 1DY
Tel: 01463 233374 Fax: 01463 713983

The Music Station

Retailer, hirer, repairer. General instrument sales (new and second hand). Acoustic and electric. Electronic repairs, music and accessories. PA hire.
49 Church Street, Inverness IV1 1DR
Tel: 01463 225523 Fax: 01463 717477

LOTHIAN

Band Parts Music Stores

Retailer. Music, records, CDs. Specialising in 12 inch dance records. Guitar strings and harmonicas.
10 Antigua Street, Edinburgh EH1 3NH
Tel: 0131 556 6621
Contact: Ronald Blacklock (Proprietor) or Keith Gray (Manager)

Blackfriars Music

Retailer, repairer. Sale of folk instruments, books, sheet music, books, cassettes, CDs, magazines, repairs.
49 Blackfriars Street, Edinburgh EH1 1NB
Tel: 0131 557 3090 Fax: 0131 557 3090

Mev Taylors Music Shop

Retailer, repairer. General instrument repairs (not keyboards). Retailer of instruments, music and books. Education rental scheme. PA hire.
212 Morrison Street, Edinburgh EH3 8EA
Tel: 0131 229 7454 Fax: 0131 228 5913

SUPPLIERS & SERVICES

Rae Macintosh
Retailer. Sale of music plus instrument accessories.
6 Queensferry Road, Edinburgh EH2 4PA
Tel: 0131 225 1171 Fax: 0131 225 9447

Rainbow Music
Retailer, hirer, repairer. General instrument sales, percussion and wind instruments not stocked but can be obtained from Dundee store. Music accessories. PA equipment sold and installed, also PA hire.
13 South Clerk Street, Edinburgh EH8 9JB
Tel: 0131 667 3030

Rikki's Music Shop
Retailer. All leading makes of guitars, drums, amplifiers and Yamaha and Casio keyboards. Second hand, part exchange, credit schemes. Repairs. Tutor books, music and accessories.
102 Leith Walk, Edinburgh EH6 8HN
Tel: 0131 553 5084

Scayles Music
Retailer, hirer, repairer. Acoustic, electric, folk instruments. Second hand keyboards, amplifiers, books and accessories.
42 West Crosscauseway, Edinburgh EH8 9JP
Tel: 0131 667 8241

Sheena McNeil Music
Retailer. Comprehensive sheet music sales, including international mail order. Directory of music tutors. Recorders and musical accessories.
7 Barclay Terrace, Edinburgh EH10 4HP
Tel: 0131 228 3666 Fax: 0131 228 3966

Sound Control
Retailer, repairer. Keyboard centre, sale of guitars, amplifiers, PA systems, etc. Music, books and accessories. Guitar workshop and engineer.
19-21 St Mary's Street, Edinburgh EH1 1TA
Tel: 0131 557 3986
Contact: Head Office Fax: 01383 725733

Varsity Music
Retailer, hirer, repairer, piano tuner. Wholesale and retail. Sale of pianos, guitars (acoustic and electric), violins, brass, music books and albums, accessories. Hire pianos for functions. Guitar tuition available.
8A-10A Nicholson Street, Edinburgh EH8 9DH
Tel: 0131 556 3273 / 557 4310 / 0831 225551 (mobile) Fax: 0131 556 3273
Contact: Ralph Hepburn or Stuart Hepburn

ORKNEY

Hillanders The Music Centre
Repairer, retailer. General instrumental repairs. Periodical brass, woodwind, piano repair specialist visits. Instruments, books, music and accessories for sale. Mail order service.
Anchor Buildings, Bridge Street, Kirkwall KW 15 1HR
Tel: 01856 872854 Fax: 01856 874854

STRATHCLYDE

Ad Lib Music
Retailer, repairer. Range of instruments, acoustic to hi-tech. Amp and PA (up to 5k) sales. Index of tutors. Accessories. School rental scheme.
8 Jamaica Street, Greenock PA15 1XU
Tel: 01475 786821 Fax: 01475 724274

The Band Room
Retailer, repairer. Drums, percussion, some guitars, woodwind and brass. Specialists in pipe band equipment and highland wear. After sales service.
172-174 West Regent Street, Glasgow G1 4RL
Tel: 0141 248 5885 Fax: 0141 248 5885

Biggars
Retailer, hirer, repairer. General instrument sales (acoustic and electric). Amplifiers, synthesisers, music, books and accessories. Instrument hire.
273 Sauchiehall Street, Glasgow G2 3HH
Tel: 0141 332 8676 Fax: 0141 332 8676

Forrest Wm and D
Retailer, repairer. Instrument and accessories. Specialise in keyboards, guitars and electronic equipment.
217 Gallowgate, Glasgow G1 5DX
Tel: 0141 552 0683
Contact: William Forrest or David Forrest

Frontline Music
Retailer, repairer, hirer. Instruments, books, sheet music and accessories. Repairs to guitars and amplifiers. Vocal PA hire.
2 Arthur Street, Ayr KA7 1QJ
Tel: 01292 265252
Contact: John Lyall

MacKay Music
Retailer, hirer, repairs. Woodwind and string instruments for retail and hire. All accessories, music and musical gifts. Postal service.
3 Cathcart Street, Ayr KA7 1BJ
Tel: 01292 289562 Fax: 01292 289562
Contact: Mrs MacKay (Manager)

Magnum Sound
Retailer. Educational suppliers. General instrument sales (new and second hand). PA system sales. General sound installation (disco, background music etc).
67 Stewarton Street, Wishaw ML2 8AG
Tel: 01698 358761 Fax: 01698 359745

McCormacks
Retailer, repairers. General instrument sales, music and accesssories. Repair brass, woodwind, guitars and amps. New and second hand instruments. School rental scheme.
33 Bath Street, Glasgow G2 1HG
Tel: 0141 332 6644 Fax: 0141 353 3095

Merchant City Music
Retailer, hirer, repairer. Acoustic to hi-tech instruments, new and second hand. Epiphone guitar specialists.
7 Garth Street, Glasgow G1 1UT
Tel: 0141 552 6290

The Music Centre
Retailer, repairer. Amplifiers and electronic equipment. Accessories and music. New and second hand.
48 Campbell Street, Hamilton ML3 6AS
Tel: 01698 283325 Fax: 01698 283330

The Music Centre
Retailer, repairer. Amplifiers and electronic equipment. Accessories and music. New and second hand.
8 Well Meadow Street, Paisley PA1 2EF
Tel: 0141 848 1033

Nortone (Glasgow) Ltd

Retailer. Sales of string instruments, keyboards, brass, woodwind, accordion, PA, amplifiers. Can arrange repairs if required.
340 Argyle Street, Glasgow G2 8LY
Tel: 0141 226 5038 Fax: 0141 221 0959
Contact: Martin Morris

P and R Howard (Wholesalers)

Retailer. General musical instrument and accessories wholesaler. Distributor of Westfield guitars and amplification.
13-17 James Watt Place, College Milton Industrial Estate, East Kilbride G74 5HG
Tel: 013552 36621 Fax: 013552 65560

RGM Music

Retailer, repairer. Musical equipment and instrument sales (new and second hand). Music and accessories. Lighting and vocal PA hire. Retail and installation of all PA systems.
24 Nelson Street, Kilmarnock KA1 1BA
Tel: 01563 537711 Fax: 01563 530209

Sound Control

Retailer, hirer, repairer. Sale of keyboards, amplifiers, etc. Music, books and accessories. Acoustic guitar warehouse. Professional audio department. PA hire.
61 and 67 Jamaica Street, Glasgow G1 4NN
Tel: 0141 204 2774
Contact: Head Office Fax: 01383 725733

Sound Thinking

Retailer, repairer. General instrument sales, music, accessories. Hire scheme on selected instruments.
7 James Street, Helensburgh G84 8AS
Tel: 01436 672230 Fax: 01436 672230

Soundfolk Music

Retailer, repairer, maker. Specialise in traditional music. Instruments, including electric guitars, cassettes, books and accessories. Folk instruments made to order, especially strings.
4 Chancellor Street, Glasgow G11 5RG
Tel: 0141 334 5137
Contact: Charles Saksena

Southside Music

Retailer, repairer. Range of new and second hand instruments including folk instruments and amplifiers, music and accessories. Repairs to guitars and amplifiers.
599 Cathcart Road, Glasgow G42 8AD
Tel: 0141 423 5474
Contact: Charlie Hepburn (Manager)

Village Music

Retailer, hirer, repairer. General instrument sales (new and second hand). All accessories, amplifiers, music and teaching videos. Vocal PA and brass instruments for hire.
31A Main Street, The Village, East Kilbride G74 4JU
Tel: 013552 44562
Contact: Colin Finn

TAYSIDE

Abbey Music

Retailer, hirer, repairer. General instrument sales, cassettes, videos, music, accessories. Hire of amplifiers and some instruments. Keyboard, guitar and piano tuition.
15 West Port, Arbroath DD1 1RF
Tel: 01241 879904 Fax: 01241 879904
Contact: Terry Wood or Rosemary Wood

Bandwagon

Retailer, repairs, hirer. Guitars, amplifiers, folk instruments (new and second hand). Vocal PA hire. Guitar tuition. Music books and videos (rock/pop).
9 St Paul's Square, Perth PH1 5QW
Tel: 01738 637714
Contact: Peter Caban

The Concorde

Retailer. Sale of guitars, violins, percussion, flutes, clarinets, recorders, practice chanters, music and books. Record sales (jazz, classical etc).
15 Scott Street, Perth PH1 5EJ
Tel: 01738 621818 Fax: 01738 639903

Forbes Musicians

Retailer, repairer. General instrument sales, specialising in accordions (new and second hand). Wholesale or retail. Some repairs. Mail order. List of local music teachers. Music and accessories.
89 Nethergate, Dundee DD1 4DH
Tel: 01382 223352 Fax: 01382 221600

Rainbow Music

Retailer, hirer, repairer. General instrument sales, music and accessories. PA equipment sold and installed. Hire of brass instruments and PA.
15 Bell Street, Dundee DD1 1HP
Tel: 01382 201405 Fax: 01382 225183
Contact: Edinburgh Branch
Tel:0131 667 3030

Sound Control

Retailer, hirer, repairer. Sale of keyboards, guitars, amplifiers, PA, etc. Acoustic pianos, brass and woodwind. Music, books, and accessories. Repairs. Guitar workshop and engineer. PA hire.
29 Castle Street, Dundee DD1 3AD
Tel: 01382 225619
Contact: Head Office Fax: 01383 725733

Wilkie's Music House

Retailer, repairer. General instrument sales (new and second hand). Music and accessories. Tuition available.
2/4 Canal Crescent, Perth PH2 8HZ
Tel: 01738 623041 Fax: 01738 633173

WESTERN ISLES

Fonn Music Shop

Retailer, hirer, repairer. General instruments and accessories, books and music. PA hire to 300w. Index of tutors.
19 Bayhead Street, Stornoway HS1 2DU
Tel: 01851 704632

PIANO REMOVALS

Gerard Removers

Piano removers.
Anniesland Industrial Estate, Netherton Road, Glasgow G13 1EU
Tel: 0141 954 3939 Fax: 0141 954 5290

Pettigrew Removal and Storage

Piano removal specialists.
2 Stoney Flatts Park, South Queensferry, Edinburgh EH30 9YL
Tel: 0131 331 5663

Love, Gerald

Piano specialists and forwarders.
The Old Smiddy, Hermiston Village, Edinburgh EH14 4AG
Tel: 0131 552 0553 / 0831 509257 (mobile) Fax: 0131 552 0553

PIANO TUNERS

CENTRAL

Forth Valley Pianos
Tuning.
23 Braeview, Stenhousemuir, Falkirk
FK5 3DS
Tel: 01324 557539
Contact: Brian Gorrie Tel: 0831 332524
(mobile)

FIFE

Forrester, Gavin
Piano tuner, repairer.
38 Glamis Road, Kirkcaldy KY2 6LL
Tel: 01592 261508

Hay, George
Piano tuner, repairer.
17 Forth Park Drive, Kirkcaldy
KY2 5TB
Tel: 01592 260621

Piano Tuning Services
Piano tuner, repairer. Pianos bought and sold.
14 Inverie Street, St Monans, Fife
KY10 2AE
Tel: 01333 730468 / 0374 266480
(mobile)

GRAMPIAN

Brown, John
Piano tuner, repairer.
23 Renny Crescent, Montrose
DD10 9BW
Tel: 01674 672237

Burnett Piano Services
Tuning, repairing, restoration, valuation, buying and selling of new and second hand pianos.
22 McIntosh Drive, Elgin, Moray
IV30 3AP
Tel: 01343 544680
Contact: Glyn Burnett (Proprietor)

David Martin Keyboards
Tuning, repair, rebuilding, hire and moving of pianos.
1 Smithy Cottages, Fetteresso,
Stonehaven AB3 2UR
Tel: 01569 764334
Contact: David Martin

Edmonstone, A
Piano tuner, repairer. Pianos bought and sold.
20 King Street, New Elgin, Morayshire
IV30 3BX
Tel: 01343 541872

J B Piano Services
Piano sales, tuning, restoration and polishing.
7 Hatton Farm Road, Hatton AB42 7QL
Tel: 01779 841723
Contact: Jeremy Eayrs

Morrison, W
Piano tuner, repairer.
83 Kirkbrae, Cults, Aberdeenshire
AB1 9QX
Tel: 01224 868517

HIGHLAND

Grant, Katherine
Piano tuner.
Tontearie, Nethy Bridge, Inverness-shire
PH25 3EF
Tel: 01479 831699

Matthews, Ian
Piano tuning, repair, sales (pianos bought and sold).
35 Laggan Road, Inverness IV2 4EW
Tel: 01463 232196

LOTHIAN

Allens Piano Services
Piano tuner, hirer, repairer. Hire upright pianos. Sales of refurbished pianos. Pianos bought and sold.
124 Gilmore Place, Edinburgh EH3 9PL
Tel: 0131 229 9544

Burnett Pianos
Piano tuning, repairs, restoration, reconditioning. Pianos bought and sold.
11 Barclay Terrace, Edinburgh
EH10 4HP
Tel: 0131 228 3638 / 0374 160195
(mobile)

Calder, James
Piano tuner, repairer. Valuations given.
26 Templeland Road, Edinburgh
EH12 8SD
Tel: 0131 334 2973

Mitchell, Leslie
Piano tuner, repairer. CTB. MIMIT.
55 Newmains Road, Kirkliston,
Edinburgh EH29 9AW
Tel: 0131 333 3436

Motion, Norman W
Piano tuner, repairs, full restoration. Concert tuner for most of Edinburgh and Glasgow, SCO, etc.
The Old Smiddy, Hermiston Village,
Edinburgh EH14 4AG
Tel: 0131 449 2968/ 0378 642911
(mobile)

S J Lynch Pianos
Piano tuner, repairer. Instruments bought and sold.
47 Falcon Avenue, Morningside,
Edinburgh EH10 4AN
Tel: 0131 452 8176

• Wilson and Son
Piano tuner, restorer. Sales.
71 Whitehill Street, Newcraighall,
Edinburgh EH21 8QZ
Tel: 0131 669 0999

Wood, George
Piano tuner, repairer.
22 Durward Rise, Livingston EH54 6HU
Tel: 01506 415800

STRATHCLYDE

Bolton, Malcolm
Piano tuner, repairer.
7 Bedcow View, Kirkintilloch G66 3JA
Tel: 0141 776 2758

W and G Brown
Piano tuner, repairer.
Wellbank, Howwood, Johnstone
PA9 1AW
Tel: 01505 702623

Campbell, Alan
Piano tuner, repairer.
46 Kirktonside, Barrhead, Glasgow
G78 2HL
Tel: 0141 881 5557

Grummitt, Brian G
Piano tuner, repairer.
48 Abbott Crescent, Clydebank G81 1AB
Tel: 0141 952 9031

Jamieson, Andrew
Piano tuner and technician.
5 Sycamore Gardens, Blackwood,
Lanarkshire ML11 9SX
Tel: 01555 893160 Fax: 01555 893160

King, Stewart A
Piano tuner, repairer.
24 John Knox Street, Clydebank, Glasgow G81 1ND
Tel: 0141 952 3142

Lauchlan, J T
Piano tuner, repairer.
156 North Shore Road, Troon, Ayrshire KA10 6RB
Tel: 01292 314131

Love, D S
Piano tuner, repairer.
47 Alexander Street, Coatbridge, Lanarkshire ML5 3JL
Tel: 01236 425362 / 0831 592601 (mobile)

McBay, Douglas
Piano tuner, repairer.
33 Bolton Drive, Glasgow G42 9DT
Tel: 0141 636 1370

McClements, Hugh
Piano tuner, repairer.
18 Machrie Place, Kilwinning KA13 6RW
Tel: 01294 553955

McDonald, David
Piano tuner, repairer.
9 Marywood Square, Glasgow G41 2BW
Tel: 0141 424 1863 / 0836 650492 (mobile)

McLauchlan, John
Piano tuner, repairer.
7 Springfield Road, Tarbolton KA5 5QU
Tel: 01292 541346

McLean, Alasdair
Piano tuner, repairer. Sales and valuations.
105 Queensborough Gardens, Hyndland, Glasgow G12 9RS
Tel: 0141 339 0905

Ottolini, Joseph
Piano tuner, repairer.
197 Byres Road, Glasgow G12 8TN
Tel: 0141 334 9587

Russel, Richard
Piano tuner, repairer, restorer.
32 Eglinton Court, Glasgow G5 9NF
Tel: 0141 429 7891

Savory, Brian
Piano tuner, repairer.
165 Waterside Road, Carmunnock, Clarkston, Glasgow G76 9AJ
Tel: 0141 644 2012

Vernal, Marjory
Piano tuner/technician.
16 St Andrews Road, Renfrew PA4 0SU
Tel: 0141 886 3952

Wilson, Dave
Piano tuner, repairer, restorer. Old instruments tuned to concert pitch. Pianos bought and sold. Free estimates - distance no object.
19 Kensington Gate, Glasgow G12 9LQ
Tel: 0141 334 1790

TAYSIDE

Anderson Pianos
Piano tuner, repairer.
35 Kinloch Terrace, Dundee DD3 6JZ
Tel: 01382 200708

McFatridge, Gordon
Piano tuner, repairer.
Edendale, Isla Road, Perth PH2 7HQ
Tel: 01738 623788

McIntyre, John
Piano tune, repairer.
10 Commercial Street, Coupar Angus, Perthshire PH13 9AD
Tel: 01382 826373 / 01828 628181 (ans mac) / 0831 166661 (mobile)

Waggott, James
Piano tuner, repairer.
40 Braehead Drive, Carnoustie, Angus DD7 7SX
Tel: 01241 853272

PA & LIGHTING

BORDERS

N and K Blake
Sales, installation and repair of most types of sound equipment. Any sound system can be supplied for hire.
17 Woodmarket, Kelso TD5 7AT
Tel: 01573 224217
Contact: Norman Blake or Keith Blake

Sound Station
PA installations and hire up to 10k.
42 High Street, Galashiels TD1 1SE
Tel: 01896 750190

CENTRAL

ABS Productions

Sound, lighting (retail, hire and installation) also events production and show production.

344 Main Street, Stenhousemuir
FK5 3JR
Tel: 01324 562010 Fax: 01324 562010
Contact: Ian Gardiner

Frontline Production Services

Sales, installation and hire of lighting equipment.

Unit 5, Castle Court, Bankside Industrial
Estate, Falkirk FK2 7UU
Tel: 01324 612367 Fax: 01324 612368
Contact: Derek McVay

GMS Recordings Ltd

Sales, installation and repair to sound equipment. Also supply background music.

Kinneil House, Kirk Entry, Polmont
FK2 0QS
Tel: 01324 711011 Fax: 01324 711533
Contact: Rodney Kennard

DUMFRIES & GALLOWAY

Alan Sound

PA systems to hire for orchestra and concerts. Operator provided. Can supply recording system for event.

43 Brooke Street, Dumfries DG1 2JL
Tel: 01387 254805
Contact: Alan Marshall

FIFE

Audio Craft Services

Sales and installation of sound equipment. Hire of PA rigs from 100w vocal PAs to 10k rigs, 24 channel mixing desk. Lighting equipment for small bands. Transport, sound operators, engineers and crew can be provided. Repairs. Also three rehearsal rooms available.

Elgin House, Elgin Street, Dunfermline
KY12 7SA
Tel: 01383 620858 Fax: 01383 620858
Contact: Allan Short (Manager)

Capital Sound and Light

Sales and installation of sound, lighting and stage equipment. Staging hire available - lighting, PA up to 30k. Repairs on all equipment.

The Studio City Hotel, Bridge Street,
Dunfermline KY12 8AQ
Tel: 01383 620610 Fax: 01383 620610
Contact: Steven Rotherham

Sounds Inc PA

Hire of PA equipment. Vocal to 30k with engineer.

17 Main Street, Strathkinness KY16 9RX
Tel: 01334 850588 / 0378 479182
(mobile)
Contact: Gordon Sedgwick

GRAMPIAN

Atmosphere Lighting and Sound

Sales and installation of sound and lighting equipment. Hire also. Crew, operator and transport supplied. Repairs. Theatrical supplies.

67-69 Nelson Street, Aberdeen AB2 3ER
Tel: 01224 622222 Fax: 01224 621162
Contact: Euan Beadie (Hire) or Andy Adam (Sales)

Creative Lighting and Sound

Sales, installation, hire and repair of lighting and sound equipment. Hire for any size of operation. Transport and crew can be arranged.

140 The Spital, Aberdeen AB2 3JU
Tel: 01224 647521 Fax: 01224 640411
Contact: Charles Flett

Granite City Rock

Hire out 3.5k PA with engineer. Agency that will organise tours for up and coming bands. Also production - can arrange staging, lighting, PA etc.

16 Thistle Drive, Port Lethen AB1 4QH
Tel: 01224 781805
Contact: Tommy Reid

J M S Promotions

Hire of vocal PA to 6k rig. Transport, lighting and staging if required.

49 Marchburn Road, Aberdeen AB2 7ND
Tel: 01224 693887
Contact: John Spiers

HIGHLANDS

Limelights

Hire of lighting rigs from 5k to 120k. Will provide a whole package. Also hire sound equipment and staging.

3 Connel Court, Ardconnel Street,
Inverness IV2 3EY
Tel: 01463 243363 Fax: 01463 710755
Contact: Craig Duncan

LOTHIAN

A and R Martin

Sell some sound equipment though not retailer. Install sound systems in theatres and arts centres. PA up to 12k, operated and dry hire. Specialise in hiring out sound equipment to promoters for acoustic music.

26 Roseneath Place, Marchmont,
Edinburgh EH9 1JD
Tel: 0131 229 4784 Fax: 0131 228 6801
Contact: Alan Martin

B B G PA Hire

Specialise in hire to bands and theatre companies. Any size and type of sound system can be put together. Transport and sound operators are provided.

19 East London Street, Edinburgh
EH7 4BN
Tel: 0131 556 9296 / 0831 482539
(mobile) Fax: 0131 556 6668
Contact: Gus Boyd

Black Light

Sales and installation of sound and lighting equipment. Hire also. Transport, stage crew and sound personnel can be arranged.

18 West Harbour Road, Granton,
Edinburgh EH5 1PH
Tel: 0131 551 2337 Fax: 0131 552 0370
Contact: Gavin Stewart

Bonskeid Music Ltd

Sound hire within the acoustic music field. 4 rigs - 500w to 5k.

6 The Steils, Edinburgh EH10 5XD
Tel: 0131 447 0991 / 0831 779920
(mobile) Fax: 0131 447 0991
Contact: Freeland Barbour

193

E F X Audio

Hire of sound systems from 300w to 40k. Transport and sound crew can be provided. Installations for studios, theatres, etc. Sound equipment can be custom built.

59-59a Muir Road, Bathgate, West Lothian EH48 2QL
Tel: 01506 633356
Contact: Johnny Ramsay or Steven Flemming

G B Professional Audio

Sales, installation and hire of sound equipment. Vocal PA to 20k. Transport, sound operators and crew included in hire. Repair of audio equipment. Also manufacture flight-cases, racks, custom-made electronics.

Unit D, 51 Brunswick Road, Edinburgh EH7 5PD
Tel: 0131 661 0022 Fax: 0131 661 0022
Contact: Graham Bodenham

The Lighthouse

Hire of lighting rigs from 20k to 200k. Includes installation, transport, lighting design and crew.

84 Myreside Road, Edinburgh EH10 5BZ
Tel: 0131 337 8329
Contact: Chris Bowman (Owner)

Northern Light

Sales, installation and repair of sound, light and audio-visual equipment. Hire from 3k to 30k rigs. Also Glasgow branch.

Assembly Street, Leith, Edinburgh EH6 7RG
Tel: 0131 553 2383 Fax: 0131 553 3296
Contact: Gordon Blackburn (Hire) or Mr Martin (Sales)

Pegasus Sound and Light

Suppliers and wholesalers of sound and lighting equipment. Specialists in design and installation. Hire and repair.

23-25 Canongate, The Royal Mile, Edinburgh EH8 8BX
Tel: 0131 556 1300 Fax: 0131 557 6466
Contact: Charles Hunter or David Hunter

Spectra Sound Systems

Hire of vocal PA to 15k rig, including transport, installation, engineer and uplift. Installations.

20 Saughtonhall Drive, Edinburgh EH12 5SQ
Tel: 0131 337 7570

Contact: Gordon Henderson

The Warehouse

Sales, installation and hire of sound equipment including DAT machines. Hire to 9k rigs.

23 Water Street, Leith, Edinburgh EH6 6SU
Tel: 0131 555 6900 Fax: 0131 555 6901
Contact: Glasgow Office
Tel: 0141 950 1757

War Productions

Suppliers of lighting.
5/6 Broughton Place Lane, Edinburgh EH1 3RS
Tel: 0131 558 3824 Fax: 0131 558 3665

STRATHCLYDE

Amp Hire (Scotland)

Installation of sound systems. PA hire from small Bose to 10k Turbosound rigs, Soundcraft desks. Packages include engineer, monitor mix. Lighting available if required.

Tel: 0141 942 2124 Fax: 0141 942 2124
Contact: Tony Moreland

Baker T G (Sound) Ltd

Sales, installation and repairs of sound equipment. Design sound systems to customer specification. Manufacture own speakers.

173-175 Glasgow Road, Clydebank, Glasgow G81 1LQ
Tel: 0141 941 3399 Fax: 0141 952 6003
Contact: Tom Baker or John Baker

Caithness Stage and Lighting

Sales and installation of range of lighting and staging equipment. Hire portable stage, mixing desks, lighting equipment, smoke machines, etc.

3 Wellington Street, Paisley PA3 2JQ
Tel: 0141 887 0949 Fax: 0141 887 1175

GAB Studio Services

Sales, installation and repairs of sound equipment. Hire from small vocal rig to 10k system. Sound operator and crew part of hire package.

6 Garden Street, Ayr KA8 0BB
Tel: 01292 267400
Contact: Jim Brian

Hyper PA Hire

Hire small vocal PA to 15k rigs. Transport and engineer included.

20 Queen Mary Avenue, Glasgow G42 8DT
Tel: 0141 424 0383 / 0850 916579 (mobile) Fax: 0141 424 0383
Contact: Campbell Forbes

Louis Grace Ltd

Wholesale and distribution of all PA systems.

25 Langside Place, Glasgow G41 3DL
Tel: 0141 632 4633 Fax: 0141 649 4772
Contact: Martin Grace or Suzanne Morris

Nightflight Entertainments Ltd

All lighting and sound equipment sold. Installations for theatres etc. PA hire up to 3k.

7 Fleming Court, Clydebank Business Park, Clydebank G81 2DR
Tel: 0141 941 1001 Fax: 0141 952 6464
Contact: John Murdoch

Northern Light

Sales, installation and repairs of sound, light and audio-visual equipment. Hire from 3k to 30k rigs. Also Edinburgh branch.

79 Loanbank Quadrant, Govan, Glasgow G51 3HZ
Tel: 0141 440 1771 Fax: 0141 445 4406
Contact: Keith Duncan (Hire) or Ken Christie (Sales)

Professional Sound Services PA Hire

Specialise in acoustic music. 2k Bose/Turbosound rigs.

21 Crosbie Street, Maryhill Park, Glasgow G20 0BQ
Tel: 0141 946 3983 / 0350 198215 (mobile)
Contact: Duncan Reid

Projek Sound and Lighting

Sales, installation, repair and hire of sound and lighting equipment. PA hire from a vocal system to a 4k rig. Custom built amplifiers and speakers.

13 The Workshops, Union Street, Greenock PA16 8JL
Tel: 01475 783626 / 0860 563337 (mobile) Fax: 01475 783626
Contact: Paul Birt

R S Sound and Light

Sales, installation and hire of sound and lighting equipment. Sound hire to 5k rigs.

158 Howard Street, Glasgow G1 4HA
Tel: 0141 204 5200 / 5201 Fax: 0141 204 5202

Rock Electronics

Sales, installation and repairs of sound and lighting equipment. Hire of PA sound systems from 100w to 2k. Also strobes and disco lights. Custom made electronic equipment.

113 Glasgow Road, Dumbarton G82 1RG
Tel: 01389 732588
Contact: Ian Clarke (Office) Tel: 01389 730300

Rock Hard

Hire of PA, 1 or 2k. Offer transport service. Band rehearsal, storage, and live pre-production.

3/5 Commerce Street, Glasgow G5 8AB
Tel: 0141 429 4807 / 0850 596573 (mobile)
Contact: Jake McGhee

Rock-It

Amplifier and speaker sales. PA hire from 2k to 40k. Repairs. Installations.

17/19 Motherwell Road, Carfin, Motherwell ML1 4EB
Tel: 01698 275581 Fax: 01698 265653
Contact: Jack Nimmo

S M Lighting

Supply lighting rigs 6k-120k with technical support.

176 Battlefield Road, Langside, Glasgow G42 9JT
Tel: 0141 649 0790 / 0860 494759 (mobile) Fax: 0141 636 0326
Contact: Scott Munroe

Squire Sound and Light (Scotland)

Sales and installation of sound and lighting equipment.

1 Queen Margaret Road, Kelvinside, Glasgow G20 6DP
Tel: 0141 946 3303
Contact: Colin Ashby (Manager)

Starstruck Professional Sound and Light

Sales, installation and repairs of all sound and lighting equipment. Hire from vocal PA to 20k rigs and range of lighting.

14 Carmyle Avenue, Tollcross, Glasgow G32 8HJ
Tel: 0141 778 4848 Fax: 0141 763 0015
Contact: Hardy Mattu

Storm Sound Systems

Sales, installation and hire of sound equipment. 2k to 24k PA, Bi-amp monitor system. Maintenance service.

Unit 2, Laird Business Park, Swanston Street, Glasgow G40 4HG
Tel: 0141 554 1065
Contact: Wilson Reid

Tannoy Audix Ltd

Sales, installation and hire of sound systems. PA manufacture.

Rosehall Industrial Estate, Coatbridge ML5 4TF
Tel: 01236 436053 Fax: 01236 426804
Contact: Peter Clark

Teknique Systems

Sales and installation of sound and lighting equipment. Equipment customised. Can arrange lighting hire.

31 Hamilton Drive, Cambuslang G72 8JQ
Tel: 0141 641 2343
Contact: Tony Kennedy

The Warehouse

Sales, installation and hire of sound equipment including DAT machines. Hire to 9k rigs.

Unit H, 7 Craigend Place, Anniesland, Glasgow G13 2UN
Tel: 0141 950 1757 Fax: 0131 555 6901
Contact: Edinburgh Office Tel: 0131 555 6900

Tone Zone

Sale, installation and hire of sound equipment. Sound hire to 20k including transport, sound operator and crew. Repair of audio equipment.

The Old Church Building, 92 Raeberry Street, Maryhill, Glasgow G20 6EG
Tel: 0141 946 0227 Fax: 0141 946 0228
Contact: Willie Knox

Zero Dee Bee

Live engineer, vast experience home and abroad. FOH and monitors. Rock/reggae/classical/rock.

17(b) Cathcart Crescent, Paisley PA2 7EL
Tel: 0141 889 9893
Contact: Tom O'Malley (Sound Engineer)

RECORDING

RECORD COMPANIES

Absolute Records

Pop/rock and celtic rock. Demos welcome.

Craig Gowan, Carr Bridge, Inverness PH23 3AX
Tel: 01479 841257

Attic Records

Specialise in traditional, fiddle and contemporary folk music.

Keldebrae, Finstown, Orkney KW17 2ER
Tel: 01856 761222
Contact: Owen Tierney

Auldgate Records

Produces cassettes and CDs of Scottish folk songs and traditional hymns in Gaelic and English, mainly taken from Alexander Carmichael's *Carmina Gadelica*. Aims to make a living connection between ancient Scottish folk music and Gaelic hymnody newly set to music by Ellen Wycherley (for voice and clarsach).

3 Auldgate, Kirkliston EH29 9HB
Tel: 0131 333 4042

Avalanche

Specialise in local bands. Re-issue of Fast Forward also.

17 West Nicolson Street, Edinburgh EH8 9DA
Tel: 0131 668 2374 Fax: 0131 668 3234
Contact: Kevin Buckle

Baghdad Radio Records

Artists include Cage and Heaven Hill. Demos welcome. Interested in moving into film music also. Scripts welcome for TV programme production side.

PO Box 508, Edinburgh EH10 4TN
Tel: 0131 229 8715
Contact: Raymond Moore

Beechwood Records

Recordings for independent record companies. Handle the mass production of CDs. One-off CDs. Computer based studio, CD ROM.

Drybridge, Moray AB56 2JY
Tel: 01542 832110
Contact: James Hunter

Big R Records

Country, classical and Scottish music label. Promoter also.

5 James Square, Biggar, Lanarkshire ML12 6DL
Tel: 01899 20202 Fax: 01899 21020
Contact: Drew Taylor

Buzz Records

Artists include Summerfield Blues and The Cotton Field. Also management and publicity services.

192 Glasgow Road, Perth PH2 0NA
Tel: 01738 638140 / 0585 437868 (mobile) Fax: 01738 638140
Contact: David Arcari

195

Cairngorm Music

Produce a mixture of Scottish and traditional music mainly for the local tourist industry. Also publishing arm.
The Warren, Woodside Avenue, Grantown On Spey, Morayshire PH26 3JR
Tel: 01479 872263
Contact: Allan Bantick

Caritas Records

Publishing arm Eschenbach Editions.
28 Dalrymple Crescent, Edinburgh EH9 2NX
Tel: 0131 667 3633 Fax: 0131 667 3633

Clubscene Records

Specialise in dance music. Publishing arm also.
PO Box 11, Bathgate, West Lothian EH48 1RX
Tel: 01506 636038 Fax: 01506 633900
Contact: Bill Grainger

Contribution Records

Soul and R and B label. Artists include Robert Ferrier, Bill Hurley and Stirling McLean. Also publishing arm.
35 Oakfield Avenue, Kelvinbridge, Glasgow G12 8LL
Tel: 0141 357 4980 Fax: 0141 357 4980
Contact: John Keenan

Corban Records

Scottish traditional and contemporary folk music. Artists include Peter Morrison, Robert Urquhart and Hanno Starosta.
PO Box 2, Glasgow G44 3LB
Tel: 0141 637 5277
Contact: Alastair McDonald

Culburnie Records

A company dedicated to exploring, expanding and regenerating the roots of pan-Celtic culture in general and that of the Scottish tradition in particular.
2 Harestanes Gardens, Kirkintilloch, Glasgow G66 2BT
Tel: 0141 776 0113 Fax: 0141 777 6097
Contact: Iain Fraser

Deeay Music

Scottish music and continental music by Scottish artists. Also music publishing.
22 Westfield Drive, Forfar, Angus DD8 1EQ
Tel: 01307 464324 Fax: 01307 464913
Contact: Doug Adamson

Dick Brothers Record Company

Produce all of Fish's solo material and have signed The Dream Disciples. International distribution point for Fish's work. (Also Funny Farm Recording Studios.)
Main House, Spittalrig Farm, Nr Haddington, East Lothian EH41 3SU
Tel: 01620 826150
Contact: Moira McGregor

Different Class Records Ltd

Student-run label signing one band each year for single deal. Previous groups include Goodbye Mr MacKenzie, Smile and Captain Shifty.
West Lothian College, Marjoribanks Street, Bathgate, West Lothian EH48 1QJ
Tel: 01506 634948 Fax: 01506 635801

Dolls House Records

Rock-indie based label.
7A Burnbank Place, Glasgow G20 6UH
Tel: 0141 331 1444 Fax: 0141 331 1444
Contact: Steve Doyle

Dunkeld Records

Scottish musicians including singer-songwriter tradition. Artists include Dougie MacLean.
Cathedral Street, Dunkeld, Perthshire PH8 0AW
Tel: 01350 727686 Fax: 01350 728606
Contact: Jennifer MacLean

Eclectic Records

With a special interest in Scottish contemporary music, artists on this label are Martyn Bennett, Cauld Blast Orchestra, The Easy Club, Michael Marra, Peter Nardini, Savourna Stevenson, Mike Travis's EH15 and Jim Sutherland.
3 Chamberlain Road, Edinburgh EH10 4DL
Tel: 0131 229 9299 Fax: 0131 229 9298

Electric Honey Records

Student-run label producing one EP per year. 1994 - Eight Miles High.
Stow College, 43 Shamrock Street, Glasgow G4 9LD
Tel: 0141 332 1786 x269
Contact: Alan Rankine

SUPPLIERS & SERVICES

Greentrax Recordings

Specialising in Scottish traditional music, artists include Aly Bain, Eric Bogle, Ceolbeg, The McCalmans, Hamish Moore, Jean Redpath, Shooglenifty and many more - on CD and cassette. Full catalogue available. Publishing arm, Grian Music.
Cockenzie Business Centre, Edinburgh Road, Cockenzie, East Lothian EH32 0HL
Tel: 01875 814155 Fax: 01875 813545
Contact: Ian D Green (Proprietor) or June M D Green (Co-proprietor)

Honey Records

Mainstream pop. Small label which is part of Streamline Music Ltd (publishers).
Streamline Music Ltd, Colinton Commercial Centre, 6D West Mill Road, Edinburgh EH13 0NX
Tel: 0131 441 6152 Fax: 0131 441 5470
Contact: Gordon Campbell

Human Condition Records

Indie/rock label. Artists include Lyd Painkillers and Sawyer. (Also Chamber Recording Studio).
120A West Granton Road, Edinburgh EH5 1PF
Tel: 0131 551 6632 Fax: 0131 551 6632
Contact: Jamie Watson or Paul Kirk

Iona Gold

Concentrating on the folk/rock scene, artists on this label include the Humpff Family, Carol Laula, Love and Money, The Pearlfishers and The Kevin McDermitt Orchestra.
27-29 Carnoustie Place, Scotland Street, Glasgow G5 8PH
Tel: 0141 420 1881

Iona Records

Specialising in contemporary folk music, artists on this label include Avalon, The Colour of Memory, The Keltz, Paul Mounsey, The Occasionals, Ossian and Rock Salt and Nails.
27-29 Carnoustie Place, Scotland Street, Glasgow G5 8PH
Tel: 0141 420 1881 Fax: 0141 420 1892

K B S Records

Established to deal with contemporary AOR artist Kitty Brewster. Publishing arm, Kitty Brewster Songs.
2 Hillhead Road, Newtonhill, Stonehaven, Kincardineshire AB3 2PT
Tel: 01569 730962 Fax: 01569 731030
Contact: Doug Stone

KRL

Audio and video recording company which controls and owns several labels: Elm (easy listening), Igus (MOR), Monarch (piping), OK (pop), Lochshore (traditional), Delux (folk). Publishing arm, Bulk Music Ltd.
9 Watt Road, Hillington, Glasgow G52 4RY
Tel: 0141 882 9060/9986 Fax: 0141 883 3686
Contact: Gus McDonald or Isobel Waugh

Kingfisher Records

Established to release The McCluskey Brothers album Favourite Colours, though not exclusive to this group. Future release forthcoming.
23 Buccleuch Street, Glasgow G3 6SJ
Tel: 0141 332 0921 / 01698 853500
Contact: Ken McCluskey or David McCluskey

Lewis Recordings

Specialist West Coast and Gaelic label.
1 Millburn Road, Inverness IV2 3PS
Tel: 01463 225621 Fax: 01463 225621
Contact: Donnie MacLean

Linn Records

Recordings cover jazz, classical and rock music. Artists include Carol Kidd, Martin Taylor and Tommy Smith.
Floors Road, Waterfoot, Eaglesham, Glasgow G76 0EP
Tel: 0141 644 5111 Fax: 0141 644 4262
Contact: Lindsay Pell

Lismor Recordings Ltd

Specialising in traditional Scottish music. Artists include Moira Anderson and Kenneth McKellar. Publishing arm, Isa Music.
27-29 Carnoustie Place, Scotland Street, Glasgow G5 8PH
Tel: 0141 420 1881 Fax: 0141 420 1892

Lough Records

Exists solely to issue recordings by Boys of the Lough, thereby enabling the artists to exert total artistic control over their product. Press and distribute within the UK and licence material to the USA.
31 Foutainhall Road, Edinburgh EH9 2LN
Tel: 0131 662 4992 Fax: 0131 662 0956
Contact: Dave Richardson (Administrator)

Macmeanmna

A Gaelic music marketing, management, recording and promotion company. Also involved in the production of live audio-visual shows. Management company for Arthur Cormack, Blair Douglas, Ishbel Macaskill, Mary Ann Kennedy. Photographer/broadcaster Cailean Maclean.
Quay Brae, Portree, Isle of Skye IV51 9DB
Tel: 01478 612990 Fax: 01478 613263
Contact: Arthur Cormack (Partner) or Blair Douglas (Partner)

Mayker Record Ltd

Concerned with the traditional and contemporary Scottish music of Moira Kerr. Future releases forthcoming.
PO Box 877, Glasgow G52 1EL
Tel: 0141 882 4218
Contact: Moira Kerr

Moonbeam Music

Record label renowned for the music of Mr Boom, the children's entertainer. Also on label is contemporary music of Andy Munro. Publishing arm, Sprockitt Music Publishing.
Lindsaylands Cottage, Biggar ML12 6NR
Tel: 01899 20471 Fax: 01899 20471
Contact: Andy Munro

My Dark Star Records

Independent record company. Artists, The Pearlfishers.
224 Renfrew Street, Glasgow G3 6TX
Tel: 0141 332 2851

Next Big Thing

Covers rock based music from the 1950s to the present. Demos welcome - will listen to any style of good music. Ties with US labels - will pass on interesting demos. Also produces magazine Next Big Thing.
20 Albert Avenue, Grangemouth, Stirlingshire FK3 9AT
Tel: 01324 482724 Fax: 01324 482724
Contact: Lindsay Hutton

Nine Gaites Music

Specialise in Scottish traditional music, mostly local talent recorded on CD and cassette.
Unit 48, The Forum Centre, Dundee DD1 1DQ
Tel: 01382 225962

Orissor Productions

Artists Orissor plus local musicians (mainly country and folk). Also available tape duplication service and recording studio.
14 Craigmore Road, Rothesay, Isle of Bute PA20 9LB
Tel: 01700 505357 Fax: 01700 505394

The Precious Organisation Ltd

Artists include Wet Wet Wet and John Harley and the Pack. Publishing arm, The Precious Music Company.

14-16 Speirs Wharf, Port Dundas, Glasgow G4 9TB
Tel: 0141 353 2255 Fax: 0141 353 3545
Contact: Elliott Davis

Q Songs

Contemporary pop record company.
99 Douglas Street, Dundee DD1 5AT
Tel: 01382 200808 Fax: 01382 201111

REL Records Ltd

Specialise in Scottish interest music and video, including traditional fiddle, accordion and pipes as well as television series such as Hooked on Scotland and The Castles of Scotland. Also publishing arm, Ad-Chorel Music.

40 Sciennes, Edinburgh EH9 1NH
Tel: 0131 668 3366 Fax: 0131 662 4463
Contact: Charles Cybulski or Neil Ross

Ridge Records

Deals with re-issues of Runrig albums Recovery, Heartland and Highland Connection.

55 Wellington Street, Aberdeen AB2 1BX
Tel: 01224 573100 Fax: 01224 572598
Contact: Gordon Ross

Ross Records

Artists include Jimmy Shand and his Band, The Gordon Family, Ian Middleton, Sandy Reid and Colin Campbell. Also publishing arm, Balnagown Music and Ross Records Distribution.

29 Main Street, Turriff, Aberdeenshire AB53 7AB
Tel: 01888 568899 Fax: 01888 568890
Contact: Gibson Ross or Audrey Reid

Rowan

Concentrate mainly on Scottish traditional artists. Released first two Wolfstone albums.

Ardross, Alness, Rossshire IV17 0YD
Tel: 01349 882039
Contact: David Foster

Schkaboogie Records

House music from garage to contemporary. Demos welcome.

Greenside House, 25 Greenside Place, Edinburgh EH1 3AA
Tel: 0131 557 9099 Fax: 0131 557 6519
Contact: George or Jason

Scotdisc

Music and video recording company specialising in traditional Scottish and easy listening music. Publishing arm, Garron Music.

Newtown Street, Kilsyth G65 OJX
Tel: 01236 821081 Fax: 01236 826900
Contact: Dougie Stevenson or Bill Garden

Scotsoun

Over 100 cassettes concentrating on Scottish language, literature, music and song.

13 Ashton Road, Glasgow G12 8SP
Tel: 0141 339 4705
Contact: Dr George Philp

Seil Recording

Specialise in re-release of unavailable Scottish material.

10 Gallowgate, Rothesay, Isle of Bute PA20 0HS
Tel: 01700 504566
Contact: Peter Hamilton

Shoop! Records

Techno music label.
34 Myrtle Crescent, Kirkcaldy KY2 5DX
Tel: 01592 205986 Fax: 01592 205986
Contact: Gordon

Soma

Dance label with releases from Rejuvination, Slam, Daft Punk, Skintrade, Mode 4 and Percy X.

62 Kelvingrove Street, Glasgow G3 7SA
Tel: 0141 331 1477 Fax: 0141 353 0017
Contact: David Clarke

Spiral Records

Limited editions of Scottish indie bands.
PO Box 661, Glasgow G41 4JL
Tel: 0141 427 6598
Contact: Justin Burns Tel: 0141 334 7752 or Keith Hawlay

Springthyme Records

New and traditional arrangements of folk, traditional and Scottish music. Publishing arm, Springthyme Music.

Balmalcom House, Kingskettle KY7 7TJ
Tel: 01337 830773 Fax: 01337 831773
Contact: Peter Shepherd

Steppin Out Records

Commercial dance music. Artists include DJ Scott, Bandido and Outer Rhythm.

4A Murderdean Road, Newton Grange, Edinburgh EH22 4PD
Tel: 0131 654 1888 Fax: 0131 654 2888
Contact: Laura McAnna or Scott Robertson

Sticky Music

Independent label specialising in quality song-writing. Current roster includes Iain Archer, Lies Damned Lies, Calvin's Dream and D B McGlynn. UK distribution through Total/BMG. (Also Heaven Recording Studios).

Cree House, 4 Townend Street, Dalry, Ayrshire KA24 4AA
Tel: 01294 833913 Fax: 01294 832460
Contact: Charlie Irvine or Steve Butler

Temple Records

Formed to create an outlet for the Scottish music that was ignored by the established record companies. Release albums that cover the broad sweep of the timeless Scottish tradition. Also British distributor for Flying Fish Records, Chicago.

Shillinghill, Temple, By Gorebridge, Midlothian EH23 4SH
Tel: 01875 830328 Fax: 01875 830392
Contact: Robin Morton (Manager) or Joyce McMillan (Secretary)

Twentythird Precinct and Limbo Records Ltd

Specialising in dance music, this company houses 23rd Precinct, Limbo and Marimba labels. Artists include Havanna and Q-Tex. Also publishing arm.

23 Bath Street, Glasgow G2 1HU
Tel: 0141 332 9740
Contact: William Kiltie or David McKenzie

Vital Spark Music Ltd

Vital Records Label, involved in publishing, record release, record production, A and R consultancy and musician guidance. Production includes Runrig (5 albums), The River Detectives (2 albums), Blair Douglas (1 album) and Steve Davies (1 album). T.H.E. Distribution (throughout UK) and Gordon Duncan Distribution (Scotland).

1 Waterloo, Breakish, Isle of Skye IV42 8QE
Tel: 01471 822484 Fax: 01471 822673
Contact: Chris Harley

Whirlie Records

Releases by Aly Bain and Phil Cunningham. Welcome demos in folk, world, or acoustic vein.

Greenside House, 25 Greenside Place, Edinburgh EH1 3AA
Tel: 0131 557 9099 Fax: 0131 557 6519
Contact: Aly Bain or Liz Wright

RECORDING STUDIOS

Abracadabra Recording
8 track studio. Classical to punk. (Also Buzz Records.)
47A Chestnut Avenue, Kirkcaldy KY1 2LS
Tel: 01592 641914 / 0585 437868 (mobile) Fax: 01738 638140
Contact: David Arcari

Apollo Recording
Full direct to disc digital multitrack recording, plus editing.
7 Garth Street, Glasgow G1 1UT
Tel: 0141 552 6290
Contact: Calum MacLean or Andy Haldane

Argyle Studios
One digital recording studio plus four practice suites.
1103 Argyle Street, Glasgow G3 8ND
Tel: 0141 221 1007

C Sharp Music Factory
Services and facilities are free to residents of Castlemilk area and some of surrounding environments. 16 track recording studio, rehearsal space; music lessons on variety of instruments, use of 1K PA and lighting.
37 Dougrie Drive, Castlemilk, Glasgow G45 9AD
Tel: 0141 631 1166 Fax: 0141 634 1156
Contact: Rab Patterson or Andrew Phillips

CA VA East
One recording studio (24 track), two rehearsal rooms (fully equipped). Also Glasgow studio and 48 track mobile studio.
The Clock House, Albion Business Centre, 78 Albion Road, Edinburgh EH7 5QZ
Tel: 0131 659 6673 Fax: 0131 661 4309
Contact: Nik Kinloch (Studio Manager)

CA VA Sound Workshops
Three studios available: one with 48 track large enough to house a 50 piece orchestra, one with 24 track and third with 8 track digital editing. Also a 48 track mobile recording studio and Edinburgh branch.
30 Bentinck Street, Kelvingrove, Glasgow G3 7TU
Tel: 0141 334 5099 / 6330 Fax: 0141 339 0271
Contact: Brian Young (Studio Manager) or Helen Clark (Bookings)

CAP Recording Studios
Fully professional 24 track digital recording studio built and equipped to the highest specifications, in a beautiful and tranquil rural area only 25 minutes from Inverness and Dalcross airport. Enquiries regarding availability, rates etc to Donna Cunningham.
Crask of Aigas, By Beauly, Inverness-shire IV4 7AD
Tel: 01463 782364 / 01463 782525 Fax: 01463 782525
Contact: Donna Cunningham

Carlton Studios
24-track digital recording studio. 4 rehearsal rooms with catering facilities.
54 Carlton Place, Glasgow G5 0TW
Tel: 0141 429 5723
Contact: Michael Price

Castle/CA VA
32 track digital recording and 24 track analogue recording.
The Old School, Pentcaitland, East Lothian EH34 5DY
Tel: 01875 340143 Fax: 01875 340557
Contact: Stuart Hamilton

Chamber Recording Studios
24 track recording studio. Amek 'Big by Langley' fully automated mix down. In house production available plus four rehearsal rooms.
120A West Granton Road, Edinburgh EH5 1PS
Tel: 0131 551 6632 Fax: 0131 551 6632
Contact: Jamie Watson (Owner)

CLM Recording Studio
16 track studio. MIDI capabilities. Country, Scottish and some pop.
26 Tay Street, Monifieth, Tayside DD5 4BG
Tel: 01382 534868
Contact: Grant MacDonald

The Cube
20 track digital recording studio plus one rehearsal room.
Calderbank Rehearsal Rooms, 81 Main Street, Calderbank, Airdrie ML6 9SJ
Tel: 01236 756056 Fax: 01236 750650
Contact: W Woodhead

Funny Farm Recording Studios Limited
32 track digital multi-tracking and 24 track analogue. Fully residential. (Also Dick Brothers record company).
Main House, Spittalrig Farm, Nr Haddington, East Lothian EH41 3SU
Tel: 01620 826150
Contact: Moira McGregor

Hart Street Studios
Four studios. All formats catered for.
4 Forth Street, Edinburgh EH1 3LD
Tel: 0131 557 0181 Fax: 0131 557 9521
Contact: Roy Ashby

Heartbeat Recording Studio
16 track with digital remastering. In-house record production team.
Guildie House Farm, North Middleton, Gorebridge EH23 4QP
Tel: 01875 821102 Fax: 01875 821102
Contact: David Valentine

Heaven
24 track studio. AMRS console (38 channels on remix). Tascam multitracks/ DAT Soundscape 8 track digital mastering/ editing. Quad amps. AR/JBL monitors. Mics, outboard, midi suite, cubase, s1000, m1, Hammond organ, daylight control room (300 sq ft). Daylight live room. (Also Sticky Music record company.)
Cree House, 4 Townend Street, Dalry, Ayrshire KA24 4AA
Tel: 01294 833913 Fax: 01294 832460
Contact: Charlie Irvine or Steve Butler

Leap Frog Mobile Recording
Mobile 24 track recording studio. Claude Harper was trained at Abbey Road and helped to install Apple Studios for the Beatles. All kinds of work undertaken including copying, maintenance, wiring installation of audio equipment.
1 Currievale Farm Cottages, Currie, Midlothian EH14 4AA
Tel: 0131 449 5808
Contact: Claude Harper

MCM Recording and Rehearsals
16 track recording facility.
Peacock Cross Industrial Estate, Hamilton ML3 9AQ
Tel: 01698 286882
Contact: Michael McGowan

Monitor Recording and Rehearsal Studio
One rehearsal room and 16 track recording studio.
24 Gairbraid Avenue, Maryhill, Glasgow G20 8YE
Tel: 0141 945 3519 / 946 3366
Contact: Findlay Robertson

Murricane and Murricane

Sound dubbing studio. Auto conforming audio from CMX EDLs (digital). Voice over recording to picture. Also write and produce music if commissioned.
Kensington House, 227 Sauchiehall Street, Glasgow G2 3EX
Tel: 0141 332 7282 Fax: 0141 332 6517
Contact: Barbara Murricane or David Murricane

Music Shack

24 track recording studios (two studios).
Brill Building, Kings Court, Southern Osborne Street, Glasgow G1 5QQ
Tel: 0141 552 6677 Fax: 0141 552 1354
Contact: Aly MacDonald

Opus One

24 track recording studio with digital mastering. Full tape and CD facilities available including all printing and packaging.
The Cottage, 14 Menstrie Road, Tullibody, Clacks FK10 2RG
Tel: 01259 218343
Contact: Dave Paterson (Owner)

Palladium Recording Studio

32 track digital and 24 track analogue recording facility.
7 Loanhead Road, Straiton Village, Edinburgh EH20 9NH
Tel: 0131 440 1084 Fax: 0131 440 1084
Contact: Jon Turner (Managing Director)

The Practice Pad

16 track and 24 track recording studio. Three practice rooms. Late night specials, midnight until 9am.
Unit B1, Enterprise West, Craigmont Street, Maryhill, Glasgow G20 9BT
Tel: 0141 946 7656 Fax: 0141 946 7656

Park Lane Studios

24 track recording studio.
974 Pollokshaws Road, Glasgow G41 2HA
Tel: 0141 636 1218 Fax: 0141 649 0042
Contact: Alan Connell (Studio Manager)

Radio Clyde Studios

Two studio rooms operating from one control room, AMEK G2520 desk. MCI 24 track recorder.
Clydebank Business Park, Clydebank, Glasgow G81 2RX
Tel: 0141 306 2200
Contact: Grae Allan (Chief Engineer)

Random Rhythms Music Workshop

16 track recording studio and rehearsal rooms. Also educational music workshops given.
Bridgehaugh Road, Stirling FK9 5AR
Tel: 01786 479082
Contact: Guy Dadge (Project Co-ordinator)

REL Studios Limited

Scotland's largest sound effects library (10,000 on CD) and worldwide digital linking using ISDN. Two fully equipped studios available for sound-to-picture, dubbing, music/jingle composition, short run custom pressing and all audio post-production needs.
40 Sciennes, Edinburgh EH9 1NH
Tel: 0131 668 3366 Fax: 0131 662 4463
Contact: Alasdair George or Bel Emslie

Revelation Recording Studios

Two studios, one with 24 track digital or analogue recording facility, other with 16 track range of midi equipment and samplers.
Archibald Simpson House, 27-29 King Street, Aberdeen AB2 3AA
Tel: 01224 625965 Fax: 01224 625962
Contact: Alan Benzie

Riverside Studios

48, 24 and 16 track recording facilities plus two rehearsal rooms.
7 Lowermill Road, Lowermill Estate, Clarkston G76 8BJ
Tel: 0141 644 5572 Fax: 0141 644 4421
Contact: Duncan Cameron

Robb, Graham

Small computer based recording studio, automated digital and analogue multi-track recording. Suitable for individuals rather than bands.
Tigh-Na-Beithe, Birnam, Dunkeld, Perthshire PH8 OBW
Tel: 01350 727371 / 0378 616151 (mobile) Fax: 01350 727371

Rowan

24 track recording facility.
Ardross, Alness, Rosshire IV17 OYD
Tel: 01349 882039
Contact: David Foster

Scotstores Studio

8 track digital and analogue recording facility, CDs and cassettes.
Muse Cottage, Allanton, Duns, Berwickshire TD11 3JZ
Tel: 01890 818884 Fax: 01890 818108
Contact: Muriel Johnstone or Bill Zobel

Scotty's Sound Studio

24 track recording studio. (Also Scotdisc record company).
Newtown Street, Kilsyth G65 OJX
Tel: 01236 823291 Fax: 01236 825683
Contact: Bill Garden

Seagate Studios

16 track digital recording studio. In-house production and CD and cassette duplication services.
97 Seagate, Dundee DD1 2EN
Tel: 01382 200725
Contact: Stewart Firm

Shabby Road Recording Studio

24 track recording studio. Six rehearsal rooms.
1 Glencairn Square, Kilmarnock, Ayrshire KA1 4AQ
Tel: 01563 536377

Skerries Music Publishing and Recording Studios

General studio recording work on 16 track digital. Production of TV film music.
29 Queen Street, Lossiemouth IV31 6PR
Tel: 01343 815454
Contact: Dave Sinton

The Sound Cafe

24 track digital recording studio.
Walston Steading, Nine Mileburn, Penicuik, Midlothian EH26 9LS
Tel: 01968 674913
Contact: David Grey

The Sound Factory

Two rehearsal rooms. 16 track digital recording studio. Adats/promix.
Queensway Industrial Estate, Glenrothes KY7 5PZ
Tel: 01592 611327 Fax: 01592 610315
Contact: James Bisset

Sound Station

8 track plus cuebase.
42 High Street, Galashiels TD1 1SE
Tel: 01896 750190

The Soundhouse

Digital hard disc recording system multi-track. In-house production available.
Forth House, Forth Street, Edinburgh EH1 3LF
Tel: 0131 557 1557 Fax: 0131 557 3899
Contact: David Balfe

Split Level Recording Studios
24 track analogue and digital recording facility. In-house production available.
3 Eastmains, Ingliston, Edinburgh EH28 8NQ
Tel: 0131 333 5024 Fax: 0131 333 5024
Contact: Neil McNaught

Stormsound
16 track recording studio.
Craighall, Deerness, Orkney KW17 2QQ
Tel: 01856 741260
Contact: Philip Anderson

Stuffhouse Studios
16 track recording studio. Two rehearsal rooms. Amplifier repairs.
7A Burnbank Place, St Georges Cross, Glasgow G20 6UH
Tel: 0141 331 1444 Fax: 0141 331 1444

The Toucan Studio
28 track recording studio. Also rehearsal studios.
Unit Number 2, West Bowhouse Workshops, Girdle Toll, Irvine KA11 1AW
Tel: 01294 221903
Contact: Danny or Mike

Waterfront Studios
24 track digital recording facility. Four studios. Tape duplication service. TV and radio post-production work.
Riverside House, 260 Clyde Street, Glasgow G1 4JH
Tel: 0141 248 9100 Fax: 0141 248 5020
Contact: Mattie Murdoch

Waveform Studio
Small 16 track studio specialising in remixes.
158 Howard Street, Glasgow G1 4HA
Tel: 0141 226 3285 / 0850 285927 (mobile)
Contact: Trevor Riley

Whitham, Keith
8 track recording studio.
c/o The Hidden Gem, Latheron Centre, Ullapool IV26 2TH
Tel: 01854 612554

REHEARSAL STUDIOS

Audio Craft Services
Three rehearsal rooms. (Also PA and lighting hire).
Elgin House, Elgin Street, Dunfermline KY12 7SA
Tel: 01383 620858
Contact: Allan Short

Babelfish Rehearsal Studios
Two rehearsal rooms.
81 Castlebank Street, Glasgow G11 6AR
Tel: 0141 357 0001
Contact: Gavin or Alan

Banana Row
Eight rehearsal rooms.
21 Constitution Place, Leith Docks, Edinburgh EH6 7DJ
Tel: 0131 553 5533 Fax: 0131 553 7551
Contact: Craig Hunter

Barrowland Rehearsals
Three rehearsal rooms.
244 Gallowgate, Glasgow G4 0TT
Tel: 0141 553 2515 Fax: 0141 552 4997
Contact: Gordon Robb

Berkley 2
Five rehearsal rooms.
54 Washington Street, Glasgow G3 8AZ
Tel: 0141 248 7290 Fax: 0141 204 1138
Contact: Steve Cheyne

Inch Community Centre
Six rooms available for bands to rehearse in.
Inch House, Gilmerton Road, Edinburgh EH16 5UF
Tel: 0131 664 4710 Fax: 0131 664 4710
Contact: John Travers

Red Eye Studios
Three rehearsal rooms.
11 Hume Street, Clydebank, Dunbartonshire G81 1XL
Tel: 0141 951 1554
Contact: John Nairn

Rock Hard
One rehearsal room. PA hire to 2.5K.
3/5 Commercial Street, Glasgow G5 8AB
Tel: 0141 429 4807 / 0850 596573 (mobile)
Contact: Jake McGhee

Stage Two Thousand
Two music rehearsal rooms.
Taybridge Station, Riverside Drive, Dundee DD1 4DB
Tel: 01382 223332
Contact: Stuart Milne

SUPPLIERS & SERVICES

201

The Toucan Studio

Hire of 1k and 2k Bose PA with transport, crew and engineer.
Unit No 2, West Bowhouse Workshops, Girdle Toll, Irvine KA11 1AW
Tel: 01294 221903
Contact: Danny or Mike

RECORDING SERVICES

Better Mousetrap Music

Location recording services and production of CD's and cassettes, specialising in jazz and classical from solo to full orchestra/choir.
85 East King Street, Helensburgh G84 7RG
Tel: 01436 672187

Bonskeid Music Ltd

All manner of production work and sound recording, mainly within the general field of Scottish music.
6 The Steils, Edinburgh EH10 5XD
Tel: 0131 447 0991 / 0831 779920 (mobile) Fax: 0131 447 0991
Contact: Freeland Barbour

C5 TVC Ltd

Tape duplication service. One-off CDs.
Bridgend House, Lasswade, Edinburgh EH18 1NA
Tel: 0131 654 2372 Fax: 0131 654 0816
Contact: Paul Blythe

Chow Productions

Cassette manufacturers and duplicators. All post-recording needs met.
571 Sauchiehall Street, Glasgow G3 7PQ
Tel: 0141 221 5058 Fax: 0141 248 8184

Digital Demos

Small company specialising in low cost, high quality recordings of chamber music. Recording and editing is digital. Operates own label Deus Ex Machina, which produces cassettes, DCC tapes and CDs.
99 Lothian Road, Edinburgh EH3 9AN
Tel: 0131 228 3706 Fax: 0131 650 6516
Contact: Geraint Wiggans

Gab Studio Services

Supply and installation of professional sound systems.
6 Garden Street, Ayr KA8 0BB
Tel: 01292 267400
Contact: Jim Bryan

Lorn House Productions

Audio cassette duplications. Precision wound blank audio cassette.
Lorn House, Links Gardens Lane, Leith, Edinburgh EH6 7JQ
Tel: 0131 553 5503 Fax: 0131 553 5550
Contact: James Lawson

MacTrack Duplicating

Tape duplication service. Runs from 50 upwards. On body printing etc.
95 Hercus Loan, Musselburgh, Edinburgh EH21 6BB
Tel: 0131 665 5377 Fax: 0131 653 6905
Contact: Donald McGregor or Alasdair McGregor

Q Logic

Producers of midi metro (visual metronome) and MBC1 (midi bar counter), enabling musicians to record without using headphones.
PO Box 109, Dundee DD1 9DF
Tel: 01382 200808 Fax: 01382 201111

Shermann Audio (Scotland)

Manufacture loud speakers for studio and PA use.
Unit D, 51 Brunswick Road, Edinburgh EH7 5PD
Tel: 0131 661 0022 Fax: 0131 661 0022

Sound Control

Professional audio department. Sales to recording studios.
61 and 67 Jamaica Street, Glasgow G1 4NN
Tel: 0141 204 2774
Contact: Head Office Tel: 01383 733353 Fax: 01383 725733

Voyager Media Ltd

Compact disc duplication. One-off CDs - mass duplication orders. Typesets artwork, promotes customers through Scottish media. Works with professionals and amateurs, all types of music.
13 Corran Gardens, Dundee DD5 3EH
Tel: 01382 480200
Contact: Brad Sutherland (Managing Director)

Zonal Limited

Manufacture CD boxes and cassette cases. Supply and distribute professional audio magnetic tape and cassette pancakes for duplication purposes.
Invergordon Industrial Estate, Invergordon IV18 0PQ
Tel: 01349 853840 Fax: 01349 853712
Contact: Dave Quinton

PUBLISHERS

Bagpipes of Caledonia

Piping and related material, music books.
Lorn House, Links Garden Lane, Leith, Edinburgh EH6 7JQ
Tel: 0131 553 5503

Balnagown Music

Publish traditional Scottish music.
29 Main Street, Turriff, Aberdeenshire AB53 7AB
Tel: 01888 568899 Fax: 01888 568890
Contact: Gibson Ross or Audrey Reid

Blackfriars Publishing

Publish Scottish folk arts directory every year. Folk song publications also.
49 Blackfriars Street, Edinburgh EH1 1NB
Tel: 0131 557 3090 Fax: 0131 557 3090
Contact: Willie Haynes

Bonskeid Music Ltd

Publishers of various items in the general field of Scottish music.
6 The Steils, Edinburgh EH10 5XD
Tel: 0131 447 0991 / 0831 779920 (mobile) Fax: 0131 447 0991 (Mobile) 0831 779920
Contact: Freeland Barbour

David Johnson Music

Small publishing house producing Scottish educational string series, Scottish 18th c. orchestral hire catalogue, selection of David Johnson's compositions, 18th c. Scottish cassettes.
1 Hill Square, Edinburgh EH8 9DR
Tel: 0131 667 7054
Contact: Dr David Johnson

Deeay Music

Publish mainly new compositions, though some traditional.
22 Westfield Drive, Forfar, Angus DD8 1EQ
Tel: 01307 464324 Fax: 01307 464913
Contact: Doug Adamson

Esslin Music

Classical music for voice and piano.
Fraserford, Dunscore, Dumfries DG2 0UU
Tel: 01387 820271 Fax: 01387 820226

Gairm Publications

Publish Gaelic choral music for the Mod. Also some Gaelic song books with translations.
29 Waterloo Street, Glasgow G2 6BZ
Tel: 0141 221 1971

Glasgow Libraries Publications

Local history publishers mainly.
The Mitchell Library, North Street,
Glasgow G3 7DN
Tel: 0141 221 9600
Contact: James Irvine

Griffin Music

Mainly publishes and promotes the music of John McLeod.
Hill House, 9 Redford Crescent,
Edinburgh EH13 0BS
Tel: 0131 441 3035 Fax: 0131 441 5218

The Hardie Press

Founded in 1984, with 23 titles in the areas of Scottish traditional fiddle music, Scottish vocal music (traditional and contemporary), Scottish baroque music, and is the publisher for the Liszt Society. Scottish music is the main interest but other projects will be considered. Distribution undertaken on behalf of other publishers.
17 Harrison Gardens, Edinburgh
EH11 1SE
Tel: 0131 313 1383 Fax: 0131 313 1388

Harper Collins Publishers

Manuscripts welcome.
PO Box, Glasgow G4 0NB
Tel: 0141 772 3200 Fax: 0141 306 3588
Contact: Christopher Riches (General Reference Section)

John Donald Publishers Ltd

Specialise in academic historical book publication, though have published several books relating to music.
138 St Stephen Street, Edinburgh
EH3 5AA
Tel: 0131 225 1146
Contact: Russell Walker (Commissioning Editor)

Kerr Music Corporation Limited

Comprises Bayley and Ferguson, James F Kerr and Mozart Allan Publishing companies. Traditional Scottish and Irish music.
65 Berkeley Street, Glasgow G3 7DZ
Tel: 0141 221 9444 / 6805
Contact: Andrew Dunn

Kinmor Music

Publish traditional and folk music.
Shilling Hill, Temple, Midlothian
EH23 4SH
Tel: 01875 830328 Fax: 01875 830392
Contact: Robin Morton

Larousse PLC

Publishers of several musical reference books.
43-45 Annandale Street, Edinburgh
EH7 4AZ
Tel: 0131 557 4571 Fax: 0131 557 2936

Limetree Arts and Music

Publishing company for the songs of Dougie MacLean.
Cathedral Street, Dunkeld, Perthshire
PH8 0AW
Tel: 01350 727686 Fax: 01350 728606
Contact: Jonathon Moses or Jenny MacLean

Lomond Music

Publishes educational music, music for bands and ensembles (woodwind, brass and string). Mainly Scottish composers.
32 Bankton Park, Kingskettle, Fife
KY15 7PY
Tel: 01337 830974 Fax: 01337 830653

Masterclass Music

Educational publishers. Sell instrumental arrangements of classical pieces, which are marketed directly to secondary schools within the UK and the Republic of Ireland. Arrangements are all suitable for mixed groups of instruments, providing teachers with flexibility . There is also an automatic limited photocopying licence.
12 Kelso Place, Dundee DD2 1SL
Tel: 01382 667251 Fax: 01382 640775
Contact: Nigel Don

Octavo Music

Specialises in traditional Scottish music, especially bagpipe music (highland and bellows-blown), contemporary compositions for the pipes, and new music of all descriptions by Scottish based composers.
1 Cheyne Street, Edinburgh EH4 1JA
Tel: 0131 332 8083
Contact: Dick Lee

SUPPLIERS & SERVICES

203

Piper Publications

Educational music, orchestral music for schools and youth orchestras, chamber music, music for steel pan, 18th century concertos and choral work.
Dochroyle Farm, Barrhill, Girvan KA26 OQG
Tel: 01465 821377
Contact: Pat Spence

Polygon

Publish books relating to folk and traditional music. Forthcoming publication: *Companion to Scottish Traditional Music.*
22 George Square, Edinburgh EH8 9LF
Tel: 0131 650 4689 Fax: 0131 662 0053

Royal Scottish Pipe Band Association

Publish piping and drumming tuition books.
45 Washington Street, Glasgow G3 8AZ
Tel: 0141 221 5414 Fax: 0141 221 1561

Scottish Music Publishing

The publishing division of the Scottish Music Information Centre. Current list includes over 20 works for solo instruments by contemporary Scottish composers, a collection of bagpipe tunes by Robert Wallace and violin sonatas by David Foulis (1710-1773).
1 Bowmont Gardens, Glasgow G12 9LR
Tel: 0141 334 6393 Fax: 0141 337 1161
Contact: Dr Kirsteen McCue (Manager)

Skirling Music

Publishers for various British and American country artistes.
James Square, Biggar, Lanarkshire ML12 6DL
Tel: 01899 20202 Fax: 01899 21020
Contact: Drew Taylor

Streamline Music Ltd

Music publishing and marketing service. Also incorporates small record label Honey Records (mainstream pop).
Colinton Commercial Centre, 6D West Mill Road, Edinburgh EH13 0NX
Tel: 0131 441 6152 Fax: 0131 441 5470
Contact: Gordon Campbell

Taigh Na Teud

Wide range of traditional music, including contemporary.
13 Upper Breakish, Isle of Skye IV42 8PY
Tel: 01471 822528 Fax: 01471 822528
Contact: Alasdair Martin

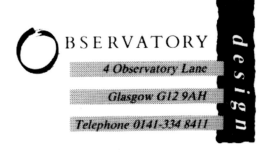

SUPPLIERS & SERVICES

Vanderbeek and Imrie Ltd

Catalogue includes Spanish and Portuguese, Franco-Flemish, English, German/Slav, Italian and Mexican Church Music; music by Orlandus Lassus (1532-1594), instrumental music and music for brass band, wind band and orchestra. Also work by David Ward, Adrian Beaumont, Ivan Moody, Christopher Painter and Robert Steadman.

15 Marvig, Lochs, Isle of Lewis
HS2 9QP
Tel: 01851 880216 Fax: 01851 880216
Contact: Martyn Imrie

Wild Goose Publications

Publish religious material, including music books and cassettes.
Unit 15, 6 Harmony Row, Glasgow
G51 3BA
Tel: 0141 440 0985
Contact: Sarelle Reid

COPYISTS

HAND

Bragg, Glynn

Hand copyist.
1 North Dumgoyne Avenue, Milngavie,
Glasgow G62 7JT
Tel: 0141 956 2480

Cull, Jeremy

Professional part-copying service, standard rates apply. Recent contracts have included SCO, Royal Opera House Covent Garden and the Composers' Ensemble. Samples available on request.
Top Floor Right, 12 Gladstone Terrace,
Edinburgh EH9 1LT
Tel: 0131 667 6765

Fowler, Tommy

B.Mus. (Hons) Glasgow University. Chiefly a composer but has a wide knowledge of arranging and copying with over twenty years' experience. Has copied for the SCO, STV and Traverse, Edinburgh. Presently on postgrad composition research.
60 Maryhill Road, Glasgow G20 7QB
Tel: 0141 353 0927

Hearne, John

Hand copyist. Terms by arrangement.
Smidskot, Fawells, Keith Hall, Inverurie
AB5 0LN
Tel: 01651 882274

Heyward, Mark

Hand copyist.
9 Garrioch Quadrant, 2/2, Glasgow
G20 8RT
Tel: 0141 946 5270

Hughes, Kevin

Hand copyist. Also computer based copying.
11 Queens Park Avenue, Glasgow
G42 8BX
Tel: 0141 423 2702

Jones, David Paul

Hand copyist
Top Floor, 7 Dunedin Street, Edinburgh
EH7 4JB
Tel: 0131 556 6031

Jukes, Aileen

Hand copyist.
13/2 Elm Row, Leith Walk, Edinburgh
EH7 4AA
Tel: 0131 557 8799

Sharrock, Jean

Hand copyist. (Also composer).
20 Bothwick Way, Foxbar, Paisley
PA2 0TT
Tel: 0141 848 3212

Strutt, Clive

Postal service offered for the manuscript preparation of performing material - orchestral/vocal parts, full scores, transposition, photocopying masters etc. Low overheads allowing competitive pricing.
Manse Bay, South Ronaldsay, Orkney
Islands KW17 2TJ
Tel: 01856 831541

Wilson, Max

Hand copyist.
19 Kensington Gate, Glasgow G12 9LQ
Tel: 0141 334 1790

COMPUTER

Chalmers Enterprises

Complete music typesetting service, laser printed etc. Copied numerous complete editions.
37 Juniper Avenue, Juniper Green,
Midlothian EH14 5EE
Tel: 0131 453 3026 Fax: 0131 453 3180
Contact: Neil Scott

Dunvournie Music

Music typesetting, printing, single songsheets, complete books, teaching resources, conventional printing.
Dunvournie, Blairninich, Strathpeffer
IV14 9AB
Tel: 01997 421124 Fax: 01997 421124

Evans, Joseph

Music typesetting by computer.
Flat 2/R, 2 Grantley Gardens, Glasgow
G41 3QA
Tel: 0141 636 1560

Fowler, David

Music typesetting by computer. Hand copying also available.
Scores, Burnfoot, Westerkirk, Langholm,
Dumfriesshire DG13 0NG
Tel: 01387 370280

GFA Publishing

Music typesetting by computer.
5 Kirkintilloch Road, Lenzie, Glasgow
G66 4RW
Tel: 0141 776 5056
Contact: Charles Ketteringham

The Hardie Press

Computer based music typesetting for traditional, classical and contemporary manuscripts: melody lines to orchestral scores. Editorial input available when required.
17 Harrison Gardens, Edinburgh
EH11 1SE
Tel: 0131 313 1383 Fax: 0131 313 1388

Kendal Music

Music typesetting by computer.
16 Trinity Crescent, Edinburgh
EH5 3ED
Tel: 0131 552 4065
Contact: Paul Flush

Mackie Music Service

Computer based copying and transposition service. Preparation of parts, scores and piano reductions. Also arranging and orchestration.
190 Lee Crescent North, Aberdeen
AB22 8FR
Tel: 01224 823256

Mitre Music

Provides a complete one stop music preparation service. Everything is available from computer based copying, brochures, programmes, photocopying and manuscript paper to customer specifications. Computer based music systems can also be designed and installed to match exact needs.
680 Anniesland Road, Glasgow
G14 0XR
Tel: 0141 954 8757 Fax: 0141 954 8757
Contact: Derek Bishop

SUPPLIERS & SERVICES

205

Music to Measure

Professional music typesetting by computer and DTP facilities, up to A3, and to film. Personal service for customers' compositions and publications. Send a sample page for free typesetting and quotation, or phone to discuss requirements.

New House, Ballachulish, Argyll PA39 4JR
Tel: 01855 811507 Fax: 01855 811507
Contact: Mary Anne Alburger

Octavo Music

Computer based typesetting and printing. (Also publishing.)
1 Cheyne Street, Edinburgh EH4 1JA
Tel: 0131 332 8083
Contact: Dick Lee

Robb, Graham

Computer based copyist.
Tigh-Na-Beithe, Birnam, Dunkeld, Perthshire, PH8 0BW
Tel: 01350 727371 / 0378 616151 (mobile) Fax: 01350 727371

Skye-Time Copying

Computer typesetting. Clear scores and parts (A4, B4, A3) ranging from single staves to full orchestral score, including lyrics, contemporary notation using Sibelius 7. Synthesized demo tapes available. Competitive rates.
12 Lochbay, Waternish, Dunvegan, Isle of Skye IV55 8GD
Tel: 01470 592253
Contact: Jane Yeats

Wright, Jane

Music typesetting by computer.
Lower Millfield, Stronsay, Orkney KW17 2AG
Tel: 01857 616329

LIBRARIES & MUSEUMS

AK Bell Library

Atholl collection of 18th and 19th century Scottish music.
Perth and Kinross District Libraries, York Place, Perth PH2 8EH
Tel: 01738 444949
Contact: Mike Moir (Depute District Librarian)

Auld Sköll

Local fiddle made in 1890s.
Utra, Fair Isle, Shetland Islands ZE2 9JU

Central Library

Walker collection: books on theory of music and some musical scores including some rare examples of early Scottish music. J M Henderson Collection: many Scottish items, especially fiddle music (most at National Library, Edinburgh), Cosmo Mitchell Collection: books on history and practice of dancing. MacBeath Collection: English and Scottish folk ballads. Also printed music.
Aberdeen City Council, Rosemount Viaduct, Aberdeen AB9 1GU
Tel: 01224 634622 x214
Contact: Michael Thomson (Music Queries)

Chambers Street Museum

Small international collection of musical instruments, partly ethnology oriented. Also the Jean Jenkins archives (ref *Man and Music*, 1984). Also Museum of Antiquities and Scottish United Services Museum.
National Museums of Scotland, Chambers Street, Edinburgh EH1 1JF
Tel: 0131 225 7534

Dean Castle

Collection of historical stringed instruments. Entrance £2 adult, 50p children (free to residents of Kilmarnock and Loudon).
Dean Road, Kilmarnock KA3 1XB
Tel: 01563 522702
Contact: James Hunter (Curator)

Dick Institute Museum and Art Gallery

Van Raalte collection - large collection of early musical instruments including harps, lutes and dulcimers.
14 Elmbank Avenue, Kilmarnock KA1 3BU
Tel: 01563 526401

Dundee Central Library

A J Wighton Collection of old Scottish music and Easson Collection of European folk music. The Wighton database can be consulted at the library and also at the National Library of Scotland in Edinburgh.
The Wellgate, Dundee DD1 1DB
Tel: 01382 434376
Contact: Christine Ferguson (Librarian in Charge)

Edinburgh University

1,000 items on display including string, woodwind, brass and percussion instruments: also some folk instruments. Open Wednesdays 3 - 5pm, Saturdays 10am - 1pm. During Edinburgh Festival open Monday - Friday 2-5pm. Party and other conducted visits can be made by arrangement with the curator. Admission free.
Collection of Historic Musical Instruments, Edinburgh University, Reid Concert Hall, Bristo Square, Edinburgh EH8 9AG
Tel: 0131 650 2423
Contact: Arnold Myers (Curator) or Miss Donaldson

Edinburgh University

General and special book collections include books of Scottish song. Special collections also include early Scottish music MSS (including the surviving leaves of the 14th c. Inchcolm antiphoner and collections of lute and pipe tunes etc), English madrigal books and the Marjorie Kennedy-Fraser collection of Hebridean folk-song recordings and books on Highland music and dance.
Main Library, George Square, Edinburgh EH8 9LJ
Tel: 0131 650 3409 / 3384

Gairloch Hertitage Museum

Collection of local printed music.
Achtercairn, Gairloch, Ross and Cromarty IV21 2BJ
Tel: 01445 712287
Contact: Curator

Glasgow University

Special collections (with major strengths): Euing music (early editions of theory of music, psalters, lute MSS); Farmer (history of Arabic and military music); Mearns (hymnology); Stillie (19th c. operas); works (including many MSS) of Drysdale, Hyllested, Lamond, McEwen, MacCunn, W B Moonie, Whittaker, Zavertal. Houses Scottish Theatre Archive, Scottish Ballet Archive. General public apply to librarian for access.
University Library, Hillhead Street, Glasgow G12 8QE
Tel: 0141 339 8855
Contact: Stella Money (Music Librarian) Tel: x6719

Highland Folk Museum

Small collection on display including clarsach, pipes, fiddle and printed music.
Duke Street, Kingussie, Badenoch and Strathspey PH21 1JG
Tel: 01540 661307

Hunterian Museum

Hague Collection - about 100 wind instruments from late 18th c. to early 20th c. Owned by Music Department, housed in the Hunterian.
University of Glasgow, 82 Hillhead Street, Glasgow G12 8QQ
Tel: 0141 330 4221
Contact: Dr Edwards
Tel: 0141 339 8855 x5288

Inverness Museum and Art Gallery

Extensive collection of fiddle material and some prototype instruments of Alexander Grant. Also collection of pipe material.
Castle Wynd, Inverness IV2 3BJ
Tel: 01463 23714
Contact: Assistant Curator, Social History

Kelvingrove Art Gallery and Museum

Organ restored 1990 - regular recitals. Large collection of European (early music collection) and non-European instruments. Glen collection held and collection from RSAMD on loan (European and non-European). Anyone interested in study/research of instruments not on display, phone for an appointment. Contact Bob Savage for information on instruments held at St Mungo's Museum, Glasgow.
Kelvingrove, Glasgow G3 8AG
Tel: 0141 221 9600
Contact: Bob Savage (European Instruments) or Antonia Lovelace (Non-European Instruments)

McManus Galleries

Small collection of keyboard instruments and hand instruments. Also worldwide ethnology instruments.
Albert Square, Dundee DD1 1DA
Tel: 01382 432020
Contact: Keeper of Human History Art Gallery and Museum Department Dundee District Council

Mitchell Library

Monday - Friday 9am - 9pm. Saturday 9am - 5pm. 50,000 scores (18,000 for loan). 20,000 books on music (6,000 for loan). 400 orchestral scores with parts for loan, 175 vocal score sets for loan. 4,000 items on recording. Also the Kidson Collection (folk song), some manuscripts in the Bayley and Ferguson Donation incl. Hugh Roberton and the *Scottish Students Song Book*, The George Gardiner Donation (dance and folk music), The Moody Manners Collection. Francis George Scott MSS (songs and sketches). Baptie Collection (1,400 items mainly madrigals, hymns etc). Also three practice rooms with piano plus two other practice rooms.
North Street, Glasgow G3 7DN
Tel: 0141 221 9600

Museum of Antiquities

Collection of international and Scottish string, keyboard and woodwind instruments, including the Glen and Ross bagpipe collection and collection of pipe making tools. Also Chambers Street Museum and Scottish United Services Museum.
National Museum of Scotland, 1 Queen Street , Edinburgh EH2 1JD
Tel: 0131 225 7534

Museum of Islay Life

Small collection of local printed music and set of bagpipes.
Port Charlotte, Isle of Islay, Argyll and Bute PA48 7UA
Tel: 01496 850358
Contact: Curator

Museum of the Isles

One set of pipes, 'the fairy pipes of Moidart' on permanent loan. Supposedly played at the battle of Bannockburn, the chanter to these pipes has an extra hole which the maker added following a dream telling him that this would create an original sound. Violin with local connections. Very small collection.
Clan Donald Visitor Centre, Armadale, Ardvasar, Isle of Skye IV45 8RS
Tel: 01471 844389
Contact: Margaret MacDonald

Music Library

Monday - Friday 9am - 9pm. Saturday 9am - 1pm. Scotland's largest public music lending library has 64,000 books and scores, 7,000 cassettes and 12,000 CDs. There are also 5,700 books and scores and 80 periodicals available for reference. Scottish music of all types and periods is strongly represented. Information files are maintained covering local music teachers, societies and organisations.
Edinburgh City Libraries, George IV Bridge, Edinburgh EH1 1EG
Tel: 0131 225 5584 Fax: 0131 225 8783
Contact: Lorna Mill

Napier University

Printed music, books, periodicals, sound recordings. General public apply to library for access.
Queen's Library, Sighthill Court, Edinburgh EH11 4BN
Tel: 0131 444 2266
Contact: Pat Napier (Music Librarian)
Tel: x3445

National Library of Scotland

UK legal deposit library. c. 250,000 scores, predominantly British music. Literature about music. Special collections: Scottish traditional music; Handle;Berlioz, Verdi. Music manuscripts: Scottish music manuscripts, including early music; piping and other traditional music; manuscripts of concert music by Scottish composers; 2,500 sound recordings. All collections are reference only.
George IV Bridge, Edinburgh EH1 1EW
Tel: 0131 226 4531
Contact: Roger Duce (Music Librarian)

Northern College

Printed music, books, periodicals. Sound recordings mainly classical though small amount of folk, jazz, sound effects and spoken word. Open to general public as reference library - contact main desk on arrival.
Dundee Campus Library, Gardyne Road, Dundee DD5 1NY
Tel: 01382 464000

Northern College Library

Scores and books relating to music.
Northern College, Aberdeen Campus, Hilton Place, Aberdeen AB9 1FA
Tel: 01224 283571 Fax: 01224 487046
Contact: Kit Corrall (Asst Senior Librarian)

SUPPLIERS &
SERVICES

207

Perth Museum and Art Gallery

Small collection including instruments from a local brass band and work band, a Niel Gow violin and a collection of Scottish song books.
George Street, Perth PH1 5LB
Tel: 01738 632488
Contact: Rebecca Shawcross

Queen Mother Library

Holds books relating to music, scores, sheet music and CD's. Also the Gavin Greig and Forbes Leith collections of folk songs, which are housed in the department of special collections, King's College.
University of Aberdeen, Meston Walk, Aberdeen AB9 2UE
Tel: 01224 272580
Contact: Richard Turbet (Music Librarian) Tel: 01224 272592

Regimental Museum of the Queen's Own Highlanders

Small collection - seven sets of pipes, two keyed bugles.
Fort George, Ardersier, Inverness IV1 2TD
Tel: 01667 462800

Reid Music Library

Kenneth Leighton Archives, Sir Donald Tovey Archives, Weiss Collection on Beethoven, Collection of early books on theory of music. Scores, printed music, books about music, sound recordings with listening facilities. Service free to members of the university. General public should apply to librarian for access. Also special collections and religious music collections in main library.
Edinburgh University Library, Alison House, 12 Nicolson Square, Edinburgh EH8 9DF
Tel: 0131 650 2436
Contact: Mr J Upton

Royal Highland Fusiliers Museum

Small collection of military instruments.
518 Sauchiehall Street, Glasgow G2 3LW
Tel: 0141 332 0961
Contact: Major Shaw

RSAMD Library

Collection of printed music, books and audio visual material, mainly classical with small ethnomusicology collection.
100 Renfrew Street, Glasgow G2 3DB
Tel: 0141 332 4101

Russell Collection of Early Keyboard Instruments

Wednesdays 2-5pm, Saturdays 2-5pm (during Edinburgh Festival: 10.30am - 12.30pm Monday to Saturday.) Demonstrations and guided tours.
St Cecilia's Hall, Niddry Street, Cowgate, Edinburgh EH1 1LJ
Tel: 0131 650 2423
Contact: Miss Donaldson or Arnold Myers (Curator)

School of Scottish Studies

Book collections include Scots and Gaelic song since the 18th c., folk music and ethnomusicology of Ireland, England, North America and the world. Archives include traditional and national Scottish music field recordings, the John Levy collection of ethnomusicological recording (mostly oriental), the Peter Cooke collection of African music recordings, the Will Forret collection of Scottish national, popular, folk revival music, and smaller collections (Chilean, Irish, Indian).
University of Edinburgh, 27 George Square, Edinburgh EH8 9LD
Tel: 0131 650 4160

Scottish United Services Museum

Military wind and percussion instruments from the 18th century including extensive bagpipe collection. Sound archives on tape of European and North American military music. Also Chambers Street Museum and Museum of Antiquities.
National Museums of Scotland, The Castle, Edinburgh EH1 2NG
Tel: 0131 225 7534

St Andrews University

Holds 113 modern manuscripts in the Finzi collection. Some in Gerald Finzi's hand. About 180 manuscripts in the catalogue of works by Cedric Thorpe Davie. Also letters to and from the composer. Printed music, books on music, periodicals and recordings. General public should apply to librarian for access.
University Library, North Street, St Andrews KY16 9TR
Tel: 01334 476161 x2283
Contact: Margot Munro

Stevenson College

Selection of books relating to musical instrument repair. Printed music also. General public apply to librarian for access.
Carrickvale Centre, Library, Stenhouse Street West, Edinburgh EH11 3EP
Tel: 0131 443 8888
Contact: Fay Watson

Stewartry Museum

Small collection. Bechstein piano designed by E A Taylor plus printed music.
6 St Mary Street, Kirkcudbright, DG6 4AQ
Tel: 01557 331643

Stirling University Library

Small collection of printed music, books and periodicals, sound recordings from early music to modern jazz and pop with a small amount of ethnic music. External readers contact librarian for access, no listening facilities available for external readers.
University of Stirling, Stirling FK9 4LA
Tel: 01786 467231
Contact: Gordon Willis Tel: x7236

West Highland Museum

Small collection including the Poltalloch harp (late 19th c. copy of the Lamont harp), bagpipes supposedly played at Culloden and Mulroy, set of cauld wind pipes which Bonnie Prince Charlie gave to his valet. Please no enquiries until after refurbishment (expected completion Spring 1997).
Cameron Square, Fort William, Lochaber PH33 6AJ
Tel: 01397 702169
Contact: Fiona Marwick

VENUES

Editorial Notes

The chapter is divided by REGION in the first instance, then further categorised by CAPACITY. For example, all venues with a capacity of under 150 in the Borders region are listed first, then venues in the Borders with a capacity of 150 to 399, followed by Borders venues of 400 to 999, and so on before proceeding to Central region. Capacity divisions are: under 150; 150 to 399; 400 to 999; and over 1,000.

The Regions used are as follows:

> Borders
> Central
> Dumfries & Galloway
> Fife
> Grampian
> Highland
> Lothian
> Orkney Islands
> Shetland Islands
> Strathclyde
> Tayside
> Western Isles

These are the local government regions as they are at the time of publication. These will undergo tremendous change in April 1996, but we felt that the current regions are familiar to everyone while the new ones would not be so easy to use at the time of printing. Future editions of the *Handbook,* of course, will need to be arranged differently.

The listings give the contact details for the venue and whom to contact to hire it, the capacity, and notes on disabled access. This chapter is intended as a guide only and groups arranging a tour, for example, will need to contact the venues directly to find out more specific details such as stage layout and lighting.

Venues which have 'The' as part of their name have been listed by the second word, e.g. The Lemon Tree is under L rather than T. However, it was decided to list venues beginning with 'An' under A, even though this is the Gaelic definitive article. An Lanntair appears under A rather than L for example, as this is probably where most people would look for it!

BORDERS

UNDER 150

Ancrum Village Hall
Capacity: 90. Disabled access and facilities.
Ancrum, Roxburghshire TD8
Tel: 01835 830348
Contact: E Smart (Treasurer)

Birgham Village Hall
Capacity: 50. No disabled access.
Eccles Road, Birgham, Coldstream TD12 4NF
Tel: 01890 830249
Contact: Jean Allan (Secretary/Treasurer (bookings))

Cockburnspath Village Hall
Capacity: 100. Disabled access.
Cockburnspath, Berwickshire TD13 5XX
Tel: 01368 830357
Contact: M Young (Secretary (bookings))

Eccles Village Hall
Capacity: 130. Disabled access.
Main Street, Eccles, Kelso TD5
Tel: 01890 840302
Contact: J White

Eckford Village Hall
Capacity: 80. No disabled access.
Eckford , Kelso TD5 8LG
Tel: 01835 850289
Contact: Lorraine Kay (Hon Secretary)

Ednam Village Hall
Capacity: 70. Disabled access and facilities.
Ednam, Kelso TD5
Tel: 01573 224006
Contact: Linda Nairn (Chairman Hall Trustees)

Foulden Parish Hall
Capacity: 120. No disabled facilities.
Foulden, Nr Berwick upon Tweed TD15 1UH
Tel: 01289 386332
Contact: E Elphinston (Hon Secretary (bookings))

Gordon Village Hall
Capacity: 120. Disabled access and facilities. Correspondence c/o Secretary, Burnbrae, Gordon, Berwickshire TD3 6JU.
Main Street, Gordon, Berwickshire TD3 6VR
Tel: 01573 410357
Contact: Mrs Fairgrieve (Secretary)

Graham Institute
Capacity: 90. Disabled access and facilities. Correspondence c/o DSO Manager, Tweeddale DC, Dovecote Road, Peebles EH45 8HW.
The Green, West Linton, Tweeddale
Tel: 01721 723354
Contact: A D Briggs (DSO Manager Tweeddale DC)

Grantshouse Village Hall
Capacity: 100. Disabled access.
Grantshouse, Duns, Berwickshire
Tel: 01368 830403
Contact: Mrs M White (Chairman Hall Committee)

Hutton Village Hall
Capacity: 120. No disabled access.
Correspondence c/o Secretary, Paddirow, Butterdean, Grantshouse, Duns, Berwickshire TD11 3RS.
Hutton, Berwickshire
Tel: 01361 850217
Contact: J Purves (Secretary/Treasurer)

Reston Village Hall
Capacity: 100. Disabled access.
Ladeside, Reston, Eyemouth, Berwickshire
Tel: 01890 761371
Contact: Mr Tait (Caretaker / bookings) or Mrs Campbell Tel: 01890 761398

Smailholm Village Hall
Capacity: 70. No disabled access.
Smailholm, Kelso TD5 7PJ
Tel: 01573 460252
Contact: Alex Taylor (Secretary Hall Committee)

Southdean Village Hall
Capacity: 80. Disabled access.
Southdean, Hawick TD9 8TG
Tel: 01450 860239
Contact: June Scott (Hallkeeper)

Swinton Village Hall
Capacity: 120. Disabled access and facilities.
Main Street, Swinton, Berwickshire
Tel: 01890 860617
Contact: Frank Barker (Hall Committee)

Volunteer Hall (Galashiels)
Capacity: 60. No disabled access.
Correspondence c/o Ettrick and Lauderdale DC, PO Box 4, Council Chambers, Albert Place, Galashiels TD1 3DL.
St John Street, Galashiels, Selkirkshire
Tel: 01896 752247 Fax: 01896 757003
Contact: David Harrison (Public Halls Supervisor) Tel: 01896 754751

Wauchope Hall
Capacity: 100. Disabled access (four steps to facilities). Correspondence c/o Isobel Herbert, Deanfield Road, Yetholm, Kelso TD5 HRS.
Main Street, Yetholm, Kelso, Roxburgh TD5
Tel: 01573 420329
Contact: Isobel Herbert (Treasurer and Booking Clerk)

Wilton Lodge Museum and Scott Gallery
Capacity: 100-150. No disabled access.
Hawick, Roxburghshire TD9 7JL
Tel: 01450 373457 Fax: 01450 373993
Contact: Fiona M Colton (District Museums Curator)

150 TO 399

Chambers Institute
Capacity: 225. Disabled access and facilities. Correspondence c/o DSO Manager, Tweeddale DC, Dovecote Road, Peebles EH45 8HW.
High Street, Peebles EH45 8AN
Tel: 01721 723354
Contact: A D Briggs (DSO Manager, Tweeddale DC)

Coldingham Village Hall
Capacity: 150. Disabled access and facilities.
c/o Burnhall Farmhouse, Coldingham, Nr Eyemouth, Berwickshire
Tel: 018907 71613
Contact: Mrs Robertson (Booking Clerk)

Corn Exchange
Capacity: 215. Disabled access and facilities.
Market Square, Melrose, Roxburghshire
Tel: 01896 754751 x173 Fax: 01896 757003
Contact: Ian Yates (Ettrick and Lauderdale DC) or Venue Tel: 01896 822463

Edgerston Village Hall
Capacity: 200. Disabled access and facilities.
Edgerston , By Camptown, Jedburgh TD8 6PW
Tel: 01835 840276
Contact: Mrs Anderson (Hon Secretary)

Floors Castle
Capacity: 150. Disabled access and facilities. Preference: small scale chamber/piano.
Kelso, Borders TD5 7SF
Tel: 01573 223333 Fax: 01573 226056
Contact: Frances Brown (Marketing Manager)

VENUES

213

Laidlaw Memorial Hall
Capacity: 180. Disabled access and facilities.
Bonchester Bridge, Hawick, Roxburgh
Tel: 01450 860255
Contact: Aileen Douglas (Treasurer) or Andrew Reith (Hallkeeper)

Memorial Hall
Capacity: 350. Disabled access and facilities. Correspondence c/o DSO Manager, Tweeddale DC, Dovecote Road, Peebles EH45 8HW.
Leithen Road, Innerleithen EH44 6HX
Tel: 01721 723354
Contact: A D Briggs (DSO Manager Tweedale DC)

Morebattle Village Hall
Capacity: 150. Disabled access.
Main Street, Morebattle, Roxburgh
Tel: 01573 440329
Contact: J Mabon (Secretary/Treasurer)

Newcastleton Village Hall
Capacity: 200. Disabled access and facilities.
Langholm Street, Newcastleton TD9 0QX
Tel: 013873 75251
Contact: Moira Rowan (bookings)

St Boswell's Village Hall
Capacity: 180. Disabled access.
Jenny Moores Road, St Boswells TV6
Tel: 01835 823344
Contact: Madge Melrose (A S and P Robb Newsagent)

Victoria Halls
Capacity: Lesser Hall 150. No disabled access. Correspondence c/o Ettrick and Lauderdale DC, Council Chambers, Albert Place, Galashiels TD1 3DL.
Scotts Place, Selkirk
Tel: 01896 754751
Contact: David Harrison (Public Halls Supervisor) or Venue Tel: 01750 21382

VENUES

400 TO 999

Hawick Town Hall
Capacity: 634. Disabled access and facilities.
High Street, Hawick TD9 9EF
Tel: 01450 375991 Fax: 01450 378526
Contact: Adie Barker (Tourist/Leisure Manager)

Tait Hall
Capacity: 700. Disabled access and facilities.
Edenside Road, Kelso, Roxburgh TD5 7B5
Tel: 01573 224233
Contact: Jim Connor (Hallkeeper)

Town Hall
Capacity: 450. Disabled access and facilities.
Abbey Place, Jedburgh, Roxburgh TD8 6BE
Tel: 01835 862261
Contact: Ian Frizzel (Hallkeeper)
Tel: 01450 375991

Victoria Halls
Capacity: Main Hall 650. Disabled access and facilities. Correspondence c/o Ettrick and Lauderdale DC, Council Chambers, Albert Place, Galashiels TD1 3DL.
Scotts Place, Selkirk
Tel: 01896 754751
Contact: David Harrison (Public Halls Supervisor) or Venue Tel: 01750 21382

Volunteer Hall (Duns)
Capacity: 400. Disabled access and facilities. Correspondence c/o Environmental Services Dept, Berwickshire DC, 44 Newtown Street, Duns TD11 3DT.
Langton Gate, Duns TD11 3AU
Tel: 01361 882600
Contact: Ian Gill (Admin Officer Environmental Services)

Volunteer Hall (Galashiels)
Capacity: 553. Disabled access and facilities. Correspondence c/o Ettrick and Lauderdale DC, PO Box 4, Council Chambers, Albert Place, Galashiels TD1 3DL. PRS Significant Venue.
St John Street, Galashiels, Selkirkshire
Tel: 01896 752247 Fax: 01896 757003
Contact: David Harrison (Public Halls Supervisor) Tel: 01896 754751

CENTRAL

UNDER 150

Albert Halls
Capacity: Lesser Hall 140. Disabled access and facilities.
Dumbarton Road, Stirling FK8 2LQ
Tel: 01786 473544 Fax: 01786 448933
Contact: Jess Brown (Senior Booking Office Assistant)

Alloa Town Hall
Capacity: Lesser Hall 80. No disabled access. Correspondence c/o Leisure Services Dept, Clackmannan DC, The Speirs Centre, 29 Primrose Street, Alloa FK10 1JJ.
Mars Hill, Alloa, Clackmannan FK10 1AB
Tel: 01259 213131 Fax: 01259 721313
Contact: Sheena Neil (Administration Officer)

Centenary Hall
Capacity: 74. No disabled access. Correspondence c/o Leisure Services Dept, Clackmannan DC, The Speirs Centre, 29 Primrose Street, Alloa FK10 1JJ.
Tillicoultry, Stirling
Tel: 01259 213131 Fax: 01259 721313
Contact: Sheena Neil (Administrator Leisure Services Dept)

Coach House Theatre
Capacity: 65. No disabled access.
Inglewood, Tullibody Road, Alloa FK10 2DY
Tel: 01259 212264
Contact: G C D Cairns (Artistic Director) Tel: 01259 213762

Cowane Centre
Capacity: 140. Disabled access and facilities. Correspondence to Community Services, Beechwood House, St Ninian's Road, Stirling FK8 2AD.
Cowane Street, Stirling FK8 1JP
Tel: 01786 473544 Fax: 01786 448933
Contact: Jess Brown (Senior Booking Office Assistant)

Glebe Hall
Capacity: 80. Disabled access and facilities. Correspondence c/o Leisure Services Dept, Clackmannan DC, The Speirs Centre, 29 Primrose Street, Alloa FK10 1JJ.
Alloa, Stirling
Tel: 01259 213131 Fax: 01259 721313
Contact: Sheena Neil (Administrator Leisure Services Dept)

MacRobert Arts Centre
Capacity: Studio 140. Disabled access and facilities. PRS Significant Venue.
University of Stirling, Stirling FK9 4LA
Tel: 01786 467155 Fax: 01786 451369
Contact: Liz Moran (Director) or Box Office Tel: 01786 461081

Muckhart Village Hall
Capacity: 100. Disabled access and facilities.
Muckhart FK14 7JP
Tel: 01259 781492
Contact: A Bryce

Shieldhill Community Hall
Capacity: 100. Disabled access.
Main Street, Shieldhill, Falkirk
Tel: 01324 632576
Contact: J Hamilton (Secretary)

Tullibody Civic Centre
Capacity: Function Suite 80. Disabled
access and facilities. Correspondence c/o
Leisure Services Dept, Clackmannan DC,
The Speirs Centre, 29 Primrose Street,
Alloa FK10 1JJ.
Tullibody, Stirling
Tel: 01259 213131 Fax: 01259 721313
*Contact: Sheena Neil (Administrator
Leisure Services Dept)*

150 TO 399

Clackmannan Town Hall
Capacity: 190 (184 + 6 wheelchair
spaces). Disabled access and facilities.
Correspondence c/o Leisure Services
Dept, Clackmannan DC, The Speirs
Centre, 29 Primrose Street, Alloa
FK10 1JJ.
Clackmannan, Stirling
Tel: 01259 213131 Fax: 01259 721313
*Contact: Sheena Neil (Administrator
Leisure Services Dept)*

Cochrane Hall
Capacity: 300 (294 + 6 wheelchair
spaces). Disabled access and facilities.
Correspondence c/o Leisure Services
Dept, Clackmannan DC, The Speirs
Centre, 29 Primrose Street, Alloa
FK10 1JJ.
Alva, Stirling
Tel: 01259 213131 Fax: 01259 721313
*Contact: Sheena Neil (Administrator
Leisure Services Dept)*

Dumyat Leisure Centre
Capacity: Main Hall 250. Disabled access
and facilities. Correspondence c/o Leisure
Services Dept, Clackmannan DC, The
Speirs Centre, 29 Primrose Street, Alloa
FK10 1JJ.
Menstrie, Stirling
Tel: 01259 213131 Fax: 01259 721313
*Contact: Sheena Neil (Administrator
Leisure Services Dept)*

Falkirk Town Hall
Capacity: Lesser Hall 200. No disabled
access. PRS Significant Venue.
Civic Centre, West Bridge Street, Falkirk
Tel: 01324 624911 x2397
*Contact: Jane Clark (Entertainments
Officer) Tel: 01324 624911 x2377*

Guildhall
Capacity: 150. Disabled access: contact
in advance for wheelchair spaces.
49 St John Street, Stirling FK8 1ED
Tel: 01786 473544 Fax: 01786 448933
*Contact: Jess Brown (Senior Booking
Office Assistant)*

Mayfield Centre
Capacity: 200. Disabled access and
facilities.
Sunnybank Road, St Ninians, Stirling
Tel: 01786 473544 Fax: 01786 448933
*Contact: Jess Brown (Senior Booking
Office Assistant)*

Sauchie Hall
Capacity: 250. No disabled access.
Correspondence c/o Leisure Services
Dept, Clackmannan DC, The Speirs
Centre, 29 Primrose Street, Alloa
FK10 1JJ.
Sauchie, Stirling
Tel: 01259 213131 Fax: 01259 721313
*Contact: Sheena Neil (Administrator
Leisure Services Dept)*

400 TO 999

Albert Halls
Capacity: Main Hall 882. Disabled
access and facilities.
Dumbarton Road, Stirling FK8 2LQ
Tel: 01786 473544 Fax: 01786 448933
*Contact: Jess Brown (Senior Booking
Office Assistant)*

Alloa Town Hall
Capacity: 500. Disabled access and
facilities. Correspondence c/o Leisure
Services Dept, Clackmannan DC, The
Speirs Centre, 29 Primrose Street, Alloa
FK10 1JJ.
*Mars Hill, Alloa, Clackmannan
FK10 1AB*
Tel: 01259 213131 Fax: 01259 721313
*Contact: Sheena Neil (Leisure Services
Administration Officer)*

VENUES

215

Devonvale Hall
Capacity: 431. Disabled access and facilities. Correspondence c/o Sheena Neil, Administration Officer, Leisure Services Dept, Clackmannan DC, 29 Primrose Street, Alloa FK10 1JJ.
Moss Road, Tillicoultry, Clackmannanshire
Tel: 01259 213131 Fax: 01259 721313
Contact: Sheena Neil (Administration Officer)

Falkirk Town Hall
Capacity: Main Hall 200-900 (flexible). Disabled access and facilities.
Civic Centre, West Bridge Street, Falkirk
Tel: 01324 624911 x2397
Contact: Jane Clark (Entertainments Officer) Tel: 01324 624911 x2377

MacRobert Arts Centre
Capacity: Main Theatre 501. Disabled access and facilities.
University of Stirling, Stirling FK9 4LA
Tel: 01786 467155 Fax: 01786 451369
Contact: Liz Moran (Director) or Box Office Tel: 01786 461081

DUMFRIES & GALLOWAY

UNDER 150

Birchvale Theatre
Capacity: 78. Disabled access and facilities.
9 Galla Avenue, Dalbeattie DG5 4JZ
Tel: 01556 611615
Contact: Miss E MacKenzie (Secretary)

Gillespie Memorial Hall
Capacity: 80. Disabled access and facilities.
Mouswald, Dumfries DG1 4LU
Tel: 01387 750362
Contact: Mrs Rae (Secretary)

Glemriddell Hall
Capacity: 100. Disabled access and facilities planned.
Dunscore, Nithsdale DG2 0TA
Tel: 01387 820455
Contact: Colin Mitchell (Secretary)

Langholm Community Centre
Capacity: 120. No disabled access.
Charles Street, Langholm DG13 0AA
Tel: 01387 381289
Contact: Barbara Jameson (Asst Community Education Worker)

Lockerbie Little Theatre
Capacity: 88. Disabled access.
Well Street, Lockerbie
Tel: 01576 202257
Contact: Betty Wilson (Secretary)

Loreburn Hall
Capacity: 100. Disabled access and facilities. Correspondence to Arts Dept, Dumfries and Galloway DC, Municipal Chambers, Buccleuch Street, Dumfries DG1 2AD. PRS Significant Venue.
Newall Terrace, Dumfries DG1 1LN
Tel: 01387 253166 x297
Contact: Chris Cook / Mari Findlay (Client Manager / Admin Officer) or Venue Tel: 01387 253166 x213

McFarlan Hall
Capacity: 94. No disabled access.
Clarencefield, Dumfries
Tel: 01387 870249
Contact: M Coulthard (Secretary/Treasurer)

McMillan Hall
Capacity: 100. No disabled access. Correspondence c/o Mrs McGaw, Council Offices, Victoria Street, Newton Stewart DG8.
Dashwood Square, Newton Stewart DG8
Tel: 01671 403346
Contact: J Fraser (Hallkeeper) or Mrs McGaw (bookings) Tel: 01671 402442

Old Well Theatre
Capacity: 74. Disabled access.
Old Well Road, Moffat DG10 9AP
Tel: 01683 300491
Contact: Graylene Clark (Hon Secretary Upper Annandale Dramatic Society)

Patrick Dudgeon Memorial Hall
Capacity: 50. No disabled access. Correspondence c/o Secretary, Whitethorn, Islesteps, Dumfries DG2 8ES.
Islesteps, Dumfries DG2 8ES
Tel: 01387 254673
Contact: E Baldwin (Hall Secretary)

Robert Burns Centre
Capacity: 69. Disabled access and facilities.
Mill Road, Dumfries DG2 7BE
Tel: 01387 264808
Contact: Kenny Eggo (Film Theatre Officer) Tel: 01387 253374

Victoria Hall
Capacity: 345. Disabled access and facilities. Correspondence to Council Chambers, Annan DG12 6AQ.
Downies Wynd, Annan
Contact: Lesley Hackitt (Cultural Services Officer) Tel: 01461 201384

150 TO 399

Barbour Memorial Hall
Capacity: 200. Disabled access and facilities.
Church Street, Glencaple, Dumfries DG1 4QY
Tel: 01387 770313
Contact: A McCall (Treasurer)

Dalbeattie Town Hall
Capacity: 250. No disabled access or facilities.
High Street, Dalbeattie, Dumfries and Galloway
Tel: 01557 330291 x214 / 323 Fax: 01557 330005
Contact: I Peacock (Leisure Services Officer) or Venue Tel: 01556 502732

Galloway Arts Theatre
Capacity: 200. Disabled access and facilities.
Lochside Road, Castle Douglas DG7 1EU
Tel: 01556 503755
Contact: J H Paterson (Treasurer)

Kirkbean Hall
Capacity: 200. Disabled access.
Kirkbean, Dumfries DG2 8BQ
Tel: 01387 880386
Contact: Isobel Hundertmark (Hallkeeper)

Kirkcudbright Town Hall
Capacity: 250. No disabled facilities.
St Mary Street, Kirkcudbright DG6 4AA
Tel: 01557 330291 x214 / 235 Fax: 01557 330005
Contact: I Peacock (Leisure Services Officer) or Venue Tel: 01557 330478

McMillan Hall
Capacity: 250. No disabled access. Correspondence c/o Mrs McGaw, Council Offices, Victoria Street, Newton Stewart DG8.
Dashwood Square, Newton Stewart DG8
Tel: 01671 403346
Contact: J Fraser (Hallkeeper) or Mrs McGaw (bookings) Tel: 01671 402442

New Galloway Town Hall
Capacity: 153. No disabled facilities.
High Street, New Galloway, Stewartry of Kirkudbright
Tel: 01557 330291 x 214 Fax: 01557 330005
Contact: Peacock (Leisure Services Officer) or E McQueen (Hallkeeper and bookings) Tel: 01644 420204

The Ryan Centre

Capacity: Theatre 263. Disabled access and facilities.
Fairhurst Road, Stranraer, Wigtownshire DG9 7AP
Tel: 01776 703535 Fax: 01776 706880
Contact: Stewart S Atkinson (Director Client Services) or David Hislop (Contracts Manager)

Theatre Royal (Dumfries)

Capacity: 219. Disabled access and facilities.
Shakespeare Street, Dumfries DG1 2JH
Tel: 01387 254209
Contact: Alan Ritson (Chairperson) Tel: 01387 255268 or Box Office Tel: 01387 254209

400 TO 999

Castle Douglas Town Hall

Capacity: 406. No disabled access.
St Andrew Street, Castle Douglas DG7 1DE
Tel: 01557 330291 x214 / 321
Fax: 01557 330005
Contact: I Peacock (Leisure Services Officer) or Venue Tel: 01556 502732

Loreburn Hall

Capacity: 800. Disabled access and facilities. Correspondence to Arts Dept, Dumfries and Galloway DC, Municipal Chambers, Buccleuch Street, Dumfries DG1 2AD.
Newall Terrace, Dumfries DG1 1LN
Tel: 01387 253166 x297
Contact: Chris Cook / Mari Findlay (Client Manager / Admin Officer) or Venue Tel: 01387 253166 x213

The Ryan Centre

Capacity: Games Hall 620. Disabled access and facilities.
Fairhurst Road, Stranraer, Wigtownshire DG9 7AP
Tel: 01776 703535 Fax: 01776 706880
Contact: Stewart S Atkinson (Director Client Services) or David Hislop (Contracts Manager)

FIFE

UNDER 150

Auchtermuchty Town Hall

Capacity: 50. No disabled access.
High Street, Auchtermuchty, North East Fife KY14 7AT
Tel: 01337 828329
Contact: Pat Johnstone (Senior Clerkess) or Mr Wyse (Hallkeeper) Tel: 01337 828720

Buckhaven Theatre

Capacity: 102. Disabled access and facilities.
Lawrence Street, Buckhaven KY8 1BQ
Tel: 01592 715577
Contact: Rev Bryce Calder (Minister)

Crawford Arts Centre

Capacity: Drama Studio 66; largest gallery also suitable for recitals. Disabled access: parking by arrangement, theatre up one step.
93 North Street, St Andrews KY16 9AL
Tel: 01334 474610
Contact: Diana A Sykes (Director)

Hill of Tarvit

Capacity: 70. Disabled access and facilities.
Cupar, Fife KY15 5PB
Tel: 01334 653127
Contact: The Manager

Wilkie Memorial Hall

Capacity: 100. No disabled access.
Ladybank Road, Pitlessie, North East Fife
Tel: 01337 830915
Contact: Mrs Davie (Hallkeeper (bookings))

150 TO 399

Auchtermuchty Victoria Hall

Capacity: 180. Disabled access and facilities.
Cupar Road, Auchtermuchty, North East Fife KY14 7DD
Tel: 01337 828329
Contact: Pat Johnstone (Senior Clerkess) or Mr Wyse (Hallkeeper) Tel: 01337 828720

Buchanan Theatre

Capacity: 386. No disabled access.
University of St Andrews, Union Street, St Andrews KY16 9AJ
Tel: 01334 462521
Contact: Linda Richardson (Reservations Secretary)

Byre Theatre

Capacity: 174. Disabled access and facilities.
Abbey Street, St Andrews KY16 9LA
Tel: 01334 476288
Contact: Tom Gardner (General Manager)

Elie and Earlsferry Town Hall

Capacity: 160. No disabled access.
High Street, Earlsferry, North East Fife
Tel: 01333 330480
Contact: Mrs Lawrie (Hallkeeper)

St Monans Town Hall

Capacity: 250. Disabled access and facilities. Correspondence c/o NE Fife DC, Local Office, West Shore, St Monans, Anstruther KY10 2BS.
Hope Place, St Monans, North East Fife KY10 2DJ
Tel: 01333 730319
Contact: Mrs Peattie (NE Fife DC (local office) or Mr and Mrs Kinnear (Hallkeepers) Tel: 01333 730277

400 TO 999

Adam Smith Theatre

Capacity: 475. Disabled access and facilities. PRS Significant Venue.
Bennochy Road, Kirkcaldy KY1 1ET
Tel: 01592 202855 Fax: 01592 640655
Contact: Sheila Thomson (Theatre Manager) or Box Office Tel: 01592 260498

Carnegie Hall

Capacity: 590. Disabled access and facilities. PRS Significant Venue.
East Port, Dunfermline KY12 7JA
Tel: 01383 720108
Contact: Jim McIsaac (Principal Arts and Ents Officer)

The Centre

Capacity: 512. Disabled access and facilities: contact in advance for wheelchair spaces, first floor lounge not fully accessible.
Commercial Road, Leven KY8 4QX
Tel: 01333 424700
Contact: Max Walker (Community Education Worker)

VENUES

217

Corn Exchange (Cupar)
Capacity: 450. No disabled access.
St Catherine Street, Cupar, North East Fife KY15 4HA
Tel: 01334 652864
Contact: Jean Hassan (Hallkeeper)

Lochgelly Centre
Capacity: 460. Disabled access and facilities.
Bank Street, Lochgelly KY5 9QU
Tel: 01592 418141 Fax: 01592 418080
Contact: Norman Lockhart (Head of Centre)

Union Theatre
Capacity: 500. Disabled access and facilities.
Student Union, St Mary's Place, St Andrews KY16 9UZ
Tel: 01334 462700 / 462701 Fax: 01334 462716
Contact: Bruce Turner (House Supervisor) or Rebecca Ashworth (Administrator)

Younger Graduation Hall
Capacity: 968. Disabled access.
North Street, St Andrews KY16 9AJ
Tel: 01334 462226
Contact: A Malcolm (Secretary) or Mrs Brechin (Secretary) Tel: 01334 476161 x2520

GRAMPIAN

UNDER 150

VENUES

Aberlour Fleming Hall
Capacity: 112 (seated). Disabled access and facilities.
Aberlour, Moray
Tel: 01343 543451
Contact: Eric McGillivray (Arts and Ents Officer) or Bookings Tel: 01340 871308

Altens Community Centre
Capacity: 140. Disabled access and facilities.
Strathburn Street, Altens, Aberdeen AB1 4SE
Tel: 01224 896798
Contact: Carol Bruce (Management Committee)

Brodie Castle
Capacity: 50. Disabled access and facilities. Correspondence to Peggie Gordon, Abertarff House, Church Street, Inverness IV1 1EU.
Nr Forres, Moray IV36 0TE
Tel: 01309 641371 Fax: 01309 641600
Contact: Peggie Gordon (Regional PRO) Tel: 01463 232034

Buckie Town House
Capacity: 140. Disabled access and facilities.
43 St Peters Road, Buckie AB56 1DP
Tel: 01343 543451
Contact: Eric McGillivray (Arts and Ents Officer) or Box Office Tel: 01542 832297

Cummings Park Community Centre
Capacity: 130. Disabled access and facilities.
Cummings Park Crescent, Northfield, Aberdeen AB2 7AQ
Tel: 01224 694060
Contact: Dorothy Park (Management Committee)

Forres Town Hall
Capacity: 100. Disabled access and facilities.
High Street, Forres, Moray
Tel: 01343 543451
Contact: Eric McGillivray (Arts and Ents Officer) or Venue Tel: 01309 675899 / 672277 (bookings)

Houldsworth Institute
Capacity: 130. Disabled access and facilities.
Main Street, Dallas, Moray IV36 0SA
Tel: 01343 890329
Contact: Mrs Garrow (Caretaker (bookings))

Insch Community Centre
Capacity: 148. Disabled access and facilities.
Insch, Gordon AB52 6HX
Tel: 01464 820860
Contact: Beth Hebenpon (Community Education Officer)

The Jazz Cellar
Capacity: 110.
Cellar 35, My Father's Moustache, 31-35 Rosemount Viaduct, Aberdeen AB1 1NQ
Tel: 01224 640483 Fax: 0131 554 0454
Contact: Suzy Melhuish (Assembly Direct) Tel: 0131 553 4000

Leadside Community Centre
Capacity: 125. Disabled access and facilities.
Leadside Road, Aberdeen AB2
Tel: 01224 647028
Contact: Mrs Benzie (Management Committee)

Lossiemouth Town Hall
Capacity: 86. No disabled access.
High Street, Lossiemouth, Moray
Tel: 01343 543451
Contact: Eric McGillivray (Arts and Ents Officer) or Venue Tel: 01343 815309 / 812002 (bookings)

Macduff Arts Centre
Capacity: Lower Hall 60. Disabled access and facilities. Correspondence c/o Arts Dev Officer, Banff and Buchan DC, 1 Church Street, Macduff AB44 1UR.
Clergy Street, Macduff AB44 1US
Tel: 01261 813388 Fax: 01261 833646
Contact: Iain Macaulay (Arts Dev Officer) or Venue Tel: 01261 83381

Monymusk Arts Centre
Capacity: 70. Disabled access and facilities.
Monymusk, AB51 7HL
Tel: 01467 651220
Contact: Lady Grant (Monymusk Arts Trust) Tel: 01467 651513

Torphins Learney Hall
Capacity: under 150. Disabled access. Correspondence c/o Barbara MacLeod, Arts Officer, Kincardine and Deeside DC, Viewmount, Arduthie Road, Stonehaven AB3 2DQ.
Torphins, Kincardine and Deeside
Tel: 01569 762001 Fax: 01569 766549
Contact: Barbara MacLeod (Arts Officer) or Venue Tel: 013398 82496

Woodside Burgh Hall
Capacity: 100. Disabled access and facilities.
360 Clifton Road, Aberdeen AB2 2DX
Tel: 01224 646333 (bookings)
Contact: Martin Milne

150 TO 399

Aberdeen Art Gallery
Capacity: 350. Disabled access and facilities.
School Hill, Aberdeen AB9 1FQ
Tel: 01224 646333 Fax: 01224 632133
Contact: Nigel King (Programmes/ Venues Manager) Tel: 01224 632080

Aberdeen Arts Centre

Capacity: 350. Disabled access and facilities: contact in advance. PRS Significant Venue.
33 King Street, Aberdeen AB2 3AA
Tel: 01224 635208
Contact: Verna Ward (Administrator) or Box Office Tel: 01224 641122

Ballater Victoria Hall

Capacity: 250. Disabled access and facilities. Contact in advance.
Correspondence c/o Gray and Kellas, Bridge Street, Ballater.
Ballater, Kincardine and Deeside
Tel: 013397 55535
Contact: Peter Crawford (Committee Member) Tel: 013397 55894

Banchory Town Hall

Capacity: 292. Disabled access and facilities: contact in advance.
Banchory, Kincardine and Deeside
Tel: 01569 762001
Contact: Barbara MacLeod (Arts Officer) or Venue Tel: 01330 824004

Beach Ballroom

Capacity: Star Room 200. No disabled access.
Beach Leisure Centre, Beach Promenade, Aberdeen AB2 1NR
Tel: 01224 647647 Fax: 01224 648693
Contact: Allen A Doig / Ken McAulay (Area Manager / General Manager) or Box Office Tel: 01224 641122

Catherine Street Community Centre

Capacity: 150. Disabled access and facilities.
Catherine Street, Aberdeen AB1 1EU
Tel: 01224 640853
Contact: Trena Clunes (Management Committee)

Cowdray Hall

Capacity: 350. Disabled access and facilities. PRS Significant Venue.
Schoolhill, Aberdeen AB9 1FQ
Tel: 01224 646333
Contact: Michael Fraser (Hallkeeper) or Alex Hidalgo (Head of Service (bookings))

Cullen Town Hall

Capacity: 300. Disabled access.
Cullen, Moray
Tel: 01343 543451
Contact: Eric McGillivray (Arts and Ents Officer) or Venue Tel: 01542 841478 / 840313 (bookings)

Dalrymple Hall

Capacity: 380. Disabled access.
Correspondence c/o Arts Development Officer, Banff and Buchan DC, 1 Church Street, Macduff AB44 1UR.
Seaforth Street, Fraserburgh AB43 5BB
Tel: 01261 813384 Fax: 01261 833819
Contact: Iain Macaulay (Arts Dev Officer) or Venue Tel: 01346 518761

Forres Town Hall

Capacity: 250. Disabled access and facilities.
High Street, Forres, Moray
Tel: 01343 543451
Contact: Eric McGillivray (Arts and Ents Officer) or Venue Tel: 01309 675899 / 672277 (bookings)

Glenkindie Towie Hall

Capacity: 226. Disabled access.
Glenkindie, Gordon
Tel: 01975 641286
Contact: L Alexander (bookings) Tel: 01975 641267

Haddo House Hall

Capacity: 350. Disabled access and facilities.
Haddo House , Aberdeen AB41 0ER
Tel: 01651 851770 Fax: 01651 851609
Contact: Charles A Barron (Arts Director) or Box Office Tel: 01224 641122

Inchgarth Community Centre

Capacity: 150. Limited disabled access (one step up) and facilities.
Aboyne Place, Garthdee, Aberdeen
Tel: 01224 325191
Contact: Alison Jopp (Management Committee) Tel: 01224 312302

Keith Longmore Hall

Capacity: 2 halls - 320 and 190. Disabled access and facilities.
Banff Road, Keith, Moray
Tel: 01343 543451
Contact: Eric McGillivray (Arts and Ents Officer) or Venue Tel: 01542 886712 / 882767 (bookings)

Kemnay Village Hall

Capacity: 156. Disabled access and facilities.
8 Aquithie Road, Kemnay AB51 9NS
Tel: 01467 642391
Contact: Mavis Wainman (Secretary)

The Lemon Tree

Capacity: Café Theatre 300 (cabaret-style), 500 (standing); Studio Theatre 150 (seating), 350 (standing). Disabled access and facilities. PRS Significant Venue.
5 West North Street, Aberdeen AB2 3AT
Tel: 01224 642230 Fax: 01224 630888
Contact: Shona Powell (Administrator) or Andy Shearer (Asst Administrator)

Lossiemouth Town Hall

Capacity: 270. Disabled access and facilities.
High Street, Lossiemouth, Moray
Tel: 01343 543451
Contact: Eric McGillivray (Arts and Ents Officer) or Venue Tel: 01343 815309 / 812002 (bookings)

Macduff Arts Centre

Capacity: Main Hall 160. Disabled access and facilities. Correspondence c/o Arts Dev Officer, Banff and Buchan DC, 1 Church Street, Macduff AB44 1UR.
Duff Street, MacDuff AB44 1US
Tel: 01261 813388 Fax: 01261 833646
Contact: Iain Macaulay (Arts Dev Officer) or Venue Tel: 01262 833819

Methlick Beaton Hall

Capacity: 200. Disabled access and facilities.
Methlick, Gordon
Tel: 01651 806417
Contact: John Pratt (Management Committee)

Peterhead Community Education Centre Theatre

Capacity: 300. Limited disabled access and facilities.
Peterhead Community Education Centre, Balmoor Terrace, Peterhead AB42 6EP
Tel: 01779 477277 Fax: 01779 471041
Contact: Donald Russell (Senior Community Education Worker) or Venue

Portsoy Town Hall

Capacity: 200. Disabled access and facilities.
Seafield Street, Portsoy, Banffshire
Tel: 01261 842739
Contact: Mr Finlay (Leisure and Recreation Dept) Tel: 01261 812521 or Mrs Wilson (Hallkeeper)

Rescue Hall

Capacity: 250. Correspondence c/o Arts Dev Officer, Banff and Buchan DC, 1 Church St., Macduff AB44 1UR.
Prince Street, Peterhead AB42 6QE
Tel: 01261 813388 Fax: 01261 833464
Contact: Iain Macaulay (Arts Dev Officer) or Venue Tel: 01779 472354 / 477958

VENUES

219

Ritchie Hall Strichen

Capacity: 300. Disabled access.
Correspondence c/o Arts Development
Officer, Banff and Buchan DC, 1 Church
Street, Macduff AB44 1UR.
Strichen, Banff and Buchan
Tel: 01261 813388 Fax: 01261 833646
*Contact: Iain Macaulay (Arts Dev
Officer) or Venue Tel: 01771 637425*

Rosehearty Public Hall

Capacity: 200. No disabled access.
*Fordyce Street, Rosehearty, Banff and
Buchan*
Tel: 01346 571253
Contact: Mrs Ritchie (Caretaker)

Stewart's Hall

Capacity: 350. Disabled access and
facilities.
*Gordon Street, Huntly, Aberdeenshire
AB54 5AJ*
Tel: 01466 792779
Contact: Morris Murdoch (Hallkeeper)

Torry St Fittick's Church Hall

Capacity: 200. Disabled access and
facilities.
Walker Road, Torry, Aberdeen
*Contact: Jim Mutch (Congregational
Board) Tel: 01224 683152*

Universal Hall

Capacity: 300. Disabled access and
facilities.
*Findhorn Foundation, The Park, Forres
IV36 0TZ*
Tel: 01309 691170 Fax: 01309 691301
Contact: David Till (Administrator)

400 TO 999

Buckie Fisherman's Hall

Capacity: 432. Disabled access and
facilities.
North Pringle Street, Buckie, Moray
Tel: 01343 543451
*Contact: Eric McGillivray (Arts and Ents
Officer) or Venue Tel: 01542 834026 /
832297 (bookings)*

Elgin Town Hall

Capacity: 723 (seated). Disabled access
and facilities. PRS Significant Venue.
*5 Trinity Place, Elgin, Grampian
IV30 1VL*
Tel: 01343 543451
*Contact: Eric McGillivray (Arts and Ents
Officer) or Venue Tel: 01343 547767*

Ellon Community Centre

Capacity: 350 or 400 using stage.
Disabled access and facilities.
Ellon Academy, Ellon AB41
Tel: 01358 720478
*Contact: Area Officer (Ellon DC) Tel:
01358 720295*

Inverurie Town Hall

Capacity: Hall 400 and Balcony 134.
Disabled access and facilities main hall
only.
Market Place, Inverurie, Aberdeenshire
Tel: 01467 621610
*Contact: Michael Knight / Kenny Gillies
(Hallkeepers)*

Macduff Town Hall

Capacity: 400. Disabled access and
facilities. Correspondence c/o Arts Dev
Officer, Banff and Buchan DC, 1 Church
Street, Macduff AB44 1UR.
*Shore Street, Macduff, Banffshire
AB44 1UB*
Tel: 01261 813384 Fax: 01261 833819
*Contact: Iain Macaulay (Arts Dev Officer)
or Venue Tel: 01261 832702*

Speyside High School and Community Education Centre Aberlour

Capacity: 500. No disabled access to
auditorium.
*Mary Avenue, Aberlour, Moray
AB38 9QN*
Tel: 01340 871641 Fax: 01340 871098
*Contact: Fiona Rolt (Community
Education Officer)*

Stonehaven Town Hall

Capacity: 475. Disabled access and
facilities. Correspondence c/o Leisure and
Recreation Dept., Kincardine and Deeside
DC, Viewmount, Arduthie Road,
Stonehaven AB3 2DQ.
*Allardice Street, Stonehaven, Kincardine
and Deeside*
Tel: 01569 762001 Fax: 01569 766549
*Contact: Barbara MacLeod (Arts
Officer) or Venue Tel: 01569 762761*

Turriff Academy Hall

Capacity: 450. Disabled access.
*Turriff Academy, Victoria Terrace,
Turriff AB53 7DZ*
Tel: 01888 563216 Fax: 01888 568966
*Contact: Area Officer (Grampian
Regional Council) Tel: 01888 562427*

OVER 1,000

Aberdeen Exhibition and Conference Centre

Capacity: Hall A 4,700 seated, 7,500
standing, 6,450 combined; Conference
area 1,300. Disabled access and
facilities. PRS Significant Venue.
Bridge of Don, Aberdeen AB23 8BL
Tel: 01224 824824 Fax: 01224 825276
*Contact: Jim Francis (Senior Sales
Executive)*

Aberdeen Music Hall

Capacity: 1,280 seated; 1,550 standing.
Disabled access and facilities. PRS
Significant Venue.
Union Street, Aberdeen AB1 1QS
Tel: 01224 632080
*Contact: Nigel King (Programmes/
Venues Manager) or Box Office Tel:
01224 641122*

Beach Ballroom

Capacity: Main ballroom 1,200.
Disabled access and facilities.
*Beach Leisure Centre, Beach Promenade,
Aberdeen AB2 1NR*
Tel: 01224 647647 Fax: 01224 648693
*Contact: Allen A Doig / Ken Macaulay
(Area Manager / General Manager) or
Box Office Tel: 01224 641122*

Capitol Theatre

Capacity: 1,990. Disabled access. PRS
Significant Venue.
431 Union Street, Aberdeen AB1 2DA
Tel: 01224 583141 Fax: 01224 573888
*Contact: Herbert Donald (Director and
Secretary) Tel: 01224 573838*

His Majesty's Theatre

Capacity: 1,456. Disabled access and
facilities.
Rosemount Viaduct, Aberdeen AB9 1GL
Tel: 01224 637788
*Contact: Robert Robson (Theatre
Director) or Box Office Tel: 01224
641122*

HIGHLAND

UNDER 150

Ackergill Tower

Capacity: 90. Disabled access and
facilities.
Wick, Caithness KW1 4RG
Tel: 01955 603556 Fax: 01955 602140
Contact: Arlette Banister (Director)

VENUES

An Tuireann Arts Centre
Capacity: 80. Disabled access and facilities.
Struan Road, Portree, Isle of Skye IV51 9ES
Tel: 01478 613306
Contact: Susan Nicholson (Administrator)

Ardvasar Village Hall
Capacity: 70. Disabled access and facilities. Correspondence to Duncan MacInnes, Administrator, SEALL Community Arts, Ostaig House, Teangue, Isle of Skye IV44 8RQ.
Isle of Skye Tel: 01471 844207
Contact: Duncan MacInnes (Administrator SEALL Community Arts)

Balnain House
Capacity: café/bar 70; two rooms 75 each.
40 Huntly Street, Inverness IV3 5HR
Tel: 01463 715757 Fax: 01463 713611
Contact: Caroline Hewat (Asst Manager)

Braes Village Hall
Capacity: 80. Disabled access and facilities.
Lower Ollach, Braes, by Portree, Isle of Skye
Tel: 01478 650233
Contact: Mrs Bruce (Treasurer)

Carbost Village Hall
Capacity: 100. Disabled access.
Carbost, Skye IV47 8SR
Tel: 01478 640256
Contact: Catherine McLeod (Secretary)

Castletown Drill Hall
Capacity: 130. Disabled access being added 1995. Correspondence c/o John Crowden, Brigga, Main Street, Castletown.
Main Street, Castletown, Caithness KW14 8TT
Tel: 01847 821407
Contact: W Nicholson (Hallkeeper) (bookings) or John Crowden (Hall Committee Chaiman) Tel: 01847 821632

The Ceilidh Place
Capacity: 60-80. No disabled access.
14 West Argyle Street, Ullapool, Ross and Cromarty IV26 2TY
Tel: 01854 612103 Fax: 01854 612886
Contact: Jean Urquhart / Julia Campbell (Organisers)

Dingwall Town Hall
Capacity: 100. Limited disabled access. Correspondence c/o Development Officer, Ross and Cromarty DC, Council Offices, Dingwall IV15 9QN.
Church Street, Dingwall IV15
Tel: 01349 863381 x570
Contact: Dennis Dunbar (Dev Officer)

Dunbar Memorial Hall
Capacity: 120. No disabled access.
High Street, Auldearn, Nairn
Tel: 01667 452347 / 454503
Contact: Rita McAndrew (Secretary)

Invergordon Arts Centre
Capacity: Auditorium 99; Café/Bar, Exhibition Area, Meeting Room. Limited disabled access.
High Street, Invergordon IV18 0EL
Tel: 01349 854414
Contact: Nick Fearne (Arts Dev Officer) Tel: 01349 830517 or Marie Corbett (Caretaker)

Inverness Museums and Art Gallery
Capacity: 60. Disabled access by stairlift.
Castle Wynd, Inverness IV2 3ED
Tel: 01463 237114 Fax: 01463 712850
Contact: Catherine Niven (Curator)

Invershin Hall
Capacity: 100. Disabled access and facilities.
Invershin, Lairg, Sutherland IV27 4ET
Tel: 01549 421275
Contact: Agnes Murray (Secretary) or Venue Tel: 01549 421309

Kilchoan Village Hall
Capacity: 120. Disabled access.
Craigard, Kilchoan, Lochaber
Tel: 01972 510250 (bookings)
Contact: Mrs Scott (Secretary)

Killearnan Public Hall
Capacity: 120. Disabled access.
Tore, Ross and Cromarty IV6
Tel: 01463 731537
Contact: Charlie Leggat (Hon Secretary/ Treasurer)

Kilmallie Hall
Capacity: 76. Disabled access and facilities.
Corpach, Fort William PH33
Tel: 01397 772664
Contact: J D Leslie (Treasurer)

Kyleakin Village Hall
Capacity: 120. Disabled access. Correspondence Duncan MacInnes, Administrator, SEALL Community Arts, Ostaig House, Teangue, Isle of Skye IV44 8RQ.
Kyleakin, Skye
Tel: 01471 844207
Contact: Duncan MacInnes (Administrator SEALL)

The Little Theatre (Nairn)
Capacity: 77. Disabled access. All correspondence c/o The Secretary, 5 Wyves Road, Nairn.
King Street, Nairn
Tel: 01667 453766
Contact: Sandra Inglis (Drama Club Secretary)

Lyth Arts Centre
Capacity: 72. Disabled access.
Lyth, Wick KW1 4UD
Tel: 01955 641270
Contact: William Wilson (Director)

Sheildaig Village Hall
Capacity: 60. Disabled access.
Sheildag, Strathcarron IV54 8XN
Tel: 01520 755239
Contact: Vivienne MacLennan (Ents Officer)

Skerray Village Hall
Capacity: 100. Disabled access and facilities.
Skerray, Thurso KW14 7TJ
Tel: 01641 521212
Contact: Gavin Lockhart

Spectrum Community Centre
Capacity: Drama Studio 100. Disabled access and facilities.
1 Margaret Street, Inverness IV1 1LS
Tel: 01463 221842 Fax: 01463 713325
Contact: Neil Thomson (Community Education Worker)

Thurso Town Hall
Capacity: Band Room 60. No disabled access.
High Street, Thurso, Caithness
Tel: 01847 894545 x14 Fax: 01847 896188
Contact: Val Smith (Higher Clerical Officer) or William Manson (Hallkeeper) Tel: 01847 892692

Treslaig Village Hall
Capacity: 100. Disabled access and facilities.
Treslaig, Fort William, Lochaber PH33
Tel: 01397 772229
Contact: Mrs Morrison (Secretary)

Waternish Village Hall
Capacity: 100. Disabled access. Correspondence Secretary, Hall Committee, 2 Ardmore, Waternish, Isle of Skye IV55 8GW.
Dunhallin, Waternish, Skye IV55 8GB
Tel: 01470 592312
Contact: Eileen Naylor (Secretary Hall Committee) Tel: 01470 592202 or Lesley MacLean (Chairperson Hall Committee)

VENUES

221

150 TO 399

Aultbea Community Hall
Capacity: 250. Disabled access.
Aultbea, Ross and Cromarty IV22
Tel: 01445 731505
Contact: D Aldrich (Vice Chairman)

Bonar Bridge Village Hall
Capacity: 200. Disabled access.
Lairg Road, Bonar Bridge IV24 3EE
Tel: 01863 766291
Contact: Lorraine Askew (bookings) or R Philcox (Treasurer) Tel: 01863 766276

Broadford Village Hall
Capacity: 150. Disabled access.
Correspondence to Duncan MacInnes, Administrator, SEALL Community Arts, Ostaig House, Teangue, Isle of Skye IV44 8RQ.
Broadford, Isle of Skye
Tel: 01471 844207
Contact: Duncan MacInnes (Administrator SEALL Community Arts)

Culduthel Hall
Capacity: 200. Disabled access.
Correspondence c/o Administrator, Leisure and Recreation Dept, Inverness DC, Town House, Inverness IV1 1JJ.
Green Drive, Culduthel, Inverness IV2
Tel: 01463 724262
Contact: Carol Cracknell (Administrator Leisure and Recreation Dept) or Mrs Jeans (Hallkeeper)

Culloden Academy Community Complex
Capacity: 338. Disabled access and facilities.
Keppoch Road, Culloden, Inverness IV1 2JZ
Tel: 01463 792794
Contact: Julia Maguire (Centre Co-ordinator)

Culloden Hall
Capacity: 360. Disabled access.
Correspondence c/o Administrator, Leisure and Recreation Dept, Inverness DC, Town House, Inverness IV1 1JJ.
Culloden, Inverness IV1
Tel: 01463 724262
Contact: Carol Cracknell (Administrator Leisure and Recreation Dept) or Mrs Stewart (Hallkeeper)

Dornie Village Hall
Capacity: 170. Disabled access and facilities.
Dornie, Skye and Lochalsh IV40 8HA
Tel: 01599 555364
Contact: Catriona Bell (Administrator)

VENUES

Duthac Centre
Capacity: Canmore Hall 350; Morangie Hall 150. Disabled access and facilities.
Shandwick Street, Tain, Ross-shire IV19 1AA
Tel: 01862 894422
Contact: Mrs Neilson (Administrator)

Edderton Village Hall
Capacity: 220. Disabled access and facilities.
Station Road, Edderton, by Tain IV19 1JZ
Tel: 01862 821305
Contact: Frank Ward (Chairman)

Findon Hall
Capacity: 150. Disabled access and facilities. Correspondence c/o Clach Bhuidhe, Greenhill, Culbokie, Ross-shire IV7 8JZ.
Culbokie, Dingwall IV17
Tel: 01349 877658
Contact: Mrs Stewart (Secretary)

Fort Augustus Public Hall
Capacity: Main Hall 320; Lesser Hall 230. Disabled access. Correspondence c/o Administrator, Leisure and Recreation Dept, Inverness DC, Town House, Inverness IV1 1JJ.
Bunoich, Fort Augustus PH32 4DG
Tel: 01463 724262
Contact: Carol Cracknell (Administrator Inverness DC) or Mr Webster (Hallkeeper)

Glenelg Village Hall
Capacity: 150. No disabled access.
Glenelg, Kyle, Skye and Lochalsh
Contact: Mrs Stork (Secretary) or Jimmy Cameron (Treasurer (bookings))
Tel: 01599 522327

Glenuig Hall
Capacity: 170. Disabled access and facilities.
Glenuig Community Association, Glenuig, by Lochailort, Inverness-shire PH38 4NG
Tel: 01687 470214 Fax: 01687 470275 / 470289
Contact: Val Hunter (Secretary) or Billy MacKail (Vice Chairman) Tel: 01687 470250

Kilmallie Hall
Capacity: 250. Disabled access and facilities.
Corpach, Fort William PH33
Tel: 01397 772664
Contact: J D Leslie (Treasurer)

Kiltarlity Hall
Capacity: 250. No disabled access. Correspondence c/o Administrator, Leisure and Recreation Dept, Inverness DC, Town House, Inverness IV1 1JJ.
Kiltarlity, Nr Beauly, Inverness IV4
Tel: 01463 724262
Contact: Carol Cracknell (Administrator Leisure and Recreation Dept) or Mrs Mainland (Hallkeeper)

Kinlochewe Village Hall
Capacity: 200. Disabled access and facilities.
Kinlochewe, Ross and Cromarty
Tel: 01445 760206
Contact: Liz Forest (Secretary Village Hall Committee (bookings)) Tel: 01445 760234

Kyle Village Hall
Capacity: 240. Disabled access and facilities.
Main Street, Kyle of Lochalsh IV40 8BB
Tel: 01599 534174
Contact: Alec Browness (Secretary)

Lochinver Village Hall
Capacity: 200. Disabled access and facilities. Correspondence c/o Cnoc Aluinn, Badnaban, Lochinver, Sutherland IV27 4LR.
Lochinver, Sutherland
Tel: 01571 844664
Contact: Irene Callas (bookings)

Memorial Hall
Capacity: 170. Disabled access. Correspondence c/o Administrator, Leisure and Recreation Dept, Inverness DC, Town House, Inverness IV1 1JJ.
Fort Augustus, Inverness PH32
Tel: 01463 724262
Contact: Carol Cracknell (Administrator Inverness DC) or Mr Webster (Hallkeeper)

Munlochy Village Hall
Capacity: 150. Disabled access. Correspondence to 48 Millbank Road, Munlochy IV8 8NL.
Millbank Road, Munlochy,
Tel: 01463 811417
Contact: Elizabeth MacCallum (Bookings Secretary) or Terry Johnstone (Secretary)

Phipps Hall

Capacity: Main Hall 370. Disabled access and facilities; Room One and Two 154 each. No disabled access. Correspondence c/o Leisure and Recreation Dept, Inverness DC, Town House, Inverness IV1 1JJ.
Station Road, Beauly, Inverness IV4 7EH
Tel: 01463 724262
Contact: Carol Cracknell (Administrator Leisure and Recreation Dept.) or Mr McKenzie (Hallkeeper)

Plockton Village Hall

Capacity: 150. Disabled access and facilities.
36 Harbour Street, Plockton IV52 8TN
Tel: 01599 544359
Contact: Mr Macrae (Secretary/ Treasurer)

The Railway Club

Capacity: 200. No disabled access.
Strothers Lane, Inverness IV1
Tel: 01463 243397
Contact: Rosalyn Marron

Spectrum Community Centre

Capacity: 250. Disabled access and facilities.
1 Margaret Street, Inverness IV1 1LS
Tel: 01463 221842 Fax: 01463 713325
Contact: Neil Thomson (Community Education Worker)

Thurso Town Hall

Capacity: 242. No disabled access.
High Street, Thurso, Caithness
Tel: 01847 894545 x14 Fax: 01847 896188
Contact: Val Smith (Higher Clerical Officer) or William Manson (Hallkeeper) Tel: 01847 892692

Ullapool Village Hall

Capacity: 150. Disabled access and facilities.
Market Street, Ullapool IV26
Tel: 01854 612103
Contact: Julia Campbell (Secretary Ullapool Entertainments)

400 TO 999

Cannich Hall

Capacity: 500. Disabled access. Correspondence c/o Administrator, Leisure and Recreation Dept, Inverness DC, Town House, Inverness IV1 1JJ.
Cannich, Inverness IV4
Tel: 01463 724262
Contact: Carol Cracknell (Administrator Inverness DC)

Dingwall Town Hall

Capacity: 500. Limted disabled access. Correspondence c/o Development Officer, Ross and Cromarty DC, Council Offices, Dingwall IV15 9QN.
Church Street, Dingwall IV15
Tel: 01349 863381 x570
Contact: Dennis Dunbar (Dev Officer)

Eden Court Theatre

Capacity: 791. Disabled access and facilities. PRS Significant Venue.
Bishops Road, Inverness IV3 5SA
Tel: 01463 239841 / 221718 Fax: 01463 713810
Contact: Paul Maurel (Theatre Director) or Box Office Tel: 01463 234234

Marco's An Aird

Capacity: Lounge 500. Disabled access and facilities.
An Aird, Fort William PH33 6AN
Tel: 01397 700707 Fax: 01397 700708
Contact: Barry Mason (Centre Manager)

Speyside Theatre

Capacity: 692. Disabled access and facilities.
Aviemore Mountain Resort, Aviemore, Inverness-shire PH22 1PF
Tel: 01479 810624 Fax: 01479 810862
Contact: Ian Miller (bookings) or Chris Helik (Cinema Manager)

Wick Assembly Rooms

Capacity: 636. Disabled access and facilities.
Sinclair Terrace, Wick, Caithness KW1 5AD
Tel: 01955 602584
Contact: Fiona Smith (Dev Officer)

OVER 1,000

Marco's An Aird

Capacity: Hall 1,500. Disabled access and facilities.
An Aird, Fort William PH33 6AN
Tel: 01397 700707 Fax: 01397 700708
Contact: Barry Mason (Centre Manager)

LOTHIAN

UNDER 150

Assembly Rooms and Music Hall

Capacity: Supper Room 120. Disabled access and facilities.
54 George Street, Edinburgh EH2 2LR
Tel: 0131 220 4348 Fax: 0131 220 6812
Contact: Simon Robson / Betty Pringle (Acting Manager / Asst Manager) or Box Office Tel: 0131 220 4349

Bedlam Theatre

Capacity: Main Stage 92; Café 50. Disabled access and facilities: contact in advance for wheelchair spaces.
11b Bristo Place, Edinburgh EH1 1EZ
Tel: 0131 225 9873
Contact: Box Office Tel: 0131 225 9893

Bonnington Resource Centre

Capacity: Main Hall 150 seated, 300 standing; Long Room 60; Drama Studio 20. Disabled access and facilities: purpose built for adults with physical and learning disabilities.
200 Bonnington Road, Edinburgh EH6 5NL
Tel: 0131 555 0920
Contact: Jane Fairgrieve (Depute Manager)

Church Hill Theatre

Capacity: Little Theatre 145. No disabled access.
Morningside Road, Edinburgh EH10 4RR
Tel: 0131 5294145 Fax: 0131 220 6813
Contact: Joyce Sibbald (Admin Assistant) or George Smart / Jo Navarro (Hallkeepers) Tel: 0131 447 7597

Craigsfarm

Capacity: Theatre 100; second space 80. Disabled access and facilities.
Maree Walk, Craigshill, Livingston EH54 5BP
Tel: 01506 432772
Contact: John Hoey (Manager)

VENUES

223

Dalkeith Arts Centre
Capacity: Large Gallery 150; Small Gallery 50. Disabled access and facilities. Correspondence c/o Nancy Newton, Community Services Division, Midlothian DC, 1 White Hart Street, Dalkeith EH22 1AJ.
White Hart Street, Dalkeith EH22 1AJ
Tel: 0131 663 6988
Contact: Nancy Newton (Community Services Division) Tel: 0131 660 7695 (bookings)

Dalkeith Leisure Centre
Capacity: 100. Disabled access and facilities.
6 Woodburn Road, Dalkeith EH22 2AR
Tel: 0131 663 3445
Contact: Mike Louden (Manager)

Danderhall Community Leisure Centre
Capacity: 80. Disabled access and facilities.
Newton Church Road, Danderhall, Dalkeith EH22 1LU
Tel: 0131 663 9280
Contact: Jim Turnbull (Manager)

Edinburgh International Conference Centre
Capacity: Galloway Suite and Harris Room each 100, or two rooms of 50; Carrick Room and Ochil Room each 100, or three rooms of 30, or one room of 60 with one room of 30. Disabled access and facilities.
Morrison Street, Edinburgh EH3 8EE
Tel: 0131 300 3000 Fax: 0131 300 3030
Contact: Trevor McCartney (Sales and Marketing Director) or Fiona Beaton (Corporate Sales Manager)

Hopetoun House
Capacity: Red Drawing Room 100. Disabled facilities and access possible with help. Preference: classical. Also outdoor concerts.
South Queensferry, West Lothian EH30 9SL
Tel: 0131 331 2451 Fax: 0131 319 1885
Contact: Alison Walkinshaw (Events Manager)

Loanhead Town Hall
Capacity: 50. No disabled access.
Academy Lane, Loanhead, Midlothian
Tel: 0131 448 2110
Contact: Tim Dent (Loanhead Leisure Centre Manager) Tel: 0131 440 4516

Mayfield Leisure Centre
Capacity: 80. Disabled access and facilities.
Mayfield Place, Mayfield, Dalkeith EH22 5JG
Tel: 0131 663 2219
Contact: Wendy West (Centre Manager)

Muirhouse Festival Activities Centre
Capacity: 75; second space 30. Disabled access and facilities.
Muirhouse Place West, Edinburgh EH4 4PX
Tel: 0131 315 2151
Contact: Martin Ayers / Sean Hay (Arts Dev Workers)

Musselburgh Town Hall
Capacity: 140. No disabled access.
High Street, Musselburgh, East Lothian EH21
Tel: 0131 665 3711
Contact: Lesley Smith (Arts and Ents Officer) Tel: 01620 824161

Netherbow Arts Centre
Capacity: 75. Disabled access and facilities.
43-45 High Street, Edinburgh EH1 1SR
Tel: 0131 556 9579 / 2647
Contact: Donald Smith (Director) or Ellis McKechnie (Asst Director)

Penicuik Arts Centre
Capacity: 120 (two spaces). No disabled access.
4 West Street, Penicuik EH26 9DL
Tel: 01968 678804
Contact: Jenni Jones (Penicuik Arts Association)

Penicuik Town Hall
Capacity: Lesser Hall 100. Disabled access and facilities.
33 High Street, Penicuik, Midlothian
Tel: 01968 672281
Contact: Nancy Shaw (bookings)

Rosebery Hall
Capacity: Large Hall 130. Disabled access.
High Street, South Queensferry
Tel: 0131 529 4145/7
Contact: Joyce Sibbald (Admin Assistant) or Eddie Farrell Tel: 0131 331 4117

Royston Wardieburn Community Centre
Capacity: 120. Disabled access and facilities.
11 Pilton Drive North, Edinburgh EH5 1NF
Tel: 0131 552 5700
Contact: Carol Dodds (Admin Assistant)

Springwell House Centre
Capacity: 120. No disabled access.
1 Ardmillan Terrace, Edinburgh EH1 2JL
Tel: 0131 337 1971 / 346 1405 Fax: 0131 337 6331
Contact: George Williamson (Project Director)

Stepping Stones Theatre
Capacity: Main Theatre 120. Studio Theatre 80. No disabled access.
112 West Bow, Grassmarket, Edinburgh EH1 2HH
Tel: 0131 226 4412
Contact: Collette Potter (Manager)

Theatre Workshop
Capacity: 143. Disabled access and facilities.
34 Hamilton Place, Edinburgh EH3 5AX
Tel: 0131 225 7942 Fax: 0131 220 0112
Contact: Robert Rae (Director) or Box Office Tel: 0131 226 5425

Traquair House
Capacity: 70. No disabled access.
Innerleithen, Peebleshire EH44 6PW
Tel: 01896 830323 Fax: 01896 830639
Contact: Catherine Maxwell Stuart (Administrator)

Traverse Theatre
Capacity: Traverse Two 100-120. Disabled access and facilities.
Cambridge Street, Edinburgh EH1 2ED
Tel: 0131 228 3223 Fax: 0131 229 8443
Contact: Lucy Mason (Administrator) or Box Office Tel: 0131 228 1404

150 TO 399

Adam House Theatre
Capacity: 164. No disabled access.
Chambers Street, Edinburgh
Tel: 0131 667 1971
Contact: C MacMillan

Bo'ness Town Hall
Capacity: Lesser Hall 180. No disabled facilities.
Glebe Park, Bo'ness EH51 0EF
Tel: 01324 624911
Contact: Craig Murray / Jane Clark (Principal Officer / Ents Officer) or Venue Tel: 01506 826098

Brunton Theatre
Capacity: Supper Room 200; Theatre 312. Disabled access and facilities.
Ladywell Way, Musselburgh, Edinburgh EH21 6AA
Tel: 0131 665 9900 Fax: 0131 665 7495
Contact: Lesley Smith (Arts and Ents Officer) Tel: 01620 824161 or Box Office el: 0131 665 2240

VENUES

Church Hill Theatre

Capacity: Theatre 360. No disabled access.
Morningside Road, Edinburgh
EH10 4RR
Tel: 0131 529 4145/7 Fax: 0131 220 6813
Contact: Joyce Sibbald (Admin Assistant) or George Smart / Jo Navarro (Hallkeepers) Tel: 0131 447 7597

Clovenstone Community Centre

Capacity: 200. Disabled access and facilities.
54 Clovenstone Park, Edinburgh
EH14 3EY
Tel: 0131 453 4561
Contact: Janet Easton (Secretary)

Dalkeith Leisure Centre

Capacity: 260. Disabled access and facilities.
6 Woodburn Road, Dalkeith EH22 2AR
Tel: 0131 663 3445
Contact: Mike Louden (Manager)

Danderhall Community Leisure Centre

Capacity: 250. Disabled access and facilities.
Newton Church Road, Danderhall, Dalkeith EH22 1LU
Tel: 0131 663 9280
Contact: Jim Turnbull (Manager)

Deans Theatre

Capacity: 240. Disabled access and facilities.
Eastwood Park, Livingston EH54 8PS
Tel: 01506 431972
Contact: Kate Turvey (Theatre Manager)

Dunbar Corn Exchange

Capacity: 200. Disabled access and facilities. Correspondence to East Lothian DC, 31 Court Street, Haddington, East Lothian EH41 3HA.
890 High Street, Dunbar, East Lothian
EH42 1ER
Tel: 01368 863434
Contact: Brian Gall (Leisure and Tourism Director) Tel: 01620 824161

Hopetoun House

Capacity: Ball Room 300. Disabled access and facilities. Preference: classical.
South Queensferry, West Lothian
EH30 9SL
Tel: 0131 331 2451 Fax: 0131 319 1885
Contact: Alison Walkinshaw (Events Manager)

Howden Park Centre

Capacity: Theatre 276; Conference Hall 200. Disabled access and facilities.
Howden Park, Livingston EH54 6AE
Tel: 01506 433634 Fax: 01506 434525
Contact: Val Bickford (Manager)

Loanhead Town Hall

Capacity: 180. Disabled access and facilities.
Academy Lane, Loanhead, Midlothian
Tel: 0131 448 2110
Contact: Tim Dent (Loanhead Leisure Centre Manager) Tel: 0131 440 4516

Nelson Hall

Capacity: 150. Disabled access.
MacDonald Road Library, MacDonald Road, Edinburgh EH7 4LX
Tel: 0131 556 5630
Contact: Peter Baxter (Asst Music Librarian)

Newtongrange Community Centre

Capacity: 150. Disabled access.
115 Main Street, Newtongrange, Midlothian
Tel: 0131 663 4276 / 4485
Contact: Mr Worrall (Manager)

Penicuik Town Hall

Capacity: Main Hall 200. No disabled access.
33 High Street, Penicuik, Midlothian
Tel: 01968 672281
Contact: Nancy Shaw (Bookings)

Pleasance Theatre Festival

Capacity: 340. No disabled access to theatre. Disabled access and facilities in bar.
60 Pleasance, Edinburgh EH8 9TJ
Tel: 0131 650 2349
Contact: Anne Elder (Administrator)

Prestonpans Community Centre

Capacity: 330. Disabled access and facilities.
Preston Road, Prestonpans EH32 9EL
Tel: 01875 813349
Contact: Heather Higgins (Senior Leisure Attendant)

Prestonpans Town Hall

Capacity: 180. Disabled access and facilities.
High Street, Prestonpans, East Lothian
Tel: 01875 810128
Contact: Lesley Smith (Arts and Ents Officer) Tel: 01620 824161

Reid Concert Hall

Capacity: 300. Limited disabled access.
14 Bristo Square, Teviot Place, Edinburgh EH8 9AH
Tel: 0131 650 4367 Fax: 0131 650 2425
Contact: Fiona Donaldson (Concert Secretary) Tel: 0131 650 2423

Royal Museum of Scotland

Capacity: Lecture Theatre 278. Disabled access and facilities.
Chambers Street, Edinburgh EH1 1JF
Tel: 0131 225 7534 Fax: 0131 220 4819
Contact: Barbara Buchan (Press and Publicity)

Royston Wardieburn Community Centre

Capacity: 300. Disabled access and facilities.
11 Pilton Drive North, Edinburgh
EH5 1NF
Tel: 0131 552 5700
Contact: Carol Dodds (Administration Assistant)

St Bride's Centre

Capacity: 320. Disabled access and facilities.
10 Orwell Terrace, Edinburgh
EH11 2DY
Tel: 0131 346 1405 Fax: 0131 337 6331
Contact: George Williamson (Project Director)

St Cecilia's Hall

Capacity: 200. Disabled access.
Niddry Street, Cowgate, Edinburgh
EH1 1LJ
Tel: 0131 650 2805 Fax: 0131 650 2812
Contact: Fiona Donaldson (Concert Secretary) Tel: 0131 650 2423

Thomas Morton Hall

Capacity: Main Hall 300. Disabled access and facilities.
28 Ferry Road, Leith
Tel: 0131 529 4145/7 Fax: 0131 220 6813
Contact: Joyce Sibbald (Admin Assistant) or John Knox (bookings) Tel: 0131 554 1408

Traverse Theatre

Capacity: Traverse One 200. Disabled access and facilities.
Cambridge Street, Edinburgh EH1 2ED
Tel: 0131 228 3223 Fax: 0131 229 8443
Contact: Lucy Mason (Administrator) or Box Office Tel: 0131 228 1404

400 TO 999

Assembly Rooms and Music Hall

Capacity: Music Hall 730, Ballroom 400. Disabled access and facilities. PRS Significant Venue.
54 George Street, Edinburgh EH2 2LR
Tel: 0131 220 4348 Fax: 0131 220 6812
Contact: Simon Robson / Betty Pringle (Acting Manager / Asst Manager) or Box Office Tel: 0131 220 4349

VENUES

225

Bo'ness Town Hall
Capacity: Main Hall 450. Disabled access.
Glebe Park, Bo'ness EH51 0EF
Tel: 01324 624911
Contact: Jane Clark (Ents Officer) or Venue Tel: 01506 826098

Brunton Theatre
Capacity: Hall 882. Disabled access and facilities.
Ladywell Way, Musselburgh, Edinburgh EH21 6AA
Tel: 0131 665 9900 Fax: 0131 665 7495
Contact: Lesley Smith (Arts and Ents Officer) Tel: 01620 824161 or Box Office Tel: 0131 665 2240

Calton Studios
Capacity: 500 downstairs, 200 upstairs. Disabled access.
24-26 Calton Road, Edinburgh EH8 8DP
Tel: 0131 558 3758
Contact: Peter Scott (Manager)

Edinburgh International Conference Centre
Capacity: Strathblane Hall 620, Lomond Suite 600, or three rooms each 200; Cromdale Hall 800 seated, 1,200 standing buffet. Disabled access and facilities. PRS Significant Venue.
Morrison Street, Edinburgh EH3 8EE
Tel: 0131 300 3000 Fax: 0131 300 3030
Contact: Trevor McCartney (Sales and Marketing Director) or Fiona Beaton (Corporate Sales Manager)

Gorebridge Leisure Centre
Capacity: 500. Disabled access and facilities.
Hunterfield Road, Gorebridge EH23 4TX
Tel: 01875 821739
Contact: Kenneth Davidson (Manager)

Haddington Corn Exchange
Capacity: 500. Disabled access and facilities.
Court Street, Haddington, East Lothian EH41
Tel: 01620 824161
Contact: Lesley Smith (Arts and Ents Officer) Tel: 01620 824161

Ladywood Leisure Centre
Capacity: 400. Disabled access and facilities.
Yarrow Court, Penicuik EH26 8HD
Tel: 01968 678473
Contact: Heather Langlands (Manager)

Loch Centre
Capacity: 404. Disabled access and facilities.
Well Wynd, Tranent, East Lothian EH33 2JX
Tel: 01875 611081
Contact: Robert Archibald (Centre Supervisor)

Mayfield Leisure Centre
Capacity: 400. Disabled access and facilities.
Mayfield Place, Mayfield, Dalkeith EH22 5JG
Tel: 0131 663 2219
Contact: Wendy West (Centre Manager)

Methodist Central Hall
Capacity: 800. Disabled access and facilities. PRS Significant Venue.
West Tollcross, Edinburgh EH3 9BP
Tel: 0131 229 7937
Contact: John Simon (Hall Manager)

Portobello Town Hall
Capacity: 771 Main Hall. Disabled access.
Portobello High Street, Edinburgh EH15 1AF
Tel: 0131 529 4145/7 Fax: 0131 220 6813
Contact: Joyce Sibbald (Admin Assistant) or Andrew Craig (Hallkeeper) Tel: 0131 669 5800

Queen's Hall (Edinburgh)
Capacity: 800. Disabled access and facilities. PRS Significant Venue.
87 Clerk Street, Edinburgh EH8 9JG
Tel: 0131 668 3456 Fax: 0131 668 2656
Contact: Beth Cavanagh (Hall Manager) or Box Office Tel: 0131 668 2019 / 667 7776 (credit cards)

Royal Lyceum Theatre
Capacity: 906. Disabled access and facilities.
Grindlay Street, Edinburgh EH3 9AX
Tel: 0131 229 7404 Fax: 0131 228 3955
Contact: Marcus Ford (Theatres Manager) or Box Office Tel: 0131 229 9697

Royal Museum of Scotland
Capacity: 500. Disabled access and facilities.
Chambers Street, Edinburgh EH1 1JF
Tel: 0131 225 7534 Fax: 0131 220 4819
Contact: Barbara Buchan (Press and Publicity)

OVER 1,000

Edinburgh Festival Theatre
Capacity: 1,915. Disabled access and facilities (no disabled parking). PRS Significant Venue.
13/29 Nicolson Street, Edinburgh EH8 9FT
Tel: 0131 662 1112 Fax: 0131 667 0744
Contact: Paul Iles (General Manager) or Box Office Tel: 0131 529 6000 / 662 1199 (fax)

Edinburgh International Conference Centre
Capacity: The Pentland Suite 1,200; can split into three theatres; Pentland Auditorium 600, Sidlaw Auditorium 300, Fintry Auditorium 300. Disabled access and facilities. PRS Significant Venue.
Morrison Street, Edinburgh EH3 8EE
Tel: 0131 300 3000 Fax: 0131 300 3030
Contact: Trevor McCartney (Sales and Marketing Director) or Fiona Beaton (Corporate Sales Manager)

Edinburgh Playhouse
Capacity: 3,075. Disabled access and facilities Circle only. PRS Significant Venue.
18/22 Greenside Place, Edinburgh EH1 3AA
Tel: 0131 557 2692 Fax: 0131 557 6520
Contact: Nicky Monk (Theatre Bookings Manager) Tel: 01865 730066 or Box Office Tel: 0131 557 2590

King's Theatre (Edinburgh)
Capacity: 1,341. Disabled access and facilities. PRS Significant Venue.
2 Leven Street, Edinburgh EH3 9LQ
Tel: 0131 229 4840 Fax: 0131 229 9180
Contact: Chris Potter (Theatre Manager) or Box Office Tel: 0131 220 4349

Marco's Forum
Capacity: Main Hall 1,600 (concerts), 3,150 (standing/seating for pop). Disabled access and facilities. Upstairs bar not accessible to disabled.
Almondvale West, Almondvale, Livingston EH54 6NB
Tel: 01506 419191 Fax: 01506 416564
Contact: Sean Duffy (Centre Manager)

Ross Theatre (outdoor)
Capacity: 2,000. Disabled access and facilities.
Princes Street Gardens, Kings Stables Road Gate, Edinburgh
Tel: 0131 529 4048
Contact: Moira Line (Halls Officer) or Stage door Tel: 0131 220 4351

VENUES

Usher Hall
Capacity: 2,500. Disabled access and facilities. PRS Significant Venue.
Lothian Road, Edinburgh EH1 2EA
Tel: 0131 228 8616 Fax: 0131 228 8848
Contact: Moira Mackenzie (Manager) or Box Office Tel: 0131 228 1155

ORKNEY ISLANDS

UNDER 150

Kirkwall Community Centre
Capacity: 40; 100. Disabled access and facilities.
Broad Street, Kirkwall, Orkney KW15 1DH
Tel: 01856 873354
Contact: Keith Donaldson (Centre Supervisor)

Pier Arts Centre
Capacity: 50. Disabled access.
Victoria Street, Stromness, Orkney KW16 3AA
Tel: 01856 850209 Fax: 01856 851148
Contact: Maureen Gray (Administration)

150 TO 399

Kirkwall Community Centre
Capacity: 180. Disabled access and facilities.
Broad Street, Kirkwall, Orkney KW15 1DH
Tel: 01856 873354
Contact: Keith Donaldson (Centre Supervisor)

Orkney Arts Theatre
Capacity: 324. Disabled access: contact in advance.
Mill Street, Kirkwall, Orkney KW15
Tel: 01856 874119
Contact: J Clark (Booking Officer) or Box Office Tel: 01856 872047

Stromness Academy Community School
Capacity: 280. Disabled access and facilities.
Garson, Stromness, Orkney KW16 3JS
Tel: 01856 850171

Stromness Town Hall
Capacity: 150. Disabled access and facilities.
Church Road, Stromness, Orkney KW16 3BH
Tel: 01856 850712
Contact: Jin McVean (bookings) or Anita Park (Caretaker)

400 TO 999

Phoenix Cinema
Capacity: 520. Disabled access and facilities. Correspondence to Orkney Islands Council, Kirkwall KW15 1NY.
Junction Road, Kirkwall, Orkney
Tel: 01856 873535 x2404 Fax: 01856 871356
Contact: Alan Clouston (Assistant Director Education and Recreation Services)

SHETLAND ISLANDS

UNDER 150

Germatwatt Centre
Capacity: 50. Disabled access and facilities.
Walls, Shetland ZE2 9PF
Tel: 01595 809348 Fax: 01595 809348
Contact: Mrs Tait (Secretary)

Lunnasting Community Hall
Capacity: 120. Disabled access and facilities.
Vidlin, Shetland ZE2 9QE
Tel: 01806 577326
Contact: Mrs Johnson (Booking Officer) or Venue Tel: 01806 577329

Muckle Roe Hall
Capacity: 100. No disabled access.
Muckle Roe, Brae, Shetland ZE2 9QW
Tel: 01806 522671
Contact: L Johnson (Secretary)

North Unst Public Hall
Capacity: 80. Disabled access and facilities.
Haroldswick, Unst, Shetland ZE2 9JJ
Tel: 01957 711369
Contact: Alison Priest (Caretaker)
Tel: 01957 711260

Quarff Public Hall
Capacity: 140. Disabled access and facilities.
Quarff, Shetland ZE2 9EY
Tel: 01950 477423
Contact: Mrs Mulley (Treasurer) or Venue Tel: 01950 477203

Sound Public Hall
Capacity: 60. Disabled access and facilities.
Sound, Lerwick, Shetland
Tel: 01595 693429
Contact: Marina Massie (Bookings Clerk)

150 TO 399

Aith Public Hall
Capacity: 184. Disabled access and facilities. Correspondence c/o Ms Anderson, Wirliegert, Aith, Shetland.
Aith, Shetland ZE2 9NB
Tel: 01595 810327
Contact: Catriona Anderson (Secretary) or Venue Tel: 01595 810714

Burra Public Hall
Capacity: 200. Disabled access and facilities.
Hamnavoe, Burra Isle, Shetland ZE2
Tel: 01595 859321
Contact: Lynda Smith (Secretary) or Venue Tel: 01595 859505

Carnegie Hall
Capacity: 200. Disabled access and facilities.
Stove, Sandwick, Shetland ZE2 9HH
Tel: 01950 431396
Contact: Kathleen Goudie (Secretary)

East Yell Community Hall
Capacity: 350. Disabled access and facilities.
East Yell, Shetland
Tel: 01957 702205
Contact: Alana Nicholson (Hall Secretary) or Venue Tel: 01957 702214

Garrison Theatre
Capacity: 287. Disabled access and facilities.
Market Street, Lerwick, Shetland ZE1 0EQ
Tel: 01595 692114
Contact: John Bulter (Manager)

Lerwick Town Hall
Capacity: 200. Disabled access and facilities.
Hillhead, Lerwick, Mainland, Shetland ZE1 0HB
Tel: 01595 696460 / 3535 Fax: 01595 694349
Contact: Richard Irvine (Town Hall Manager)

VENUES

227

North Unst Public Hall
Capacity: 200. Disabled access and facilities.
Haroldswick, Unst, Shetland ZE2 9JJ
Tel: 01957 711369
Contact: Alison Priest (Caretaker) or Venue Tel: 01957 711260

Sound Public Hall
Capacity: 330. Disabled access and facilities.
Sound, Lerwick, Shetland
Tel: 01595 693429
Contact: Marina Massie (Bookings Clerk)

Symbister Public Hall
Capacity: 200. Disabled access.
Whalsay, Shetland ZE2 9AQ
Tel: 01806 566263
Contact: Vida Williamson (bookings)

400 TO 999

Clickimin Leisure Complex
Capacity: Bowls Hall 500. Disabled access and facilities.
Lochside, Lerwick, Mainland, Shetland Islands ZE1 0PJ
Tel: 01595 741000 Fax: 01595 741001
Contact: Andy Mayers (General Manager) or James Johnston (Centre Manager)

OVER 1,000

Clickimin Leisure Complex
Capacity: 1,200. Disabled access and facilities.
Lochside, Lerwick, Mainland, Shetland Islands ZE1 0PJ
Tel: 01595 741000 Fax: 01595 741001
Contact: Andy Mayers (General Manager) or James Johnston (Centre Manager)

STRATHCLYDE

UNDER 150

Arches Theatre
Capacity: Theatre 112. Disabled access and facilities.
30 Midland Street, Glasgow G1 4PR
Tel: 0141 221 9736 Fax: 0141 221 8605
Contact: Andy Arnold (Artistic Director) or Lori Frater (General Manager)

Ardrishaig Public Hall
Capacity: Small Hall 60. Disabled access and facilities.
Chalmers Street, Ardrishaig PA30
Tel: 01546 603877
Contact: Irene Clarke (Booking Secretary)

Auchinairn Hall
Capacity: 90. Disabled access and facilities. Correspondence c/o Dept of Leisure and Recreational Services, Strathkelvin DC, The Triangle, Kirkintilloch Road, Bishopbriggs, Glasgow G64 2TR.
Auchinairn Road, Bishopbriggs G64 1NF
Tel: 0141 772 3210 Fax: 0141 762 0934
Contact: Russell Laurie (Halls Manager)

Baird Institute Museum
Capacity: 30. No disabled access.
Lugar Street, Cumnock, Ayrshire KA18 1AD
Tel: 01290 421701
Contact: Charles Woodward (Community Museums Dev Officer)

Bellshill Cultural Centre
Capacity: 146. Disabled access.
John Street, Bellshill, Motherwell ML4 1RJ
Tel: 01698 267515
Contact: Lizanne McMurrich (Venue Manager)

Biggar Little Theatre
Capacity: 100. Disabled access and facilities.
Broughton Road, Biggar ML12 6HA
Tel: 01899 20631 Fax: 01899 20750
Contact: Jill Purves (Company Director)

Bonnyton Community Centre
Capacity: 127. Disabled access. Correspondence c/o Kilmarnock and Loudoun DC, Leisure Services Dept, PO Box 13, Civic Centre, Kilmarnock KA1 1BY.
Garrier Place, Kilmarnock KA1 2NG
Tel: 01563 578422 Fax: 01563 578426
Contact: Derek Spence (Director of Recreation) or Venue Tel: 01563 521140

Bowling Public Hall
Capacity: 120. Disabled access and facilities. Correspondence c/o Gillian Graham, Dept Environmental Services, Dumbarton DC, Castle Street, Dumbarton G82 1JY.
Dumbarton Road, Bowling G60
Tel: 01389 765100 x208
Contact: Gillian Graham (Arts Officer) or Venue Tel: 01389 878801

Budhill and Springboig Hall
Capacity: 100. Disabled access. Correspondence c/o Performing Arts and Venues Dept, Glasgow DC, Exchange House, 229 George Street, Glasgow G1 1QU.
Hallhill Road, Budhill, Glasgow G33
Tel: 0141 227 5005/8/9/ 5015 / 5258 Fax: 0141 227 5533
Contact: Supervisor (Venues Dept, Glasgow DC) or Venue Tel: 0141 774 8142

Burgh Hall
Capacity: 100. Disabled access and facilities. Correspondence c/o Gillian Graham, Environmental Services Dept, Dumbarton DC, Castle Street, Dumbarton G82 1JY.
Shore Road, Cove G84
Tel: 01389 765100
Contact: Gillian Graham / Jane McPhail (Arts Officer / Clerical Assistant)

Calderbank Community Centre
Capacity: Lesser Hall 60. No disabled access. Correspondence c/o Leisure and Recreation Dept, Monklands DC, 101 Bank Street, Coatbridge ML5 1ET.
Main Street, Calderbank, by Airdrie, Monklands
Tel: 01236 441442
Contact: Agnes Rodgers (Booking Assistant) or Venue Tel: 01236 767354

Caldwell Hall
Capacity: 89. No disabled access. Correspondence c/o Dept of Leisure and Recreational Services, Strathkelvin DC, The Triangle, Kirkintilloch Road, Bishopbriggs, Glasgow G64 2TR.
Campsie Road, Torrance G64 4BW
Tel: 0141 772 3210 Fax: 0141 762 0934
Contact: Russell Laurie (Halls Manager) or Venue Tel: 01360 620776

Cambuslang Institute
Capacity: Lesser Hall 122. Disabled access and facilities. Correspondence c/o Performing Arts and Venues Dept, Glasgow DC, Exchange House, 229 George Street, Glasgow G1 1QU.
Greenlees Road, Glasgow G72
Tel: 0141 227 5005/8/9 / 5015 / 5258 Fax: 0141 227 5533
Contact: Supervisor (Venues Section Glasgow DC) or Venue Tel: 0141 641 1727

VENUES

228

VENUES

230

Carluke District Hall

Capacity: Lesser Hall 100. Disabled access and facilities.
Carnwath Road, Carluke ML8
Tel: 01555 772501
Contact: P Thomson (Hallkeeper)

Centre for Contemporary Arts

Capacity: Studio Theatre 96; Performance Space 90. Disabled access and facilities for Studio Theatre only.
350 Sauchiehall Street, Glasgow G2 3JD
Tel: 0141 332 7521 Fax: 0141 332 3226
Contact: Mark Waddell (Performance Programme Director) or Box Office Tel: 0141 332 0522

Citizens' Theatre

Capacity: Circle Studio 120; Stalls Studio 60. Disabled access (Stalls Studio only) and facilities.
Gorbals, Glasgow G5 9DS
Tel: 0141 429 5561 Fax: 0141 429 7374
Contact: Sharman Weir (General Manager) or Box Office Tel: 0141 429 0022

Cumbernauld Theatre

Capacity: Studio 60. Disabled access and facilities.
Braehead Road, Kildrum, Cumbernauld G67 2BN
Tel: 01236 737235 / 458680 Fax: 01236 738408
Contact: Simon Sharkey (Artistic Director) or Box Office Tel: 01236 732887

Dixon Hall

Capacity: North Room 112. Disabled access and facilities. Correspondence to Performing Arts and Venues Dept, Glasgow DC, Exchange House, 229 George Street, Glasgow G1 1QU.
650 Cathcart Road, Glasgow G42
Tel: 0141 227 5005/8/9 / 5015 / 5258 Fax: 0141 227 5533
Contact: Supervisor (Venues Dept Glasgow DC) or Venue Tel: 0141 423 0469

East Kilbride Arts Centre

Capacity: 108. Disabled access and facilities.
51-53 Old Coach Road, East Kilbride G74 4DU
Tel: 013552 61000
Contact: Evan Henderson (Recreation Manager)

Fairhill Civic Centre

Capacity: Lesser Hall 80. Disabled access and facilities. Correspondence c/o Cultural Services Dept, Hamilton DC, 98 Cadzow Street, Hamilton ML3 6HQ.
Neilsland Road, Hamilton
Tel: 01698 282030
Contact: Gillian Annetts (Arts Dev Officer) Tel: 01698 894083 or Rosemary Brown (Hallkeeper)

Fort Theatre

Capacity: 100. Disabled access: no toilets for disabled.
Kenmure Avenue, Bishopbriggs, Glasgow G64 2DW
Tel: 0141 772 7054
Contact: Mary Little (Box Office Manager) Tel: 0141 772 8382

Fulton Hall

Capacity: 120. Disabled access and facilities. Correspondence c/o Kilmarnock and Loudoun DC, Leisure Services Dept, PO Box 13, Civic Centre, Kilmarnock KA1 1BY.
91 Main Road, Fenwick KA3 6DY
Tel: 01563 578437 Fax: 01563 578426
Contact: Derek Spence (Director of Recreation) or Venue Tel: 01560 600809

Gamble Halls

Capacity: 100. Disabled access and facilities. Correspondence c/o Dept of Recreational Services, Municipal Buildings, Clyde Square, Greenock PA15 1QL.
Shore Street, Gourock, Renfrewshire
Tel: 01475 882308
Contact: Amanda Way (Inverclyde DC) or Venue Tel: 01475 633248

Gartcosh Hall

Capacity: 95. Disabled access and facilities. Correspondence c/o Dept of Leisure and Recreational Services, Strathkelvin DC, The Triangle, Kirkintilloch Road, Bishopbriggs, Glasgow G64 2TR.
61 Lochend Road, Gartcosh G69 8AB
Tel: 0141 772 3210 Fax: 0141 762 0934
Contact: Russell Laurie (Halls Manager) or Venue Tel: 01236 874861

Gatehead Hall

Capacity: 100. Disabled access and facilities. Correspondence c/o Kilmarnock and Loudoun DC, Leisure Services Dept, PO Box 13, Civic Centre, Kilmarnock KA1 1BY.
Fairlie View, Gatehead KA2 0AU
Tel: 01563 578437 Fax: 01563 578426
Contact: Derek Spence (Director of Recreation) or Venue Tel: 01563 521140

The Glasgow Royal Concert Hall

Capacity: Buchanan Suite 80 theatre-style. Disabled access and facilities. Accessibility Hotline x4179. PRS Significant Venue.
2 Sauchiehall Street, Glasgow G2 3NY
Tel: 0141 332 6633 Fax: 0141 333 9123
Contact: Karen Taylor (Events Administration Manager) or Box Office Tel: 0141 227 5511 / 353 4134 (fax)

Glenhead Community Education Centre

Capacity: 120. No disabled access.
Duntiglennan Road, Duntocher, Clydebank G81 6HS
Tel: 0141 952 3046
Contact: Kirsteen Logan (Community Education Worker) or Venue Tel: 01389 874130

The Grand Hall

Capacity: Reception Room 40. Disabled access and facilities. Correspondence c/o Kilmarnock and Loudoun DC, Leisure Services Dept, PO Box 13, Civic Centre, Kilmarnock KA1 1BY.
London Road, Kilmarnock KA3 7AA
Tel: 01563 578437 Fax: 01563 578426
Contact: Derek Spence (Director of Recreation) or Venue Tel: 01563 521545

Greengairs Community Centre

Capacity: 120. No disabled access. Correspondence c/o Leisure and Recreation Dept, Monklands DC, 101 Bank Street, Coatbridge ML5 1ET.
Greengairs Road, Greengairs, Monklands
Tel: 01236 441442
Contact: Agnes Rodgers (Booking Assistant) or Venue Tel: 01236 830595

Greenock Arts Guild

Capacity: Wallace Bennett Theatre 80. No disabled access.
Campbell Street, Greenock, Renfrewshire PA16 8AP
Tel: 01475 723038 Fax: 01475 723038
Contact: Liz Muir (Administration)

Haggs Castle

Capacity: 75. No disabled access. Correspondence c/o Mark Hughes, Events Officer, Art Galleries and Museums Dept, Glasgow DC, McLellan Galleries, 270 Sauchiehall Street, Glasgow G2 3EH.
St Andrews Drive, Glasgow G41
Tel: 0141 331 1854 Fax: 0141 332 9957
Contact: Mark Hughes (Events Officer) or Venue Tel: 0141 427 2725

Harbour Arts Centre
Capacity: 96. Disabled access and facilities.
114-116 Harbour Street, Irvine KA11 8PZ
Tel: 01294 274059
Contact: Laura Brown (Centre Dev Manager)

Henderson Theatre
Capacity: 140. Disabled access and facilities.
Shotts Community Education Centre, Kirk Road, Shotts, Lanarkshire ML7 5NE
Tel: 01501 821826
Contact: Dorothy Adams (House Committee Member)

Hutcheson's Hall
Capacity: 120. PRS Significant Venue.
158 Ingram Street, Glasgow G1 1EJ
Tel: 0141 552 8391 Fax: 0141 552 7031
Contact: Property Manager

Institute Hall
Capacity: Ante-room 50. No disabled access. Correspondence c/o Kilmarnock and Loudoun DC, Leisure Services Dept, PO Box 13, Civic Centre, Kilmarnock KA1 1BY.
1 Avenue Street, Stewarton KA3 5AP
Tel: 01563 578422
Contact: Derek Spence (Director of Recreation) or Venue Tel: 01560 484386

Isle of Jura Village Hall
Capacity: 140. Disabled access and facilities.
Craighouse, Jura, Argyll PA60 7XW
Tel: 01496 820323
Contact: Rose Fletcher (Secretary Hall Committee)

Kilmardinny House
Capacity: 140. Disabled access.
50 Kilmardinny Avenue, Bearsden, Glasgow G61 3NN
Tel: 0141 943 0312 (24hrs)
Contact: The Organising Secretary

Linwood Community Education Centre
Capacity: 80. Disabled access and facilities.
Brediland Road, Linwood PA3 3RA
Tel: 01505 322233
Contact: Jeanette Anderson (Community Work Assistant)

McLean Museum and Art Gallery
Capacity: 100. Disabled access and facilities.
15 Kelly Street, Greenock PA16 8JX
Tel: 01475 723741 Fax: 01475 882010
Contact: Valerie Boa (Curator)

Milton of Campsie Hall
Capacity: 106. Disabled access and facilities. Correspondence c/o Dept of Leisure and Recreational Services, Strathkelvin DC, The Triangle, Kirkintilloch Rd., Bishopbriggs, Glasgow G64 2TR.
School Lane, Milton of Campsie G65 8DD
Tel: 0141 772 3210 Fax: 0141 762 0934
Contact: Russell Laurie (Halls Manager) or Venue Tel: 01360 310046

Mull Little Theatre
Capacity: 43. Disabled access and facilities.
Dervaig, Isle of Mull PA75 6QW
Tel: 01688 400267
Contact: Anne MacDonald / David Smith (Administration) or Box Office Tel: 01688 400245

The NACDU Arts Centre
Capacity: 45. Disabled access: five minutes notice required.
North Glasgow College, 110 Flemington Street, Glasgow G21 4TG
Tel: 0141 558 9313
Contact: Joe Hampson (Asst Cultural Dev Officer)

Paisley Museum and Art Galleries
Capacity: Lecture Hall 100; Gallery One 100. Disabled access and facilities in Lecture Hall only.
High Street, Paisley PA1 2BA
Tel: 0141 889 3151 Fax: 0141 889 9240
Contact: Andrea Kerr (Principal Museums Officer)

Pavilion
Capacity: Lesser Hall 120; Bowls Room 120. Disabled access and facilties.
Argyle Street, Rothesay, Isle of Bute
Tel: 01546 602127
Contact: Willie Young (Leisure and Recreation Officer) or Douglas MacCombe (Manager) Tel: 01700 504250

Pearce Institute Studio Theatre
Capacity: 92. Limited disabled access.
840 Govan Road, Glasgow G51 3UU
Tel: 0141 445 1941
Contact: Alan Davidson

Pollockshaws Burgh Hall
Capacity: Lesser Hall 130. Disabled access and facilities. Correspondence c/o Performing Arts and Venues Dept, Exchange House, 229 George Street, Glasgow G1 1QU.
2025 Pollockshaws Road, Glasgow G43
Tel: 0141 227 5005/8/9 / 5015 / 5258
Fax: 0141 227 5533
Contact: Supervisor (Venues Section Glasgow DC) or Venue Tel: 0141 632 0043

Pollok Community Education Centre
Capacity: 50. Disabled facilities planned.
Langton Road, Pollok, Glasgow G53
Tel: 0141 882 5869
Contact: Thomas Lloyd (Community Education Worker)

Pollok House
Capacity: 100. Disabled access by arrangement. Correspondence c/o Mark Hughes, Events Officer, Art Galleries and Museums Dept, Glasgow DC, McLellan Galleries, 270 Sauchiehall Street, Glasgow G2 3EH.
Pollock Country Park, 2060 Pollokshaws Road, Glasgow G43 1AT
Tel: 0141 331 1854 Fax: 0141 332 9957
Contact: Mark Hughes (Events Officer)
Tel: 0141 331 1854 or Venue Tel: 0141 632 0274

Port Glasgow Town Hall
Capacity: Lesser Hall 130; Provost's Room 40. Disabled access and facilities.
35 King Street, Port Glasgow PA14 5HD
Tel: 01475 882308
Contact: J A Douglas (Recreational Services Director) or Venue Tel: 01475 741305

Provands Lordship
Capacity: 30. No disabled access. Correspondence c/o Mark Hughes, Events Officer, Art Galleries and Museums Dept, Glasgow DC, McLellan Galleries, 270 Sauchiehall Street, Glasgow G2 3EH.
Castle Street, Glasgow G4
Tel: 0141 331 1854 Fax: 0141 332 9957
Contact: Mark Hughes (Events Officer) or Venue Tel: 0141 552 8819

Ramshorn Theatre
Capacity: 80-100. Disabled access and facilities.
98 Ingram Street, Glasgow G1 1ES
Tel: 0141 552 3489
Contact: Susan Triesman (Director) or Box Office Tel: 0141 227 5511

VENUES

231

Royal Scottish Academy of Music and Drama

Capacity: Chandler Studio Theatre 128; Guinness Room 108. Disabled access and facilities.
RSAMD, 100 Renfrew Street, Glasgow G2 3DB
Tel: 0141 332 4101 Fax: 0141 332 8901
Contact: Anna Fenge (Marketing and Public Relations Manager) or Box Office Tel: 0141 332 5057

Rutherglen Burgh Hall

Capacity: Lesser Hall 50. Disabled access and facilities. Correspondence c/o Performing Arts and Venues Dept, Exchange House, 229 George Street, Glasgow G1 1QU.
East King Street, Glasgow G72
Tel: 0141 227 5005/8/9 / 5015 / 5258
Fax: 0141 227 5533
Contact: Supervisor (Venues Section Glasgow DC) or Venue Tel: 0141 647 2254

St Mungo Museum of Religious Life and Art

Capacity: 100. Disabled access by arrangement. Correspondence c/o Mark Hughes, Events Officer, Art Galleries and Museums Dept, Glasgow DC, McLellan Galleries, 270 Sauchiehall Street, Glasgow G2 3EH.
2 Castle Street, Glasgow G4 0RH
Tel: 0141 331 1854 Fax: 0141 332 9957
Contact: Mark Hughes (Events Officer) or Venue Tel: 0141 553 2557

St Ninian's Youth Activity Centre

Capacity: 100. Disabled access and facilities.
Blackstoun Road, Ferguslie Park, Paisley PA3 1NR
Tel: 0141 887 3514
Contact: Anne Nelson (Community Education Worker)

Scottish Mask and Puppet Centre

Capacity: 70. Disabled access and facilities.
8-10 Balcarres Avenue, Kelvindale, Glasgow G12 0QF
Tel: 0141 339 6185 Fax: 0141 357 4484
Contact: Malcolm Knight (Hon Secretary)

Sighthill Community Education Centre

Capacity: 100. Disabled access and facilities.
Fountainwell Square, Sighthill, Glasgow G21
Tel: 0141 557 0710
Contact: Linda Biggarstaff (Senior Community Education Worker)

Sir John Wilson Town Hall

Capacity: 110. No disabled access. Correspondence c/o Leisure and Recreation Dept, Monklands DC, 101 Bank Street, Coatbridge ML5 1ET.
Stirling Street, Airdrie
Tel: 01236 763211
Contact: Agnes Rodgers (Booking Assistant) Tel: 01236 441442

Stepps Hall

Capacity: 108. Disabled access and facilities. Correspondence c/o Dept of Leisure and Recreational Services, Strathkelvin DC, The Triangle, Kirkintilloch Road, Bishopbriggs, Glasgow G64 2TR.
Cardowan Drive, Stepps G33 6HD
Tel: 0141 772 3210 Fax: 0141 762 0934
Contact: Russell Laurie (Halls Manager) or Venue Tel: 0141 779 1320

Strathclyde Arts Centre

Capacity: Theatre 100; Gallery 100. Disabled access and facilities.
12 Washington Street, Glasgow G3 8AZ
Tel: 0141 221 4526
Contact: George Cherrie (Head of Centre)

Summerlee Heritage Trust

Capacity: 60. Disabled access and facilities. Preference: organ recitals.
West Canal Street, Coatbridge, Strathclyde ML5 1QD
Tel: 01236 431261 Fax: 01236 440429
Contact: Jillian Ferrie (Head of Administration and Support Services)

Tramway

Capacity: Café/Bar 30; Area Three 125; Area Four 125. Disabled access and facilities.
25 Albert Drive, Pollockshields, Glasgow G41 2PE
Tel: 0141 422 2023 / 227 5511 (box office) Fax: 0141 422 2021
Contact: Robert Palmer (Director Performing Arts Venues Glasgow DC) Tel: 0141 227 5429 or Steven Slater / Susan Dieghan (Programmers)

Turret Theatre

Capacity: 60. Disabled access and facilities.
9 Eastside, Kirkintilloch G66 1PY
Tel: 0141 776 2570
Contact: Bill Todd (President) Tel: 0141 776 7613

Valley ARC

Capacity: 96. Disabled access.
10 Garnockside, Glengarnock, Beith KA25 7JT
Tel: 01505 683917
Contact: Marie Blackwood (Administrator)

Victoria Hall

Capacity: Pillar Hall 120; Ante-room 50; Room Four 70. Disabled access and facilities. Correspondence c/o Gillian Graham, Environmental Services Dept, Dumbarton DC, Castle Street, Dumbarton G82 1JY.
Sinclair Street, Helensburgh, Dumbartonshire G84
Tel: 01389 765100 x280 Fax: 01389 743256
Contact: Gillian Graham / Jane McPhail (Arts Officer / Clerical Assistant) or Venue Tel: 014386 673275

War Memorial Hall

Capacity: 145. Disabled access and facilities. Correspondence c/o Dept of Leisure and Recreational Services, Strathkelvin DC, The Triangle, Kirkintilloch Road, Bishopbriggs, Glasgow G64 2TR.
Balmuildy Road, Bishopbriggs G64 3BS
Tel: 0141 772 3210 Fax: 0141 762 0934
Contact: Russell Laurie (Halls Manager) or Venue Tel: 0141 772 6884

Westbridgend Community Centre

Capacity: 80. Disabled access. Correspondence c/o Gillian Graham, c/o Environmental Dept, Dumbarton DC, Castle Street, Dumbarton G82 1JY.
Dalreoch, Dumbarton G82
Tel: 01389 765100
Contact: Gillian Graham / Jane McPhail (Arts Officer / Clerical Assistant)

Woodside Hall

Capacity: Mid Hall 80. Disabled access and facilities. Correspondence c/o Performing Arts and Venues Dept, Exchange House, 229 George Street, Glasgow G1 1QU.
36 Glenfarg Street, Glasgow G21
Tel: 0141 227 5005/8/9 / 5015 / 5258
Fax: 0141 227 5533
Contact: Supervisor (Venues Section Glasgow DC) or Venue Tel: 0141 332 3651

150 TO 399

Airdrie Arts Centre

Capacity: 168. Disabled access: contact in advance.
Anderson Street, Airdrie ML6 0AA
Tel: 01236 755436
Contact: M Patterson (Hon Secretary (bookings))

VENUES

232

Altonhill Community Centre

Capacity: 200. Disabled access and facilities. Correspondence c/o Kilmarnock and Loudoun DC, Leisure Services Dept, PO Box 13, Civic Centre, Kilmarnock KA1 1BY.
10 Auchencar Drive, Kilmarnock KA3 1PP
Tel: 01563 578422 Fax: 01563 578426
Contact: Derek Spence (Director of Recreation) or Venue Tel: 01563 572847

Ardrishaig Public Hall

Capacity: Main Hall 230-250. Disabled access and facilities.
Chalmers Street, Ardrishaig PA30
Tel: 01546 603877
Contact: Irene Clarke (Booking Secretary)

Ardrossan Civic Centre

Capacity: 350. Disabled access and facilities.
Glasgow Street, Ardrossan, Ayrshire KA22
Tel: 01294 602615
Contact: Carol Fleming (Leisure Clerkess Cunninghame DC) or Venue Tel: 01294 602242

Beach Pavilion

Capacity: Atlantic suite 210. Disabled access and facilities: contact in advance for wheelchair spaces.
Knockcushan Street, Girvan, Ayrshire KA26 9AQ
Tel: 01465 714545 / 714294
Fax: 01465 713492
Contact: William Fulton (Contract Manager) or Box Office Tel: 01465 714294

Beechwood Community Centre

Capacity: 200. Disabled access and facilities.
Shortroods Road, Paisley PA3 2NR
Tel: 0141 848 6471 Fax: 0141 848 6253
Contact: Elsie Mitchell (Community Arts Coordinator)

Bellfield Community Centre

Capacity: 200. Disabled access and facilities. Correspondence c/o Kilmarnock and Loudoun DC, Leisure Services Dept, PO Box 13, Civic Centre, Kilmarnock KA1 1BY.
193b Whatriggs Road, Kilmarnock KA1 3TG
Tel: 01563 578422 Fax: 01563 578426
Contact: Derek Spence (Director of Recreation) or Venue Tel: 01563 572832

Boglestone Community Centre

Capacity: 150. Disabled access and facilities.
Dubbs Place, Port Glasgow PA15 5UD
Tel: 01475 704948
Contact: A Mathieson (Manager)

Borderline Theatre

Capacity: 182. Disabled access and facilities.
North Harbour Street, Ayr KA8 8AA
Tel: 01292 281010
Contact: Beverley Robb (Theatre Manager) or Box Office Tel: 01292 288998

Brodick Public Hall

Capacity: 215. Disabled access and facilities. Correspondence c/o District Council Offices, Lamlash, Isle of Arran.
Brodick, Arran KA27 8DL
Tel: 01770 600338
Contact: Eileen Griffin (bookings) or Jean Blackwood (Caretaker) Tel: 01770 302375

Burgh Hall

Capacity: 350. Disabled access and facilities. Correspondence c/o Environmental Services Dept, Dumbarton DC, Castle Street, Dumbarton G82 1JY.
Church Street, Dumbarton
Tel: 01389 765100 x208
Contact: Gillian Graham / Jane McPhail (Arts Officer / Clerical Assistant) or Venue Tel: 01389 731281

The Burrell Collection

Capacity: 180. Disabled access and facilities. Correspondence c/o Mark Hughes, Events Officer, Art Galleries and Museums Dept, Glasgow DC, McLellan Galleries, 270 Sauchiehall Street, Glasgow G2 3EH.
Pollok Country Park, 2060 Pollokshaws Road, Glasgow G43 1AT
Tel: 0141 331 1854 Fax: 0141 332 9957
Contact: Mark Hughes (Events Officer) or Venue Tel: 0141 649 7151

Calderbank Community Centre

Capacity: 250. No disabled access. Correspondence c/o Leisure and Recreation Dept, Monklands DC, 101 Bank Street, Coatbridge ML5 1ET.
Main Street, Calderbank, By Airdrie, Monklands
Tel: 01236 441442
Contact: Agnes Rodgers (Booking Assistant) or Venue Tel: 01236 767354

Cambuslang Institute

Capacity: 266. Disabled access and facilities. Correspondence c/o Performing Arts and Venues Dept, Glasgow DC, Exchange House, 229 George Street, Glasgow G1 1QU.
Greenlees Road, Glasgow G72
Tel: 0141 227 5005/8/9 / 5015 / 5258
Fax: 0141 227 5533
Contact: Supervisor (Venues Dept Glasgow DC) or Venue Tel: 0141 641 1727

Campsie Memorial Hall

Capacity: 176. Disabled access and facilities. Correspondence c/o Dept of Leisure and Recreational Services, Strathkelvin DC, The Triangle, Kirkintilloch Road, Bishopbriggs, Glasgow G64 2TR.
Main Street, Lennoxton, Glasgow G65 7HA
Tel: 0141 772 3210 Fax: 0141 762 0934
Contact: Russell Laurie (Halls Manager) or Venue Tel: 01360 310123

Cardinal Newman High School Theatre

Capacity: 200. Disabled access: contact in advance.
Main Street, Bellshill, Lanarkshire ML4 3DW
Tel: 01698 844607
Contact: S Wright (Area Community Education Officer)

Carluke Recreation Centre

Capacity: 350. Disabled access and facilities (no parking).
Carnwath Road, Carluke ML8 4EA
Tel: 01555 751384
Contact: Hazel Nimmo (Manager)

Carstairs Junction Community Hall

Capacity: 160. Disabled access and facilities.
St Charles Avenue, Carstairs Junction ML11
Tel: 01555 870889
Contact: M Thomson (Hallkeeper)

Civic Theatre

Capacity: 345. Disabled access.
Content Avenue, Craigie, Ayr KA8 0ET
Tel: 01292 264630 Fax: 01292 288383
Contact: Alan Davies (Principal Arts and Entertainments Officer) or Box Office Tel: 01292 264639

VENUES

233

Clydebank Town Hall
Capacity: Lesser Hall 170. Disabled access and facilities. Correspondence to Dept of Environmental Health, Amenities Dept, Clydebank District Council, Municipal Buildings, Clydebank.
Dumbarton Road, Clydebank G81
Tel: 0141 941 1331 Fax: 0141 952 0573
Contact: Iain McAdam (Chief Amenities Officer)

Connel Village Hall
Capacity: 200. Disabled access and facilities.
Connel, Argyll PA37 1PA
Tel: 01631 710278
Contact: Claire Grierson (Hon Secretary)

The Cottier
Capacity: 350. Disabled access and facilities.
Hyndland Street, Partick, Glasgow G11 5JE
Tel: 0141 339 9407 Fax: 0141 337 1644
Contact: Sandy Maxwell or Box Office Tel: 0141 357 3868

Couper Institute
Capacity: 204. Disabled access and facilities. Correspondence c/o Performing Arts and Venues Dept, Glasgow DC, Exchange House, 229 George Street, Glasgow G1 1QU.
86 Clarkston Road, Glasgow G44
Tel: 0141 227 5005/8/9 / 5015 /5258 Fax: 0141 227 5533
Contact: Supervisor (Venues Section Glasgow DC) or Venue Tel: 0141 637 1409

Craigie Campus Theatre
Capacity: 320. Disabled access: ramp at entrance but stairs to all house facilities.
University of Paisley, Beech Grove, Ayr KA8 0SR
Tel: 01292 260321
Contact: Mr McLean (Hospitalities Manager)

Crawfurd Theatre
Capacity: 392. Disabled access and facilities.
Jordanhill Campus, 76 Southbrae Drive, Glasgow G13 1PP
Tel: 0141 950 3437 / 3438
Contact: Shona McKee (Theatre Manager)

Cumbernauld Theatre
Capacity: Theatre 250. Disabled access and facilities.
Braehead Road, Kildrum, Cumbernauld G67 2BN
Tel: 01236 737235 / 458680 Fax: 01236 738408
Contact: Simon Sharkey (Artistic Director) or Box Office Tel: 01236 732887

Dalrymple Community Centre
Capacity: 200. Disabled access.
Dalrymple, Cumnock and Doon Valley
Tel: 01292 560469
Contact: M McClure (Centre Supervisor)

Denny Civic Theatre
Capacity: 345. Disabled access and facilities.
c/o Dept Environmental Services, Dumbarton District Council, Castle Street, Dumbarton G82 1JY
Tel: 01389 765538
Contact: Gillian Graham (Arts Officer) Tel: 01389 765100 or Jane McPhail (Clerical Assistant)

Dervaig Community Hall
Capacity: 200. Disabled access.
Dervaig, Mull PA75
Tel: 01688 400324
Contact: Sarah Spence (Secretary)

Dixon Hall
Capacity: 198. Disabled access and facilities. Correspondence to Performing Arts and Venues Dept, Glasgow DC, Exchange House, 229 George Street, Glasgow G1 1QU.
650 Cathcart Road, Glasgow G42
Tel: 0141 227 5005/8/9 / 5015 / 5258 Fax: 0141 227 5533
Contact: Supervisor (Venues Dept Glasgow DC) or Venue Tel: 0141 423 0469

Dunlop Public Hall
Capacity: 300. Disabled access. Correspondence c/o Kilmarnock and Loudoun DC, Leisure Services Dept, PO Box 13, Civic Centre, Kilmarnock KA1 1BY.
48 Main Street, Dunlop KA3 4AG
Tel: 01563 578437 Fax: 01563 578426
Contact: Derek Spence (Director of Recreation) or Venue Tel: 01563 521140

Duntocher Hall
Capacity: 200. No disabled access.
New Street, Duntocher G81
Tel: 0141 941 1313 Fax: 0141 952 0573
Contact: Iain McAdam (Chief Amenities Officer)

Easdale Village Hall
Capacity: 150. Disabled access.
Easdale, Oban PA34 4RF
Tel: 01852 300209
Contact: David Mason (Hallkeeper (bookings)) or Venue Tel: 01852 300435

Eastwood Theatre
Capacity: 300. Disabled access and facilities.
Eastwood Park, Rouken Glen Road, Giffnock, Glasgow G46 6UG
Tel: 0141 638 8399
Contact: Halls Officer (Eastwood District Council) Tel: 0141 638 1101 x330

Fairhill Civic Centre
Capacity: 300. Disabled access and facilities. Correspondence c/o Cultural Services Dept, Hamilton DC, 98 Cadzow Street, Hamilton ML3 6HQ.
Neilsland Road, Hamilton
Tel: 01698 282030
Contact: Gillian Annetts (Arts Dev Officer) Tel: 01698 894083 or Rosemary Brown (Hallkeeper / bookings)

Gamble Halls
Capacity: 240. Disabled access and facilities. Correspondence c/o Dept of Recreational Services, Municipal Buildings, Clyde Square, Greenock PA15 1QL.
Shore Street, Gourock, Inverclyde
Tel: 01475 882308
Contact: Amanda Way (Inverclyde DC) or Venue Tel: 01475 633248

The Glasgow Royal Concert Hall
Capacity: Exhibition Hall 250 cabaret-style, 350 theatre-style; Strathclyde Suite 350 cabaret-style, 500 theatre-style. Disabled access and facilities. Accessibility Hotline x4179. PRS Significant Venue.
2 Sauchiehall Street, Glasgow G2 3NY
Tel: 0141 332 6633 Fax: 0141 333 9123
Contact: Karen Taylor (Events Administration Manager) or Box Office Tel: 0141 227 5511 / 353 4134 (fax)

Govan Town Hall
Capacity: Lesser Hall 200; Upper Hall 150. No disabled access. Correspondence c/o Performing Arts and Venues Dept, Exchange House, 229 George Street, Glasgow G1 1QU.
Summertown Road, Glasgow G51
Tel: 0141 227 5005/8/9 / 5015 / 5258 Fax: 0141 227 5533
Contact: Supervisor (Venues Section Glasgow DC) or Venue Tel: 0141 445 1610

VENUES

234

The Grand Hall
Capacity: Art Hall One 200; Art Hall Two 150; Pillar Hall 200. Disabled access to ground floor only, no disabled access to art halls. Correspondence c/o Kilmarnock and Loudoun DC, Leisure Services Dept, PO Box 13, Civic Centre, Kilmarnock KA1 1BY.
London Road, Kilmarnock KA3 7AA
Tel: 01563 578437 Fax: 01563 578426
Contact: Derek Spence (Director of Recreation Kilmarnock and Loudoun DC) or Venue Tel: 01563 521545

Greengairs Community Centre
Capacity: 200. No disabled access. Correspondence c/o Leisure and Recreation Dept, Monklands DC, 101 Bank Street, Coatbridge ML5 1ET.
Greengairs Road, Greengairs, Monklands
Tel: 01236 441442
Contact: Agnes Rodgers (Booking Assistant) or Venue Tel: 01236 830595

Hamilton Town Hall
Capacity: Lesser Hall 394. Disabled access. Contact in advance. Correspondence c/o Cultural Services, Hamilton DC, 98 Cadzow Street, Hamilton, ML3 6HQ.
Lower Auchingramont Road, Hamilton
Tel: 01698 894060
Contact: Gillian Annetts (Arts Dev Officer) Tel: 01698 894083 or Mr Burke Tel: 01698 282323 x2421

Hardgate Hall
Capacity: 150. No disabled access.
Glasgow Road, Hardgate G81
Tel: 0141 941 1313 Fax: 0141 952 0573
Contact: Iain McAdam (Chief Amenities Officer)

Highland Theatre
Capacity: 277. Disabled access and facilities.
George Street, Oban PA34 5NX
Tel: 01631 562444 Fax: 01631 566160
Contact: David Webster (Managing Director) Tel: 01631 563794 / 565083

Institute Hall
Capacity: Main Hall 380. No disabled access. Correspondence c/o Kilmarnock and Loudoun DC, Leisure Services Dept, PO Box 13, Civic Centre, Kilmarnock KA1 1BY.
1 Avenue Street, Stewarton KA3 5AP
Tel: 01563 578422
Contact: Derek Spence (Director of Recreation) or Venue Tel: 01560 484386

Iona Public Hall
Capacity: 200. Disabled access and facilities.
Iona, Argyll PA76 6SJ
Tel: 01681 700567
Contact: Judith Jardine (Secretary)

Langside Hall
Capacity: 226. No disabled access. Correspondence to: Performing Arts and Venues Dept, Exchange House, 229 George Street, Glasgow G1 1QU.
5 Langside Avenue, Glasgow G41
Tel: 0141 227 5005/8/9 / 5015 / 5258
Fax: 0141 227 5533
Contact: Supervisor (Venues Section Glasgow DC) or Venue Tel: 0141 632 0096

Lenzie Hall
Capacity: 177. Disabled access and facilities. Correspondence c/o Dept of Leisure and Recreational Services, Strathkelvin DC, The Triangle, Kirkintilloch Road, Bishopbriggs, Glasgow, G64 2TR.
Kirkintilloch Road, Lenzie G66 4LD
Tel: 0141 772 3210 Fax: 0141 762 0934
Contact: Russell Laurie (Halls Manager) or Venue Tel: 0141 775 2902

Linwood Community Education Centre
Capacity: 175. Disabled access and facilities.
Brediland Road, Linwood PA3 3RA
Tel: 01505 322233
Contact: Jeanette Anderson (Community Work Assistant)

McLellan Galleries
Capacity: 150. Disabled access and facilities. Correspondence c/o Mark Hughes, Events Officer, Art Galleries and Museums Dept, Glasgow DC, McLellan Galleries, 270 Sauchiehall Street, Glasgow G2 3EH.
270 Sauchiehall Street, Glasgow G2 3EH
Tel: 0141 331 1854 Fax: 0141 332 9957
Contact: Mark Hughes (Events Officer)

Magnum Theatre
Capacity: Theatre 323. Disabled access and facilities: contact in advance. Correspondence to District Entertainments Office, Cunninghame District Council, Cunninghame House, Irvine KA12 8EE. PRS Significant Venue.
Magnum Leisure Centre, Harbourside, Irvine KA12 8PP
Tel: 01294 278381 Fax: 01294 311228
Contact: Willie Freckleton (Ents Officer)
Tel: 01294 274166

Merchant's House
Capacity: 200. Disabled access poor. PRS Significant Venue.
7 West George Street, Glasgow G2 1BA
Tel: 0141 221 8272
Contact: A D Barr (Assistant to the Collector)

Molendinar Community Education Centre
Capacity: 200. Disabled access and facilities.
45 Craighead Avenue, Blackhill, Glasgow G33 3LH
Tel: 0141 770 7248
Contact: Moira Stewart (Clerkess)

Morton Hall
Capacity: 300. Disabled access and facilities. Correspondence c/o Kilmarnock and Loudoun DC, Leisure Services Dept, PO Box 13, Civic Centre, Kilmarnock KA1 1BY.
123 Main Street, Newmilns KA16 9DG
Tel: 01563 578422 Fax: 01563 578426
Contact: Derek Spence (Director of Recreation) or Venue Tel: 01560 320071

Motherwell Theatre
Capacity: 395. Disabled access and facilities.
Civic Centre, Motherwell ML1 1TW
Tel: 01698 267515 Fax: 01698 268806
Contact: Lizanne McMurrich (Venue Manager) Tel: 01698 266166 x2354

Muirhead Hall
Capacity: 172. Disabled access and facilities. Correspondence c/o Dept of Leisure and Recreational Services, Strathkelvin DC, The Triangle, Kirkintilloch Road, Bishopbriggs, Glasgow G64 2TR.
Cumbernauld Road, Muirhead, Glasgow G69 9ND
Tel: 0141 772 3210 Fax: 0141 762 0934
Contact: Russell Laurie (Halls Manager) or Venue Tel: 0141 779 2733

Napier Hall
Capacity: 240. Disabled access.
Dumbarton Road, Old Kilpatrick
Tel: 0141 941 1331 Fax: 0141 952 0573
Contact: Iain McAdam (Chief Amenities Officer)

Old Athenaeum Theatre
Capacity: 345. Disabled access: contact in advance.
179 Buchanan Street, Glasgow G1 2JZ
Tel: 0141 332 5127 Fax: 0141 333 1021
Contact: Neil Mowat (House Manager) or Box Office Tel: 0141 332 2333

VENUES

235

Paisley Arts Centre
Capacity: 165. Disabled access and facilities.
New Street, Paisley PA1 1EZ
Tel: 0141 887 1010 Fax: 0141 887 6300
Contact: Paul Hogan (Principal Arts Officer)

Park Mains Theatre
Capacity: 370. Disabled access and facilities.
Park Mains, Erskine PA8 6EY
Tel: 0141 812 2801
Contact: Mr Fox (Headmaster)

Partick Burgh Hall
Capacity: Lesser Hall Suite 200; Mid Hall 150. No disabled access. Correspondence c/o Performing Arts and Venues Dept, Exchange House, 229 George Street, Glasgow G1 1QU.
9 Burgh Hall Street, Glasgow G11
Tel: 0141 227 5005/8/9 / 5015 /5258 Fax: 0141 227 5533
Contact: Supervisor (Venues Section Glasgow DC) or Venue Tel: 0141 339 8386

Pearce Institute
Capacity: 250. Disabled access and facilities.
840 Govan Road, Glasgow
Tel: 0141 445 1941
Contact: Alan Davidson

Pivot Community Education Centre
Capacity: 220. Disabled access and facilities.
Glenmanor Avenue, Moodiesburn, Chryston, Strathkelvin G69
Tel: 01236 874941
Contact: Carolyn McKeown (Community Education Worker)

Pollok Community Education Centre
Capacity: 200. Disabled facilities planned.
Langton Road, Pollok, Glasgow G53
Tel: 0141 882 5869
Contact: Thomas Lloyd (Community Education Worker)

Riccarton Community Centre
Capacity: 250. Disabled access and facilities. Correspondence c/o Kilmarnock and Loudoun DC, Leisure Services Dept., PO Box 13, Civic Centre, Kilmarnock, KA1 1BY.
23 Campbell Street, Kilmarnock KA1 4HL
Tel: 01563 578422 Fax: 01563 578426
Contact: Derek Spence (Director of Recreation) or Venue Tel: 01563 571138

Robin Anderson Theatre
Capacity: 182. Disabled access and facilities: contact in advance for wheelchair spaces.
Scottish Ballet, 261 West Princes Street, Glasgow G4 9EE
Tel: 0141 331 2931 Fax: 0141 331 2629
Contact: Liz Roger (Admin Secretary)

Royal Scottish Academy of Music and Drama
Capacity: New Athenaeum Theatre 346; Stevenson Hall 360. Disabled access. Stevenson Hall is a PRS Significant Venue.
100 Renfrew Street, Glasgow G2 3DB
Tel: 0141 332 4101 Fax: 0141 332 8901
Contact: Anna Fenge (Marketing and Public Relations Manager) or Box Office Tel: 0141 332 5057

Rutherglen Burgh Hall
Capacity: 200. No disabled access. Correspondence c/o Performing Arts and Venues Dept, Exchange House, 229 George Street, Glasgow G1 1QU .
East King Street, Glasgow G72
Tel: 0141 227 5005/8/9 / 5015 / 5258 Fax: 0141 227 5533
Contact: Supervisor (Venues Dept Glasgow DC) or Venue Tel: 0141 647 2254

Shettleston Hall
Capacity: Lesser Hall 150. No disabled access . Correspondence c/o Performing Arts and Venues Dept, Glasgow DC, Exchange House, 229 George Street, Glasgow, G1 1QU.
150 Wellshot Road, Glasgow G32
Tel: 0141 227 5005/8/9 / 5015 / 5258 Fax: 0141 227 5533
Contact: Supervisor (Venues Section Glasgow DC) or Venue Tel: 0141 778 1288

Tron Theatre
Capacity: 272. Disabled access and facilities.
63 Trongate, Glasgow G1 5HB
Tel: 0141 552 3748 Fax: 0141 552 6657
Contact: Michael Boyd (Artistic Director) or Box Office Tel: 0141 552 4267

Troon Concert Hall
Capacity: Walker Hall 288. Disabled access and facilities.
Kyle and Carrick DC, Municipal Buildings, South Beach, Troon KA10 6EF
Tel: 01292 313555 Fax: 01292 318009
Contact: Carol Murray (Registrar)

Village Theatre
Capacity: Main Theatre 333. Disabled access and facilities.
Maxwell Drive, East Kilbride G74 4HG
Tel: 013552 48669
Contact: Maggie Campbell (Theatre Manager) or Sandy McBain (Arts and Ents Officer) Tel: 013552 61000

Volunteer Rooms
Capacity: 400 (close seating), 250. Disabled access and facilities.
High Street, Irvine
Tel: 01294 311995 / 276377 Fax: 01294 277113
Contact: Bobby McGhee (Community and Leisure Officer)

Woodside Hall
Capacity: Lesser Hall 160. No disabled access. Correspondence c/o Performing Arts and Venues Dept, Exchange House, 229 George Street, Glasgow, G1 1QU.
36 Glenfarg Street, Glasgow G21
Tel: 0141 227 5005/8/9 / 5015 / 5258 Fax: 0141 227 5533
Contact: Supervisor (Venues Section Glasgow DC) or Venue Tel: 0141 332 3651

400 TO 999

Adelaide's
Capacity: 550. Disabled access.
209 Bath Street, Glasgow G2 4HZ
Tel: 0141 248 4970
Contact: Sandy Meiklejohn (Centre Director)

Arches Theatre
Capacity: Café/Bar 650. Disabled access and facilities.
30 Midland Street, Glasgow G1 4PR
Tel: 0141 221 9736 Fax: 0141 221 8605
Contact: Andy Arnold (Artistic Director) or Lori Frater (General Manager)

Art Gallery and Museum
Capacity: 400. Disabled access and facilities. Correspondence c/o Mark Hughes, Events Officer, Art Galleries and Museums Dept, Glasgow DC, McLellan Galleries, 270 Sauchiehall Street, Glasgow G2 3EH.
Kelvingrove, Glasgow G3 8AG
Tel: 0141 331 1854 Fax: 0141 332 9957
Contact: Mark Hughes (Events Officer) or Venue Tel: 0141 221 9600

VENUES

Ayr Town Hall

Capacity: 712. Disabled access: contact in advance. Correspondence c/o Kyle and Carrick DC, Burns House, Burns Statue Square, Ayr.
New Bridge Street, Ayr KA7 1LX
Tel: 01292 281511 Fax: 01292 610650
Contact: Ewan Coventry (Customer Services Officer)

Ballerup Hall

Capacity: 400. Disabled access and facilities.
Civic Centre, Andrew Street, East Kilbride, Strathclyde G74 1AB
Tel: 013552 71296 Fax: 013552 71376
Contact: Jeanette Mulholland (Clerical Assistant) or Venue Tel: 013552 71301

Beach Pavilion

Capacity: 610. Disabled access and facilities: wheelchair spaces by arrangement.
Knockcushan Street, Girvan, Ayrshire KA26 9AQ
Tel: 01465 714545 Fax: 01465 713492
Contact: William Fulton (Contract Manager) or Box Office Tel: 01465 714794

Boglestone Community Centre

Capacity: 400. Disabled access and facilities.
Dubbs Place, Port Glasgow PA15 5UD
Tel: 01475 704948
Contact: A Mathieson (Manager)

Carluke District Hall

Capacity: 580. Disabled access and facilities.
Carnwath Road, Carluke ML8
Tel: 01555 772501
Contact: P Thomson (Hallkeeper)

Citizens' Theatre

Capacity: Main Theatre 600. Disabled access and facilities. Extensive services available for the disabled, visually impaired and hard of hearing in all theatres.
Gorbals, Glasgow G5 9DS
Tel: 0141 429 5561 Fax: 0141 429 7374
Contact: Sharman Weir (General Manager) or Box Office Tel: 0141 429 0022

Clydebank Town Hall

Capacity: Large Hall 500. Disabled access and facilities. Correspondence to Dept of Environmental Health, Amenities Dept, Clydebank District Council, Municipal Buildings, Clydebank.
Dumbarton Road, Clydebank G81
Tel: 0141 941 1331 Fax: 0141 952 0573
Contact: Iain McAdam (Chief Amenities Officer)

Corran Hall

Capacity: 758. Disabled access. PRS Significant Venue.
Esplanade, Oban PA34 5AB
Tel: 01631 564046
Contact: Alan Black (Manager)

Couper Institute

Capacity: 650. Disabled access and facilities. Correspondence c/o Performing Arts and Venues Dept, Glasgow DC, Exchange House, 229 George Street, Glasgow G1 1QU.
86 Clarkston Road, Glasgow G44
Tel: 0141 227 5005/8/9 / 5015 /5258
Fax: 0141 227 5533
Contact: Supervisor (Venues Section Glasgow DC) or Venue Tel: 0141 637 1409

Darvel Town Hall

Capacity: 476. Disabled access and facilities. Correspondence c/o Kilmarnock and Loudoun DC, Leisure Services Dept, PO Box 13, Civic Centre, Kilmarnock KA1 1BY.
10/12 West Main Street, Darvel KA17 0AQ
Tel: 01563 578437 Fax: 01563 578426
Contact: Derek Spence (Director of Recreation) or Venue Tel: 01560 322437

Gaiety Theatre

Capacity: 570. Disabled access and facilities: no disabled parking (car park next door).
Carrick Street, Ayr KA7 1NU
Tel: 01292 264630 Fax: 01292 288383
Contact: Alan Davies (Arts and Ents Officer) or Box Office Tel: 01292 264639

The Grand Hall

Capacity: 979. Disabled access and facilities ground floor only. All correspondence c/o Kilmarnock and Loudoun DC, Leisure Services Dept, PO Box 13, Civic Centre, Kilmarnock KA1 1BY.
1a London Road, Kilmarnock KA3 7AA
Tel: 01563 578437 Fax: 01563 578426
Contact: Derek Spence (Director of Recreation) or Venue Tel: 01563 521545

Greenock Arts Guild

Capacity: Arts Guild Theatre 469. No disabled access.
Campbell Street, Greenock, Renfrewshire PA16 8AP
Tel: 01475 723038
Contact: Liz Muir (Administration)

Henry Wood Hall

Capacity: 500. Disabled access and facilities. PRS Significant Venue.
73 Claremont Street, Glasgow G3 7HA
Tel: 0141 226 3868 / 204 4540 Fax: 0141 221 4317
Contact: Ann Elliot (Administrator)

Kirkintilloch Town Hall

Capacity: 543. Disabled access and facilities. Correspondence c/o Dept of Leisure and Recreational Services, Strathkelvin DC, The Triangle, Kirkintilloch Road, Bishopbriggs, Glasgow G64 2TR.
Union Street, Kirkintilloch, Glasgow G66 1DH
Tel: 0141 772 3210 Fax: 0141 762 0934
Contact: Russell Laurie (Halls Manager) or Venue Tel: 0141 776 2266

Lanark Memorial Hall

Capacity: 536. Disabled access and facilities.
19 St Leonard's Street, Lanark, Clydesdale ML11 7DU
Tel: 01555 665383
Contact: Raymond Anderson (Hall Supervisor)

Langside Hall

Capacity: 468. Disabled access and facilities. Correspondence to Performing Arts and Venues Dept, Exchange House, 229 George Street, Glasgow G1 1QU.
5 Langside Avenue, Glasgow G41
Tel: 0141 227 5005/8/9 / 5015 / 5258
Fax: 0141 227 5533
Contact: Supervisor (Venues Dept Glasgow DC) or Venue Tel: 0141 632 0096

Mitchell Theatre and James Moir Hall Complex

Capacity: Mitchell Theatre 418; James Moir Hall 400. Disabled access and facilities. PRS Significant Venue.
3 Granville Street, Glasgow G3 7DR
Tel: 0141 227 4855 Fax: 0141 221 0695
Contact: Steven Kelly or Box Office Tel: 0141 227 5033

Museum Of Transport

Capacity: 800. Disabled access and facilities. Correspondence c/o Mark Hughes, Events Officer, Art Galleries and Museums Dept, Glasgow DC, McLellan Galleries, 270 Sauchiehall Street, Glasgow G2 3EH.
Kelvin Hall, 1 Bunhouse Road, Glasgow G3
Tel: 0141 331 1854 Fax: 0141 332 9957
Contact: Mark Hughes (Events Officer) or Venue Tel: 0141 357 3929

VENUES

237

New Farm Loch Community Centre

Capacity: 400. Disabled access. Correspondence c/o Kilmarnock and Loudoun DC, Leisure Services Dept, PO Box 13, Civic Centre, Kilmarnock KA1 1BY.

2a Fraser Walk, Kilmarnock KA3 7PH
Tel: 01563 578422 Fax: 01563 578426
Contact: Derek Spence (Director of Recreation) or Venue Tel: 01563 535333

Palace Theatre

Capacity: 503. Disabled access and facilities.

9 Green Street, Kilmarnock KA1 3BN
Tel: 01563 537710 Fax: 01563 573047
Contact: Bruce Gilmour (Theatre Manager) or Box Office Tel: 01563 523590

Partick Burgh Hall

Capacity: 550. Disabled access and facilities. Correspondence c/o Performing Arts and Venues Dept, Exchange House, 229 George Street, Glasgow G1 1QU.

9 Burgh Hall Street, Glasgow G11
Tel: 0141 227 5005/8/9 / 5015 / 5258
Fax: 0141 227 5533
Contact: Supervisor (Venues Dept Glasgow DC) or Venue Tel: 0141 339 8386

Pollockshaws Burgh Hall

Capacity: 450. Disabled access and facilities. Please contact in advance. Correspondence c/o Performing Arts and Venues Dept, Exchange House, 229 George Street, Glasgow G1 1QU.

2025 Pollockshaws Road, Glasgow G43
Tel: 0141 227 5005/8/9 / 5015 / 5258
Fax: 0141 227 5533
Contact: Supervisor (Venues Dept Glasgow DC) or Venue Tel: 0141 632 0043

Port Glasgow Town Hall

Capacity: 623. Disabled access and facilities.

35 King Street, Port Glasgow PA14 5HD
Tel: 01475 882308
Contact: J A Douglas (Recreational Services Director) or Venue Tel: 01475 741305

Queen's Hall

Capacity: 888. Disabled access and facilities.

Gateway Leisure, Argyll Street, Dunoon PA23 7HH
Tel: 01369 702800 Fax: 01369 705150
Contact: Mrs Whyte (Administrator) or Lorna Murphy (Admin Assistant)

Shettleston Hall

Capacity: 450. Disabled access and facilities. Correspondence c/o Performing Arts and Venues Dept, Glasgow DC, Exchange House, 229 George Street, Glasgow G1 1QU.

150 Wellshot Road, Glasgow G32
Tel: 0141 227 5005/8/9 / 5015 / 5258
Fax: 0141 227 5533
Contact: Supervisor (Venues Dept Glasgow DC) or Venue Tel: 0141 778 1288

Sir John Wilson Town Hall

Capacity: 708. Disabled access and facilities. Correspondence c/o Leisure and Recreation Dept, Monklands DC, 101 Bank Street, Coatbridge ML5 1ET.

Stirling Street, Airdrie
Tel: 01236 763211
Contact: Agnes Rodgers (Booking Assistant) Tel: 01236 441442

Tramway

Capacity: Area One 600 (seated) - 740. Disabled access and facilities.

25 Albert Drive, Pollockshields, Glasgow G41 2PE
Tel: 0141 422 2023 / 227 5511 (box office) Fax: 0141 422 2021
Contact: Robert Palmer (Performing Arts Venues Director) Tel: 0141 227 5429 or Steven Slater / Susan Dieghan (Programmers)

Troon Concert Hall

Capacity: Concert Hall 860. No disabled access.

Kyle and Carrick DC, South Beach, Troon, Ayrshire KA10 6EF
Tel: 01292 313555 Fax: 01292 318009
Contact: Carol Murray (Registrar)

Victoria Hall

Capacity: 450. Disabled access and facilities. Correspondence c/o Gillian Graham, Dept of Environmental Services, Dumbarton DC, Castle Street, Dumbarton G82 1JY.

Sinclair Street, Helensburgh, Dumbartonshire G84
Tel: 01389 765100 x208 Fax: 01389 743256
Contact: Gillian Graham / Jane McPhail (Arts Officer / Clerical Assistant) or Venue Tel: 014386 763275

Woodside Hall

Capacity: 600. Disabled access and facilities. Correspondence c/o Performing Arts and Venues Dept, Exchange House, 229 George Street, Glasgow G1 1QU.

36 Glenfarg Street, Glasgow G21
Tel: 0141 227 5005/8/9 / 5015 / 5258
Fax: 0141 227 5533
Contact: Supervisor (Venues Section Glasgow DC) or Venue Tel: 0141 332 3651

OVER 1,000

Barrowlands

Capacity: 1,900 (standing). Disabled access and facilities: stewards willing to help with stairs etc, contact venue in advance. PRS Significant Venue.

244 Gallowgate, Glasgow G4 0TT
Tel: 0141 552 4601 Fax: 0141 552 4997
Contact: Tom Joyes / Stan Riddet / Anne Dick

City Hall

Capacity: 1,184. Disabled access (facilities added soon). Correspondence to Performing Arts and Venues Dept, Glasgow DC, Exchange House, 229 George Street, Glasgow G1 1QU. PRS Significant Venue.

Candleriggs, Glasgow G1 1NQ
Tel: 0141 227 5005/8/9 / 5015 / 5258
Fax: 0141 227 5533
Contact: Supervisor (Venues Dept Glasgow DC) or Venue Tel: 0141 227 5024

The Glasgow Royal Concert Hall

Capacity: Main Auditorium 2,475. Disabled access and facilities. Accessibility Hotline x4179. PRS Significant Venue.

2 Sauchiehall Street, Glasgow G2 3NY
Tel: 0141 332 6633 Fax: 0141 333 9123
Contact: Karen Taylor (Events Administration Manager) or Box Office Tel: 0141 227 5511 / 353 4134 (fax)

Govan Town Hall

Capacity: 1,172. Disabled access and facilities. Correspondence c/o Performing Arts and Venues Dept, Exchange House, 229 George Street, Glasgow G1 1QU.

Summertown Road, Glasgow G51
Tel: 0141 227 5005/8/9 / 5015 / 5258
Fax: 0141 227 5533
Contact: Supervisor (Venues Dept Glasgow DC) or Venue Tel: 0141 445 1610

VENUES

238

Hamilton Town Hall

Capacity: 1,020. Disabled access and facilities. Correspondence c/o Cultural Services, Hamilton DC, 98 Cadzow Street, Hamilton ML3 6HQ.
Lower Auchingramont Road, Hamilton
Tel: 01698 894060
Contact: Gillian Annetts (Arts Dev Officer) Tel: 01698 894083 or Mr Burke Tel: 01698 282323 x2421

King's Theatre (Glasgow)

Capacity: 1,785. Disabled access and facilities.
297 Bath Street, Glasgow G2 4JN
Tel: 0141 227 5022 Fax: 0141 248 3361
Contact: William Differ (General Manager) or Box Office Tel: 0141 227 5511

Magnum Theatre

Capacity: Main Hall 1,200. Disabled access and facilities. Correspondence to District Entertainments Office, Cunninghame District Council, Cunninghame House, Irvine KA12 8EE.
Magnum Leisure Centre, Harbourside, Irvine KA12 8PP
Tel: 01294 278381 Fax: 01294 311228
Contact: Willie Freckleton (Entertainments Officer) Tel: 01294 274166

Motherwell Concert Hall

Capacity: Concert Hall 1008 seated, 1800 standing. Disabled access and facilities. PRS Significant Venue.
Civic Centre, Motherwell ML1 1TW
Tel: 01698 267515 Fax: 01698 268806
Contact: Lizanne McMurrich (Venue Manager) Tel: 01698 266166 x2354

Pavilion

Capacity: 1,250. Disabled access and facilities.
Argyle Street, Rothesay, Isle of Bute
Tel: 01546 602127
Contact: Willie Young (Leisure and Recreation Officer) or Douglas MacCombe (Manager) Tel: 01700 504250

Pavilion Ballroom

Capacity: 1,000. Disabled access and facilities.
Esplanade, Ayr KA7 1DT
Tel: 01292 265489
Contact: C McIntyre (General Manager)

Pavilion Theatre

Capacity: 1,449. Disabled access and facilities. PRS Significant Venue.
121 Renfield Street, Glasgow G2 3AX
Tel: 0141 332 7579
Contact: Iain Gordon (Theatre Manager) or Box Office Tel: 0141 332 1846

Scottish Exhibition and Conference Centre

Capacity: Hall One 2,000; Halls Two and Three 3,600; Hall Four 9,676; Hall Five 5,500 (standing). Disabled access and facilities. PRS Significant Venue.
Scottish Exhibition Centre, Glasgow G3 8YW
Tel: 0141 248 3000 Fax: 0141 226 3423
Contact: Mike Closier (Chief Executive) or Box Office Tel: 0141 248 9999

Theatre Royal (Glasgow)

Capacity: 1,547. Disabled access and facilities.
282 Hope Street, Glasgow G2 3QA
Tel: 0141 332 3321 Fax: 0141 332 3965
Contact: Peter Price (Theatre Manager) or Box Office Tel: 0141 332 9000

Tramway

Capacity: Area Two 1,000 (seated) -1,500. Disabled access and facilities.
25 Albert Drive, Pollockshields, Glasgow G41 2PE
Tel: 0141 422 2023 / 227 5511 (box office) Fax: 0141 422 2021
Contact: Robert Palmer (Performing Arts Venues Director) Tel: 0141 227 5429 or Steven Slater / Susan Dieghan (Programmers)

TAYSIDE

UNDER 150

Bridge of Earn Institute and Hall

Capacity: 110. Disabled access and facilities.
Station Road, Bridge of Earn PH2 9EA
Tel: 01738 812036
Contact: Allan Jack Tel: 01738 813241 or Sue Bell (Caretaker (bookings)) Tel: 01738 813646

Damacre Centre

Capacity: 80. Disabled access and facilities.
26 Damacre Road, Brechin DD9 6DU
Tel: 01356 623491
Contact: Davina Campbell (Community Education Worker)

Dibble Tree Theatre

Capacity: 48. Disabled access and facilities.
99a High Street, Carnoustie DD7
Tel: 01241 856294
Contact: Peter Waggott (Treasurer) Tel: 01241 856140

Dundee Arts Centre

Capacity: 112. Disabled access and facilities: please contact in advance.
St Mary Place, Dundee DD1 5RB
Tel: 01382 201035
Contact: George Docherty (Team Leader (Arts))

Inchture Village Hall

Capacity: 120. Disabled access and facilities.
Main Street, Inchture, Perth and Kinross
Tel: 01828 686430
Contact: Christine Allan (Booking Secretary)

McManus Galleries

Capacity: Victoria Gallery 50-100, Albert Hall 70, café 50. Disabled access and facilities.
Albert Square, Dundee, Tayside DD1 1DA
Tel: 01382 432020 Fax: 01382 432052
Contact: Parveen Rodger (Museum Services Officer) Tel: 01382 432034

Panmure Community Education Centre

Capacity: 40. Disabled access.
141 Kinloch Street, Carnoustie, Angus
Tel: 01241 853091
Contact: Community Education Worker

Perth Theatre

Capacity: Studio 100. Disabled access and facilities.
185 High Street, Perth PH1 5UW
Tel: 01738 638123 Fax: 01738 624576
Contact: Andrew McKinnon (Artistic Director) or Box Office Tel: 01738 621031

Rainbow Theatre

Capacity: 92. No disabled access.
71 Murray Street, Montrose DD10 8JZ
Tel: 01356 622201
Contact: J Anderson (Chief Executive (bookings))

Upper Springland Theatre and Community Centre

Capacity: 100. Disabled access and facilities.
Scottish Council for Spastics, Isla Road, Perth
Tel: 01738 632995 Fax: 01738 633537
Contact: Hugh Murdoch (Art Co-ordinator)

VENUES

239

150 TO 399

Bonar Hall
Capacity: Ustinov Room 180. Disabled access and facilities.
Park Place, University of Dundee, Dundee DD1 4HN
Tel: 01382 229450 Fax: 01382 229450
Contact: John Cassels (Manager) or Sheena Jack (Asst Manager)

Gardyne Theatre
Capacity: 367. Disabled access and facilities.
Gardyne Road, Dundee DD5 1NY
Tel: 01382 464000 x4312
Contact: D Wilson (Box Office Manager) or Box Office Tel: 01382 464002 x4433

Panmure Community Education Centre
Capacity: 200. Disabled access.
141 Kinloch Street, Carnoustie, Angus
Tel: 01241 853091
Contact: Community Education Worker

Perth City Hall
Capacity: Lesser hall 350. Disabled access and facilities. PRS Significant Venue.
Perth and Kinross DC, King Edward Street, Perth PH1 5UG
Tel: 01738 639911 x4863 Fax: 01738 441690
Contact: John Gilmour (Leisure and Recreation Dept) or Venue Tel: 01738 624055

Town Hall
Capacity: 368. Disabled access, except to balcony area.
Reform Street, Kirriemuir
Tel: 01307 465100 Fax: 01307 466220
Contact: Freda Milne (Halls Administrator) or Venue Tel: 01575 572357

400 TO 999

Bonar Hall
Capacity: Main Hall 494. Disabled access and facilities.
Park Place, University of Dundee, Dundee DD1 4HN
Tel: 01382 229450 Fax: 01382 229450
Contact: John Cassels (Manager) or Sheena Jack (Asst Manager)

Caird Hall
Capacity: Marryat Hall 400. Disabled access and facilities.
City Square, Dundee DD1 4BD
Tel: 01382 223141 x4287
Contact: Susan Gillan (Leisure Activities Officer) or Box Office Tel: 01382 434940 / 434941 (credit cards)

Carnoustie Leisure Centre
Capacity: Beach Hall 480. Disabled access and facilities.
Links Parade, Carnoustie, Angus DD7 7JB
Tel: 01241 853246
Contact: Archie Dick (Centre Manager)

Dundee Repertory Theatre
Capacity: 450. Disabled access and facilities.
Tay Square, Dundee DD1 1PB
Tel: 01382 227684 Fax: 01382 228609
Contact: Hamish Glen (Artistic Director) or Box Office Tel: 01382 223530

Marryat Hall
Capacity: 400. Disabled access and facilities.
City Square, Dundee DD1 3BD
Tel: 01382 223141 x4287
Contact: Susan Gillan (Leisure Activities Officer) or Box Office Tel: 01382 434288

Montrose Town Hall
Capacity: 669. Disabled access and facilities.
Melville Gardens, Montrose, Angus DD10 8HG
Tel: 01241 876221 x222 Fax: 01241 870090
Contact: Catherine Wallace (Halls Administrator (Coastal)) or Venue Tel: 01674 672435

Perth Theatre
Capacity: Theatre 490. Disabled access and facilities.
185 High Street, Perth PH1 5UW
Tel: 01738 638123 Fax: 01738 624576
Contact: Andrew McKinnon (Artistic Director) or Box Office Tel: 01738 621031

Pitlochry Festival Theatre
Capacity: 544. Disabled access and facilities.
Port-na-Craig, Pitlochry PH16 5DR
Tel: 01796 473054 Fax: 01796 473054
Contact: Sheila Harborth (Administrator) or Box Office Tel: 01796 472680

Reid Hall
Capacity: 829. Disabled access: no access to balcony area.
Castle Street, Forfar DD8 1BX
Tel: 01307 465100 Fax: 01307 466220
Contact: Freda Milne (Halls Administrator) or Venue Tel: 01307 462958

Webster Memorial Theatre
Capacity: 606. Disabled access. Correspondence c/o Halls Administrator, Parks and Recreation Dept, Angus DC, 12 Hill Terrace, Arbroath DD11 1AJ.
High Street , Arbroath DD11 1AW
Tel: 01241 874637 Fax: 01307 466220
Contact: Catherine Wallace (Halls Administrator) Tel: 01241 876221 x222 or Box Office Tel: 01241 872609 / 876680

Whitehall Theatre
Capacity: 750. Disabled access and facilities. Correspondence c/o Treasurer, Whitehall Theatre, 24 Torridon Road, Broughty Ferry, Dundee. PRS Significant Venue.
Bellfield Street, Dundee DD1 5JA
Tel: 01382 322684
Contact: Alastair Walker (Treasurer) Tel: 01382 477513 or Box Office Tel: 01382 202513

OVER 1,000

Caird Hall
Capacity: 2,400. Disabled access and facilities. PRS Significant Venue.
City Square, Dundee DD1 4BD
Tel: 01382 223141 x4287
Contact: Susan Gillan (Leisure Activities Officer) or Box Office Tel: 01382 434940 / 434941 (credit cards)

Perth City Hall
Capacity: Main Auditorium: 1,624 (seated). Disabled access and facilities.
King Edward Street, Perth, Tayside PH1 5UG
Tel: 01738 639911 x4863 Fax: 01738 441690
Contact: John Gilmour (Leisure and Recreation Dept) or Venue Tel: 01738 624055

VENUES

240

WESTERN ISLES

UNDER 150

An Lanntair
Capacity: 55. Disabled access.
South Beach Street, Stornoway, Isle of
Lewis HS1 2BX
Tel: 01851 703307
Contact: Alex McDonald (Programmes
Officer)
Eriskay Village Hall
Capacity: 110. Disabled access.
Rubain, Eriskay, Western Isles HS8 5JL
Tel: 01878 720277
Contact: Neilina McInnes (Booking
Agent) or Venue Tel: 01878 720281
Taigh Chearsabhagh
Capacity: 30-40. Disabled access and
facilities.
Lochmaddy, North Uist, HS6 5AA
Tel: 01876 500293
Contact: Norman McLeod (bookings)

150 TO 399

Sabhal Bornais
Capacity: 200. Disabled access and
facilities.
Bornish, South Uist HS8 5SA
Tel: 01878 710376
Contact: M T MacInnes (Caretaker)
Sgoil Lionacleit Benbecula
Capacity: 150. Disabled access and
facilities.
Sgoil Lionacleit, Benbecula HS7 5PJ
Tel: 01870 602107 Fax: 01870 602817
Contact: Donald John MacDonald
(Senior Community Education Officer)

400 TO 999

Stornoway Town Hall
Capacity: 300. Disabled access.
South Beach, Stornoway, Isle of Lewis
HS1 2BE
Tel: 01851 703773 x448
Contact: Norman McLean (Community
Education Service)

VENUES

241

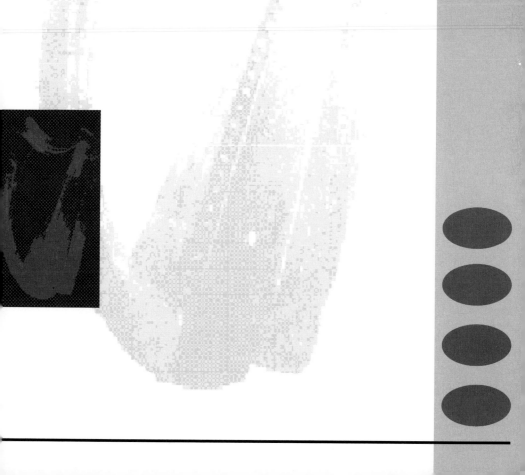

CLUBS AND PROMOTERS

Editorial Notes

The chapter is divided into four categories: FOLK CLUBS, JAZZ, MUSIC SOCIETIES AND CLUBS, and PROMOTERS, and entries are arranged alphabetically. This division was believed to be necessary to ensure the widest possible use of the Handbook. It should, for example, facilitate its use both by audience members looking for a concert to attend, and by performers hoping to arrange a club or concert booking.

MUSIC SOCIETIES AND CLUBS tend to offer around six concerts a year, mainly classical. Many of the FOLK CLUBS, however, have weekly meetings. More detailed information including artists etc. is given on Radio Scotland's *Travelling Folk* programme (Thursdays 7-9pm).

The JAZZ category contains both clubs and promoters. This is a relatively small section and it seemed useful to group all jazz related entries together.

The PROMOTERS category will be of use to musicians looking for concert dates, and includes both venues and organisations which promote concerts regularly during the year. Various types of music are covered by these promoters. Musicians looking for bookings might also find it worthwhile to look through the FESTIVALS section.

FOLK CLUBS

Aberdeen Folk Club

Club meets at The Lemon Tree, West North Street, Aberdeen. There is a guest artist every week. Piano available. All kinds of folk music but 40-50% of artists are Scottish.
77 Polmuir Road, Aberdeen AB1 2SJ
Tel: 01224 642230 (venue) Fax: 01224 630888 (venue)
Contact: Roger Inns (Organiser)
Tel: 01224 591005

Aberdour Folk Club

Woodside Hotel, Aberdour. One concert, first Thursday of every month. Folk music of all kinds - other countries, contemporary etc.
Kenmore, 18 Seaside Place, Aberdour KY3 0TX
Tel: 01383 860540
Contact: Jean Watt (Secretary) or Ian Richard (Publicity) Tel: 01383 735023

Alyth Folk Club

Meets on last Friday of the month year round in the Alyth Hotel with additional ad hoc sessions. All kinds of acoustic folk music from all over the world. Graham Marshall, the organiser, broadcasts on Heartland FM on Saturday lunchtime Scene Around which is a live folk music programme.
Alyth Hotel, Alyth, Perth PH11 8AF
Tel: 01828 632447 Fax: 01828 632355
Contact: Graham Marshall (Organiser)

Ancrum Folk Club

Last Sunday in every month at the Cross Keys. Traditional folk. No guest sessions. Folk weekend towards the end of August.
The Cross Keys Inn, Ancrum, Jedburgh TD8 6XH
Tel: 01835 830344 (venue)
Contact: Christine Chisholm Tel: 01835 830546

Babbity Bowster

Sunday evening at the Babbity Bowster is folk night. All kinds of folk music. Guest artists are frequently invited.
Babbity Bowster, 16 Blackfriars Street, Glasgow G1 1PE
Tel: 0141 552 5055 Fax: 0141 552 5215
Contact: Stevie McGeady Tel: 0141 552 5055 (W) or Mr F Laurie (Proprietor)

Balerno Folk Club

Meet last Thursday of the month, sometimes has a guest (usually autumn and spring months). Traditional/Scottish/ contemporary. Venue is the Kestrel Hotel, Balerno.
30 Marchbank Gardens, Balerno, Midlothian EH14 7EJ
Tel: 0131 449 5014
Contact: Morag Dunbar (Bookings Secretary) or Robin Murdoch (Treasurer) Tel: 0131 449 3744

Black Bull Folk Club (Milngavie)

Every second Sunday evening from about 8pm in the Black Bull Hotel, Main Street, Milngavie. Various types of folk music.
14 Inchmurrin Drive, Burnside, Glasgow G73 5RT
Tel: 0141 634 1095
Contact: Roseann Gilchrist (Organiser/ Secretary) or Bob Gilchrist (Organiser)

Clydesdale Folk Club

8 - 9 concerts January to December, but not July. Usually last Thursday in the month in the Elphinstone Hotel, High Street, Biggar and other venues. Traditional and modern, folk/roots based music. British/American.
St Oswalds, South Back Road, Biggar, Lanarkshire ML12 6AL
Tel: 01899 21090 (day) / 01899 21236 (eve) Fax: 01899 21201
Contact: Jim O'Neill (Treasurer) or Denholm McDougal (Chairman) Tel: 01899 3312

Deeside Folk and Blues Club

10 - 15 concerts year round. No piano. Skinner's Restaurant is the venue. Folk, blues and contemporary music.
Scott Skinner's Restaurant, North Deeside Road, Banchory AB31 3YR
Tel: 01330 824393
Contact: Brian Pearl (Organiser)

Denholm Folk

Thursday evenings. Guest artists invited regularly. A very busy gathering which meets in the Cross Keys Inn, Denholm. All kinds of folk music.
Cross Keys Inn, Denholm TD9 8NU
Tel: 01450 870305
Contact: Kenny Speirs (Organiser) or Peter Ferguson (Proprietor of Inn)

The Dunfermline Folk Club

Club meets on Wednesdays once a month at the Roadhouse, Pilmuir Street, Dunfermline. All instruments welcome. Various types of acoustic folk music. Members are offered £1 off for guest nights and receive a newsletter.
30 Pitcorthie Road, Dunfermline KY11 5DR
Tel: 01383 729673 Fax: 01383 622167
Contact: Gifford Lind (Chairman) or Mike Brown (Secretary) Tel: 01383 724799

Edinburgh Folk Club

About 45 Wednesday concerts year round. Venue is The Pleasance Cabaret Bar, 60 The Pleasance. Acoustic and amplified. No piano. Folk and related music.
17 Lady Menzies Place, Edinburgh EH7 5BE
Tel: 0131 652 1471 Fax: 0131 652 1471
Contact: Nancy Purves (Hon Secretary) or Graham Devlin (Vice-chair) Tel: 0131 558 3284

Falkirk Folk Club

Excepting July and August, The Drookit Duck, Grahams Road, Falkirk, is the venue for weekly meetings. There is a guest artist each week. Mostly Scottish folk music, but other kinds as well. Thursday is folk night. No piano.
3 Colonsay Avenue (Adj. Grahamston Railway Station), Polmont FK2 0UY
Tel: 01324 712142
Contact: Grace Brown (Entertainment Secretary)

The Ferry Boat Inn Folk Club

Weekly music on Thursday, Friday or Saturday at the Ferry Boat Inn. Mostly traditional, but rock and jazz bands are occasionally brought in.
The Ferry Boat Inn, Lochalsh Hotel, Kyle of Lochalsh IV40 8AF
Tel: 01599 534202
Contact: Jason Band (Organiser)

Fifie Folk Club

Brig o'Tay Hotel, Boat Brae, Newport-on-Tay is the venue on Fridays (at least monthly) for guest artists. All kinds of folk music.
61 Kirk Road, Newport-on-Tay, Fife DD6 8HY
Tel: 01382 542112
Contact: Citty Finlayson (Organiser)

CLUBS & PROMOTERS

247

Folk at the Egg

Every second Monday at the Eglinton Arms Hotel, Eaglesham. Various types of folk music.
14 Inchmurrin Drive, Burnside, Glasgow G73 5RT
Tel: 0141 634 1095
Contact: Roseann Gilchrist (Organiser/ Secretary) or Bob Gilchrist (Organiser)

Glasgow Folk Club

Wednesday evenings, Saturday and Sunday afternoons. Wednesdays and Saturdays are mainly folk music. Sunday afternoon is mainly blues.
The Scotia Bar, 112 Stockwell Street, Glasgow G1 4LW
Tel: 0141 552 8681
Contact: Robin Kerr (Organiser)

Glassford Folk Club

44 concerts on Tuesdays throughout the year, except July at the Glassford Inn, Glassford. Club starts at 8.30 pm.
2 Druid Street, Glassford, Nr Strathaven, Lanarkshire ML10 6JJ
Tel: 01357 20769
Contact: Liz MacIntyre (Booking Agent)

Glenfarg Village Folk Club

Club meets every Monday plus 3 days Folk Feast in the Glenfarg Hotel, Glenfarg. Traditional and contemporary music.
11 Scott Street, Perth PH1 5EJ
Tel: 01738 623274
Contact: Jim McIver (Chairman) or Doris Rougrie (Publicity Officer)
Tel: 01738 583698

Haddington Folk Club

6 Wednesday concerts in the Pheasant Hotel, Market Street. No piano. Traditional and contemporary folk. Also, blues, country and acceptable standard pop music. The club is essentially singaround/session. Guest artists are only invited when funds are available.
53 Seggarsdean Court, Haddington, East Lothian EH4 4LZ
Tel: 01620 822925
Contact: Gordon Pearson (Organiser) or Laurie Brett (Booking Secretary)

Inverness Folk Club

Club meets every Sunday evening at 8pm. There is a guest artist every 2nd week. Music - traditional, contemporary, blues.
Beaufort Hotel, Culduthel Road, Inverness IV2 4AG
Tel: 01463 238586
Contact: Jackie Sinclair (Organiser) or Ian McGillivray (Committee)
Tel: 01463 225947

Irvine Folk Club

Now in its 28th year. Meetings held fortnightly in the Redburn Hotel, Kilwinning, near Irvine (Wednesdays 8.30pm). All kinds of folk, blues, contemporary, guitar and traditional - mainly traditional.
Redburn Hotel, Kilwinning Road, Irvine, Ayrshire KA12 8SU
Contact: Joyce Hodge (Secretary) Tel: 01294 551047

Keith Folk Club

Club meets on the 1st Thursday of the month in the Fife Arms Hotel, Regent's Square, Keith. Club meets year round. All kinds of folk music. There are occasional guests.
127 Moss Street, Keith, Morayshire AB55 3EY
Tel: 01542 882826
Contact: Bob Sharp (Organiser)

Kilmarnock Folk Club

Club meets every Thursday year round. 2 guest artists each month except July, when there are none. Traditional music of many countries.
Hunting Lodge, Glencairn Square, Kilmarnock
Tel: 01560 321102
Contact: Maggie McCrae (Organiser)

Lerwick Folk and Blues Club

Saturdays in the Islesburgh Community Centre, Lerwick. All kinds of folk including bluegrass and jazz.
20 Hayfield Lane, Lerwick, Shetland ZE 0PZ
Tel: 01595 695005
Contact: Steve Davidson (Organiser)

Lossiemouth Folk Club

Club meets every Tuesday year round at the Beach Bar, Commerce Street, Lossiemouth. Occasional guest nights. Folk music. Folk weekend around 3rd week in July.
Beach Bar, Commerce Street, Lossiemouth, Moray IV31 6BW
Tel: 01343 818000
Contact: Malcolm Leiper or Sheena Muir Tel: 01343 830682

Montrose Folk Club

22 concerts year round except July. Held on Tuesdays at the Corner House Hotel, High Street, Montrose. No piano. Any kind of non-electrical popular music, including folk, blues, country, bluegrass etc.
5 Furlongs, Main Road, Hillend, Montrose DD10 9HH
Tel: 01674 830688 Fax: 01674 673812
Contact: Ken Bruce (Organiser)

Nairn Folk Club

Club meets every second Monday in the Milford Hotel year round and every week during the summer. Small membership. Traditional music.
2 Stuart Avenue, Ardersier, Inverness IV1 2SA
Tel: 01667 462194
Contact: Mary Bell (Committee Member)

New Dawn Folk Club

Every Thursday year round. Guest artist each week. Occasional singer's night. Scottish traditional to blues.
The Press Club, 94 West Regent Street, Glasgow G2 2QD
Tel: 0141 332 1674 (Press Club)
Contact: Kenny Caird (Organiser) Tel: 0141 445 6271 (H) or Ian Clelland (Sound Engineer) Tel: 0141 775 0306

Nitten Folk Club

10 concerts, 1 per 1st Thursday of each month except July and August. Acoustic contemporary/traditional folk music in the Dean Tarim, Main Street, Newtongrange, Midlothian. No piano. On the other Thursdays, there is a singaround but no guest artist.
114 Newbattle Abbey Crescent, Dalkeith, Midlothian EH22 3LP
Tel: 0131 660 3025
Contact: Denis Wilson (Booking Agent) or Chris Barnett (Secretary) Tel: 0131 663 1514

Penicuik Folk Club

Guest nights 2nd Tuesday of the month but not July, August or October. Open club on the other Tuesdays. Traditional and contemporary folk music. Venue is Navar House Hotel, Bog Road, Penicuik.
36 Greenhill Park, Penicuik EH26 9EX
Tel: 01968 678153
Contact: Brian Miller (Chairman) or Alan Murray (Secretary) Tel: 01968 678610

Regular Music

300 concerts in various venues throughout the year. Mainly folk but also rock and jazz.
The Loft, 25 Greenside Place, Edinburgh EH1 3AA
Tel: 0131 557 6578 Fax: 0131 557 6579
Contact: Barry Wright (Director) or Mark Mackie (Director)

Rowantree Folk Club

The Club meets every Friday at the Rowantree Inn. Guest artists are invited once a month on average. Any kind of music is welcome on a singer's night. Guest artists are folk or blues.
c/o Rowantree Inn, Old Mill Road, Uddingston G71 7PfF
Tel: 01698 425029
Contact: John Adamson (Organiser)

Stirling Folk Club

3 booked artists per month, year round, but weekly meetings in the Terrraces Hotel, 4 Melville Terrace, Stirling. No piano. Acoustic and amplified traditional folk. Contemporary music and song, blues and jazz. Bands, groups, solos, duos. Club provides access for singers and musicians who wish to play to a listening audience.
136 Carseview, Tullibody, Alloa FK10 9ST
Tel: 01259 218521
Contact: Isobel Methven (Bookings Organiser) or Kathie Costello (Secretary) Tel: 01236 735324

Stonehaven Folk Club

Club meets weekly on Fridays in St Leonards Hotel, Bath Street, Stonehaven. Piano available. Small, friendly club. Guest artists must supply their own PA. Traditional/contemporary folk music.
45 Forest Park, Stonehaven, Kincardineshire AB3 2GF
Tel: 01569 762781
Contact: Maggie Crowe (Bookings Secretary) or Charlie West (Publicity)

Straiton Folk Club

12 Friday concerts at the Black Bull Hotel, Straiton or the Straiton Village Hall. American folk music through to Irish and Scottish. Piano available. Small club.
The Smithy, Maybole, Ayrshire KA19 7NE
Tel: 01655 770630
Contact: David Hunter (Organiser)

Stranraer Folk Club

Scheuchen Arms, Glebe Street, Stranraer is the venue for Wednesday weekly concerts. All kinds of acoustic folk music. Guest artists are booked once every 6 weeks.
Wee Knockinam, Port Patrick, Wigtonshire DG9 9AD
Tel: 01766 810473
Contact: Tony Frank (Chairman) or Elaine Palmer (Treasurer) Tel: 01776 810477

The Shetland Accordion and Fiddle Club

Shetland Hotel, Lerwick is the venue for this club which is regularly attended by 200 people. 2nd and 4th Thursday of each month between October and April plus special events. Traditional Scots fiddle and accordion music, especially music from Shetland. Organise tune competitions.
12 Lover's Loan, Lerwick ZE1 OBA
Tel: 01595 692276
Contact: Gussie Angus (Organiser) or Cecil Hughson (Treasurer) Tel: 01595 694345

The Tron Folk Club

Saturday night is folk night at the Tron Bar year round, except during the Edinburgh Festival. There is a guest artist each week. Piano available. All kinds of folk music.
The Tron, 9 Hunter Square, Edinburgh EH1 1QW
Tel: 0131 667 9390
Contact: Alan Cameron (Proprietor/ Manager) Tel: 0131 220 1550

JAZZ

Aberdeen Jazz Club

Monthly meetings between September and May presenting major visiting American and British artists. Piano available. Mainstream/modern jazz. Venue - The Lemon Tree.
24 Chestnut Row, Aberdeen AB2 3SD
Tel: 01224 642230 (Lemon Tree)
Fax: 01224 630888 (Lemon Tree)
Contact: Ian Watt (Committee)
Tel: 01224 648316

Assembly Direct

Promotes jazz and blues throughout Scotland, England and Europe. Handles all sizes of concerts, ranging from small club gigs to concert hall performances and festivals. Three levels: (1) Jazz Cellar; (2) Jazz Club; (3) Jazz Directions.
89 Giles Street, Edinburgh EH6 6BZ
Tel: 0131 553 4000 Fax: 0131 554 0454
Contact: Roger Spence or Fiona Alexander

Basement Jazz

Weekly jazz at the Ramshorn Theatre, Ingram Street, Glasgow on Fridays. Mostly modern, contemporary, jazzfunk, Latin, mainstream, be-bop. Profiles Scottish artists but once a month well-established artists from throughout the UK and abroad are invited to perform.
1c Main Road, Castlehead, Paisley PA2 6AH
Tel: 0141 959 3325 (W) Fax: 0141 959 1161 (W)
Contact: Iain Copeland (Organiser) Tel: 0141 552 3489 (Ramshorn Theatre)

Cowal Jazz Forum Ltd

12 concerts, on the 2nd Saturday of every month. No piano, no regular venue. All forms of jazz from early to modern and avant-garde. Latin American and blues to be included in the future. Prefer amplified. Regular workshops/master classes in modern music and jazz for young people - no charge for these.
34 Argyll Road, Dunoon, Argyll PA23 8EL
Tel: 01369 705118
Contact: Barry Kaye (Company Secretary) or Elizabeth Davies (Director) Tel: 01369 705378

Edinburgh International Jazz and Blues Festival

150 concerts during August at the Edinburgh Festival Theatre, 13/29 Nicolson Street and the Queens Hall, Clerk Street. Upright and grand pianos in both venues. Mainstream, blues, New Orleans, be-bop, big bands and some contemporary styles. Acoustic and amplified.
116 Canongate , Edinburgh EH8 8DD
Tel: 0131 557 1642 Fax: 0131 556 0012
Contact: Michael Hart (Festival Director) or James Thomson (Administrator)

Glasgow Jazz Services

Jazz consultants, small venue promotion, co-operative band agency, all styles accommodated, gigs available for MU members. Demo tapes, bookings accepted Greater Glasgow area.
Tel: 0141 649 4044 (afternoons only)
Contact: Mr Zigman

Inverness Jazz Platform

10 concerts year round except July and August. Concerts take place in the restaurant area of the Eden Court Theatre. Piano available. Artists from around the world perform mainstream jazz.
7 Oakdene Court, Culloden IV1 2XL
Tel: 01463 790937
Contact: Jim Love (Programme Co-ordinator)

Jazz at the Tron

There is jazz in the Tron Cellar 2 nights a week, Sunday and Wednesdays. Preference is given to Scottish bands but there are also international bands. Modern jazz. No piano. Capacity 120.
The Tron Jazz Cellar, 9 Hunter Square, Edinburgh EH1 1QW
Tel: 0131 667 9390
Contact: Flora Harrold (Hon Secretary)

Rammage Jazz

About 15 concerts year round. Artists from around the world perform in various venues round Nairn. Occasional local artists.
4 Marine Cottages, Nairn IV12 4EA
Tel: 01667 455262 (W) Fax: 01667 453364
Contact: Kenneth Rammage

The Shetland Jazz Club

6 concerts, 1 every 2 months. Local and visiting artists. Upright piano available. Hold workshops. Usually held in Islesburgh Community Centre. All types of jazz.
Sundside, Bressay, Shetland ZE2 9ER
Tel: 01595 820205
Contact: Lesley Roberts (Secretary) or Marjory Bain (Asst Secretary) Tel: 01595 694035

MUSIC SOCIETIES & CLUBS

Aberdeen Chamber Music Club

Usually 6 Monday concerts between October and March. Always acoustic. Mainly string quartets but other forms of chamber music now being introduced (rarely voice or solo piano). Regular venue is The Cowdray Hall, Aberdeen which has a grand piano.
31 Gladstone Place, Queen's Cross, Aberdeen AB1 6UX
Tel: 01224 322631
Contact: Mrs M Paternoster (Hon Secretary) or Mr W Ewen (Hon Treasurer) Tel: 01224 315027

Ayr Music Club

5 or 6 classical, acoustic concerts between October and March on Saturdays. Grand piano in the regular venue, the Assembly Hall at Craigie Campus in Ayr.
9 Shawfield Avenue, Ayr KA7 4RE
Tel: 01292 442086
Contact: Pamela Martin (Hon Secretary)

Biggar Music Club

6 - 8 acoustic classical concerts in Biggar Municipal Hall, High Street, Biggar, between October and early April.
16 Coulter Road, Biggar, Lanarkshire ML12 6EP
Tel: 01899 20119
Contact: Margaret Filshie (Hon Secretary) or Miss A Jean Sloan (Hon President) Tel: 01899 20512

Carnoustie Music Club

6 concerts in the Carnoustie Public Library Reading Room on Sundays between October and March. Classical/light classical music. Priority given to Scottish based artists.
21 Kinloch Street, Carnoustie, Angus DD7 7EL
Tel: 01241 852 086
Contact: Isobel Allan (Hon Secretary) or Mrs M Bremner (Treasurer) Tel: 01241 853411

Cowal Music Club

7 Sunday afternoon concerts between October and April in the Kirn Church Centre, Dunoon. Grand piano available. Various types of music, usually chamber to light classical.
Veriwill, 79 Alexander Street, Dunoon, Argyll PA23 7BB
Tel: 01369 702860
Contact: Vera Ponton (Secretary) or Mary Turner (Treasurer) Tel: 01369 702371

Cumnock Music Club

5, plus 1 informal, acoustic concerts on Thursdays between October and March. Upright piano. Concerts take place in the Royal Hotel, Cumnock.
14 Bank Avenue, Cumnock, Ayrshire KA18 1PQ
Tel: 01290 421492
Contact: Isobel Crawford (Hon Secretary)

Dollar Music Club

4 - 5 acoustic concerts in Dollar Academy, New Concert Hall. Grand piano. Concerts take place between September and March. These are mainly classical, but there is occasional jazz or folk.
7 Sorley's Brae, Dollar, Clackmannanshire FK14 7AS
Tel: 01259 742014
Contact: Andrea Ross (Concert Secretary)

Dumfries Music Club

6 monthly classical concerts between October and March. Steinway Grand. Acoustic performances. Dumfries High School is the regular venue.
5 Victoria Road, Dumfries DG2 7NU
Tel: 01387 255879
Contact: Margaret Carruthers (Concerts Secretary) or Mr MacLennan (Chairman) Tel: 01387 255283

Dundee Chamber Music Club

5 acoustic classical concerts which take place between October and March on Tuesdays or Thursdays in the Bonar Hall, Park Place, Dundee. Grand piano available. Music tends to concentrate on chamber repertoire, string quartets, etc.
10 Nesbitt Street, Dundee DD4 7HN
Tel: 01382 461743
Contact: Duncan McDonald (Hon Secretary)

CLUBS & PROMOTERS

Dunkeld and Birnam Music Club

6 - 7 concerts on Sunday evenings during May to August in Dunkeld Cathedral. Upright piano available. Various types of music.

Ladylands, Dunkeld, Perth PH8 OAA
Tel: 01350 728869
Contact: Elizabeth Reid (Concert Secretary) or Joy Reid (Treasurer) Tel: 01350 727350

Gatehouse Music Society

4 concerts, November, December, February and March. Thursday evenings or Sunday afternoon. Classical acoustic concerts in Gatehouse Primary School. No piano - occasionally hire one. No contemporary music.

Mansewood, Gatehouse-of-Fleet, Kircudbrightshire DG7 2EQ
Tel: 01557 814428
Contact: Sheila Russell (Hon Secretary) or Mr R Bryson (Secretary in 1996) Tel: 01557 814558

Glenkens and District Music Club

4 concerts, 2 in autumn, 2 in spring on Saturdays in Dalry Town Hall, Dalry School Hall and New Galloway Town Hall. Grand piano. Acoustic, classical chamber concerts.

4 Thoroughgate, Dalry, Castle Douglas, Kirkcudbrightshire DG7 3UU
Tel: 01644 30352
Contact: Isobel Jackson (Secretary) or Dr J Neil (Chairman) Tel: 01644 20275

Haddington Music Club

6 concerts between September/October and March/April. Concerts, which mostly take place in the Town House, Linlithgow, are classical/light classical, including one jazz. Grand piano available.

3 West Saltoun, By Pencaitland, East Lothian EH34 5EJ
Tel: 01875 340472
Contact: Carol Millar (Programme Secretary) or Norman Lawrie (Membership Secretary) Tel: 01620 823242

Hawick Music Club

5 Saturday evening concerts between October and March in Drumlanrig-St Cuthberts School Hall, Hawick. Acoustic concerts, grand piano. A good mixture of music.

Scauredge, Haysike, Hawick, Roxburghshire TD9 ONT
Tel: 01450 372999
Contact: Sheila Ellis (Programme Secretary) or Mrs C Whillans (President) Tel: 01450 376211

Helensburgh Music Society

5 Saturday evening concerts between September and March/April in the Victoria Halls, Sinclair Street, Helensburgh. Grand piano available. Various types of classical ensemble and solos.

7 East Montrose Street, Helensburgh G84 7ER
Tel: 01436 678827
Contact: Linsey Aitken (Programme Organiser) or Chris Packard (Chairman) Tel: 01436 674130

Inverness Chamber Music Society

A new society which will have 5 - 6 concerts between September and March, possibly in Charleston Academy, Inverness. 3 string quartets and 2 other ensembles will probably be the musical mix. Until the Society is established, traditional classical music will be the fare. Contemporary music will be introduced in future years. No piano yet.

42 Lovat Road, Inverness IV2 3MS
Tel: 01463 711693
Contact: Colin Brown (Chairman) or Niall Ramsay (Secretary) Tel: 01463 230803

The Irvine Burns Club

A long established club which holds 6 concerts per year between September and May. They are held in the Irvine Burns Club, Wellwood, Eglinton Street, Irvine on Wednesdays. Acoustic music: Scottish, light classical and classical. Grand piano available.

Craigknowe, 7 Kilwinning Road, Irvine, Cunninghame KA12 8RR
Tel: 01294 312673
Contact: George Watson (Hon Secretary) or J J Caldwell (Committee) Tel: 01294 278553

Isle of Arran Music Society

6 - 7 concerts on Saturdays between September and March in the Brodick Public Hall. Electric Rolland SSDOS piano available. Acoustic chamber music of any period.

Achabhealaidh, Machrie, Isle of Arran KA27 8DZ
Tel: 01770 840201 Fax: 01770 840201
Contact: Mike Lunan (Secretary)

Kelso Music Society

6 - 7 Friday concerts in Kelso High School between October and March. Grand piano available. Strong preference for instrumental, acoustic and chamber music as opposed to vocal.

Kelso Pottery, The Knowes, Kelso TD5 7BH
Tel: 01573 224027
Contact: Ian Hird (President) or Deirdre Hutton (Vice President) Tel: 01573 224368

Kintyre Music Club

7 classical acoustic concerts on Tuesdays in the Lorne and Lowland Church Hall, Campbeltown between September and April. Grand piano available. Concerts range from chamber music to light opera.

Dunlossit, Machrihanish, Campbeltown PA28 6PT
Tel: 01586 810301
Contact: John Lawrie (Secretary) or Cathy Ken (Chairperson) Tel: 01586 552500

Kirkcaldy Music Society

6 acoustic chamber music concerts between October and March in St Peter's Church, Townsend Place, Kirkcaldy. Grand piano. Concert day is Wednesday.

17 Swan Road, Kirkcaldy KY1 1VQ
Tel: 01592 264632
Contact: J L Boase (Secretary)

Lanark Music Club

6 acoustic concerts on Tuesdays in the Greyfriars Church Hall. Grand piano. Season - October to March. Mainly classical music but like to have 1 jazz concert during the season.

The Priory, 11 Friars Lane, Lanark ML10 9EL
Tel: 01555 662190
Contact: Rachel Hill (Hon Secretary) or Dr Duncan Rae (Treasurer) Tel: 01555 662519

CLUBS & PROMOTERS

251

Lochaber Music Club

6 concerts between September and April in Lochaber High School, Fort William, which has an upright piano. Wide ranging choice of music.

Serenata, 15 Mossfield Drive, Lochyside, Fort William, Inverness-shire PH33 7PE
Tel: 01397 703368
Contact: David Maitland (Hon Secretary) or Sheila Maitland (Hon Treasurer)

Lockerbie Musical Society

5 acoustic concerts September to February excluding December in the Dryfesdale Hotel, Lockerbie. There is a piano. Usually last Tuesday in the month.

2 Church Crescent, Lochmaben, Dumfriesshire DG11 1QQ
Tel: 01387 811480
Contact: Miss M Riddell (Secretary) or Mrs M Sloan (President) Tel: 01387 811801

Melrose Music Society

5 Saturday (occasionally Friday) classical concerts between October and March in Melrose Parish Church Hall. Grand piano. Conservative taste in music.

Setter, Aldie Crescent, Darnick, Melrose TD6 9AY
Tel: 01896 822368
Contact: Margaret Paterson (Hon Secretary) or R Collins (Hon Treasurer) Tel: 01896 753208

Milngavie Music Club

6 Friday classical concerts in Milngavie Town Hall between October and April. Grand piano available. Chamber music, piano recitals, song recitals. Always acoustic.

11 Buckingham Street, Glasgow G12 8DL
Tel: 0141 334 3498
Contact: Karl Overton (Concert Secretary) or Mrs M Thorp (Secretary) Tel: 0141 956 1572

Moffat and District Musical Society

6 middle of the road classical concerts between October and March. Usual day is Friday in Moffat Academy, Moffat. Acoustic music. Grand piano available.

Kawartha, Ball Play Road, Moffat, Dumfriesshire DG10 9JX
Tel: 01683 20541
Contact: R Peters (Secretary)

Motherwell and District Music Society

4 - 6 concerts, autumn to spring, ranging from serious classical to operettas and jazz. Performances usually acoustic.

47 Lyman Drive, Wishaw ML2 8TJ
Tel: 01698 381936
Contact: Mary Kuklinski (Hon Secretary)

Newton Stewart and District Music Club

4 concerts October - March, varies spectrum to cover most tastes. Venue is St Penninghame Primary School, piano available. Concerts Saturday, Sunday and sometimes Friday.

High Baltersan, Newton Stewart, Wigtonshire DG8 6BN
Tel: 01671 402543 Fax: 01671 402543
Contact: M C Dunlop (Treasurer) or J B Hunter (Chairman)

Oban Music Society

4 acoustic classical concerts between autumn and spring. If a piano is required, the venue is St John's Cathedral, Oban. If no piano required, venue is Christ Church, Esplanade, Oban.

25 Albany Apartments, Albany Street, Oban, Argyll PA34 4AL
Tel: 01631 564468 Fax: 01631 564463 (W)
Contact: Sarah MacDonald (Hon Secretary)

Perth Chamber Music Society

5 - 6 concerts between September and March. Usually Tuesday or Thursday but can be flexible. Perth Art Gallery, George Street is the regular venue. Grand piano. Acoustic chamber music from any period but mostly classical, i.e. 18th and 19th c.

35 St Mary's Drive, Perth PH2 7BY
Tel: 01738 621379
Contact: Ruth Harris (Secretary) or Marjory Watson (President) Tel: 01738 625069

St Andrews Music Club

5 or 6 concerts between October and April in the Town Hall, Queens Gardens, St Andrews. Grand piano. Acoustic chamber concerts by artists of national and/or international repute.

36 Kilrymont Road, St Andrews KY16 8DE
Tel: 01334 477458
Contact: Heather Chisholm (Secretary) or Dr J A Ashcroft (Treasurer) Tel: 01334 473733

Stonehaven Music Club

6 chamber concerts in St Leonard's Hotel, Bath Stret, Stonehaven between October and March. Piano available, no specific concert day. Various kinds of classical/light classical concerts, which are democratically chosen by the members.

Rutlands, 13 Arduthie Road, Stonehaven, Kincardineshire AB3 2EH
Tel: 01569 762712
Contact: Archie Watt (Chairman/ Secretary) or Edwin Keith (Treasurer) Tel: 01569 762698

Strathearn Music Society

6 classical concerts on Wednesdays in the Crieff Hydro Hotel between October and April.

Langside, 28 Ochil View Gardens, Crieff PH7 3EW
Tel: 01764 652792
Contact: Frances Farr (Secretary) or James Gray (Treasurer) Tel: 01764 670302

West Kilbride Music Club

6 acoustic, mainstream classical, Friday concerts in the West Kilbride Community Centre, Corse Street, West Kilbride, between October and April.

12 Orchard Street, West Kilbride, Ayrshire KA23 9AF
Tel: 01294 8123093
Contact: Elizabeth Fry (Secretary) or David Hutchison (Chairman) Tel: 01294 823321

West Linton Music Society

6 acoustic Saturday concerts between October and April in the Graham Institute, West Linton. Upright piano.

7 Lyne Park, West Linton, Peeblesshire EH46 7HP
Tel: 01968 660026
Contact: Mrs H Hastings (Secretary)

PROMOTERS

Airdrie Arts Guild
About 6 concerts between September and April in The Theatre, Arts Centre, Airdrie. Piano available (upright). Light classical music which has a wide appeal.
Airdrie Arts Centre, Anderson Street, Airdrie ML6 0AA
Tel: 01236 755436
Contact: Mrs M Paterson

An Lanntair
About 12 concerts throughout the year. An Lanntair is the venue. No piano. Acoustic and amplified music. Gaelic, traditional, folk, classical, jazz, blues, cajun, world.
South Beach, Isle of Lewis HS1 2BX
Tel: 01851 703307
Contact: Meg Mitchell (Programme Officer) or Annie Maynard (Manager) Tel: 01851 703307

An Tuireann Arts Centre
Concerts take place Thursday, Friday, Saturday. Only promote local groups pop to classical music. Take HI Arts Touring companies which are pre-funded by HI Arts and Arts Council. Venue is An Tuireann Arts Centre. Baby grand piano available.
An Tuireann Arts Centre, Struan Road, Portree, Isle of Skye IV51 9BS
Tel: 01478 613306 Fax: 01478 613176
Contact: Susan Nicolson (Administrator) or Kate Tetley (Management Team)

Arisaig Arts Society
4 - 5 concerts year round in the Village Hall. Scottish, traditional/Gaelic music but may expand into classical and jazz. Small audiences.
Achnaskia, Arisaig, Inverness-shire PH39 4NS
Tel: 01687 45060 Fax: 01687 45060
Contact: Mike Kingwood (Chairman) or Mary Stewart (Treasurer) Tel: 01687 450300

Ayr Arts Guild
6 orchestral concerts between September and April and a further chamber concert in June. Concerts take place in the Town Hall and Holy Trinity Church, Fullarton Street, Ayr. Grand piano.
28F River Street, Ayr, Ayrshire KA8 0AX
Tel: 01292 281960
Contact: Pamela Royle (Promotions Secretary) or Michael Hitchow (Treasurer) Tel: 01292 520331 (W)

Ballachulish Community Arts Society
12 - 20 concerts throughout the year in Ballachulish Village Hall. Upright piano. Mainly traditional music; also a fair amount of blues. Would like to encourage more classical performers.
38 West Laroch, Ballachulish, Argyll PA39 4JS
Tel: 01397 700574 (day) / 01855 811383 (eve) Fax: 01397 700574
Contact: Robert Gardiner (Secretary) or Brian Dickie (Chairperson) Tel: 01855 811419

Balnain House
20 concerts throughout the year in Balnain House. Upright piano available. Traditional, highland, Scottish contemporary music. Acoustic concerts.
40 Huntly Street, Inverness IV3 5HR
Tel: 01463 715757 Fax: 01463 713611
Contact: Caroline Hewat (Asst Manager)

Banffshire Arts Guild
4 acoustic classical concerts between October and February, plus 1 concert from the Aberdeen International Youth Festival. Various venues. At Keith there is a grand piano, other venues have an upright.
Cowhythe, Portsoy, Banff AB45 2TB
Tel: 01261 842802
Contact: Sheena Young (Secretary) or Doris Gibson (Chairperson) Tel: 01261 842355

Bearsden and Milngavie Arts Guild
4 events between October and March. Grand and upright piano available. Usually Friday or Saturday. Various types of music.
Kilmardinny House, Kilmardinny Avenue, Bearsden, Glasgow G61 3MN
Tel: 0141 943 0312
Contact: Pamela McJannet (Organising Secretary) or Thelma Struthers (Organising Secretary) Tel: 0141 943 0312

Beith Arts Club
6 concerts between September and March (not December) on Sunday afternoons. They take place in Beith Community Centre, Kings Road, Beith, which has an upright piano. Mainstream classical music. Also some jazz.
12 Wilson Street, Beith KA15 2BG
Tel: 01505 502663
Contact: Margaret Turner (Booking Secretary) or Gordon Isbister (President)

Bute Arts Society
4 classical chamber concerts between October and March/April. The venue is Rothesay Academy where a grand piano is available. Concert day is Friday.
Montford House, Rothesay, Isle of Bute PA20 9ES
Tel: 0700 503157 (day) / 503752 (eve)
Contact: Ian Munro (Secretary)

Caithness Arts Association
Promotes about 18 concerts annually. Various types of music, various venues.
Council Offices, Market Square, Wick, Caithness KW1 4AB
Tel: 01955 603761 x247
Fax: 01955 602481
Contact: Fiona Smith (Secretary) Tel: 01955 602891 (H) or Hamish Holmes (Depute Director Leisure Services) Tel: x241

Caithness District Council
Promotes 2 or 3 concerts annually, usually groups or individual performers who are on a Highland tour. Various types of music. Regular venues are Wick Assembly Rooms and Thurso Town Hall, both of which have a piano.
Council Offices, Market Square, Wick, Caithness KW1 4AB
Tel: 01955 603761 Fax: 01955 602481
Contact: Fiona Smith (Tour Co-ordinator) or Hamish Holmes (Depute Director Leisure Services)

The Carnegie Hall
6 - 10 concerts throughout the year in the Carnegie Hall, Clashmore, Dornoch. Variety of concerts. No piano at present.
Briarhill, Spinningdale, Ardgay, Sutherland IV24 3AD
Tel: 01862 881253 Fax: 01862 881253
Contact: Jennifer Cameron (Chairperson)

The Ceilidh Place
50 concerts mainly during summer months May to September. The Ceilidh Place is the venue and an upright piano is available. Mainly traditional folk music. Some jazz and classical also. Acoustic music.
The Ceilidh Place, 14 West Argyll Street, Ullapool, Ross-shire IV 26 2TV
Tel: 01854 612103 Fax: 01854 612103
Contact: Julia Campbell (Arts Administrator) or Jean Urquhart (General Manager) Tel: 01854 612103

The Council for Music in Hospitals
1,600 concerts throughout the year in hospitals and homes for the elderly. Electric piano is available. All kinds of music. Would be performers have to apply to the Council for an audition which usually takes place once a year, in spring.
10 Forth Street, Edinburgh EH1 3JX
Tel: 0131 556 5848
Contact: Nella Kerr (Scottish Director)

Cultural Connections
Promotes traditional music and provides advice. Enquiries welcome from individuals and organisations at home and abroad.
15 Portland Terrace, Troon KA10 6AJ
Tel: 01292 313205
Contact: David Dewar

Culzean Arts Guild
7 - 8 concerts April to September on Wednesdays in Culzean Castle, Maybole, Ayrshire. Grand piano. Acoustic concerts. Classical through Romantic. Occasional forays into early 20th c.
25 Happy Hills, West Kilbride, Ayrshire KA23 9EP
Tel: 01294 822 317
Contact: David Armstrong (Hon Secretary)

DEALAN Arts Administration
Coordinates all touring arts coming into Skye and Lochalsh and runs an anti-clash diary. A first point of call for advice and information.
Ostaig House, Teangue, Isle of Skye IV44 8RQ
Tel: 01471 844207 Fax: 01471 844411
Contact: Duncan MacInnes (Director) or Fiona Maclean (Secretary)

Dualchas
6 acoustic concerts between June and August on Tuesday evenings: 5 at Tigh-na-Sgire, Park Road, Portree and 1 in Plockton. Promoters of Gaelic music and song. The Council have produced 2 tapes of Gaelic music which are particularly based on local music. These tapes are also combined on a CD.
Museums Service, Skye and Lochalsh District Council, Portree, Isle of Skye IV51 9EP
Tel: 01478 612341 Fax: 01478 612543
Contact: Roger Miket (Museum Officer)

Dumfries and Galloway Arts Association
Variable number of concerts between February and May, and September and November. Various venues. Will consider all music forms on their own merit in relation to programme guidelines each season.
28 Edinburgh Road, Dumfries DG1 1JQ
Tel: 01387 260445 / 6
Contact: Jenny Wilson (Director) or Susie Roper-Caldbeck (Programme Asst)

Dunblane Cathedral Arts Guild
3 - 4 adult and 3 children's concerts between October and December, and March and June. Venue is usually Dunblane Cathedral or the Cathedral Hall. Chamber classical concerts on Saturday evenings. If a suitable artist/programme is touring, then a children's (primary age) concert can be given on the Sunday afternoon. Piano available.
Applegarth, Glen Road, Dunblane FK15 0DT
Tel: 01786 825448
Contact: Ruth Bamforth (Chairperson)

Dundee University Lunchtime Concerts
26 concerts during the academic year, Fridays in the Chaplaincy Centre. Mainly amateur performers but occasionally a professional or semi-professional artist is asked to perform. Classical/light classical/jazz music. Hall seats 120.
University of Dundee, Park Place, Dundee DD1 4HW
Tel: 01382 344407 Fax: 01382 202830
Contact: Dr John Brush (Organiser) or John Cassels (Asst Organiser) Tel: 01382 344 173

Dunfermline Arts Guild
6 acoustic classical/light classical concerts which take place in the Carnegie Music Institute Annexe, Dunfermline on Sunday evenings between October and March. Grand piano available.
13 Park Place, Dunfermline KY12 7QL
Tel: 01383 722368
Contact: Fay Mann (Secretary)

ECAT
Charitable organisation promoting performance and composition of new music. Now in its 16th season and has been responsible for commissioning over 40 works. Headed by 3 composers, Geoffrey King, James MacMillan and Peter Nelson. Initiates a wide variety of events in Scotland and abroad.
16 Clerwood Gardens, Edinburgh EH12 8PT
Tel: 0131 539 887 Fax: 0131 539 2211
Contact: Hazel Sheppard (Administrator)

Etive Promotions
Freelance tour management / guitar tech / backline. Extensive live music experience working with Marquee Promotions, Mean Fiddler Organisation, MCP and DF Concerts. Tour managed for Capercaillie and Pearlfishers (from Troon to Tokyo).
49 Derby Street, Kelvingrove, Glasgow G3 7TU
Tel: 0141 337 2666 / 357 0361 Fax: 0141 357 1577
Contact: Ali Murdoch

Feis Eige
6 concerts between Easter and August including the first weekend in July. Ceilidh music and traditional Scottish music. Concerts take place in the Isle of Eigg Hall, which will be replaced in 2 years' time. May offers week-long workshops as a holiday package.
Cuagach, Isle of Eigg PH42 4RL
Tel: 01687 482410
Contact: Camille Dressler (Secretary) or David Robertson (Chairman)

Forfar Arts Guild
6 concerts September to March (not December), Thursdays in the Angus Music Centre, Montrose Road, Forfar. Grand piano. Acoustic concerts of a varied nature. Prefer not too much contemporary.
8 East Hillbank, Kirriemuir DD8 4HQ
Tel: 01575 572324 Fax: 01575 575158
Contact: Anne Smith (Secretary) or Jane Lendrum (Vice President)
Tel: 01575 573619

Fraserburgh Arts Group
Established 1981 to provide a platform for local talents and encourage professional touring groups to visit. Organises an annual arts festival.
37 Grattan Place, Fraserburgh AB34 5SD
Tel: 01346 23802
Contact: Chris Reid (Secretary) or Margaret Adams (Chairman)
Tel: 01346 510891

CLUBS & PROMOTERS

Gadie Music

Year round meetings (except January and February) on the first Tuesday of every month. Occasionally there are Thursday or Friday meetings. Venue is the Station Hotel, 1-3 Commercial Road, Insch. Amplified music. Venue seats 450. Music is traditional/contemporary/reggae.
Fernlea, South Road, Insch,
Aberdeenshire AB52 6XM
Tel: 01464 820725
Contact: Ian MacDonald (Bookings Secretary)

Galashiels Arts Association

5 - 6 concerts in the Volunteer Hall, Galashiels between September and April. Grand piano available, acoustic performances of classical chamber music (small ensembles and solo players). We also like to include some contemporary music and encourage Scottish artists and composers.
Craiglatch, Nr Clovenfords, Galashiels,
Selkirkshire TD1 1TR
Tel: 01896 850324
Contact: Stanley Ross-Smith (Hon Secretary) or Barbara Wright (Chairperson) Tel: 01896 755509

Glenalmond Concert Society

6 acoustic concerts in the Music Hall of Glenalmond College on Wednesdays between September and March. The majority of the audience is college pupils, therefore programmes are required to be entertaining as well as educational. The occasional contemporary piece goes down well but standard repertoire is preferred. Grand piano.
Glenalmond College, Perth PH1 3RY
Tel: 01738 880340 / 880265
Fax: 01738 880 410
Contact: Nicholas Smith (Administrator)

Glenuig Community Association

2 concerts per month throughout the year in Glenuig Hall. No piano. Acoustic and amplified but not to too high a degree. Traditional/folk, blues, classical, jazz, Gaelic.
Glenuig Hall, Glenuig, By Lochailort,
Inverness-shire PH38 4NG
Tel: 01687 470214
Fax: 01687 470275 / 470289
Contact: Val Hunter (Secretary) or Billy McKail (Vice-Chairman) Tel: 01687 470250

Gordonstoun Concerts Society

10 classical concerts in the South Room of the school between September and May. Grand piano. Early to contemporary music with positive discrimination towards contemporary.
Gordonstoun School, Elgin, Morayshire
IV30 2RF
Tel: 01343 830264 Fax: 01343 830074
Contact: Kenneth Beus (Secretary)

Greenock Arts Guild Ltd

5 to 10 concerts throughout the year. Upright and grand piano available. Acoustic and amplified concerts.
Arts Guild Theatre, Campbell Street,
Greenock PA16 8AP
Tel: 01475 723038
Contact: Liz Muir (Administrator)

Hamilton District Arts Guild

4 acoustic light classical concerts between October and February on Wednesdays. Usually invite Scottish performers. Inferior upright piano. Concerts take place in Hamilton District Museum, 129 Muir Street, Hamilton.
6 Woodhead Gardens, Bothwell, Glasgow
G71 8AS
Tel: 01698 853362
Contact: Ann Watt (Secretary/Concert Convener)

Invergordon Arts Society

8 or 9 acoustic concerts between September and March. Held in Invergordon Academy where there is a grand piano. Concerts are mainly classical but there are occasional folk and jazz evenings.
Cliff Cottage, Hilton of Cadboll, Ross-shire IV20 1XP
Tel: 01862 871247
Contact: Jimmy Maxwell (Secretary)

Inverness Arts Forum

6 concerts, no particular time. Inverness Arts Forum and Inverness District Council convened a joint promotions programme in 1995. Various types of music.
4 Bruce Gardens, Inverness IV3 5EN
Tel: 01463 233902
Contact: E F Davis (Hon Treasurer) or Adrian Clark (Arts Officer)
Tel: 01463 724261

Islay Arts Association

About 5 concerts year round but not October or February. 2 - 3 classical, 1 jazz, 1 folk. No piano, venue varies.
Tigh Beag, Crown Street, Portnahaven,
Islay PA47 7SW
Tel: 01496 86216
Contact: Stuart Todd (Secretary)

Kilmardinny Music Circle

6 concerts plus 1 children's concert, October to March inclusive, on Fridays in Kilmardinny House, Kilmardinny Avenue, Bearsden. Grand piano. Acoustic concerts, all types of classical chamber groups considered. Keen to promote young artists, eg high calibre music students, at a performance held after AGM in May.
8 Drumgoyne Drive, Bearsden, Glasgow
G61 3AD
Tel: 0141 942 8332
Contact: Margaret Mehta (Concert Secretary) or John Summers (Advertising and Publicity)
Tel: 0141 942 1929

Lamp of Lothian Collegiate Trust

6 summer concerts between April and September. Prefer Wednesdays. Venues: St Mary's Parish Church or Holy Trinity Church or Toun House, Haddington. Two Steinways available B or D. Classical concerts ranging from solo performers to chamber orchestra.
The Mault House, Poldrate, Haddington,
East Lothian EH41 4DA
Tel: 01620 823738 Fax: 01620 823738
Contact: Mrs D Holme (Administrator)

Leisure Promotions

All year round concerts, various venues. Most styles of traditional and contemporary folk music and some jazz. No classical. Amplified music. Promotes 4 - 10 day tours throughout Scotland.
44 Mamore Terrace, Inverness IV3 6PF
Tel: 01463 710151 Fax: 01463 222234
Contact: Steve Bain (Owner/Manager)

Lighthouse Arts Production

8 - 12 concerts spread throughout the year, no specific concert day but prefer Friday or Saturday night. Grand piano in Universal Hall, Forres. Different types of music. Not much classical. Acoustic and amplified.
Universal Hall, Findhorn Foundation,
The Park, Forres IV36 0TZ
Tel: 01309 691170 Fax: 01309 691301
Contact: Margo Van Greta (Artistic Director) or Dave Till (Manager)

CLUBS &
PROMOTERS

255

Linlithgow Arts Guild

9 - 10 Saturday concerts in the Town Hall. Music ranges from large scale choral and orchestral concerts to solo artists. Piano is hired when necessary.
26 Highfield Crescent, Linlithgow, West Lothian EH49 7BG
Tel: 01506 842507
Contact: John MacDonald (Hon Secretary) or Robert Lennox (Treasurer) Tel: 01506 842630

Live Music Now

Young artists who have passed an audition perform in a variety of venues: prisons and young offenders' institutions, hospices, hospitals and homes for the elderly, adult training centres, and for children with special needs. Electric piano available. All year round. Mainly Western classical music but world music, jazz etc as well.
14 Lennox Street, Edinburgh EH4 1QA
Tel: 0131 332 6356 Fax: 0131 332 6356
Contact: Carol Main (Director) or The Hon Mrs Fairbairn

Living Tradition Concerts

Working mainly in South West area co-ordinating and presenting a range of concerts related to traditional music. Also give advice and support for people such as local authorities who want to include traditional music events in their normal programming.
The Living Tradition, PO Box 1026, Kilmarnock KA2 0LG
Tel: 01292 678277 Fax: 01563 544855

Lochan (Lochalsh Arts Network)

8 - 10 concerts in various village halls throughout the year. No piano. Acoustic music of all types is appreciated but traditional pulls the biggest audience.
Ravenscraig, Plockton, Ross-shire IV52 8UB
Tel: 01599 544265 Fax: 01599 544414
Contact: Ruth Fisken (Member) or Fiona Begg (Member) Tel: 01599 534 388

Lochinver Arts

15 - 20 year round musical evenings (includes ceilidhs) in the Village Hall, Lochinver. Mainly Scottish music, some classical, some jazz. Piano available.
10 Inverkirkaig, Lochinver, Sutherland IV27 4LR
Tel: 01571 844254
Contact: Wilma McKay (Organiser) or Irene Callas (Asst Organiser) Tel: 01571 844400

Loretto School

3 - 4 concerts, September, January and May, taking place in the school, usually on a Saturday evening. Grand piano. Music - usually larger ensembles, classical or Scottish music. Occasional chamber groups or soloists. Sometimes performers can contribute work with examination candidates on their composition coursework.
Loretto, Musselburgh, Midlothian EH21 7RE
Tel: 0131 6656829 Fax: 0131 6532773
Contact: Tim Goulter (Director of Music)

Lyth Arts Centre

Closed in winter. 10 concerts between April and September. Promote world music, new music, jazz and fusion. No classical or rock. Also promote modern Scottish folk music during July and August. We sometimes set up tours to other Scottish venues.
Lyth, Wick, Caithness KW1 4UP
Tel: 01955 641270
Contact: William Wilson (Director)

Maryburgh Amenities Association

2 or 3 concerts during the year. No piano. No musical preferences. Concerts take place in the Maryburgh Amenities Centre.
Rowanville, Proby Street, Maryburgh, Ross-shire IV7 8DU
Tel: 01349 861853
Contact: Len MacLachlan (President)

Mid-Argyll Arts Association

Around 6 Saturday concerts in Ardrishaig Hall, Chalmers Street, Ardrishaig between October and March. Upright piano available - not recommended for piano solo. Various kinds of acoustic music.
5 Glenfyne Park, Ardrishaig, Argyll PA30 8HQ
Tel: 01546 603088
Contact: Margaret Thomson (Secretary) or Baxter Nisbet (Chairman) Tel: 01546 605203

Monymusk Arts Trust

6 - 10 concerts between October and March on Sunday afternoons at Monymusk Arts Trust. Grand piano and organ available. Small venue, so maximum number of performers is 12-15. Acoustic performances of classical chamber music.
14 The Village, Monymusk, Inverurie AB51 7HJ
Tel: 01467 651466 Fax: 01467 651250
Contact: Lady Barbara Grant (Chairperson) or John Hearne (Concert Manager) Tel: 01651 882274 (tel/fax)

Moray Arts Club

6 to 8 concerts, throughout the year, which take place in Elgin Town Hall in North Street. Grand piano. Various types of music to cover all tastes.
Landlash, Nr Elgin, Moray IV30 3TW
Tel: 01343 547835
Contact: Grace Aitchison (Hon Secretary) or Mrs A McEwan (Chairman) Tel: 01343 542703

Moving Arts

Variable number of concerts March to November. No piano. Most kinds of music including early, Scottish/Irish traditional music, new wave, old blues, world music and classical. Good quality jazz also. Big audiences by Highland standards.
Cononbrae, Cononbridge, Ross-shire IV7 8AG
Tel: 01349 863726
Contact: Lizzie MacDougall (Projects Co-ordinator)

Music in Glasgow University

30 concerts during term time, 1.15 pm start, 40 minutes duration. Two grand pianos. Lunchtime concerts take place in the University Concert Hall. 40% of programme is contemporary. Scottish based artists and composers are encouraged. Also two concerts in the Bute Hall and two University Choir concerts in the University Chapel each year.
Music Department, Glasgow University, University Avenue, Glasgow G12 8QH
Tel: 0141 330 4092 Fax: 0141 307 8019
Contact: Judy Kilpatrick (Administrator)

Music in Peebles

7 Tuesday concerts between September and March in the Old Parish Church Centre, Peebles. Grand piano available. Classical chamber music.

36 Dean Park, Peebles EH45 8DD
Tel: 01721 721 830
Contact: I S Currie (Hon Secretary) or Elizabeth Luke (President) Tel: 01721 720418

Nairn Performing Arts Guild

8 - 9 acoustic concerts between end September and end March. Grand piano. Intimate setting. Ideal for chamber music. Clifton House, Nairn, is the venue.

Clifton House, Viewfield Street IV12 4HW
Tel: 01667 453119 Fax: 01667 452836
Contact: Gordon McIntyre (Convener) or Dr Joan Noble (Secretary) Tel: 01667 453119

NEAT (North East of Scotland Touring Arts)

Some concerts are organised in conjunction with Moray Arts. 4 to 6 of the concerts are more classical, including 1 jazz. 8 - 10 concerts of traditional music. One day Fiddlers Rally in spring. Venue is Elgin Town Hall where there are 2 Steinway pianos.

Moray District Council, Leisure and Libraries Dept, High Street, Elgin, Moray IV30
Tel: 01343 545121 Fax: 0131 557 6579
Contact: Eric McGillivray (Administrator)

New Town Concerts Society

5 Monday concerts in Queen's Hall, Edinburgh. Grand and upright pianos available. Acoustic classical chamber concerts.

Queen's Hall, Clerk Street, Edinburgh EH8 9JG
Tel: 0131 668 3456
Contact: Simon Crookall (General Manager)

Orkney Arts Society

4 concerts between September and April. Classical (early to contemporary) and occasional jazz. Venue alternates between Stromness and Kirkwall, one of which has a Steinway C and the other a smaller Steinway piano.

Bringagareth, Innertown, Stromness, Orkney KW16 3JP
Tel: 01856 850003
Contact: Fiona Cumming (Chairman)

Plockton High School (Good Night Out Network)

Only 4 promoted concerts spread throughout the year. Upright piano available. Opera is popular as is folk music. The school is mainly host to outside companies.

Plockton High School, Plockton, Ross-shire IV52 8TU
Tel: 01599 544235
Contact: Mrs G Coe (Office Clerk) or Mrs F Douglas (Admin Assistant)

Prestwick Arts Guild

4 Friday concerts between November and March in Prestwick Community Centre. All tastes are taken into account when programming and a mix of classical/light classical/folk and jazz is provided. A responsive audience is willing to listen to contemporary music as long as it is approachable.

57 Orangefield Drive, Prestwick KA9 1HF
Tel: 01292 478934
Contact: Betty McPhie (Hon Secretary) or Margaret Moultrie (President) Tel: 01292 470186

Reid Concerts

20 Tuesday lunchtime concerts mainly in the Reid Concert Hall where there is a brand-new Steinway. There are occasional organ recitals. Musically, a balance is struck between mainstream and contemporary classical. Artists are mainly Scottish.

Dept of Music, Edinburgh University, Alison House, 12 Nicholson Square, Edinburgh EH8 9DF
Tel: 0131 650 1000 Fax: 0131 650 2425
Contact: Fiona Donaldson (Administrator)

SEALL Community Arts

Several community venues in south Skye are used for about 30 concerts year round. Various types of music.

Ostaig House, Teangue, Isle of Skye IV44 8RQ
Tel: 01471 844207
Contact: Duncan McInnes (Administrator) or Brian Show (Committee) Tel: 01471 844342

Shetland Arts Trust

5 - 6 concerts between September and March (not January) in Lerwick Town Hall. Upright piano. Various types of music.

Pitt Lane, Lerwick, Shetland ZE1 0DW
Tel: 01595 694001 Fax: 01595 692941
Contact: Winnie Armitage (Asst Arts Officer)

Shetland Folk Festival Society

Folk. Founded 1981 with the aim to promote international folk music on the Shetland Isles as well as to support Shetland's own traditional music. Organises The Shetland Folk Festival and enables a wide and varied selection of folk bands to visit Shetland throughout the year.

5 Burns Lane, Lerwick, Shetland ZE1 0EJ
Tel: 01595 694757 Fax: 01595 695381

Shieldaig Village Association

4 traditional concerts between May and September. Can't guarantee large audience.

Hillside, Shieldaig, Strathcarron, Wester Ross IV54 8XN
Tel: 01520 755239
Contact: Vivienne MacLennan (Committee member) or Mrs E Cameron (Treasurer) Tel: 01520 755295

Skerray Community Arts

There are 10 concerts year round. Any night except Sunday. Music varies from folk to classical. Concerts are held in Skerray Community Hall, capacity 100.

91 Lamigo, Skerray, Sutherland KW14 7TJ
Tel: 01641 521212
Contact: Gavin Lockhart (Vice-chairman Hall Committee)

Skye Arts Guild

5 to 6 concerts between October and April in either Broadford or Portree in various venues. No piano. Chamber, choral, jazz etc.

Glenn Alainn, Treaslane, By Portree, Isle of Skye IV51 9NX
Tel: 01470 532392
Contact: Peter Wright (Secretary)

Slam Events

Club promoters including live dance bands. Clubs include The Arches and the Renfrew Ferry.

62 Kelvinside Street, Glasgow G3 7SA
Tel: 0141 353 2552 Fax: 0141 353 0017
Contact: Pedro

Stranraer Music Association

5 classical concerts beween October and March in the Ryan Centre, Stranraer.

Culgroat, Stoneykirk, Stranraer DG9 9DZ
Tel: 01776 830215
Contact: Wendy MacMaster (Secretary) or John Harkness (Treasurer) Tel: 01776 702717

CLUBS & PROMOTERS

257

Strathaven Arts Guild

6 - 8 professional concerts, mainly on Saturdays, in the Town Mill Theatre, Strathaven. Grand piano available. Various kinds of music.

Laigh Kilmeny, Strathaven, Lanarkshire ML10 6RZ
Tel: 01357 300392 (H) / 22327 (W) Fax: 01357 22327
Contact: Yvonne Howat (Secretary/ Treasurer) or G McAllan (Chairman) Tel: 01357 40339

Summer Music in Balquhidder

10 Sunday concerts in Balquhidder Church, last Sunday in June to last Sunday in August at 7pm. Piano available. Concerts always acoustic. Good platform for young Scottish based musicians and singers at the start of their career. Opera, chamber music, small orchestras, recitals.

Balquhidder Manse, Lochearnhead, Perthshire FK19 8N8
Tel: 01877 384235
Contact: Rev J W Benson (Chairman) or Nisbet Cunningham (Treasurer) Tel: 01764 685249

Tain Gala Association

2 or 3 concerts in the Duthac Centre, Shandwick Street, Tain. Upright piano. Folk/Irish/country music.

Cuileann, Arthurville Gardens, Tain, Ross-shire IV19 1PU
Tel: 01862 892886 Fax: 01862 894411
Contact: Mrs C Finlayson (Secretary) or S Mackay (Treasurer) Tel: 01862 894411

The Queen's Hall

Grand and upright pianos in this venue which promotes about 200 concerts around the year. A further 100 concerts are booked in by performers and organisations themselves (see also Queen's Hall under venues). All kinds of music acoustic and amplified, chamber, orchestral, folk, jazz, etc.

The Queen's Hall, Clerk Street, Edinburgh EH8 9JG
Tel: 0131 668 3456 Fax: 0131 668 2656
Contact: Paul Gudgin (General Manager) or Beth Cavanagh (Hall Manager)

Thurso Live Music Association

8 acoustic classical concerts in Thurso High School between September and March. Grand piano. Preferably not Fridays or Saturdays.

Skinandi, Braal, Halkirk, Caithness KW12 6XE
Tel: 01847 831437
Contact: Barbara Myatt (Secretary) or Mrs M Smedly (Treasurer) Tel: 01847 892013

Thurso Players

5 - 10 concerts in the Mill Theatre, Millbank Road, Thurso, between January and October. Clavinova piano available. Jazz/folk concerts preferred.

Sithean, Duncanshill, Thurso, Caithness KW1 8YN
Tel: 01847 892019
Contact: Betty Bradstreet (Programme Manager)

University Music (Aberdeen)

20 Tuesday lunchtime concerts and 18 full length concerts, some of which take place in the evening and some on Sunday afternoons. Piano available. The choral concerts take place in St Machers or St Andrew's Cathedral. Most other concerts take place in the Mitchell or Elphinstone Halls.

Department of Music, Powis Gate, College Bounds, Old Aberdeen AB9 2UG
Tel: 01224 272571 Fax: 01224 272515
Contact: Recitals Secretary

University of Strathclyde Music Society

20+ Tuesday lunchtime concerts, October to December and February to May, in Hutchesons' Hall, Ingram Street, Glasgow. Grand piano. Acoustic concerts. Classical (medieval to contemporary).

University of Strathclyde, Livingstone Tower, Richmond Street, Glasgow G1 1XH
Tel: 0141 552 4400 x3444 Fax: 0141 552 4053
Contact: Alan Taverner (Director of Music)

Upper Deeside Music

8-10 acoustic concerts between April and October. Sunday pm is the concert day in Ballater, Braemar and Crathie Churches (Church of Scotland). Acoustic classical concerts with the accent on Scottish composers from 16th c. onwards.

34 Craigendarroch Walk, Ballater, Aberdeenshire AB35 5ZB
Tel: 013397 56040 Fax: 013397 55960
Contact: James Dunster (Hon Secretary)

Urras an Eilean

2 concerts in October. Skye and Lochalsh Fiddlers always take part in one of these and the Oban and Lorne Strathspey and Reel Society. There are also singers and pipers.

Urrasaneil, Eilean Iarmain, Isle of Skye IV43 8QR
Tel: 01471 833266 Fax: 01471 833260
Contact: Kathleen Morrison (Secretary)

West Coast Arts

6 concerts. Various types of music. Midweek preferred. No piano. Village Hall, Poolewe is the venue.

Strondubh, Poolewe, Wester Ross IV22 2LB
Tel: 01445 781252
Contact: Sally Murray (Chairperson)

Westbourne Music

Westbourne Music promotes concerts on fortnightly lunchtimes throughout the year at the Merchants' House, 7 West George Street, Glasgow. Seats 200. Excellent piano. All kinds of chamber music (string quartets, vocal) to jazz, covering all periods.

2 Falkland Avenue, Newton Mearns, Glasgow G77 5DR
Tel: 0141 639 3176 Fax: 0141 639 3176
Contact: Sheila Osborne (Administrator) or Robert Logan (Chairman) Tel: 0141 339 2820

CLUBS & PROMOTERS

258

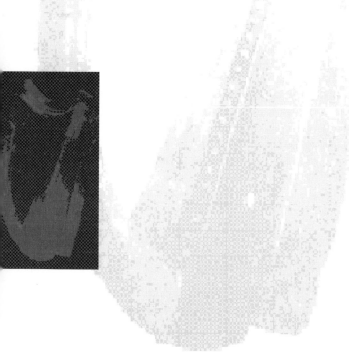

FESTIVALS AND COMPETITIONS

Editorial Notes

The chapter is divided into two main categories: FESTIVALS, which are performance oriented, and COMPETITIVE FESTIVALS AND COMPETITIONS.

FESTIVALS are arranged by month, so if you're looking for somewhere to go in July for example then it's easy to find. If you are looking for a particular festival and do not know when it is then check the index for the page reference. There are also 'Summer', 'Autumn/Winter' and 'Various' headings after the standard twelve months as some festivals are not always held at the same time every year.

It should be noted that FEISEAN have been placed either in the Education chapter or the chapter on Young People's Music as they are mainly tuition based festivals for young people. See the entry for FEISEAN NAN GAIDHEAL for more information.

COMPETITIVE FESTIVALS AND COMPETITIONS have been listed together under alphabetical order, as it was decided that people looking for information would be more interested in a particular event rather than an event on at a particular time. Most of the competitive festivals are affiliated to THE BRITISH FEDERATION OF FESTIVALS FOR MUSIC, DANCE AND SPEECH, who may be contacted at:

> Festivals House
> 198 Park Lane
> Macclesfield
> Cheshire SK11 6UD
> Tel: 01625 428297
> Fax: 01625 503229

Some of the COMPETITIONS are based outwith Scotland but have been included in the *Handbook* as musicians living in Scotland are eligible to enter them.

Piping competitions have not been listed in this edition of the *Handbook*. Dates and venues for Pipe Band competitions can be obtained from the ROYAL SCOTTISH PIPE BAND ASSOCIATION, who may be contacted at:

> 45 Washington Street
> Glasgow G3 8AZ
> Tel: 0141 221 5414
> Fax: 0141 221 1561

FESTIVALS

JANUARY

Celtic Connections

One of the world's largest folk gatherings featuring a wide variety of artists from all the Celtic nations. Extensive concert line-up announced in September, complimented by art exhibitions, displays, ceilidhs, workshops, sessions, talks and daily radio broadcasts. Free brochures available.
Glasgow Royal Concert Hall, 2 Sauchiehall Street, Glasgow G2 3NY
Tel: 0141 332 6633 Fax: 0141 333 9123
Contact: Colin Hynd (Festival Administrator)

FEBRUARY

Aberdeen Jazz Festival

10 days of performances covering all forms of jazz in both concert halls and clubs. Also jazz films, community projects, club nights, Salsa dances, educational opportunities for all ages and exhibitions.
Assembly Direct, 89 Giles Street, Edinburgh EH6 6BZ
Tel: 0131 553 4000 Fax: 0131 554 0454
Contact: Roger Spence or Fiona Alexander

MARCH

Central Region Music Festival

Held annually and after years of emphasis on competition is now weighted toward non-competitive participation. Performances involve groups ranging from string quartets to 60-strong primary school choirs. Competitive element retained in a competition for Young Musician of Central Region.
18 Polmont Park, Polmont, Falkirk FK2 0XT
Tel: 01324 713746
Contact: Christine Tait

Gatehouse of Fleet

A family festival of traditional music, arts and crafts in an amphitheatre-like setting sheltered by Galloway Forest Park. Plenty of music sessions and singalongs. Song contest. Wide variety of accommodation at affordable prices. Children catered for with their own events. Superb two-day crafts fair.
4 Carney's Corner, Gatehouse of Fleet, Castle Douglas, Kirkcudbrightshire DG7 2HW
Tel: 01557 814030 Fax: 01557 814030
Contact: George McCulloch (Secretary/PRO) or Roger Hampshire (Chairman)
Tel: 01557 814799

Milnathort Folk Festival

Mainly a folk music weekend. Afternoon sessions, children's concerts, the Orwell World Gird Championship, concerts, ceilidhs and informal sessions.
8 Rannoch Place, Kinross, Tayside KY13 7BQ
Tel: 01577 864164
Contact: Brenda Warwick (Secretary)

APRIL

Artsfeast

General arts festival. Biennial (next one 1997). Main events are 2 large outdoor concerts - one featuring the Scottish Chamber Orchestra and one featuring Carol Kidd. Wide range of music with performances in a variety of venues such as the park, the swimming pool and the shopping mall.
Eastwood District Council, Eastwood Park, Rouken Glen Road, Giffnock G46 6UG
Tel: 0141 638 6511 Fax: 0141 620 0884
Contact: R J Hawkins (Depute Chief Executive)

Easterhouse Folk Doo

Launched 1995. A week of performances, workshops and competitions held in a variety of venues.
Easterhouse Arts Project, 32 Aberdalgie Road, Glasgow G34 9HT
Tel: 0141 771 9368
Contact: Jim Cathcart or Paul McKinlay

Edinburgh Fling

Runs into May. Multi-media community festival with music tending to focus on rock, folk and ceilidh. Most performances take place in council venues including the 4 community halls in Edinburgh District.
219 High Street, Edinburgh EH1 1PE
Tel: 0131 529 4247
Contact: Lynne Halfpenny (Principal Officer (Arts))

Edinburgh Harp Festival

There are concerts, ceilidhs, workshops, classes and a harp makers' exhibition.
Clairsair, 14 Bells Mains, Gorebridge, Midlothian EH23 4QD
Tel: 01875 820532
Contact: John Campbell (Administrator)

Edinburgh International Folk Festival

Established in 1979, covers everything from ceilidhs and ballads to crossovers with jazz and rock. There is also a piping festival.
PO Box 528, Edinburgh EH10 4DU
Tel: 0131 556 3181 Fax: 0131 556 4177
Contact: Jack Evans (Director)

Glenfarg Folk Feast

Weekend event with sessions throughout and 2 singarounds. Friday ceilidh. Saturday charity singing competition and main concert . Sunday children's concert. The World Puff-a-Box Championship. Final fling in the evening.
15 Glenlochay Road, Perth PH2 0AX
Tel: 01738 626167 Fax: 01738 626167
Contact: Athole Fleming (Secretary)

Mull Traditional Music Festival

Always last weekend in April. Full 'islanders' weekend' - Wednesday to Tuesday! Informal competitions, dancing, ceilidhs, concerts, piping competition, pub sessions.
Mishnish Hotel, Tobermory, Mull PA75 6NU
Tel: 01688 302009 Fax: 01688 302462
Contact: Robert McLeod (Chairman)

Rootin' Aboot

Celebration of folk, roots and traditional music. Week long variety of events with local, national and international performers and workshops.
The Lemon Tree, 5 West North Street, Aberdeen AB2 3AT
Tel: 01224 642230 Fax: 01224 630888
Contact: Luisa Stucchi

Shetland Folk Festival

Run by Folk Festival Society founded in 1981 to promote international folk music and support Shetland's traditional music.
5 Burns Lane, Lerwick ZE1 0EJ
Tel: 01595 694757 Fax: 01595 695381
Contact: John Jamieson (Secretary)
Tel: 01595 692624 (W) or Jane Moncreiff (Publicity)

MAY

The Arts Is Magic

Developed in Glasgow in 1989. Dedicated to developing and promoting the arts and education. To this end it promotes an annual free festival which is representative of all the arts and focuses on integrating people with and without special needs. Reaches an audience of over 6,000 and provides a platform for everyone in the community to perform, exhibit and participate.
St Andrews College, Duntocher Road, Bearsden, Glasgow G61 4QA
Tel: 0141 943 1489 Fax: 0141 943 0106
Contact: Sheila McCubbin (Co-ordinator) or Lawrence Riccio (Director)

Ballachulish Music Festival

A weekend festival of folk and blues as well as a general mixture of other music. The festival is run by members of the Ballachulish Community Arts Society.
13 Croft Road, Ballachulish PA39 4JW
Tel: 01855 811419 Fax: 01855 811704
Contact: Brian Dickie (Organiser)

Banchory Festival of Traditional Music

Always the second Saturday of May. A competitive festival of traditional music mainly for the fiddle with some piano and accordion. Run by the Banchory Strathspey and Reel Society. Evening concert followed by a ceilidh.
19 Dalvenie Road, Banchory AB31 3UX
Tel: 01330 822705
Contact: Duncan Menzies

BT Scottish Ensemble Annual Island Festival

As a prelude to the summer season, on a different island every year with the Ensemble and guests playing contemporary classical, jazz and folk music. Also workshops in schools, informal sessions and special performances aimed at new audiences.
2 Anchor Lane, Glasgow G1 2HW
Tel: 0141 221 2222 Fax: 0141 221 4444
Contact: Jane Greig

Buchan Heritage Festival

Traditional music concerts, pub sessions and competitions centred around the Buchan village of Strichen.
28 School Place, New Pitsligo, Fraserburgh AB43 4NJ
Tel: 01771 653761
Contact: Evelyn Mundie

Caol and Lochaber Music Festival

A weekend festival featuring a mix of traditional music including Cajun and Celtic rock. Ceilidhs and sessions.
22 Maryburgh Court, Fort William PH33 6QP
Tel: 01397 702974 Fax: 01397 700695
Contact: Benny MacDonald

Clackmannan District Mayfest

Since 1987 a series of district festivals of mainly music (including opera, C and W, blues, jazz, musicals, dance shows), and including writers, workshops, dance tuition, visual arts exhibitions, beerfests, etc. Other festivals in October and December.
29 Primrose Street, Alloa FK10 1JJ
Tel: 01259 213131 Fax: 01259 721313
Contact: Rosa McPherson (Senior Recreation Officer (Arts and Entertainment))

Double K Country Music Festival

In its 9th year. Concerts and dances.
82 Pleasance Avenue, Dumfries DG2 7JX
Contact: Jim Kerr Tel: 01387 267451.

Dumfries and Galloway Arts Festival

Ten days of music, theatre, dance, film, literature and exhibitions. 1995 had a Franco/Scottish music programme from Purcell to Poulenc and including Ravel, Faure, Saint-Saens and Celtic music. Also folk, jazz and Viennese salon music culminating with Berlioz' *Symphonie Fantastique* featuring the BBC Scottish Symphony Orchestra under Alexander Titov.
Gracefield Arts Centre, 28 Edinburgh Road, Dumfries DG1 1JQ
Tel: 01387 260447 Fax: 01387 260447
Contact: Sheena Widdall (Administrative Assistant) or Jennifer Taylor (Secretary)

The Girvan Traditional Folk Festival

The festival features traditional music and song from all over Britain in formal and informal, amateur and professional concerts. There are also ceilidhs, workshops, competitions and childrens' events.
PO Box 1026, Kilmarnock KA2 0LG
Tel: 01563 544855
Contact: Peter Heywood (Director)

The Highland Festival

The festival celebrates and promotes an awareness of the range and the quality of the work of the artists and craftspeople of the Highlands. In addition the festival hopes to introduce the work of national and international artists and companies to the area.
Balnain House, 40 Huntly Street, Inverness IV3 5HR
Tel: 01463 719000 Fax: 01463 716177
Contact: Eona Craig (Administrator) or Ian Ritchie (Director)

Highland Harp Festival

Established in 1994. Weekend of concerts, workshops and sessions with some of the most experienced performers. Exhibition of harps also.
Balnain House, 40 Huntly Street, Inverness IV3 5HR
Tel: 01463 715757 Fax: 01463 713611
Contact: Caroline Hewat (Asst Manager)

Isle of Bute Jazz Festival

Essentially a traditional jazz festival although it also presents a wide variety of international jazz styles. Offers particular encouragement to younger musicians. 1996 will be the 9th annual event. The host band is Phil Mason's New Orleans All-Stars and the booking office opens on 1 January.
Shalunt, Isle of Bute PA20 0QI
Tel: 01700 841283 Fax: 01700 505313
Contact: Phil Mason (Director)

Kind of Blue Festival

Held on Fridays in May. Forward-looking, fresh new sounds that take music beyond the popular notion of modern jazz. Professional, international, national and local artists performances.
Assembly Direct, 89 Giles Street, Edinburgh EH6 6BZ
Tel: 0131 553 4000 Fax: 0131 554 0454
Contact: Roger Spence or Fiona Alexander

Mayfest

Large multi-media festival held in various venues throughout Glasgow with a strong community element as well as international performers. Wide range of music.
18 Albion Street, Glasgow G11 1LH
Tel: 0141 552 8000
Contact: William Kelly (General Manager)

Monklands Festival

Takes place from the end of May into June. Involves Airdrie and Coatbridge in a varied programme including model yacht racing, fair days and Highland games with dance and pipe band competitions. Plus primary schools events in speech and drama, music festival and theatrical productions by children, youth and adult groups.
Monklands District Council, 101 Bank Street, Coatbridge ML5 1ET
Tel: 01236 441200 Fax: 01236 428191
Contact: J O'Hara (Secretary) or Nicky Botting (Administrator)

Orkney Festival of Country and Irish Music

1996 has the 3rd annual festival, which is organised by Orkney Country Club. Features a variety of artists.
Morvin, Finstown, Orkney KW17 2ET
Tel: 01856 761204 Fax: 01856 761422
Contact: Colin Kirkness

Orkney Traditional Folk Festival

Held the last full weekend in May taking in the English bank holiday Monday. Events at this festival are based in Stromness although performances do branch out to the smaller islands. It features many concerts, pub sessions, ceilidhs, workshops, competitions and a fiddlers' rally.
Dept F1, PO Box 4, Stromness, Orkney KW16 3BJ
Tel: 01856 851331
Contact: John Mowat (Festival Director)
Tel: 01856 850773

Perth Festival of the Arts

Runs into June. A blend of visual and performing arts, this festival is professional apart from concerts given by school orchestras. The music leans towards classical although there is a good deal of light music plus theatre and dance.
35 Kincarrathie Crescent, Perth PH2 7HH
Tel: 01738 621672
Contact: Hector Calder (Publicity Officer)

Silver Spur Festival

One-day biennial event run by the Silver Spur Country and Western Club. First one in Paisley 1993, then Johnstone 1995 featuring 7 UK bands including Rambling Fever, The Rye Brothers and TJ McCall. Proceeds went to charity.
9 Carolside Drive, Glasgow G15 7RA
Tel: 0141 944 5289
Contact: Anne MacPhie

JUNE

Arran Folk Festival

Annual on second week of June. Music at pub sessions and village halls as well as major tent event on the final weekend.
Maol-Don, Brodick, Isle of Arran KA27 8HZ
Tel: 01770 302311
Contact: Nigel Walker or Sue Archer
Tel: 01770 700366

Ayrshire Arts Festival

A mostly professional festival featuring Scottish artists and concentrating on music. One claim to fame is that it helped an emerging Ayrshire composer James Macmillan.
Festival Office, Gaiety Theatre, Carrick Street, Ayr KA7 1NU
Tel: 01292 264630 Fax: 01292 288383
Contact: Alan Davies (Director) or Gordon Taylor (Festival Director)

Bonnetguild Festival

Gala festival mainly for children but has escalated to cater for adults. Held over 8 days. Variety of music including folk night, fiddle concert, brass band concert.
22 Arran View, Stewarton KA3 5EX
Tel: 01560 482082
Contact: Ian Hamilton (Secretary) or Eric Brown (President) Tel: 01560 482979

Craigmillar Community Festival

The festival aims to involve the community in a wide range of the arts and local amateurs are assisted by professionals. Music tends to vary but previous years have featured jazz and rock concerts.
63 Niddrie Mains Terrace, Edinburgh EH16 4NX
Tel: 0131 661 5877
Contact: Jack O'Donnell (Organising Secretary)

Cunninghame Festival

This is a district-wide event with the aim of bringing all sectors of the community together through arts based activities. One of the major events
Cunninghame District Council, Cunninghame House, Irvine KA12 8EE
Tel: 01294 274166 Fax: 01294 311058
Contact: Kim Jamieson (Community Arts Officer)

Dundee Blues Bonanza

Set up 1995 to encourage the city's blues circuit featuring several forms of blues - Chicago, Delta, Hillbilly etc. Gigs from noon to midnight. Club set up to encourage more pubs to feature live music.
Dundee Tourist Board, 4 City Square, Dundee DD1 3BA
Tel: 01382 434282 Fax: 01382 434665
Contact: Chris Campbell (Asst Tourism Development Officer)

Dundee Jazz Festival

Week long festival featuring a wide range of jazz forms, performed by professional national and international artists.
Assembly Direct, 89 Giles Street, Edinburgh EH6 6BZ
Tel: 0131 553 4000 Fax: 0131 554 0454
Contact: Roger Spence or Joanna Reid (Dundee Rep Theatre) Tel: 01382 223530

Dundee Summer Festival

A festival featuring all aspects of the arts. Music, both indoor and outdoor, is a major part of the festival involving all age groups.
c/o Dundee District Council, Leisure and Recreation Department, Earl Grey Place, Dundee DD1 4DF
Tel: 01382 434287 Fax: 01382 434601
Contact: Susan Gillan (Leisure Activities Officer) or Alex Stuart (Leisure and Recreation Manager)

Dunkeld and Birnam Arts Festival

The festival includes classical, folk and jazz concerts by professionals and amateurs as well as art exhibitions, talks and a craft fair.
Carrick Mhor, Dunkeld, Perthshire PH8 0ES
Tel: 01738 625134 Fax: 01738 620701
Contact: Walter Barbour (Secretary)

Festival of Original Music

Held on National Music Day, Saturday to Sunday, noon to midnight. Around 30 bands play new music in a variety of styles from rock to jazz, reggae and rave. Money raised goes to charity.
Brunton Theatre, Ladywell Way, Musslelburgh EH21 6AA
Tel: 0131 665 2240
Contact: Jake Scott

Fleadh

A one-day outdoor event with a celtic influence held on Glasgow Green.
Festival Office, 3a Parkway, London NW1 7PG
Tel: 0171 916 6060
Contact: Melvin Benn

Fraserburgh Arts Festival

Established 1990. Began with a week, now events cover a month. Features classical, traditional and jazz music as well as the visual arts. Free concerts for senior citizens. 1995 featured the Edinburgh Quartet, Crooked Jack and his Giant Jeely Piece Show, the Granite City Jazz Band and Scottish Ballet.
37 Grattan Place, Fraserburgh AB43 5SD
Tel: 01346 513802
Contact: Chris Reid (Secretary) or Margaret Adams (Chairman)
Tel: 01346 510891

Glasgow International Folk Festival

Large international festival with wide variety of amateur and professional performances and sessions.
Blackfriars Court, 23 Blackfriars Street, Glasgow G1 1BL
Tel: 0141 552 8605 Fax: 0141 552 8605
Contact: Charles Harrigan (Festival Director) or Robert Noakes (Chairman)

Glasgow International Jazz Festival

Runs into July with around 150 concerts. Varied jazz styles with emphasis on contemporary and modern. Has a history of promoting international names as well as emerging artists.
18 Albion Street, Glasgow G1 1LH
Tel: 0141 552 3552 Fax: 0141 552 3592
Contact: Derek Gorman (Director) or Jill Rodger (Administrator)

Highland Traditional Music Festival

A concert-based festival which takes place in Dingwall featuring sessions and some workshops. Tends to concentrate on Scottish traditional music but also includes other folk music from the Highlands. Established in 1981. Local young musicians are encouraged.
Rudha Alainn, Upper Knockbain Road, Dingwall IV15 9NR
Tel: 01349 863270
Contact: Sandra Gibson

Keith Traditional Music Festival

One of the largest TMSA festivals with concerts, competitions and sessions in every nook and cranny of the town.
Whitelees, Nether Dallochy, Speybay, Fochabers IV32 7PL
Tel: 01343 820074
Contact: Jim Smart

Kelvingrove Music Festival

A free one-day festival held at Kelvingrove Park Bandstand which provides a platform for new Scottish bands performing original material. Highlights are broadcast on Clyde Radio. The venue is scheduled for redevelopment but the future of the festival is assured.
Clyde One FM, Clydebank Business Park, Clydebank, Glasgow G81 2RX
Tel: 0141 306 2200 Fax: 0141 306 2265
Contact: John MacCalman

Killin Traditional Music and Dance Festival

Three-day event with Scots/Irish traditional music. Pub sessions. Children's shows. Heavy dancing element. A few competitions. Boat trips on Loch Tay.
126 Renfrew Road, Paisley PA3 4BL
Tel: 0141 887 9991
Contact: Danny Kyle or John Mallinson Tel: 01567 82070

Leith Jazz Festival

Third week of June, concentrates on traditional jazz although some modern can be heard in the bars and restaurants around the shore area of Leith. Also outside bandstand and marching bands
Kirkbrae House, Dean Bridge, Edinburgh EH3 7UA
Tel: 0131 225 9460
Contact: Alan Thomson (Chairman)

Livingston and District Festival

The festival committee acts as an umbrella group for various organisations. There is a wide range of music which can include rock, classical, opera, blues and traditional.
26 Dawson Avenue, Howden, Livingston EH54 6AL
Tel: 01506 431702
Contact: Raymond Birrell (Secretary)

Mendelssohn on Mull

Runs into July. Main feature series of concerts and recitals by students and professionals. Music ranging from Beethoven to Bartok. Lectures and workshops. During the festival a violin is made and awarded for a one year to the most deserving student.
D M Vaughan and Co., 10 Gloucester Place, Edinburgh EH3 6EF
Tel: 0131 225 8282 Fax: 0131 225 6889
Contact: Marilyn Jeffcoat (Administrator)

Muness Rock Festival

Launched in 1991. Held around midsummer, same weekend as Glastonbury, in a tented village near Muness Castle. Modest beginning with one Shetland band increased to three in 1995. 400 attendance - 7pm to 3am. Camping sites available.
Hamar, Baltasound, Unst, Shetland ZE2 9DS
Tel: 01957 711695 Fax: 01957 711676
Contact: Gordon Thomson
Tel: 01957 711316

Newcastleton Traditional Music Festival

Runs into July. Features large number of amateur competitions for original composition, singing, fiddle, whistle, pipes and accordion.
Green Knoll, Roans Green, Bailey, Newcastleton, Roxburghshire TD9 0TW
Tel: 016977 48033
Contact: Carole Sanderson (Secretary)

Paisley Festival

Funded by Renfrew District Council. Started in 1983. Features indoor and outdoor events by amateur and professional performers. Incorporates Sma' Shot Day - an historic celebration of Paisley weavers.
Paisley Museum and Art Gallery, High Street, Paisley PA1 2BA
Tel: 0141 889 3151 x222
Fax: 0141 889 9240
Contact: Claire Findlay (Co-ordinator)

St Magnus Festival

This festival features choral and instrumental concerts in the classical, jazz and folk fields, mostly performed by professionals. Launched in 1977, it has drama and visual arts as well as music.
Strandal, Nicholson Street, Kirkwall, Orkney KW15 1BD
Tel: 01856 872669 Fax: 01856 872204
Contact: Dorothy Rushbrook (Administrator)

Strathfest

Music, art and drama. Workshops and other events. Around 6 professional concerts/ceilidhs. Other events in spring and autumn. Mix of amateur and professional, international musicians, workshops, barbecue. Wide range of music, blues, rock, traditional, innovative. Different theme every year, 1995 was 'Change'.
Heughhead, Strathdon, Aberdeenshire AB36 8XJ
Tel: 019756 51329
Contact: J Aylet (Administrator) or Helen Denerley (Artistic Director)

JULY

Aberdeen Arts Carnival

A festival with a variety of creative arts. Runs into August. There are 20-30 events, half of which are musical including folk, jazz, blues, and rock, both professional and amateur, mostly local.
Aberdeen Arts Centre, 33 King Street, Aberdeen AB2 3AA
Tel: 01224 635208 Fax: 01224 626390
Contact: Annie Inglis (Artistic Director) or Arthur Deans (Administrator)

Arran Fleadh

Run by the Arran Celtic Music Association during the second weekend in July. High profile celebration of Scottish music which has featured artists such as The Rankine Family, Barbara Dickson, Savourna Stevenson, Mairi MacInnes and Archie Fisher.
The Jewellery Studio, Brodick, Isle of Arran KA27 8AJ
Tel: 01770 302680
Contact: Ailsa MacNicol (Secretary)

Balnain House Summer Festival of Music

Sessions and concerts of traditional music held in Balnain House. Festival runs into August and September. Midweek sessions are held in a licensed café. Many peformances are outwith, but promoted by, Balnain House.
Balnain House, 40 Huntly Street, Inverness IV3 5HR
Tel: 01463 715757 Fax: 01463 713611
Contact: Caroline Hewat

Crail Festival Society

Programme caters for wide range of tastes and ages. Events have included classical concerts, folk music, an evening of Latvian music and dance, the local children's orchestra, rock bands, fiddlers' rally, ceilidh dance and more.
1 Tolbooth Wynd, Crail KY10 3UA
Tel: 01333 450909
Contact: Jill Saunderson (Events Organiser)

Dundee Folk Festival

A well-established festival featuring professional performers in the Dundee Rep Theatre. There are also workshops and free concerts at lunchtime and before and after each event.
27 Strathearn Road, Broughty Ferry, Dundee DD5 1PP
Tel: 01382 775031
Contact: Stewart Brown (Director)

Dundee Guitar Festival

The festival features a series of concerts and workshops focusing mainly on classical music.
29 Baldovan Terrace, Dundee DD4 6NQ
Tel: 01382 461306
Contact: Selina Madeley

Dunvegan Castle Arts Festival

A major part of the festival is devoted to classical chamber music although traditional music has been featured. 1995 was the 15th annual festival.
Dunvegan Castle, Dunvegan, Isle of Skye IV55 8WF
Tel: 01470 521206 Fax: 01470 521205
Contact: John MacLeod of MacLeod

Glasgow Fair Festival

Takes place on Glasgow Green. Wide ranging entertainment including folk, jazz and popular music.
64 Tollcross Road, Glasgow G31 4XA
Tel: 0141 774 0259 Fax: 0141 554 0323
Contact: Angela Hogg (Co-ordinator) or Wendy Niblock

Highland Country Music Jamboree

Takes place at The Court Mundole near Forres and has recently featured well-known country music names such as The John C King Family Band, Dez Walters Band, The Haleys Band and Jimmy Frizzell.
56 Kilmuir Road, Inverness IV3 6EP
Tel: 01463 221268
Contact: Ann Carmody (President/ Organiser)

FESTIVALS & COMPETITIONS

267

Inverness Tattoo

Military tattoo with dancing, displays and bands over 6 nights on the Northern Meeting ground.
18 Annfield Road, Inverness IV2 3HY
Tel: 01463 235571
Contact: Major R G Wood

Isle of Bute International Folk Festival

Held 3rd week of July. Wide range of Scottish music plus large input from Ireland. Features the Blues Palace and a heavy dance element. Sea trips on the Waverley. Hosts the World Ceilidh Band Championships. 1996 is the festival's 5th anniversary year.
17 Roslin Crescent, Rothesay, Isle of Bute PA20 9HT
Tel: 01700 505721
Contact: Ann Bonnacorsi or Danny Kyle Tel: 0141 887 9991

Music in Blair Atholl

Concerts take place in converted farm steading. Strathgarry Concert Hall is four miles from Pitlochry and 35 north of Perth. 1996 concerts featuring nine international musicians, four evenings of chamber music, piano, string quartet, soprano, tenor, flute and guitar.
The Steading, Lude, Blair Atholl, Perthshire PH18 5TR
Tel: 01796 481230 Fax: 01796 481237
Contact: Lavinia Gordon (Administrator) or Henrietta Phewes (Secretary) Tel: 01796 481216

North Fife Family Festival

One-day festival with ceilidh previous night. Variety of music, mostly folk, all happens in village hall. Mix of professional, amateur, local, national and international performers. 1995 featured Peruvian folk group and Scottish harper Alison Kinnaird.
Roadside Cottage, West Flisk, Nr Newburgh KY14 6HW
Tel: 01337 870319
Contact: Douglas Dawson

Pennan Arts Week

Annual festival which began as a modest art exhibition but now attracts the likes of the Calgary Fiddlers, a French marching band and many folk music artists. The 'Local Hero' village hosts a week of singing, busking and dancing - and the red telephone box is still there.
Pennan Arts, 23 Pennan, Pennan, by Fraserburgh AB43 4JB
Tel: 01346 561201 Fax: 01346 561437
Contact: Norrie Grierson

Skye and Lochalsh Festival/ Feis an Eilean

Classical, traditional, folk music, dance, Gaelic poetry and story-telling. The festival has featured the BT Scottish Ensemble, Ballet West, and Middle Ground Theatre and the Celtic based Feis - Alasdair Fraser, Buddy McMaster and Kevin Burke on fiddle plus traditional dance with Harvey Beaton and Maggie Moore. Workshops in spoken and sung Gaelic.
Ostaig House, Teangue, Isle of Skye IV44 8RQ
Tel: 01471 844207 Fax: 01471 844411
Contact: Duncan MacInnes

Stonehaven Folk Festival

A weekend festival based around a series of concerts in the town hall and sessions in hotels and bars. There is a ceilidh, workshops and children's concert. Hosts the Arthur Argo Memorial Concert - a celebration of traditional singing from throughout the UK.
Newbigging, Mill of Forest Road, Stonehaven AB3 2GB
Tel: 01569 765063
Contact: Charlie West (Publicity) or Pat Cruse (Booking Officer) Tel: 01569 763519

Summer Music at Ayton Castle

Combines a daytime summer school with evening concerts. Annual event launched 1995.
Music Makers, 17 North Gardener Street, Glasgow G11 5BU
Tel: 0141 339 2708 Fax: 0141 339 2708

Tarlair Music Festival

Held in the natural amphitheatre at Tarlair open-air swimming pool. Developed from a small event into 10,000 capacity. Has featured Runrig, Wet Wet Wet, Jethro Tull, Fish. Cross section of rock, Celtic, blues and dance music. Held annually but 1995 cancelled when sponsor pulled out at last minute.
Rhythm and Rock Limited, 51 St Catherine Street, Banff AB45 1JT
Tel: 01261 812552 Fax: 01261 812549
Contact: John Sutherland

AUGUST

Aberdeen International Youth Festival

This festival includes leading youth orchestras, choirs and other ensembles including dance and theatre groups.
3 Nutborn House, Clifton Road, London SW19 4QT
Tel: 0181 946 2995 Fax: 0181 944 6507
Contact: Nicola Wallis (Director) or Aberdeen Box Office Tel: 01224 641122

Auchtermuchty Festival

A festival covering traditional and folk music held in venues throughout the village. First weekend for the local community, the second for visiting artists. Friday to Sunday pub sessions. Saturday night barn dance and ceilidhs. Sunday afternoon open-air dancing in square.
Auchtermuchty Community Centre, 1 Distillery Street, Auchtermuchty KY14 7BY
Tel: 01337 828907
Contact: Nick Pragnell (Chairman) or Lois Lothian Tel: 01337 827098

Blairgowrie Live

The festival caters for contemporary as well as traditional music both amateur and professional, featuring concerts, workshops, dances, children's events and informal pub sessions.
Brooklyn Mill, Riverside, Blairgowrie PH10 6TB
Tel: 01250 873090
Contact: Catharine Jones

Caithness Country Music Festival

New festival in 1995. Held on one Sunday and planned to run annually.
Waterfront Night Club, Wick KW1 4JW
Tel: 01955 602550 Fax: 01955 605907
Contact: John Sutherland Tel: 01955 605472

Dundee Water Festival

Celebrating Dundee's maritime past, featuring traditional and folk music including sea shanties and ballads. Has had marching bands and Chinese dragon music. Workshops.
Dundee Tourist Board, 4 City Square, Dundee DD1 3BA
Tel: 01382 434282 Fax: 01382 434665
Contact: Toni McPherson (Tourism Development Officer)

Edinburgh Festival Fringe Society

Worldwide reputation for three weeks of theatre, comedy, music and dance. Thousands of performers from around 35 countries.

180 High Street, Edinburgh EH1 1QS
Tel: 0131 226 5257 / 5259
Contact: Hilary Strong (Administrator)

Edinburgh International Festival

One of the world's largest arts festivals, founded in 1947. Three weeks of music, theatre and dance performed by some of the world's leading artists. Runs on to September. The music encompasses recitals, chamber and symphonic concerts, operas, and late night cabaret. From world premières to the classical repertory.

21 Market Street, Edinburgh EH1 1BW
Tel: 0131 226 4001 Fax: 0131 225 1173
Contact: Brian McMaster (Artistic Director) or James Waters (Associate Director)

Edinburgh International Jazz and Blues Festival

One of Britain's oldest jazz festivals. Many jazz forms stretching into blues and soul. Free jazz trail around eight pubs. Two free events - Mardi Gras attracts 10,000 and Jazz on a Summer's Day attracts 20,000. Concerts in Festival Theatre, Queen's Hall, St Giles Cathedral and Cotton Club.

116 Canongate, Edinburgh EH8 8DD
Tel: 0131 557 1642 Fax: 0131 556 0012
Contact: Mike Hart (Director)

Edinburgh Military Tattoo

Annual outdoor event with music, dance and drama staged on the esplanade at Edinburgh Castle. Massed pipes and drums and a variety of military display teams, dancers and bands from all over the world. Attended by a large cosmopolitan audience and seen by over 50 million people worldwide.

22 Market Street, Edinburgh EH1 1QB
Tel: 0131 225 1188 Fax: 0131 225 8627
Contact: Alan Smith

Faultline Festival

Held over first 2 weeks of August. Set up to encourage new art forms to the Highlands. Multi-media including jazz, folk, theatre, comedy, rock and pop.

15 Telford Road, Inverness IV3 6HJ
Tel: 01463 243397
Contact: Rosalyn Marron

Festival of British Youth Orchestras

Runs into September. An international festival which has included symphony orchestras, early music groups, wind, pipe and jazz bands. Festival is open to members of the National Association of Youth Orchestras. While most of the concerts are in Edinburgh and Glasgow, some of the participants may tour elsewhere.

Ainslie House, 11 St Colme Street, Edinburgh EH3 6AG
Tel: 0131 225 4606 Fax: 0131 225 3568
Contact: Carol Main (Director) or Jenny Brockie (Administrator)

Glasgow International Early Music Festival

Fully professional festival established 1990, held in alternate years. Features internationally known performers alongside and in collaboration with Scottish artists in concerts, music-theatre and opera. Instrument-making exhibitions, fringe performances, workshops. Centrepiece is early opera production by SEMC who promote the festival.

Scottish Early Music Consort, 2 Port Dundas Place, Glasgow G2 3LD
Tel: 0141 333 1178 Fax: 0141 333 1179
Contact: Mary Carmichael (Administrator) or Warwick Edwards (Artistic Director)

Jazz Festival

Features mainstream jazz. 1995 had two top piano trios, Carol Kidd and international players. A week of concerts.

4 Marine Cottage, Nairn IV12 4EA
Tel: 01667 455262 Fax: 01667 453364
Contact: Ken Ramage

Kintyre Music Festival

Barochan House, Argyll Street, Campbeltown PA28 6AZ
Tel: 01586 551141
Contact: David O McEwan (Secretary)

Marymass Folk Festival

One of Scotland's longest running folk festivals. A 4-day community event featuring music, song and dance plus world championship events in Whammy Diddling and Chuckie Chucking. Run by Irvine Folk Club.

7 Machrie Place, Kilwinning KA13 6RW
Tel: 01294 551047
Contact: Joyce Hodge

Millport-Nashville Country and Western Festival

Run by Millport Promotions and Trading. Music in large marquees strategically placed around the town. Family orientated weekend. Paint and props used to create western atmosphere with a corral, a reservation and even a High Chaparral. Series of well-known bands perform.

31 Cardiff Street, Millport, Isle of Cumbrae KA28 0AS
Tel: 01475 530153 Fax: 01475 530625
Contact: Robert Reid

Paisley International Organ Festival

This festival has classical and folk concerts and workshops and there are various competitions the main feature of which is an international organ competition.

Paisley Abbey, Paisley PA1 1JG
Tel: 0141 889 7654 Fax: 0141 889 7654
Contact: Jeanette Fenyo (Administrator)

Peebles Arts Festival

Always 2 weeks starting last Saturday of the month, featuring music as well as a variety of the performing and visual arts. Folk, jazz, traditional Border music, annual organ recital, other music, choral, classical, varies annually.

Cabbage Hall, Tweed Green, Peebles EH45 8AP
Tel: 01721 720371
Contact: Peter Norris (Chairman) or Ian McFadyen (Publicity)
Tel: 01721 720566

Pittenweem Arts Festival

Traditional Scots music in variety of venues including Kellie Castle. 1995 featured Knee Deep in Claret with writer Billy Kay and singer Rod Paterson, Edinburgh Clarsach Society and Live Music Now!

The Gingerbread Horse, 9 High Street, Pittenweem KY10 2LA
Tel: 01333 311495
Contact: Paul Moodie or Bill Stevenson
Tel: 01333 312168

Round Midnight Jazz Festival

Covers many forms of jazz, soul and blues with a number of well-known artists featured every year. All concerts are held in the Queen's Hall during the last week of the Edinburgh Festival Fringe.

Assembly Direct, 89 Giles Street, Edinburgh EH6 6BZ
Tel: 0131 553 4000 Fax: 0131 554 0454
Contact: Roger Spence or Fiona Alexander

T in the Park

Saturday-Sunday rock event launched in 1994. Now features 60 bands from headliners to locals. Last year Paul Weller, The Prodigy, Massive Attack, M People, Kylie Minogue, Beautiful South. Tickets £25 per day or £45 for two days. Over 20,000 attend on each day from noon.

DF Concerts, 272a St Vincent Street, Glasgow G2 5RL
Tel: 0141 221 5279 Fax: 0141 248 5202
Contact: Geoff Ellis

Tearing Up The Tartan

Started in 1994. The theme is 'new Scottish music which is going places'. All events are in small venues to preserve intimacy and bands can be heard in concert or at ceilidhs. The music carries influences from many other cultures.

Lyth Arts Centre, Nr Wick, Caithness KW1 4UD
Tel: 01955 641270
Contact: William Wilson (Director)

SEPTEMBER

Beauly Music Festival

A young weekend festival covering cajun, blues, rock, country and western, and jazz in a marquee, hall and open air.

Flat No 2, Shore St, Beauly IV4 7BY
Tel: 01463 782309 Fax: 01463 782531
Contact: Blair Sinclair

Carrbridge Festival of Music

Festival concentrates on country and folk music with some blues and rock. Has been running since the mid-eighties but underwent some re-vamping in 1994.

Pine Ridge, Carrbridge, Inverness-shire PH23 3AA
Tel: 01479 841646
Contact: Patrick Blease (Co-ordinator) or James Ross (Chairman)
Tel: 01479 841242

Dunbar Traditional Music Festival

Sessions around town, instrumental music, traditional singing and original song competitions, winners' concert and evening ceilidh. Held over one weekend.

2 Beveridge Row, Belhaven, Dunbar, East Lothian EH42 1TP
Tel: 01368 863593 Fax: 01368 863593
Contact: Pauline Jaffray

Dunfermline District Arts Festival

Promoting and encouraging the best in local, national and international arts - drama, dance, music (in all its guises), visual arts, crafts, literature and events aimed specifically at young people. A blend of professional and community performances, residences, workshops and happenings.

Leisure Services Division, Music Institute, East Port, Dunfermline KY12 7JA
Tel: 01383 731885 Fax: 01383 622633
Contact: J T E McIsaac (Principal Officer, Arts Theatre and Entertainments) or Lesley O'Hare (Administrator)

Glasgow International Gala Season (GIGS)

A season featuring some of the world's finest orchestras, conductors, soloists and recital performances. The season will be available on subscription from autumn. Past seasons have included concerts from the St Petersburg and Berlin Philharmonic Orchestras and recitals by Montserrat Caballé, Jessye Norman and Cecilia Bartoli.

Glasgow Royal Concert Hall, 2 Sauchiehall Street, Glasgow G2 3NY
Tel: 0141 332 6633 Fax: 0141 333 9123
Contact: Colin Hynd

Glasgow Mela

Biggest Asian festival in Scotland with music and dance from India, Pakistan, Bangladesh, China, Sri Lanka, Indonesia, Singapore and Switzerland. Exhibition stalls, street performances and different types of food from various nations.

101 Centre Street, Glasgow G5 8BU
Tel: 0141 429 6024 Fax: 0141 420 1049
Contact: A S Sandhu (Chairman)

Highland Fiddle Festival

Weekend of ceilidhs, concerts, sessions, workshops, and slow jams led by experienced fiddlers. Mainly targetting Scottish fiddling but with a hint of Cape Breton because of the strong links.

Balnain House, 40 Huntly Street, Inverness IV3 5HR
Tel: 01463 715757 Fax: 01463 713611
Contact: Caroline Hewat (Asst Manager)

Isle of Bute Country Festival

Launched 1995. Wide cross section of trans-American country, cajun and bluegrass music. Professional international bands. Line dancing. Children's events.

126 Renfrew Road, Paisley PA3 4BL
Tel: 0141 887 9991
Contact: Danny Kyle or Gerry Chambers
Tel: 01700 502612

Kirriemuir Festival

A festival of traditional music and song featuring local and national artists. Competitions. Programme available from July by sending A5 sae.

Rose Cottage, Cortachy, Kirriemuir, Angus DD8 4LX
Tel: 01575 540261
Contact: Patrick Newman (Chairman) or Mrs M Affleck (Secretary)
Tel: 01577 862979

Largs Viking Festival

Celebration of the Viking era with a wide range of entertainment and events. Music includes traditional Scottish, pipes, folk/rock and Scandinavian, Norwegian folk dancing and a Celtic ceilidh.

Cunninghame District Council, Cunninghame House, Irvine, Ayrshire KA12 8EE
Tel: 01294 274166 Fax: 01294 311058
Contact: Gary Hamilton (Events Officer) or Clare Watson Tel: 01475 689777

Melrose Music Festival

Featuring a mix of concerts, dances, children's and street events. Largely folk based with some world music. Competitions and fringe activities.

Eskdaill, Main Road, Newtown St Boswells TD6 0RY
Tel: 01835 823592
Contact: Hector Christie (Secretary)

Musica Nova

This festival has been a cornerstone of new music in Scotland for around 30 years. However, the last festival was held in 1990 and it is currently dormant pending future developments.
c/o Royal Scottish National Orchestra, 73 Claremont Street, Glasgow G3 7HA
Tel: 0141 226 3868 Fax: 0141 221 4317
Contact: Jacqueline Noltingk (Head of Planning)

Northlands Festival

Features ensembles from the north of Scotland and Scandinavia. While most of the music is classical and opera, there is some traditional and popular music and also film.
Scapa House, Castlegreen Road, Thurso, Caithness KW14 7LS
Tel: 01847 896802 Fax: 01847 896804
Contact: Allen Perrin (Festival Manager) or John Henderson

Sutherland Festival

This is an outdoor festival with Celtic, rock and folk music.
Crask Inn, by Lairg, Sutherland IV27 3AB
Tel: 01408 641353
Contact: Nick Hayhurst (Organiser)

Tarbert Music Festival

Scottish and Irish traditional folk music. Held over two days. Main concert in the hall with open air concert and barbecue on Sunday. Musicians on fishing trips. Steel band.
Mealdarroch House, Tarbert, Argyll PA29 6UG
Tel: 01880 820752
Contact: Shona Martin (Secretary) or Jane Elliott (Joint Secretary)
Tel: 01880 820560

OCTOBER

Aberdeen Alternative Festival

The festival embraces a wide mix of music and drama, visual arts, street entertainment and community projects. Although it has an international flavour, the festival encourages local semi-professional artists.
10 Belmont Street, Aberdeen AB1 1JE
Tel: 01224 635822 Fax: 01224 641931
Contact: Duncan Hendry (Director) or Box Office Tel: 01224 641122

Aviemore Music Festival

Week-long programme of afternoon and evening events. Official programme augmented by many fringe performances. 1995 - Alexander Brothers, Calum Kennedy, Jim McLeod, Revolver.
Highland Visitor Services, 28 Grampian View, Aviemore, Inverness-shire PH22 1TF
Tel: 01479 810754 Fax: 01479 810754
Contact: Peter Stienley

Borders Festival

Biennial, celebrating the cultural heritage of the Borders, includes music, dance, drama and the visual arts.
c/o Council Chambers, Albert Place, Galashiels TD1 3DL
Tel: 01896 754751 Fax: 01896 757003
Contact: Ian Yates (Administrator)

Clackmannan District Octoberfest

Since 1987 one of a series of district festivals of mainly music (including opera, C and W, blues, jazz, musicals, dance shows), and including writers, workshops, dance tuition, visual arts, exhibitions, beerfests, etc. Other festivals in May and December.
29 Primrose Street, Alloa FK10 1JJ
Tel: 01259 213131 Fax: 01259 721313
Contact: Rosa McPherson (Senior Recreation Officer (Arts and Entertainment))

Doric Festival

Focuses on the music traditionally associated with the north-east such as bothy ballads, fiddle music, mouth music and so on. The organisers are keen to promote anything with a north-east connection involving not only traditional but classical/contemporary music - the Scottish Opera For All and composer David Munro project *Song For Jamie* being an example of this.
Gordon District Council, Gordon House, Blackhall Road, Inverurie AB5 3WA
Tel: 01467 620981 Fax: 01467 624285
Contact: Jim McDonald (Director of Leisure and Recreation) or Sheila Bassett (Asst Leisure and Entertainment Officer)

Dunoon Jazz Festival

Held on mid October weekend. Over 60 performances involving more than 200 musicians in 16 venues. Artists have included Harry Beckett, Janusz Carmello, Art Farmer, Buddy de Franco, Spike Robinson, Martin Taylor and Jean Toussaint. Weekend rover tickets give access to all events.
69 Hunter Street, Kirn, Dunoon PA23 8JR
Tel: 01369 705202 Fax: 01369 705202
Contact: Russell Cowieson (Secretary)

Glasgay!

One of Europe's largest lesbian and gay arts festivals. Inaugural event 1993 attracted 23,000 to over 70 events. Second event in 1994 featured music at its heart with theatre, dance, film, visual and performance art, literature and special events. Runs over 10 days from the end of October into November.
PO Box 1590, Glasgow G12 9YZ
Tel: 0141 553 1511 Fax: 0141 553 2068
Contact: Ian McKay or Cordelia Ditton
Tel: 0141 339 5898

Motherwell Music Festival

The festival celebrates all types of music by presenting an enormous range of concerts and workshops for all ages and tastes. It takes place in Motherwell Concert Hall and Theatre, Bellshill Cultural Centre and community centres throughout the district.
Motherwell District Council, PO Box 14, Civic Centre, Motherwell ML1 1TW
Tel: 01698 266166 Fax: 01698 259224
Contact: Norman Turner (Director of Motherwell Leisure)

Penicuik Folk Festival

Weekend event with professional concerts, ceilidh, fiddle workshops and sessions. Traditional singing competition. Fairly broad definition of folk music. Tends to favour traditional side but touches on blues and contemporary.
36 Greenhill Park, Penicuik EH26 9EX
Tel: 01968 678153
Contact: Brian Miller or Alan Murray
Tel: 01968 678610

Rhythms of the North

Established in 1990, this festival is held in Eden Court Theatre at which the region's pupils are invited to perform items which they have prepared. The emphasis is on folk, rock and jazz as well as all aspects of the indigenous music of Scotland.
Curriculum Development Centre, Highland Regional Council, Central School, Kenneth Street, Inverness IV3 5DW
Tel: 01463 225449
Contact: H C Richardson (Adviser in Music) Tel: 01349 863441

Ten Day Weekend

Launched 1995 as follow up to Sound City. Organised by Glasgow District Council Department of Performing Arts to promote live music citywide from headliners but with more emphasis on local bands. There is also a strong educational component with workshops and other learning events.
92 Raeberry Street, Glasgow G20 6EG
Tel: 0141 945 5515 Fax: 0141 945 5585
Contact: John Williamson or Julie MacCaskill

NOVEMBER

Castlemilk Folk Festival

The festival is a pleasantly ambiguous three-day annual event which began in 1992. Concert tickets are £5 with £1 concessions. Past artists have included Loudon Wainwright III, Alan Price, John Martyn, Hue and Cry, Steve Harley, June Tabor, John Renbourn, Robin Williamson, Martin Stephenson and Carol Laula.
37 Dougrie Drive, Castlemilk, Glasgow G45 9AD
Tel: 0141 631 1166 Fax: 0141 634 1156
Contact: Rab Paterson

Ceilidh House Folk Festival

Week long event always taking in St Andrew's Day. Some major names in concert and sessions every day and night. Linked with a beer festival in 1995.
9 Hunter Square, Edinburgh EH1 1QW
Tel: 0131 220 1550
Contact: Allan Cameron or Cy Laurie

Women Makmerry Festival

This festival celebrates St Catherine's Day, the patron saint of lacemakers and virgins. Based in Govan, the festival's aim is to provide a platform for female talent.
111 Hill Street, Glasgow G3 6TY
Tel: 0141 332 8847
Contact: Fiona McGowran

DECEMBER

Clackmannan District Festival of Christmas

Since 1987 a series of district festivals of mainly music (including opera, C and W, blues, jazz, musicals, dance shows), and including writers, workshops, dance tuition, visual arts exhibitions, beerfests etc. Other festivals in May and October.
29 Primrose Street, Alloa FK10 1JJ
Tel: 01259 213131 Fax: 01259 721313
Contact: Rosa McPherson (Senior Recreation Officer (Arts and Entertainment))

SUMMER

Ancient Kingdom of Dalriada Festival

Festival dates depend on ferry arrangements. Contact Danny Kyle for details. Based on Scottish/Irish traditional music and dance and utilising the ferry to transport performers and audience between Campbeltown and Ballycastle.
126 Renfrew Road, Paisley PA3 4BL
Tel: 0141 887 9991
Contact: Danny Kyle (Festival Director) or Gerry Chambers Tel: 01700 502612

Pitlochry Festival

Although this festival is better known for its theatre events, it does include some classical, light and opera music from professionals who are invited to perform. It runs from April to October and the first festival was in 1951.
Pitlochry Festival Theatre, Port-na-Craig, Pitlochry, Perthshire PH16 5DR
Tel: 01796 473054 Fax: 01796 473054
Contact: Roy Wilson (General Manager)

Scottish Proms

A series of classical music concerts in Aberdeen, Dundee, Edinburgh and Glasgow during May and June. These concerts are aimed at family audiences as an introduction to classical music.
Royal Scottish National Orchestra, 73 Claremont Street, Glasgow G3 7HA
Tel: 0141 226 3868 Fax: 0141 221 4317
Contact: Graeme McKinnon (Marketing Manager)

AUTUMN/ WINTER

Borders Master Music Series

A season of concerts (usually 3) featuring mainly orchestral-based music. Venue is the Volunteer Hall, Galashiels.
Council Chambers, Albert Place, Galashiels TD1 3DL
Tel: 01896 754751 Fax: 01896 757003
Contact: Ian Yates (Administrator)

Nelson Hall Concerts

This series of 6 classical chamber music concerts (established in 1901) are given on a Tuesday in each month between October and March in the Nelson Hall, McDonald Road Library, Edinburgh (capacity 150). Previous performers have included the Edinburgh Quartet, John Wallace, David Nicholson and the Apollo Saxophone Quartet.
Music Library, Edinburgh City Libraries, George IV Bridge, Edinburgh EH1 1EG
Tel: 0131 225 5584 Fax: 0131 225 8783
Contact: Peter Baxter (Asst Music Librarian)

VARIOUS

The Burns International Festival

One-off 1996 celebration of the life and works of Robert Burns on the 200th anniversary of his death. Starts with birthday celebrations in January, continues from May to October and ends with a Hogmanay party and fireworks. Recitals, concerts, pub parties, events for schools. Festivals of women's arts, rock and pop and street theatre. Events happening all around Scotland.
24 Sandgate, Ayr KA7 1BY
Tel: 01292 288080 Fax: 01292 619622
Contact: John Struthers (Director)

Festival of Country and Western

Maravale, 51 Land Street, Keith
AB55 3AN
Tel: 01542 886182
Contact: Jenny Brown

International Festival of Music and Dance

Two-week, alternate year, event run by Highland Region's community education service. Week one - performances, workshops and ceilidhs with local groups in Lochaber, Skye and Lochalsh, Ross and Cromarty, Caithness and Sutherland. Week two - all groups in Inverness. Street performances a strong feature. Culminates in concerts at Eden Court Theatre.
Community Education, 3 High Street, Dingwall IV15 9HL
Tel: 01349 864962 Fax: 01349 863781
Contact: Jim Morrison

COMPETITIVE FESTIVALS & COMPETITIONS

Aberdeen and North East of Scotland Music Festival

Annual competitive festival of music, Scottish country dance, speech and drama. Held in two parts, dance in March and the remainder in June. Music classes are solo and ensemble in singing, keyboards, strings, woodwind, brass and recorder. Two bursary prizes among the awards - singing and piano.
16 Osborne Place, Aberdeen AB2 4DA
Tel: 01224 647792
Contact: Jean Henderson (Secretary)

Arbroath and District Musical Festival

24 Gallowden Avenue, Arbroath
DD11 3EX
Tel: 01241 874635
Contact: Mrs A Dear

Arran Music Festival

Various classes including singing, choirs, instrumental, bagpipes and verse speaking - individually and in groups both for children and adults. Scottish country dancing.
The Sheeans, Whiting Bay, Isle of Arran KA27 8QL
Tel: 01770 700203
Contact: Tony Smith (secretary)

Ayrshire Music Festival

Competitive festival with over 246 classes - over 180 in music for strings, woodwind, brass, piano, ensembles, bands, orchestras, singing. Also 36 speech and drama competitions and 27 competitions for Scottish country dancing.
Newton Centre, Green Street Lane, Ayr KA8 8BH
Tel: 01292 260325 Fax: 01292 611115
Contact: May Swan (Secretary) Tel: 01292 442836 or Andrew H Keachie (Principal Teacher of Instrumental Service)

Badenoch and Strathspey Music Festival

A competitive festival with a variety of classes.
Cornerways, Newtonmore Road, Kingussie, Inverness-shire PH21 1HE
Tel: 01540 661446
Contact: Jean Cunningham (Secretary)

BBC TV Young Musician of the Year

Biennial award gives over 150 prizes (including the Lloyds Bank Young Composers Award) for players aged 19 and under on January 1. Five categories: keyboard, strings, woodwind, brass, percussion. Also series of televised masterclasses. Concert final held in March.
BBC Television, Kensington House, Richmond Way, London W14 0AX
Contact: Marion Friend (Administrator)

Bernard Shore Award

Biennial award of £2,500 for composition of original work for viola. Funded by the Ralph Vaughan Williams Trust. 1996 closing date 31 March. Entry fee £5.
Royal Over-Seas League, Overseas House, 100 Princes Street, Edinburgh EH2 3AB
Tel: 0131 225 1501 Fax: 0131 226 3936
Contact: James Wilkie (Scottish Development Officer)

Birmingham Accompanist of the Year

Started by Incorporated Society of Musicians. Substantial monetary award plus the chance to perform in lunchtime recitals. Masterclass included for finalists. Biennial, 1995 closing date July 12. Age limit 30 on 30 September . Entry fee £10, £5 to ISM members.
Birmingham Conservatoire, Paradise Place, Birmingham B3 3HG

Brant Pianoforte Competition

Brant (Robert William and Florence Amy) annual competition since 1980 to encourage pianists aged 20-30 wishing to pursue solo careers. Limited to 20 entries. Three prizes £1,000, £500 and £250. Winner gives Stephen Brant Memorial Concert. Entry fee £30. Prospectus available; send sae.
83 Windsor Road, Oldbury, Warley, West Midlands B68 8PB
Contact: Miss G L Brant

British Contemporary Piano Competition

Triennial (next 1997) competition to encourage pianists over 18 to expand their contemporary repertoire. In three rounds. Set work for piano/electronics in final round. First prize £1,000 plus ten engagements.
31 Longholme Close, Cambridge CB4 3HW
Tel: 01223 357431
Contact: Philip Mead (Artistic Director)

British Gas Young Organist of the Year Competition

To encourage organists under 19 and to provide a platform and recital opportunities. First prize £1,000 and other prizes total £1,000. Apply by audition.
The Cathedral, Liverpool L1 7AH
Tel: 0151 709 6271
Contact: Eleanor Wright (Administrator)

Caithness Music Festival

Annual festival in Wick and Thurso. Competition classes include vocal, choral, piano, verse speaking, drama, storytelling, speech-making, woodwind, Scots fiddle, bagpipe, chanter and Caithness dialect. No age limits.
8 Castle Street, Thurso, Caithness KW14 7JB
Tel: 01847 892260
Contact: Mrs H Urquhart (Secretary) or Trevor Williams (Chairman)
Tel: 01847 892951

Cambuslang Music Festival

All the usual classes combine to make a whole week of music running into March.
72 Stewarton Drive, Cambuslang, Glasgow G72 8DG
Tel: 0141 641 1352
Contact: Ms E Owen (Secretary) or John Breslin (Treasurer) Tel: 0141 641 3053

Cardiff Singer of the World Competition

For singers over 18 on 1 June with no substantial professional experience but at the beginning of a career. First prize £10,000. Finalists receive £2,000. Lieder prize of £2,000. Apply by September with CV and future engagements listing.

BBC Wales, Broadcasting House, Llandaff, Cardiff CF5 2YQ
Tel: 01222 572888
Contact: Anna Williams (Administrator)

Clements Memorial Chamber Music Competition

To encourage composition for 3 - 8 unmodified, non-electronic instruments. No prizewinners of other competitions. No publicly performed works. Winning piece remains copyright of composer but required to present copy of score and parts to South Place Sunday Concerts. Apply by letter with sae and key details. Biennial £500 prize.

Fernside Copthal Green, Upshire, Waltham Abbey, Essex EN9 3SZ
Tel: 01992 711191
Contact: Raymond Cassidy (Hon Secretary)

Clouter Opera

Annual competition, valued at £1,500, for those nominated by heads of opera departments and academies of music. Also provides training and performance opportunites for professional singers embarking on a career. Bursaries are sometimes available to cover costs of coaching and accommodation.

Clouter Opera Farm, Swettenham, Congleton, Cheshire CW12 2LR
Contact: Administrator

Cornelius Cardew Composition Prize

Annual competition for different combinations of instruments. Around ten pieces selected for workshop day for discussion between performers, audience, adjudicators and composers. Total prize money around £400.

c/o 17 Pontcanna Place, Cardiff CF1 9JY
Tel: 01222 342329
Contact: The Administrator

Daily Telegraph Young Jazz Competition

To encourage and reward good jazz performance by young people. First rounds in ITV regions. Open to individuals, organisations, schools and music centres. Must be jazz groups, soloists, composers or arrangers. Apply by cassette tape before end January.

Royal Northern College of Music, 124 Oxford Road, Manchester M13 9HD
Tel: 0161 273 6283
Contact: Clark Rundell (Director)

Donatella Flick Conducting Competition

Aims to advance careers of conductors under 35 in performance and specialist study. Winner becomes assistant conductor with LSO. Biennial award of £10,000 to subsidise study and concert engagements across Europe. Applicants must be EC citizens. November deadline.

47 Brunswick Gardens, London W8 4AW
Tel: 0171 792 2885
Contact: Judy Strang (Administrator)

Dr Harold Smart Competition

Competition to compose a short anthem.

Royal School of Church Music, Addington Place, Croydon CR9 5AD
Tel: 0181 654 7676 Fax: 0181 655 2542
Contact: Richard Lawrence

Dr William Baird Ross Trust Prize for Composition in Church Music

Triennial, next 1996. Open to composers resident and working in Scotland. Aims to promote church music.

10 Strathalmond Park, Barnton, Edinburgh EH4 8AL
Tel: 0131 339 1113
Contact: Mr K. Hatton (Trustee)

Dudley Piano Competition

Biennial international competition for pianists aged 18 - 30 which gives the chance to play through London debut in series of engagements. First prize £3,000. 1995 closing date 31 July.

11 Peartree Drive, Pedmore, Stourbridge DY8 2LB
Tel: 01384 379306 Fax: 01384 379306
Contact: Barbara Healy (Administrator)

Dumfries and District Music Festival

Runs over two weeks with Scottish country dancing, piping, drumming, Scots verse, prose reading, bible reading, poetry, all disciplines of music, vocal, choral, strings and so on. Hundreds of trophies.

11 Kelwood Place, Dumfries DG1 4HJ
Tel: 01387 267800
Contact: Jane Brown (Secretary) or Donald McCuaig (Chairman)

Dumfries and Galloway Regional Council (Western Area) Festival

The festival is affiliated to the British Federation of Festivals for Music, Dance and Speech. It begins on the last Monday of May. The syllabus offers over 100 classes covering a wide range of instrumental, vocal, choral and Scots verse competitions.

Department of Education, Foundry Lane, Stranraer DG9 0DY
Tel: 01776 702437 x23
Contact: Davida Allison (Secretary)

Dundee Schools Festival of Music and Drama

Established in 1936. Extensive syllabus. There are competitive classes for instrumental, keyboard, vocal and ensemble work as well as aspects of drama. Each evening there are concerts in the Caird Hall given by pupils from all Dundee schools. Takes place in alternate years.

Regional Educational Development Service, Floor D, Gardyne Road, Dundee DD5 1NY
Tel: 01382 462857 Fax: 01382 462862
Contact: Fiona McIntosh (Adviser in Music)

East Glasgow Music Festival

Competitive festival with the usual classes.

51 Hallhill Road, Springboig, Glasgow G32 0NW
Tel: 0141 774 4159
Contact: Mrs E McCaffrey

Edinburgh Competition Festival

Classes for most instruments (some non-competitive), voice, speech and drama and Scottish country dancing. The preliminary round for the concerto class takes place in April.

Flat 1, 1 Correnime Drive, Edinburgh EH10 6EQ
Tel: 0131 447 1557
Contact: Miss H Thomson (Secretary)

Evelyn Glennie Award for Percussion Composition

Open to composers of all ages for new works written for percussion ensemble or accompanied percussion. Register by 31 December.

Royal Military School of Music, Twickenham, Middlesex TW2 7DU
Contact: Paul Cameron (Professor of Percussion)

Festival of Scottish Fiddle Music

One day festival with competitive classes in Scottish fiddle music for various age groups and orchestras. Usually an evening concert as well.

21 Birnie Place, New Elgin IV30 3EB
Tel: 01343 542100
Contact: Doris Allan (Secretary to Strathspey and Reel Society)

Fife Festival of Music

A one-week festival which seeks to promote music making in Fife. Usually staged in the first week of February in Kirkaldy, Dunfermline and St Andrews. Non-competitive and competitive choral, instrumental ensembles, solo instrumental, vocal, music making. Open to schools and wider community.

7 Ramsay Gardens, Leslie KY6 3NG
Tel: 01592 742637 Fax: 01592 721937
Contact: Mrs A Stephens (Secretary) or Robert Tait (Administrator)
Tel: 01592 414699

Gerald Moore Award

For under 29s residing/studying full-time in UK. Fifteen minute programme featuring piano accompaniment and singer to test playing and accompanying talent as well as initiative and skill as programme builder. £2,000 to the winner and £200 for most impressive singer. Nomination from college or obtain application form.

Courtyard House, Neopardy, Crediton, Devon EX17 5EP
Contact: Katie Arey (Administrator)

Glasgow Music Festival

Syllabus published October with details of over 220 classes in music and speech attracting 1,000 entries involving some 4,000 people. Held mostly in City Hall and Renfield St Stephen's Church Centre.

16 Drumlin Drive, Milngavie, Glasgow G62 6LN
Tel: 0141 956 1183 Fax: 0141 956 3091
Contact: Mrs M Peacock or R H MacDonald Tel: 0141 339 5887

Great Elm Music Festival Vocal Award

Biennial, next 1996, for individual singers aged between 22 and 32. First prize £2,000. 1994 deadline 30 September.

Bridge House, Great Elm, Frome, Somerset BA11 3NY
Tel: 01373 812383 Fax: 01373 812083
Contact: Maureen Lehane Wishart

Gregynog Composers Award

No nationality or age limit. For composers of works for violin or piano of around 15 minutes' duration. Special award for under 25s. Suitable material used for workshops. 1994 deadline 26 March.

Festival Office, Gregynog, Newton, Powys SY16 3PW
Tel: 01686 650224
Contact: Ian Morgan-Williams

Grimsby International Singers Competition

Alec Redshaw Memorial Award. Triennial competition, next in 1998, open to professional singers and students between 20 and 30 before the closing date 31 March. Four vocal categories plus individual song and aria prizes. Engagement opportunities and accompanist's prize. Entry fee £40, £25 for accompanists. Send sae for details.

23 Enfield Avenue, New Waltham, Grimsby, South Humberside DN6 5RD
Tel: 01472 812113
Contact: Dr A Holmes

Haverhill Sinfonia Soloist Competition

For individual performers in woodwind, brass, singers, piano and strings; may apply by sending sae. Four prizes and the winner performs solo work with an orchestra.

8 Templars Court, Haverhill, Suffolk CB9 9AJ
Tel: 01440 63799
Contact: Kevin Hill (Musical Director)

Highlands and Islands Music and Dance Festival

Normally held in May but in March for 1996 only. Competitive festival with invitation pibroch, piping (senior and junior), Highland dancing (Scottish area final), accordion, fiddle, clarsach, singing, recorder, piano.

Argyll Street, Oban PS34 5SG
Tel: 01631 565338
Contact: Christine Hill or Neil Sinclair
Tel: 01631 710201

International Lionel Tertis Viola Competition and Workshop

Triennal, next August 1997, for solo violists.

Secretariat, Port Erin, Isle of Man
Tel: 01279 422567
Contact: John White (Executive Committee)

International Young Instrumentalist of the Year

Llangollen International Musical Eisteddfod, an annual event held in July, is open to instrumentalists (including pianists) under 25 on day of competition who give a recital of well-contrasted music of their own choice. First prize £200 plus trophy, second £100, third £50. Entry fee £2.

Eisteddfod Office, Llangollen, Clwyd LL20 8NG
Tel: 01978 860236
Contact: Music Director

International Young Singer of the Year

Llangollen International Musical Eisteddfod, an annual event held in July, is open to amateur singers over 16 and under 25 on day of competition who sing two well-contrasted songs of their own choice. First prize £200 plus trophy, second £100, third £50. Entry fee £2.

Eisteddfod Office, Llangollen, Clwyd LL20 8NG
Tel: 01978 860236
Contact: Music Director

Inverclyde and Renfrew Musical Festival

Competitive festival which runs over two weeks into February. Aims to encourage competition and promote music, speech and dance. Syllabus offers 279 classes and entries are usually around 1,300 individuals, groups and choirs. Well established festival, 1996 is its 71st year.
79 Brisbane Street, Greenock, Renfrewshire PA16 8NX
Tel: 01475 727139
Contact: Dorothy Banks (Secretary)

Inverness Music Festival

Competitive festival taking place in schools and culminating in concerts at Eden Court Theatre. There are classes for all kinds of instruments and voices - mostly classical music but lately incorporating traditional music classes. 1996 is the 47th annual festival. Two gala evenings are non-competitive.
4 Bruce Gardens, Inverness IV3 5EN
Tel: 01463 233902
Contact: Elizabeth Davis

Isle of Wight International Oboe Competition

Biennial competition, next 1997, takes place in May. Open to oboists under 30 before date of finals audition who have not won an international oboe competition. First prize £1,000, the Wightlink Trophy and a Wigmore Hall recital. Additional prizes. 1995 closing date 29 October. Entry fee £20.
32 Gregory Avenue, Poudwell, Near Ryde, Isle of Wight PO33 1PZ
Tel: 01983 612451 Fax: 01983 568388
Contact: The Administrator

Jacqueline Du Pré International Cello Competition

First competition 1996 in Birmingham. Open to professional cellists under 30. Prize fund £50,000 plus record contracts and concert engagements. Deadline previous September.
Melbury House, The Crescent, Crapstone, Yelverton, Devon PL20 7PS
Tel: 01822 855201
Contact: Michael Johnson (Director)

John Noble Bursary

Scottish Opera Endowment Trust awards £2,000 annually to most deserving singer. Applicants must have a Scottish connection and be aged between 18 and 26. Preliminary auditions held in October. Entry fee £20.
Scottish Opera Competitions, 39 Elmbank Crescent, Glasgow G2 4PT
Tel: 0141 248 4567 Fax: 0141 221 8812
Contact: Music Secretary

Kathleen Ferrier Awards

Competitive annual awards, totalling £17,500, open to singers under 30. 1995 closing date 1 March. Entry fee £25.
52 Rosebank, Holyport Road, London SW6 6LY
Tel: 0171 381 0985 Fax: 0171 381 0985
Contact: Shirley Barr (Administrator)

Leeds International Pianoforte Competition

Triennal, next 1996, for pianists aged up to 30.
University of Leeds, Leeds LS9 9JT
Tel: 0113 446586 Fax: 0113 391006
Contact: Francoise Logan

Leeds Jerusalem Song Contest

Biennial, next May 1998, for composers of songs with an Israeli or Jewish content, interest or lyric.
c/o 476 Street Lane, Leeds LS17 6HA
Tel: 0113 2685191
Contact: Michael Saville

Lochaber Music Festival

Affiliated to the British Federation with the usual competitive classes.
Serenata, Mossfield Drive, Lochyside, Fort William PH33 7PE
Tel: 01397 703368
Contact: D C B Maitland

London International Piano Competition

Triennial competition (next 1997) providing financial and career assistance for international concert pianists under 29. Cash prizes and international engagements, plus scholarships for further study for competitors under 22. Selected by international auditions.
28 Wallace Road, London N1 2PG
Tel: 0171 354 1087 Fax: 0171 704 1053
Contact: The Administrator

London International String Quartet Competition

Triennial competition (next 1997). Closing date 1 December 1996. Entry fee £50.
62 High Street, Fareham, Hants PO16 7BG
Tel: 01329 283603 Fax: 0705 321080
Contact: Dennis Sayer (Competition Administrator)

London Philharmonic Pioneer Young Soloist of the Year Competition

Biennial competition for one group of instruments (strings, piano or woodwind and brass). 1996 - piano. Preliminary rounds November 1995, finals with orchestra in January 1996 at Queen Elizabeth Hall. Age limit 26. Finalists receive £1,000 product voucher. Winner receives £2,500 and opportunity to perform concert with orchestra at Royal Festival Hall.
35 Doughty Street, London WC1N 2AA
Tel: 0171 833 2744 Fax: 0171 837 1224
Contact: James Wilson

Mario Lanza Educational Foundation

Annual competition in conjunction with Birmingham Conservatoire. Prizes £150, £75. No age limit but entrants expected to be engaged in the advanced study of classical singing.
7 Lionfields Avenue, Allesley Village, Coventry CV5 9GN
Contact: Hon Secretary

Mid Argyll Music Festival

Affiliated to the British Federation of Festivals for music, dance and speech, this annual festival started in 1978. Classes include piano, woodwind, brass, accordion, bagpipes, singing, Scottish country dancing. Entrants attracted from Argyll and the islands, and also central Scotland. More details from the secretary.
Ballymeanoch House, Kilmichael-Glassary, Argyll PA31 8QE
Tel: 01546 605220
Contact: Sheila McCallum (Secretary) or John Hay (Chairman) Tel: 01546 604295

Moray Music Festival

Biennial (next 1996) over 10 days with all the usual competitive classes, workshops and a variety of venues.
8 Woodside Road, Fochabers IV32 7HD
Tel: 01343 820586
Contact: Gaye Cadenhead (Secretary) or Annella McEwan (Publicity)
Tel: 01343 542703

Music in Scotland Trust

Annual awards competition providing £15,000 in recording studio prizes to unsigned Scottish-based artists and groups who are asked to submit demonstration cassette tapes of their material.
PO Box 183, Glasgow G3 8DG
Tel: 0141 204 3520
Contact: John Dingwall

National Mod

A festival celebrating Gaelic music, drama, poetry and literature. It features piping, singing and accordion competitions, choral singing and The Day of the Big Choirs. Takes place in October in a different location each year.
An Comunn Gaidhealach, 91 Cromwell Street, Stornoway, Isle of Lewis HS1 2DG
Tel: 01851 703487 Fax: 01851 704734
Contact: Donnie Maclean (Director)

National Mozart Competition

Annual but alternates each year between singers and pianists. Recitals of Mozart's work. Winners and semi-finalists selected for various concert engagements. 1995 deadline 9 October. Entry fee £25. Male singers under 30, females under 28, pianists under 22. Age limits may be altered.
66 Talbot Street, Southport, Merseyside PR8 1LU
Tel: 01704 530903
Contact: Barbara Dix (Secretary)

Newport International Competition for Young Pianists

Triennial competition (next 1997) for under 25s to provide platform for professional career. Audition in London in July. Three finalists perform with BBC National Orchestra of Wales in November. Winner receives £2,000 with additional prizes to runners-up. Entry fee £30.
Leisure and Amenities Department, Newport Borough Council, Civic Centre, Newport, Gwent NP9 4UR
Tel: 01633 244491 Fax: 01633 232839

NFMS/Esso Young Concert Artist Award

Assists young solo performers at start of professional careers. Age limit 27 for instrumentalists, 29 for singers. Four-year cycle: 1994 instrumentalists, 1995 male voices, 1996 pianists, 1997 female voices. Four performers share 75 engagements with affiliated societies. Spring auditions.
National Federation of Music Societies, Francis House, Francis Street, London SW1P 1DE
Tel: 0171 828 7320
Contact: Kate Fearnley (Award Administrator)

Northern Meeting

Originally a race meeting, this grew into Highland Games and a ball in the 18th c. and now is primarily a premier competitive piping festival. Takes place in Inverness.
c/o Ernst and Young, Moray House, 16 Bank Street, Inverness IV1 1QY
Tel: 01463 237581 Fax: 01463 226098
Contact: Angus MacKenzie (Secretary)

Organ Composition Competition

Music Department, Leeds Leisure Services, 19 Wellington Street, Leeds LS1 4DG
Tel: 0113 478334
Contact: Simon Lindley

Paisley International Organ Festival Competition

Biennial, next August 1996, competition for interpretation and improvisation.
Paisley Abbey, Paisley PA1 1JG
Tel: 0141 889 7654 Fax: 0141 889 7654
Contact: Jeanette Fenyo (Administrator)

Park Lane Group Composers Award

Annual award of £2,000.
Russell Chambers, Covent Garden Piazza, London WC2E 8AA
Tel: 0171 240 4919
Contact: The Administrator

Performing Right Society Award

Biennial award of £1,250 for composition funded by PRS for an original vocal or instrumental work for solo or any combination of instruments/singers to a maximum of 16 performers. Piece not to last longer than 20 minutes. Live/electronic considered. 1995 deadline 30 June.
Royal Over-Seas League, Overseas House, 100 Princes Street, Edinburgh EH2 3AB
Tel: 0131 225 1501 Fax: 0131 226 3936
Contact: James Wilkie (Scottish Development Officer)

Perthshire Musical Festival

Founded in 1921 and attracts over 1,000 entries. Music section classes includes vocal (solo, duet, choral), piano, strings, woodwind, brass, accordion, percussion (solo, duo, ensemble), band and orchestra. Also Scottish country dancing and verse speaking. Syllabus issued September/October.
6 Mercer Terrace, Perth PH1 2HD
Tel: 01738 631979
Contact: William Neish (Secretary)

Royal College of Organists Performer of the Year Award

Biennial. Open to Fellows of the Royal College of Organists. First prize £1,000. Finals in May, application deadline 31 March.
7 St Andrew Street, Holborn, London EC4A 3LQ
Tel: 0171 936 3606 Fax: 0171 353 8244
Contact: Michael Nicholas (Chief Executive)

Royal Over-Seas League Music Competition

Many cash prizes awarded as well as promotion by concerts. Age limits - 28 for instrumentalists, 30 for singers, 35 for composers. 1996 closing date in February. Entry fee £20.
Royal Over-Seas League, Overseas House, 100 Princes Street, Edinburgh EH2 3AB
Tel: 0131 225 1501 Fax: 0131 226 3936
Contact: James Wilkie (Scottish Development Officer)

FESTIVALS & COMPETITIONS

277

Royal Philharmonic Society Composition Prize

Annual award of £2,000 open to past or present students (under 26) of any conservatory or university. All entries must include a letter from the Principal or Head of Department confirming the entrant's student status. Previous winners not eligible. Entry fee £10.
10 Stratford Place, London W1N 9AE
Tel: 0171 491 8110 Fax: 0171 493 7463

Sainsbury's Choir of the Year Competition

For amateur and professional choirs between 20 and 120, all styles, adult and youth. First auditions March-May, finals November. Judged on musicianship, choral technique, programme choice and presentation.
2 Portland Road, Holland Park, London W11 4LA
Tel: 0171 221 7883 Fax: 0171 229 4595
Contact: Monika Clifford (Manager)

Saltire Scots Song Competition

Three classes - two comprising the primary and secondary school music festival winners and the third for those unsuccessful at that stage. Each school that enters is awarded a certificate and those with top marks receive a crystal trophy.
9 Fountain Close, 22 High Street, Edinburgh EH1 1TF
Tel: 0131 556 1836 Fax: 0131 557 1675
Contact: Mrs K. Munro

Scots Song Recital Competition

Biennial, next on 27 April 1996, Henry Wood Hall, Glasgow. Competitors required to sing 2 traditional songs with piano accompaniment (group A); 1 unaccompanied traditional song (group B); 2 prescribed songs (group C). Age range: 18 - 26 (female); 18 - 30 (male). Substantial cash prizes.
22 Queen Street, Stirling FK8 1HN
Tel: 01786 472074
Contact: George MacVicar

Shetland Schools Music Festival

A diverse week-long programme of competitive and non-competitive classes culminating in a gala concert featuring traditional, classical, jazz and light music involving soloists, duos, ensembles and bands, highlighting the wide range of music education on Shetland.
Education Department, Schlumberger Base, Grelista Industrial Estate, Lerwick, Shetland ZE1 0PX
Tel: 01595 693800 Fax: 01595 692810
Contact: Gordon Yeaman (Education Adviser) or Lesley Leask (Secretary)

Stephen Oliver Prize

Biennial competition worth £10,000 to encourage young people working in contemporary opera. Awarded for composition of a chamber opera. Entrants invited to set a given libretto. Registration fee £10.
Stephen Oliver Trust, PW Productions, 11 Goodwins Court, London WC2N 4LL
Tel: 0171 379 7909
Contact: The Secretary

Vivian Ellis Prize

National competition for under 35s to write music for the stage. Five finalists will have two pieces performed and judged before an invited audience at the Guildhall School of Music and Drama. First prize £1,000 and cash prizes for runners-up. Entry fee £10.
Performing Right Society, 29-33 Berners Street, London W1P 4AA
Tel: 0171 580 5544
Contact: The Administrator

Yehudi Menuhin International Violin Competition

Held in Folkestone, Kent. Seniors under 22 and juniors under 16. Cash prizes. Entry fee £50.
72 Leopold Road, London SW19 7JQ
Tel: 0181 944 5171 Fax: 0181 946 0581
Contact: Mrs Noel Masters

Young Artists Platform

No cash prizes. Winners give public performances in St George's Brandon Hall, Bristol; Fairfield Hall, Croydon and Wigmore Hall, London where BBC Radio record the recital for transmission. Application deadline mid November. Singers aged 23 - 27, instrumentalists aged 20 - 24 or ensembles. Must have UK music college performer's diploma or equivalent.
Courtyard House, Neopardy, Crediton, Devon EX17 5EP
Contact: Katie Arey (Administrator)

LATE ENTRIES

LATE ENTRIES

Artlink

Escort Service: c. 125 volunteer escorts accompany disabled people to performances; waiting list for clients. Urban Aid: 4 arts development workers run projects, including music, in Craigmillar, Wester Hailes, Muirhouse/Pilton and West Lothian.
13a Spittal Street, Edinburgh EH3 9DY
Tel: 0131 229 3555 Fax: 0131 228 5257
Contact: Clare Stirling (Escort Service) or Alison Stirling (Urban Aid)

Glasgow District Council Music Business Development Fund

Introduced to help existing music businesses to develop and to help individuals who wish to set up a new music related business. Grants are of 50% of costs up to a maximum £5,000, paid in retrospect. Firms must be located in Glasgow and employ less than 25 people.
Economic Policy Unit, Town Clerk's Office, City Chambers, Glasgow G2 1DU
Contact: Paul Doherty

Highlander Music Ltd

Records and distributes Highland music with particular emphasis on recording talented young Highland musicians, and on dance music. Also provides a distribution service for other labels and artists and runs a mail order service for Scottish music.
Upper Leanassie, Kilmorack, Beauly, Inverness-shire IV4 7AF
Contact: William Crawford

Maestro Music

Computer typesetting and processing. All types of music scores, binding and part copying. Also offer an arranging and orchestration service.
190 Lee Crescent North, Bridge of Don, Aberdeen AB22 8FR
Tel: 01224 823256

Scottish Record Industry Association

An association of record companies, music publishers and general music organisations who are equipped and prepared to debate points of national and international importance of relevance to the record industry.
PO Box 516, Glasgow G5 8PZ
Tel: 0141 429 4174
Contact: Ronnie Simpson (Chairman)

Shepley-Shepley Trust

A youth arts fund for people aged between 16 and 25 who live in Scotland and want to launch an arts project showing enterprise, innovation and potential for development. Grants of £50 or more available, up to £2,000 in exceptional cases.
12 Manor Place, Edinburgh EH3 7DD

Skene Aberdeen Festival Award

A cash sum of £1,000 plus assistance with the development of the career of the young person adjudged to be the most outstanding musician at the festival.
23 Rubislaw Den North, Aberdeen AB2 4AL
Tel: 01224 326221
Contact: Dr Norman Cooper

Watercolour Music

24 track digital recording studio, 500 sq feet of recording area in a converted barn on the banks of Loch Leven. Can also stage and record live gigs. Studio available for rehearsals. Also offer a range of post-recording services.
The New House, Loch Leven Hotel, North Ballachulish, by Fort William PH33 6SA
Tel: 01855 821513 Fax: 01855 821513
Contact: Nick or Julie Turner

INDEX

INDEX

INDEX

INDEX

INDEX

INDEX

INDEX

INDEX

INDEX

INDEX

INDEX

INDEX

INDEX

INDEX

INDEX

INDEX

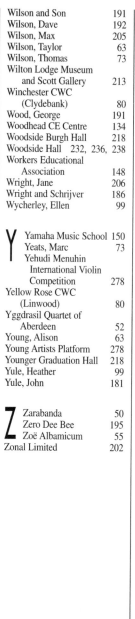

INDEX